OUTLINE OF GENERAL TOPOLOGY

OUTLINE OF GENERAL TOPOLOGY

R. ENGELKING

Institute of Mathematics of the Polish Academy of Sciences

Translated from the Polish by
K. SIEKLUCKI

1968

NORTH-HOLLAND PUBLISHING COMPANY — AMSTERDAM
JOHN WILEY & SONS, INC. — NEW YORK
(Interscience Publishers Division)

Library of Congress Catalog Card Number: 67-31048

PUBLISHERS:

NORTH-HOLLAND PUBLISHING COMPANY – AMSTERDAM

PWN – POLISH SCIENTIFIC PUBLISHERS

Sole distributors for U.S.A. and Canada:
Interscience Publishers, a division of
JOHN WILEY & SONS, INC. – NEW YORK

To Professor
Kazimierz Kuratowski

PREFACE

The theorems and concepts of general topology are presently used in many fields of mathematics and have become especially important in various branches of analysis. The concept of a topological space and a compact space, the concept of a Cartesian product, as well as the Tychonoff theorem on the compactness of the Cartesian product of compact spaces, and the Stone-Weierstrass theorem have found many applications. A knowledge of these concepts and facts, therefore, is indispensable for reading many mathematical papers and monographs.

As there exist in mathematical literature several books with a good exposition of general topology, the publication of a new book must be justified by its being different from its predecessors. This book has several distinctive characteristics. It devotes a fair amount of thought to examples, which are fully described in the main body of the book and not, as is a frequent practice, relegated to exercises. Above all, however, this book is distinctive in that it gives a modernization of the classical exposition of general topology and in the inclusion of some "non-classical" sections (for example Chapter seven, which is devoted to the dimension theory of general topological spaces).

This book is intended primarily for senior students and scientific workers pursuing various branches of mathematics. They will profit by the "classical" part of the book. The "non-classical" concepts (for example: real-compact spaces; weak, strong and countable para-compactness; dimension theory; proximity spaces) are included for mathematicians particularly interested in topology, the problems are also meant for them. The short exercises at the end of each paragraph are not difficult and give a good indication of the reader's comprehension of the material.

As for reference notation, when we refer to a theorem in the same paragraph we state its number only; for example we write — see Theorem 12. When we refer to a theorem in another paragraph but of the same chapter we state the number of the paragraph and the number of the theorem — Theorem 1.12 denotes Theorem 12 of Paragraph 1; and when we refer to a theorem in another chapter we give the number of the chapter, of the paragraph, and of the theorem — Theorem 3.1.12

means Theorem 12 of Paragraph 1 in Chapter 3. A similar system is used in denoting exercises, only here letters are used. Exercise 3.1.A refers to Exercise A of Paragraph 1 in Chapter 3.

Numbers in square brackets refer to the bibliography at the end of the book.

The mark ■ signifies the end of a proof or of an example. If it appears after the statement of a theorem (or a corollary), it denotes that the theorem (corollary) is obvious.

Many persons have been kind enough to help me in writing this book and in preparing the English edition. I render my sincere thanks to all of them. I am particularly obliged to Professor A. Lelek for his valuable comments. Thanks are also due to Dr K. Sieklucki, who translated the book, and to Mrs J. Smólska and Professor D. B. A. Epstein for verifying the translation.

Ryszard Engelking

Warsaw, January 1966

CONTENTS

INTRODUCTION

§ 1. Algebra of sets. Functions 13
§ 2. Power of a set. Cardinal numbers 15
§ 3. Ordering relations. Ordinal numbers 16
§ 4. Axiom of choice 20
§ 5. Real numbers 22
Historical remarks and bibliographic notes 23

CHAPTER 1

TOPOLOGICAL SPACES

§ 1. Topological spaces. Open and closed sets. Base. Closure and interior of a set 25
§ 2. Various methods of generation of a topology 33
§ 3. Boundary of a set and derived set. Dense sets and boundary sets. F_σ-sets and G_δ-sets 37
§ 4. Mappings. Real-valued functions. Homeomorphisms 40
§ 5. Axioms of separation 46
§ 6. Nets and filters 53
Historical remarks and bibliographic notes 58
Problems 59

CHAPTER 2

OPERATIONS ON TOPOLOGICAL SPACES

§ 1. Subspaces 65
§ 2. Sum of spaces 70
§ 3. Cartesian product 73
§ 4. Quotient spaces 83
§ 5. Limits of inverse systems 87
§ 6. Function spaces: the topology of uniform convergence. Mapping spaces: the pointwise topology 91
Historical remarks and bibliographic notes 94
Problems 95

CHAPTER 3

COMPACT SPACES

§ 1. Compact spaces 101
§ 2. Operations on compact spaces 110
§ 3. Mapping spaces: the compact-open topology 121
§ 4. Compactifications 125
§ 5. Čech-Stone compactification 129
§ 6. Locally compact spaces 135
§ 7. Lindelöf spaces 140
§ 8. Spaces complete in the sense of Čech 142
§ 9. Countably compact spaces. Pseudo-compact spaces 146
§ 10. Real-compact spaces 151
Historical remarks and bibliographic notes 157
Problems 159

CHAPTER 4

METRIC AND METRIZABLE SPACES

§ 1. Metric spaces. Metrizable spaces 169
§ 2. Operations on metrizable spaces 177
§ 3. Totally bounded spaces and complete spaces 184
§ 4. Metrization theorems 193
Historical remarks and bibliographic notes 198
Problems 199

CHAPTER 5

PARACOMPACT SPACES

§ 1. Paracompact spaces 206
§ 2. Countably paracompact spaces 220
§ 3. Weakly paracompact spaces and strongly paracompact spaces 225
Historical remarks and bibliographic notes 230
Problems 231

CHAPTER 6

CONNECTED SPACES

§ 1. Connected spaces. Operations on connected spaces 240
§ 2. Various kinds of disconnectedness 247
Historical remarks and bibliographic notes 258
Problems 259

CHAPTER 7

DIMENSION OF TOPOLOGICAL SPACES

§ 1. Definitions and basic properties of the dimensions: ind, Ind, and dim . . 264
§ 2. Further properties of the dimension dim 274

§ 3. Dimension of metrizable spaces 285
Appendix. Proof of the fixed-point theorem 296
Historical remarks and bibliographic notes 304
Problems 306

CHAPTER 8

UNIFORM SPACES. PROXIMITY SPACES

§ 1. Uniformities. Uniform spaces 313
§ 2. Operations on uniform spaces 326
§ 3. Complete and totally bounded uniform spaces. Compactness in uniform spaces 334
§ 4. Proximity spaces 342
Historical remarks and bibliographic notes 351
Problems 352

Bibliography 357
List of special symbols 371
Author index 373
Subject index 375

INTRODUCTION

In understanding this book it is sufficient to be familiar with the basic facts of set theory and with some fundamental properties of the set of real numbers. The purpose of this introduction is to enumerate those facts and to establish the notation and terminology which we will use. With one exception (the proof of the equivalence of the axiom of choice and a few theorems of set theory) the introduction does not contain any proofs and cannot be considered as a short course in set theory. With the exception of the axiom of choice, the axioms of set theory are not considered here.

§ 1. Algebra of sets. Functions. The *union*, the *intersection*, and the *difference* of sets A and B are denoted respectively by $A \cup B$, $A \cap B$, and $A \setminus B$. The symbol 0 is used to denote the *empty* set. Throughout the book we use the rules of the algebra of sets; very often we shall use the *de Morgan formulas*:

$$A \setminus (B \cup C) = (A \setminus B) \cap (A \setminus C)$$

and

$$A \setminus (B \cap C) = (A \setminus B) \cup (A \setminus C).$$

To indicate that x is an *element* of a set A we write $x \in A$; if x does not belong to A, we write $x \notin A$. The notation $A \subset B$ or $B \supset A$ means that the set A is *contained* in the set B (in this case we say that A is a *subset* of B), i.e. that each element of the set A is an element of the set B.

The set of all elements of the set X which satisfy the propositional function $\varphi(x)$ is denoted by

$$\{x \in X: \varphi(x)\} \quad \text{or by} \quad \{x: \varphi(x)\}$$

if there is no doubt which set X is being considered.

The set consisting of a finite number of elements $x_1, x_2, \ldots, x_k$ is denoted by the symbol $\{x_1, x_2, \ldots, x_k\}$ or $\{x_i\}_{i=1}^{k}$. Sometimes we do not distinguish between the element x and the set $\{x\}$ containing only x.

The set $\{\{x\}, \{x, y\}\}$ is called an *ordered pair* with *antecedent* x and *successor* y. An ordered pair is denoted by the symbol (x, y). Pairs (x_1, y_1) and (x_2, y_2) are equal if and only if $x_1 = x_2$ and $y_1 = y_2$.

The *Cartesian product* of the sets A and B is the set $A \times B$ consisting of all pairs (x, y) with antecedent in A and successor in B.

Every subset of the product $A \times B$ is called a *binary relation* between elements of the set A and elements of the set B. The relation $f \subset A \times B$ is called a *function* defined on A with values in B or a function of A into B if for every $x \in A$ there exists a $y \in B$ such that $(x, y) \in f$, and if for every $x \in A$

$$(x, y) \in f \text{ and } (x, y') \in f \text{ implies } y = y'.$$

If f is a function defined on A with values in B, then for an arbitrary $x \in A$ the unique element $y \in B$ such that $(x, y) \in f$ is denoted by $f(x)$. The set

$$f(M) = \{y \in B : y = f(x) \text{ for some } x \in M\}$$

is called the *image* of the set $M \subset A$ under f, and the set

$$f^{-1}(N) = \{x \in A : f(x) \in N\}$$

is called the *inverse image* of the set $N \subset B$.

In this book we use formulas for images and inverse images, in particular

$$ff^{-1}(N) \subset N \quad \text{and} \quad f^{-1}f(M) \supset M.$$

If f is a function of the set A into the set B such that $f(A) = B$, then f is called a function of the set A *onto* the set B. A function f defined on the set A is called a *one-to-one* function if for every $x_1, x_2 \in A$

$$f(x_1) = f(x_2) \text{ implies } x_1 = x_2.$$

We use symbols $\bigcup_{s \in S} A_s$ and $\bigcap_{s \in S} A_s$ to denote the *union* and the *intersection* of a family of sets $\{A_s\}_{s \in S}$ and $\bigcup_{i=1}^{\infty} A_i$ or $\bigcap_{i=1}^{\infty} A_i$ for a sequence of sets $A_1, A_2, \ldots$ A set consisting of elements of an infinite sequence $x_1, x_2, \ldots$ is denoted by $\{x_i\}_{i=1}^{\infty}$.

The *Cartesian product* of the family of sets $\{A_s\}_{s \in S}$, i.e. the set of all functions f of the set S into the set $\bigcup_{s \in S} A_s$ such that $f(s) \in A_s$ for every $s \in S$, is denoted by $\mathop{\boldsymbol{P}}_{s \in S} A_s$ or by $\mathop{\boldsymbol{P}}_{i=1}^{\infty} A_i$ in the case of a sequence $A_1, A_2, \ldots$

For every $f \in \mathop{\boldsymbol{P}}_{s \in S} A_s$ the point $f(s) \in A_s$ is called the *s-th coordinate* of the point f.

That element of the product $\mathop{\boldsymbol{P}}_{s \in S} A_s$ for which the point $x_s \in A_s$ is the s-th coordinate, we will continue to denote by $x = \{x_s\}$. An infinite sequence $x_1, x_2, \ldots$ of elements of the set A, i.e. an element of the product $\mathop{\boldsymbol{P}}_{i=1}^{\infty} A_i$, where $A_i = A$ for $i = 1, 2, \ldots$, is often denoted by $\{x_i\}$.

A relation R in a set A, i.e. a subset of the product $A \times A$, is called an *equivalence relation* if it is subject to the following conditions (we write xRy instead of $(x, y) \in R$):

(E1) *xRx.*

(E2) *xRy implies yRx.*

(E3) *xRy and yRz imply xRz.*

Every equivalence relation R in the set A determines a decomposition of that set into disjoint sets (*equivalence classes* of the relation R). Two elements belong to the same equivalence class if they are R-related:

$$A = \bigcup_{s \in S} A_s, \quad A_s \cap A_{s'} = 0 \text{ for } s \neq s' \text{ and } s, s' \in S$$

$$x, y \in A_s \text{ for some } s \in S \text{ if and only if } xRy.$$

The equivalence class containing the element $x \in A$ is denoted by $[x]$.

Conversely, for every decomposition of an arbitrary set A into the union of disjoint sets $\{A_s\}_{s \in S}$ there exists in A an equivalence relation R such that

$$xRy \text{ if and only if } x, y \in A_s \text{ for some } s \in S.$$

§ 2. Power of a set. Cardinal numbers. Sets A and B are said to have *the same power* if there exists a one-to-one function of the set A onto the set B. To every set A we assign a *cardinal number* denoted by $\overline{\overline{A}}$ and called the *power* of the set A; the equality $\overline{\overline{A}} = \overline{\overline{B}}$ holds if and only if the sets A and B have the same power. The power of a finite set is the number of its elements. The cardinal number assigned to the set of all integers is denoted by $\aleph_0$ (*aleph zero*); the cardinal number assigned to the set of all real numbers is denoted by $\mathfrak{c}$ (*continuum*). A set is said to be *countable* if it is finite or if it is of power $\aleph_0$.

The operations of addition and multiplication on cardinal numbers are defined as follows: The *sum* of two cardinal numbers $\mathfrak{m}$ and $\mathfrak{n}$ is the power of the set $A \cup B$ where $\overline{\overline{A}} = \mathfrak{m}$, $\overline{\overline{B}} = \mathfrak{n}$ and $A \cap B = 0$. The *product* of two cardinal numbers $\mathfrak{m}$ and $\mathfrak{n}$ is defined as the power of the set $A \times B$ where $\overline{\overline{A}} = \mathfrak{m}$ and $\overline{\overline{B}} = \mathfrak{n}$. The sum of cardinal numbers $\mathfrak{m}$ and $\mathfrak{n}$ is denoted by $\mathfrak{m}+\mathfrak{n}$ and their product — by $\mathfrak{m}\cdot\mathfrak{n}$. The *sum* of an arbitrary family $\{\mathfrak{m}_s\}_{s \in S}$ of cardinal numbers is defined as the power of the set $\bigcup_{s \in S} A_s$ where $\overline{\overline{A_s}} = \mathfrak{m}_s$ for $s \in S$ and $A_s \cap A_{s'} = 0$ for $s \neq s'$; to denote this sum we use the symbol $\sum_{s \in S} \mathfrak{m}_s$. For every cardinal number $\mathfrak{m}$ we define the number $2^{\mathfrak{m}}$ as the power of the family of all subsets of an arbitrary set A of the power $\mathfrak{m}$. It can be proved that $2^{\aleph_0} = \mathfrak{c}$.

Suppose that two cardinal numbers $\mathfrak{m}$ and $\mathfrak{n}$ are the powers of sets A and B respectively. We shall say that $\mathfrak{m}$ is *not greater* than $\mathfrak{n}$ or that $\mathfrak{n}$ is *not less* that $\mathfrak{m}$ (and write $\mathfrak{m} \leqslant \mathfrak{n}$ or $\mathfrak{n} \geqslant \mathfrak{m}$) if and only if there exists a one-to-one function of the set A onto a subset of the set B. The following *Cantor-Bernstein theorem is* fundamental for inequalities of cardinal numbers:

$$\textit{if } \mathfrak{m} \leqslant \mathfrak{n} \textit{ and } \mathfrak{n} \leqslant \mathfrak{m}, \textit{ then } \mathfrak{m} = \mathfrak{n}.$$

It can also be proved that for an arbitrary set A and a function f defined on A the inequality $\overline{\overline{f(A)}} \leqslant \overline{\overline{A}}$ always holds.

If $\mathfrak{m}$ and $\mathfrak{n}$ are two cardinal numbers, $\mathfrak{m} \geqslant \mathfrak{n} \geqslant 1$, and $\mathfrak{m}$ is infinite, then $\mathfrak{m}+\mathfrak{n} = \mathfrak{m}$ and $\mathfrak{m}\cdot\mathfrak{n} = \mathfrak{m}$. In particular

$$\mathfrak{m}+\mathfrak{m} = \mathfrak{m}\cdot\mathfrak{m} = \mathfrak{m} \quad \text{for} \quad \mathfrak{m} \geqslant \aleph_0.$$

If $\mathfrak{m} \leqslant \mathfrak{n}$ and $\mathfrak{m} \neq \mathfrak{n}$, then we say that $\mathfrak{m}$ is *less* than $\mathfrak{n}$ and write $\mathfrak{m} < \mathfrak{n}$. It can be proved that

$$\mathfrak{m} < 2^{\mathfrak{m}} \textit{ for an arbitrary cardinal number } \mathfrak{m};$$

therefore, in particular $\aleph_0 < \mathfrak{c}$.

§ 3. Ordering relations. Ordinal numbers. Suppose that we are given a set A and a relation $<$ between its elements. We say that this relation establishes an *ordering* of the set A or it is an ordering in A, if the following conditions are satisfied:

(OR1) *If* $x < y$ *and* $y < z$, *then* $x < z$.

(OR2) *If* $x < y$, *then the relation* $y < x$ *does not hold.*

(OR3) *If* $x \neq y$, *then either* $x < y$ *or* $y < x$.

A set A with a relation $<$ which establishes its ordering is called an *ordered* set.

The element x_0 of the set A which is ordered by the relation $<$ is said to be the *first* element of that set if $x_0 < x$ for each element $x \in A$ which is different from x_0. We define analogously the *last* element of an ordered set and — since the relation $<$ ordering the set A orders its every subset — the first and the last elements of an arbitrary subset of an ordered set. Not every ordered set, of course, has a first and a last element.

A pair (D, E) of subsets of the set A ordered by the relation $<$ such that $D \cup E = A$, $D \neq 0 \neq E$ and

$$x \in D,\ y \in E \text{ imply } x < y$$

is called a *cut* of the set A. The set D is called the *lower class*, and the set E the *upper class* of the cut; upper and lower classes are disjoint.

For every cut of the set A the following cases are possible:

(1) The lower class has a last element and the upper class has a first element.

(2) The lower class has a last element but the upper class has no first element.

(3) The lower class has no last element and the upper class has a first element.

(4) The lower class has no last element and the upper class has no first element.

In case (1) we say that the cut determines a *jump*; in case (4) we say that the cut determines a *gap*.

An ordered set A, no cut of which determines a jump, is said to be *ordered in a dense manner*; moreover, if there is no cut in A which determines a gap, then A is said to be *ordered in a continuous manner*. The set A is ordered in a dense manner if and only if for each pair of elements $x, y \in A$ such that $x < y$, there exists a $z \in A$ satisfying the condition $x < z < y$, i.e. if A does not contain any pair of neighbouring elements. The set A is ordered in a continuous manner if and only if, in addition to the above, we have that for every non-empty subset $A_0 \subset A$ the set $\{x \in A: a < x \text{ for each element } a \in A_0 \text{ different from } x\}$ is empty or has a first element.

The ordering of the set A determined by a relation $<$ is called a *well-ordering* (and the set A with the relation $<$ — a *well-ordered* set) if the following condition is satisfied:

(WO) *In every non-empty subset $A_0 \subset A$ there exists a first element.*

Every set of cardinal numbers is well ordered by the relation $<$ defined in the preceding paragraph.

Let A be a set ordered by the relation $<$ and B a set ordered by the relation $<'$. We say that the function f of the set A into the set B *preserves the ordering* if for every $x_1, x_2 \in A$, the condition $x_1 < x_2$ implies the condition $f(x_1) <' f(x_2)$. If for the ordered sets A and B there exists a function of the set A onto the set B which preserves the ordering, we say that the sets A and B are *similarly ordered*.

An arbitrary ordered set A is ordered similarly to a part of a set without gaps: namely the set of all cuts of the set A ordered by the relation

$$(D_1, E_1) < (D_2, E_2) \text{ if } D_1 \subset D_2 \text{ and } D_1 \neq D_2.$$

If the set A is dense, then the set of its cuts is continuous.

To every well-ordered set A we assign an *ordinal number* called the *order type* of the set A. Order types assigned to the sets A nad B are equal if and only if A and B are similarly ordered.

If sets A and B are similarly ordered, they have the same power because the function f preserving the ordering is one-to-one. Therefore, every ordinal number α has a corresponding cardinal number which is the power of an arbitrary ordered set of the type α; that cardinal number is called the *power* of the number α and denoted by $\overline{\alpha}$.

Suppose that two ordinal numbers α and β are the order types of sets A and B. The ordinal number α is said to be *less* than the ordinal number β (in this case we write $\alpha < \beta$) if and only if there exists an element $b_0 \in B$ such that the sets A and $\{b \in B: b < b_0\}$ are similarly ordered.

Every set of ordinal numbers is well ordered by the relation $<$. An arbitrary well-ordered set A of type α is ordered similarly to the set of all ordinal numbers less than α ordered by the relation $<$.

An ordinal number λ is called a *limit number* if no ordinal number immediately precedes the number λ, i.e. if for every number $\alpha < \lambda$ there exists such a number ξ that $\alpha < \xi < \lambda$.

If a number ξ immediately precedes the number λ, then λ is called the *successor* of the number ξ (and ξ — the *predecessor* of the number λ) and we write $\lambda = \xi + 1$.

An infinite ordinal number λ (i.e. the ordinal type of a well-ordered infinite set) is called an *initial number* if λ is the least number of all α such that $\overline{\alpha} = \overline{\lambda}$, i.e. if $\xi < \lambda$ implies $\overline{\xi} < \overline{\lambda}$.

For every cardinal number $\mathfrak{m}$ there exists an initial number of power $\mathfrak{m}$ (see Zermelo's Theorem in the following paragraph). The initial number of power $\aleph_0$ is denoted by ω_0; it is the ordinal type of the set of all natural numbers with the usual ordering.

The least ordinal number whose power is greater than $\aleph_0$ is denoted by ω_1. For an arbitrary sequence $\alpha_1, \alpha_2, \ldots$ of ordinal numbers less than ω_1 there exists an ordinal number $\alpha < \omega_1$ such that $\alpha_i < \alpha$ for $i = 1, 2, \ldots$

The first ordinal number in the set of all numbers with power greater than $\overline{\omega}_1$ is denoted by ω_2.

Suppose that an ordinal number α and a set A are given. An arbitrary function f of the set of all ordinal numbers less than α into the set A is called a (*transfinite*) *sequence of the type* α with values in A. The element of the sequence assigned to the ordinal number $\xi < \alpha$ is often denoted by x_ξ (instead of $f(\xi)$) and the sequence itself by $x_0, x_1, \ldots, x_\xi, \ldots, \xi < \alpha$.

Definitions of transfinite sequences are often based on the following theorem.

THEOREM ON DEFINING BY TRANSFINITE INDUCTION. *Let a set Z and an ordinal number α be given. Let us denote by G the set of all transfinite sequences, whose types are less than α and whose values belong to Z. For an arbitrary function h, which assigns an element of the set Z to every sequence $g \in G$,* *there exists exactly one transfinite sequence f of the type a such that*

$$f(\xi) = h\big(f|\, W(\xi)\big) \quad \textit{for every } \xi < a,$$

where $f|\, W(\xi)$ denotes the sequence obtained by the restriction of f to the set $W(\xi)$ of all ordinal numbers less than ξ.

The above theorem is usually applied to the case where Z is a family of subsets of a set X; the function h is then generally defined by three formulas. The first formula gives the value of h for the sequence g of type 0 (the ordinal type of the empty set) i.e. the value $h(0)$; the second the value $h(g)$ for sequences g whose type has a predecessor, i.e. whose type is of the form $\xi+1$; and the third gives the value $h(g)$ for sequences whose type λ is a limit number. For example, the first formula is of the form (we write X_ξ instead of $g(\xi)$):

$$h(0) = A;$$

the second is of the form:

$$h(g) = F(X_\xi);$$

and the third

$$h(g) = G\big(\bigcup_{\xi<\lambda} X_\xi\big) \quad \text{or} \quad h(g) = G\big(\bigcap_{\xi<\lambda} X_\xi\big),$$

where F and G are given functions and A is a fixed set.

The sequence $A_0, A_1, \ldots, A_\xi, \ldots, \xi < \lambda$, which exists by virtue of the theorem on defining by transfinite induction, is subject to the following conditions:

$$A_0 = A,$$

$$A_{\xi+1} = F(A_\xi),$$

$$A_\lambda = G\big(\bigcup_{\xi<\lambda} A_\xi\big) \quad \text{or} \quad A_\lambda = G\big(\bigcap_{\xi<\lambda} A_\xi\big).$$

Therefore, in order to define a transfinite sequence $A_0, A_1, \ldots, A_\xi, \ldots,$ $\xi < a$, it is sufficient to determine A_0 and to describe how $A_{\xi+1}$ depends on A_ξ and A_λ on $\bigcup_{\xi<\lambda} A_\xi$ or $\bigcap_{\xi<\lambda} A_\xi$.

Let A be a set well-ordered by the relation $<$. Every subset B of the set A, which for every $x_0 \in A$ satisfies the condition

$$\text{if } \{x \in A\colon\, x < x_0\} \subset B, \text{ then } x_0 \in B,$$

is equal to the set A. Inductive proofs are based on this fact. In this book we will use this fact when A is either the set of all natural numbers (proofs by induction) or the set of ordinal numbers less than a chosen ordinal number a ordered by the relation $<$ (proofs by transfinite induction).

A relation $\leqslant$ defined between elements of the set A is said to be a *partial ordering* if the following conditions are satisfied:

(PO1) *If* $x \leqslant y$ *and* $y \leqslant z$, *then* $x \leqslant z$.

(PO2) $x \leqslant x$.

(PO3) *If* $x \leqslant y$ *and* $y \leqslant x$, *then* $x = y$.

The set A together with the partial ordering relation $\leqslant$ is called a *partially ordered set.* A subset A_0 of the partially ordered set A is called *linearly ordered* if for every $x, y \in A_0$ either $x \leqslant y$ or $y \leqslant x$.

If A is a set ordered by a relation $<$, then, assuming

$$x \leqslant y \text{ if and only if either } x < y \text{ or } x = y,$$

we define a partial ordering in A; moreover, in this case the set A is linearly ordered. Thus any ordered set can be considered as a partially ordered set. Conversely, any linearly ordered subset of a partially ordered set is ordered by a relation $<$ defined by the condition

$$x < y \text{ if and only if } x \leqslant y \text{ and } x \neq y.$$

An element u of a partially ordered set A is called the *least upper bound* of a subset A_0 of A if $x \leqslant u$ for every $x \in A_0$ and if every element $v \in A$ such that $x \leqslant v$ for any $x \in A_0$ satisfies the condition $u \leqslant v$. The *greatest lower bound* of a subset of a partially ordered set is defined analogously. Let us note that the least upper bound (if it exists) of the set A is the greatest element of A; the least upper bound (if it exists) of the empty set is the least element of A.

We say that the set A is *directed* by the relation $\leqslant$ if it has the following properties:

(D1) *If* $x \leqslant y$ *and* $y \leqslant z$, *then* $x \leqslant z$.

(D2) $x \leqslant x$.

(D3) *For every* $x, y \in A$ *there exists a* $z \in A$ *such that* $x \leqslant z$ *and* $y \leqslant z$.

A subset A_0 of the set A which is directed by the relation $\leqslant$ is called *cofinal* in A if for every $x \in A$ there exists a $y \in A_0$ such that $x \leqslant y$. A cofinal subset of a partially ordered set is defined analogously.

Let us suppose that A and B are sets partially ordered (directed) by the relations $\leqslant$ and $\leqslant'$ respectively. The function f of A into B is called *monotone* if for every $x, y \in A$ where $x \leqslant y$ we have $f(x) \leqslant' f(y)$.

§ 4. Axiom of choice. In this book we often use the axiom of choice without special mention. It is often more convenient, however, to use not the axiom of choice in its classical wording but some theorems of set theory equivalent to the axiom of choice. We shall prove the equivalence of the axiom of choice to three such theorems, but first we need some definitions to formulate those theorems.

An element a belonging to a partially ordered set A is called a *maximal element* of that set if the relation $a \leqslant b, b \in A$ holds only for $b = a$.

Suppose that subsets of a certain set A can have a property $\mathfrak{W}$. Property $\mathfrak{W}$ is said to be of *finite character* if the empty set has this property and for every $A_0 \subset A$ the set A_0 has property $\mathfrak{W}$ if and only if every finite subset of the set A_0 has this property.

We will now formulate the axiom of choice and three theorems equivalent to it.

AXIOM OF CHOICE. *For every family $\{A_s\}_{s \in S}$ composed of non-empty sets there exists a function f defined on the set S such that $f(s) \in A_s$ for every $s \in S$.*

ZERMELO'S THEOREM ON WELL-ORDERING. *For every set A there exists a relation $<$ which well-orders the set A.*

TUKEY'S LEMMA. *If $\mathfrak{W}$ is a property of finite character which can be exhibited by subsets of a set A, then an arbitrary subset of the set A which has property $\mathfrak{W}$ is contained in a maximal set A_0 which has that property, i.e. in such a set A_0 having property $\mathfrak{W}$ that for every $A_1 \subset A$ having that property and satisfying the inclusion $A_0 \subset A_1$ the equality $A_0 = A_1$ holds true.*

THE KURATOWSKI-ZORN LEMMA. *If for every linearly ordered subset A_0 of a partially ordered set A there exists an element $a_0 \in A$ such that $a \leqslant a_0$ for every $a \in A_0$, then there exists a maximal element in A.*

The fact that *the Theorem on well-ordering follows from the axiom of choice* is well known and will not be proved here (see for example K. Kuratowski [1961a], p. 96). ∎

Tukey's Lemma follows from the Theorem on well-ordering.

Suppose we are given a set A and a property $\mathfrak{W}$ of finite character which can be exhibited by its subsets. Let us consider a subset $M \subset A$ which has property $\mathfrak{W}$ (M can be empty). By the Theorem on well-ordering, the set $A \setminus M$ can be well ordered; since every well-ordered set is similar to the set of all ordinal numbers less than an ordinal number a, this proves that elements of the set $A \setminus M$ can be set into the following transfinite sequence of type a:

$$x_0, x_1, \ldots, x_\xi, \ldots, \qquad \xi < a.$$

By virtue of the Theorem on defining by transfinite induction, the proof of which does not require the application of the axiom of choice, the conditions:

$$A_0 = M,$$

$$A_{\xi+1} = \begin{cases} A_\xi \cup \{x_\xi\} & \text{if } A_\xi \cup \{x_\xi\} \text{ has property } \mathfrak{W}, \\ A_\xi & \text{otherwise} \end{cases}$$

and

$$A_\lambda = \bigcup_{\xi<\lambda} A_\xi \quad \text{for limit ordinal number } \lambda$$

define a transfinite sequence $A_0, A_1, \ldots, A_\xi, \ldots, \xi < \alpha$ of subsets of the set A which have property $\mathfrak{W}$ (in passing through the limit numbers this follows from the finite character of $\mathfrak{W}$). It can easily be observed that $\bigcup_{\xi<\alpha} A_\xi$ is the maximal subset of A having property $\mathfrak{W}$. ■

Tukey's Lemma implies the Kuratowski-Zorn Lemma.

The property "X is a linearly ordered set" is a property of finite character. Let $A_0 \subset A$ be a maximal linearly ordered subset of the set A which contains the empty set (such a set exists by the Tukey Lemma). Let $a_0 \in A$ be an element of the set A such that $a \leqslant a_0$ for every $a \in A_0$. The element a_0 is a maximal one for the set A. Indeed, for every $a \in A$ such that $a_0 \leqslant a$ it follows from the maximality of A_0 that $a \in A_0$ (otherwise the set $A_0 \cup \{a\}$ would be a linearly ordered set greater than A_0); therefore $a \leqslant a_0$ and $a_0 = a$. ■

The Kuratowski-Zorn Lemma implies the axiom of choice.

Given a family $\{A_s\}_{s\in S}$ consisting of non-empty sets, let us denote by $\mathfrak{A}$ the set of all pairs of the form (T, f), where T is a subset of the set S and f is a function defined on T with values in $\bigcup_{s\in S} A_s$ and such that $f(s) \in A_s$ for every $s \in T$. For $(T_1, f_1), (T_2, f_2) \in \mathfrak{A}$ let us set $(T_1, f_1) \leqslant (T_2, f_2)$ if $T_1 \subset T_2$ and we have the equality $f_1(s) = f_2(s)$ for $s \in T_1$. It can easily be verified that the set $\mathfrak{A}$ is partially ordered by the relation $\leqslant$ and that for any subset $\mathfrak{A}_0 = \{(T_r, f_r)\}_{r\in T}$ of the set $\mathfrak{A}$ that is linearly ordered by $\leqslant$ we have, for any $r \in R$, the inequality $(T_r, f_r) \leqslant (T_0, f_0) \in \mathfrak{A}$, where $T_0 = \bigcup_{r\in R} T_r$ and $f_0(s) = f_r(s)$ for $s \in T_r$. For the maximal element $(T, f) \in \mathfrak{A}$, which exists by the Kuratowski-Zorn Lemma, the equality $T = S$ holds because, otherwise, for some $s_0 \in S \setminus T$ and arbitrary $a_{s_0} \in A_{s_0}$ the formulas

$$T' = T \cup \{s_0\}, \quad f'(s) = f(s) \quad \text{for } s \in S \quad \text{and} \quad f'(s_0) = a_{s_0}$$

would define an element (T', f') greater than (T, f). ■

§ 5. Real numbers. In this book we use the properties of arithmetic operations in the set of real numbers, the properties of the relation $<$ ordering that set, and the notion of absolute value. We assume that the reader is familiar with the notions of a least upper bound, of a limit of a sequence of real numbers, and of a continuous real-valued function. We also use the fact that a non-empty set of real numbers bounded above has a least upper bound, i.e. that the set of real numbers is continuous. An open segment with end-points a and b, where $a < b$, is denoted by (a, b); a closed one by $[a, b]$. To denote segments where only one end-point is included we use the symbols $(a, b]$ or $[a, b)$. The use of the same symbol to denote a pair of real numbers and an open segment does not lead to ambiguity in view of the context. When describing a few examples of topological spaces we use a system of coordinates in the plane.

HISTORICAL REMARKS AND BIBLIOGRAPHIC NOTES

A concise course in set theory is contained in K. Kuratowski's book [1961a]. A more extensive and detailed exposition is given in W. Sierpiński's book [1965] or Hausdorff's book [1914]. Tukey's Lemma has been proved in J. W. Tukey's paper [1940] and the Kuratowski-Zorn Lemma in papers of K. Kuratowski [1922] and M. Zorn [1935].

CHATEPR 1

TOPOLOGICAL SPACES

The present chapter is an introduction to the fundamental notions of general topology.

In Paragraph 1 we define topological spaces and prove some properties of open sets and of families of open sets; we also define a base, a subbase, and a base at a point. We consider the notion of weight and formulate the axioms of countability. Next, we consider closed sets, the closure operator, and the interior operator.

In Paragraph 2 we describe various methods of generating a topology in an arbitrary set.

Paragraph 3 is a continuation of Paragraph 1; we discuss in it the boundary operator and the derived set operator and distinguish more classes of subsets of a topological space: namely dense sets, boundary sets, F_σ-sets, and G_δ-sets.

In Paragraph 4 the notion of a mapping is defined, which is as fundamental for the whole book as the notion of a topological space. Mappings into the segment $[0,1]$ and into the set of all real numbers are treated separately. The notions of a homeomorphism and homeomorphic spaces are also introduced there.

In Paragraph 5 we discuss axioms of separation; they are restrictions imposed on general topological spaces which concern the separation of points and closed sets. In that paragraph we also prove the Urysohn Lemma.

The last paragraph is devoted to nets and filters, i.e. to the two ways of approaching the concept of convergence in topological spaces.

§ 1. Topological spaces. Open and closed sets. Base. Closure and interior of a set. A *topological space* is a pair $(X, \mathfrak{O})$ consisting of a set X and a family $\mathfrak{O}$ of its subsets which is subject to the following conditions:

(O1) $0 \in \mathfrak{O}$, $X \in \mathfrak{O}$.

(O2) *If* $U_1 \in \mathfrak{O}$ *and* $U_2 \in \mathfrak{O}$, *then* $U_1 \cap U_2 \in \mathfrak{O}$.

(O3) *If* $U_s \in \mathfrak{O}$ *for every* $s \in S$, *where* S *is an arbitrary set, then* $\bigcup_{s \in S} U_s \in \mathfrak{O}$.

The set X will be called a *space*, its elements *points* of the space, and subsets belonging to the family $\mathfrak{O}$, sets *open* in the space. The family $\mathfrak{O}$ is also called a *topology* in the set X. Properties (O1)-(O3) of the family of open sets can be formulated in the following manner:

(O1) *The empty set and the whole space are open.*

(O2) *The intersection of two open sets is open.*

(O3) *The union of arbitrarily many open sets is an open set.*

From property (O2) it follows immediately that the intersection of an arbitrary finite number of open sets is an open set.

If for some $x \in X$ and for an open set $U \subset X, x \in U$ holds, then we say that U is a *neighbourhood* of the point x.

A set $V \subset X$ is open if and only if every point $x \in V$ has a neighbourhood U_x contained in V. Indeed, if V is open, then for every $x \in V$ one can set $U_x = V$; conversely, if the condition is satisfied, then $V = \bigcup_{x \in V} U_x$, and by virtue of (O3) the set V is open.

A family $\mathfrak{B} \subset \mathfrak{O}$ is called a *base* of the topological space $(X, \mathfrak{O})$ if every non-empty open set U in the space X is the union of a number of sets belonging to the family $\mathfrak{B}$. It can easily be verified that $\mathfrak{B}$ is a base if and only if for any $x \in X$ and any neighbourhood V of the point x there exists a $U \in \mathfrak{B}$ such that $x \in U \subset V$.

Every base $\mathfrak{B}$ has the following properties:

(B1) *For every $U_1 \in \mathfrak{B}$, $U_2 \in \mathfrak{B}$ and every point $x \in U_1 \cap U_2$ there exists a $U \in \mathfrak{B}$ such that $x \in U \subset U_1 \cap U_2$.*

(B2) *For every $x \in X$ there exists a $U \in \mathfrak{B}$ such that $x \in U$.*

Indeed, property (B1) follows from the fact that $U_1 \cap U_2$ is open; property (B2) follows from the fact that X is open.

A topological space can possess many bases—one of them is the whole family $\mathfrak{O}$. It follows from properties of cardinal numbers that in every space there exists a base of minimal power, i.e. a base $\mathfrak{B}_0$ such that for an arbitrary base $\mathfrak{B}$ of this space the inequality $\overline{\overline{\mathfrak{B}}} \geqslant \overline{\overline{\mathfrak{B}}}_0$ holds. Every base possessing this property will be called a *minimal base*. All minimal bases of a topological space $(X, \mathfrak{O})$ are of the same power. This common power is called the *weight* of the space and is denoted by $w((X, \mathfrak{O}))$.

A family $\mathfrak{S} \subset \mathfrak{O}$ is said to be a *subbase* of the topological space $(X, \mathfrak{O})$ if the family of all finite intersections $U_1 \cap U_2 \cap \ldots \cap U_k$, where $U_i \in \mathfrak{S}$ for $i = 1, 2, \ldots, k$, is a base of the space $(X, \mathfrak{O})$.

A *base* of the space $(X, \mathfrak{O})$ *at the point* $x \in X$ is a family $\mathfrak{B}(x)$ of neighbourhoods of the point x such that for every open set V containing x there exists a $U \in \mathfrak{B}(x)$ such that $x \in U \subset V$. Let a base $\mathfrak{B}$ of the topological space $(X, \mathfrak{O})$ be given. It can easily be verified that the family $\mathfrak{B}(x)$ consisting of all elements of $\mathfrak{B}$ which contain x is a base at the point x.

The *weight* of the space $(X, \mathfrak{O})$ *at the point* $x \in X$ is defined as the least power of bases at this point. Of course, the weight of the space $(X, \mathfrak{O})$ at an arbitrary point is not greater than the weight of the whole space $(X, \mathfrak{O})$.

We say that the space $(X, \mathfrak{O})$ satisfies the *first axiom of countability* if the weight of the space at every point $x \in X$ is not greater than $\aleph_0$.

Spaces of weight not greater than $\aleph_0$ are said to satisfy the *second axiom of countability*.

Let $(X, \mathfrak{O})$ be an arbitrary topological space. Let us consider the collection $\{\mathfrak{B}(x)\}_{x \in X}$, where $\mathfrak{B}(x)$ is a base of the space $(X, \mathfrak{O})$ at the point x.

We are going to show that this collection has the following properties:

(BP1) $\mathfrak{B}(x) \neq 0$ *for every* $x \in X$ *and* $x \in U$ *for every* $U \in \mathfrak{B}(x)$.

(BP2) *If* $x \in U \in \mathfrak{B}(y)$, *then there exists a* $V \in \mathfrak{B}(x)$ *such that* $V \subset U$.

(BP3) *If* $U_1 \in \mathfrak{B}(x)$ *and* $U_2 \in \mathfrak{B}(x)$, *then there exists an* $U \in \mathfrak{B}(x)$ *such that* $U \subset U_1 \cap U_2$.

Condition (BP1) is satisfied by the definition of the family $\mathfrak{B}(x)$. Conditions (BP2) and (BP3) are also satisfied, for $U \in \mathfrak{B}(y)$ and $U_1 \cap U_2$ are open sets containing the point x, and $\mathfrak{B}(x)$ is a base of the space at this point.

The collection $\{\mathfrak{B}(x)\}_{x \in X}$, where $\mathfrak{B}(x)$ is a base of the space $(X, \mathfrak{O})$ at the point x, is called a *neighbourhood system* of the topological space $(X, \mathfrak{O})$.

Let us suppose that a topological space $(X, \mathfrak{O})$ is given. A set F is said to be *closed* in X if the complement $X \setminus F$ is open. From the de Morgan formulas and from (O1)-(O3) the following properties of closed sets follow:

(C1) *The empty set and the whole space are closed.*

(C2) *The union of two closed sets is closed.*

(C3) *The intersection of arbitrarily many closed sets is a closed set.*

As an example, we give a proof for property (C3). Let a family $\{F_s\}_{s \in S}$ of closed sets be given. By definition, the set $U_s = X \setminus F_s$ is open for every $s \in S$. Since

$$\bigcap_{s \in S} F_s = \bigcap_{s \in S} (X \setminus U_s) = X \setminus \bigcup_{s \in S} U_s,$$

and since the set $\bigcup_{s \in S} U_s$ is open, $\bigcap_{s \in S} F_s$ is a closed set.

Sets which are simultaneously open and closed are called *open-and--closed.*

Let us suppose that a set $A \subset X$ is given. Let us consider the family $\mathfrak{C}_A$ of all closed sets containing A. By virtue of (C1), this family is non void and, by (C3), the intersection $\bar{A}$ of all elements of the family $\mathfrak{C}_A$ is closed. It may easily be observed that $\bar{A}$ is the smallest closed set containing A; we call it the *closure* of the set A. In particular, it follows that a set is closed if and only if it is equal to its closure.

For arbitrary subsets A and B of the space X

$$\text{(1)} \qquad \textit{if } A \subset B, \textit{ then } \bar{A} \subset \bar{B}.$$

Indeed, if $A \subset B$, then $\mathfrak{C}_B \subset \mathfrak{C}_A$, therefore $\bar{A} \subset \bar{B}$.

We shall now prove

THEOREM 1. *Let* $(X, \mathfrak{O})$ *be a topological space and let* A *denote an arbitrary subset of* X. *The following conditions are equivalent*:

(i) *The point* x *belongs to* $\bar{A}$.

(ii) *For every base* $\mathfrak{B}(x)$ *at the point* x *and for every* $U \in \mathfrak{B}(x)$, $U \cap A \neq 0$.

(iii) *For a certain base* $\mathfrak{B}(x)$ *at the point* x *and for every* $U \in \mathfrak{B}(x)$, $U \cap A \neq 0$.

Proof. To prove the implication (i) $\Rightarrow$ (ii) let us suppose that condition (ii) is not satisfied, i.e. that $U \cap A = 0$ for a certain base $\mathfrak{B}(x)$ and a certain $U \in \mathfrak{B}(x)$. In this case $A \subset X \setminus U$ and $X \setminus U \in \mathfrak{C}_A$; hence $\bar{A} \subset X \setminus U$ and $x \notin \bar{A}$, i.e. condition (i) is not satisfied.

Since the implication (ii) $\Rightarrow$ (iii) is evident, it is sufficient to prove that (iii) $\Rightarrow$ (i). Let us suppose that condition (i) is not satisfied, i.e. that $x \notin \bar{A}$. There exists, therefore, a set $F \in \mathfrak{C}_A$ such that $x \notin F$. For $V = X \setminus F$ we have

$$\text{(2)} \qquad x \in V \in \mathfrak{O} \quad \text{and} \quad V \cap A = 0.$$

For an arbitrary base $\mathfrak{B}(x)$ at the point x there exists, by definition, an element $U \in \mathfrak{B}(x)$ such that $x \in U \subset V$. It follows from (2) that $U \cap A = 0$, whence (iii) is not satisfied. ∎

COROLLARY. *If for two open sets* U *and* V *we have that* $U \cap V = 0$, *then* $\bar{U} \cap V = U \cap \bar{V} = 0$.

Proof. Let us assume that there exists an $x \in \bar{U} \cap V$ and let $\mathfrak{B}(x)$ denote the family of all open sets containing x. It follows from Theorem 1 that $U \cap V \neq 0$, which is contrary to our assumption. Therefore $\bar{U} \cap V = 0$, and, by the symmetry of the assumptions, $U \cap \bar{V} = 0$. ∎

We shall now examine the closure operator in more detail.

THEOREM 2. *In the topological space* $(X, \mathfrak{O})$ *the closure operator has the following properties*:

(CO1) $\overline{0} = 0$.

(CO2) $A \subset \bar{A}$.

(CO3) $\overline{A \cup B} = \bar{A} \cup \bar{B}$.

(CO4) $\overline{(\bar{A})} = \bar{A}$.

Proof. Properties (CO1) and (CO2) are obvious. Property (CO4) follows from the fact that $\bar{A}$ is a closed set.

It follows from (1) that $\bar{A} \subset \overline{A \cup B}$ and $\bar{B} \subset \overline{A \cup B}$; therefore we have

$$\bar{A} \cup \bar{B} \subset \overline{A \cup B}. \tag{3}$$

By (CO2), $A \subset \bar{A}$ and $B \subset \bar{B}$; therefore $A \cup B \subset \bar{A} \cup \bar{B}$. Since $\bar{A} \cup \bar{B}$ is the union of two closed sets, it is closed. By the definition of closure we have

$$\overline{A \cup B} \subset \bar{A} \cup \bar{B}. \tag{4}$$

Formulas (3) and (4) imply equality (CO3). ■

The largest open set contained in A or, equivalently, the union of all open sets contained in A, is called the *interior* of the set A. The interior of the set A is denoted by $\operatorname{Int} A$. It can easily be observed that a set is open if and only if it is equal to its interior.

The following theorem results immediately from the definition of interior:

THEOREM 3. *Let $(X, \mathfrak{O})$ be a topological space and let A denote an arbitrary subset of X. The point x belongs to* $\operatorname{Int} A$ *if and only if $U \subset A$ for a neighbourhood U of the point x.* ■

The interior operator is closely connected with the closure operator, as is shown by the following theorem.

THEOREM 4. *For an arbitrary $A \subset X$*

$$\operatorname{Int} A = X \setminus (\overline{X \setminus A}).$$

Proof. By virtue of (CO2),

$$X \setminus A \subset \overline{X \setminus A}.$$

Therefore

$$X \setminus \overline{X \setminus A} \subset X \setminus (X \setminus A) = A.$$

Since $X \setminus (\overline{X \setminus A})$ is an open set,

$$X \setminus (\overline{X \setminus A}) \subset \operatorname{Int} A. \tag{5}$$

For every open set U contained in A

$$X \setminus A \subset X \setminus U = \overline{X \setminus U},$$

whence, by (1) and (CO4),

$$\overline{X \setminus A} \subset X \setminus U \quad \text{and} \quad U \subset X \setminus (\overline{X \setminus A}).$$

In particular

$$\operatorname{Int} A \subset X \setminus (\overline{X \setminus A}).$$

This inclusion together with (5) proves our theorem. ■

Theorem 2 and the de Morgan formulas imply

THEOREM 5. *The interior operator in the topological space* $(X, \mathfrak{O})$ *is subject to the following conditions:*

(I1) $\operatorname{Int} X = X$.

(I2) $\operatorname{Int} A \subset A$.

(I3) $\operatorname{Int}(A \cap B) = \operatorname{Int} A \cap \operatorname{Int} B$.

(I4) $\operatorname{Int}(\operatorname{Int} A) = \operatorname{Int} A$. ■

EXAMPLE 1. Let X be an arbitrary set and let $\mathfrak{O}$ denote the family of all its subsets. Evidently $(X, \mathfrak{O})$ is a topological space. Every subset $A \subset X$ is open-and-closed. Every set containing x is a neighbourhood of x. The base of the space is the family of all sets consisting of a single point. It is a minimal base, whence the weight of $(X, \mathfrak{O})$ is equal to $\overline{\overline{X}}$. The family consisting of one set $\{x\}$ is the base of the space at the point x; hence $(X, \mathfrak{O})$ satisfies the first axiom of countability. An arbitrary set $A \subset X$ is equal to its closure and to its interior. ■

The space described above is called the *discrete space.*

EXAMPLE 2. Let X be an arbitrary infinite set. Let us choose a point $x_0 \in X$ and let $\mathfrak{O}$ be the family consisting of all sets which do not contain the point x_0 and of all sets of the form $X \setminus F$, where F is a finite subset of X. The reader can verify that $(X, \mathfrak{O})$ is a topological space. Every point different from x_0 is open-and-closed in X. The point x_0 is closed but not open. The family consisting of the sets $\{x\}$ for every $x \neq x_0$, and of the sets $X \setminus F$, where F is a finite subset of X, is a minimal base. The family consisting of sets of the form $\{x\}$, for $x \neq x_0$, and of sets of the form $X \setminus \{x\}$, is a subbase. The weight of the space $(X, \mathfrak{O})$ and the weight of the space $(X, \mathfrak{O})$ at the point x_0 are equal to $\overline{\overline{X}}$. For an arbitrary $A \subset X$ we have

$$\overline{A} = \begin{cases} A, & \text{if } A \text{ is finite,} \\ A \cup \{x_0\}, & \text{if } A \text{ is infinite} \end{cases}$$

and

$$\operatorname{Int} A = \begin{cases} A, & \text{if } X \setminus A \text{ is finite,} \\ A \setminus \{x_0\}, & \text{if } X \setminus A \text{ is infinite.} \end{cases}$$

This implies, in particular, that no two closed and infinite sets in X are disjoint. ■

The spaces which will be described in Examples 3 and 4 are of special importance for further consideration.

EXAMPLE 3. Let us consider the set R of all real numbers. Let us define $\mathfrak{O}$ as the family of all sets U which are subject to the following condition:

For every $x \in U$ there exists an $\varepsilon > 0$ such that $(x-\varepsilon, x+\varepsilon) \subset U$.

Of course, the family $\mathfrak{O}$ defined in this manner possesses properties (O1)-(O3). It follows from the definition of limit that a set A is closed if and only if together with every convergent sequence it contains its limit. A base of the space consists of open intervals with rational end-points; this is the minimal base. Therefore, $(R, \mathfrak{O})$ satisfies the second (and thus also the first) axiom of countability. The topology $\mathfrak{O}$ is called the *natural topology* in the set of all real numbers. ■

EXAMPLE 4. Let I denote the segment $[0, 1]$. Let us define the family $\mathfrak{O}$ of open sets in I as the family of all intersections of open sets in R (with respect to the natural topology) with the segment I. A base of open sets in I is the family $\mathfrak{B}$ consisting of all sets of the form (r_1, r_2), $[0, r_1)$, $(r_2, 1]$, where r_1 and r_2 are rational numbers of I and $0 < r_1 < r_2 < 1$. Sets of the second and of the third classes form a subbase of the segment. The space $(I, \mathfrak{O})$ satisfies the second axiom of countability. A set $A \subset I$ is closed in I if and only if it is closed in R. The topology defined in this manner is called the *natural topology* of the segment I. ■

From the above examples it follows that in the same set X there are many ways of selecting a family $\mathfrak{O}$ such that the pair $(X, \mathfrak{O})$ is a topological space. Let $\mathfrak{O}_1$ and $\mathfrak{O}_2$ be two such families; we shall say that the topology $\mathfrak{O}_1$ is *stronger* than the topology $\mathfrak{O}_2$ (or that $\mathfrak{O}_2$ is *weaker* than $\mathfrak{O}_1$) if $\mathfrak{O}_1 \supset \mathfrak{O}_2$. The strongest topology in the set X is the topology $\mathfrak{O}$ consisting of all subsets of X, i.e. the topology of the discrete space.

Let us consider an arbitrary infinite set X and let the family of open sets $\mathfrak{O}_1$ be as in Example 2; Let the family $\mathfrak{O}_2$ be analogously constructed for a point $x_1 \neq x_0$. The topologies $\mathfrak{O}_1$ and $\mathfrak{O}_2$ in the set X are not comparable as one is not stronger than the other.

In general, we shall consider only one family of open sets in X. Consequently we shall denote the topological space by the letter X instead of the symbol $(X, \mathfrak{O})$, as we have done before. This notation is not absolutely correct, but the context will always clarify which topology $\mathfrak{O}$ in the set X is considered. Often, we shall simply say "a space" instead of "a topological space".

We shall now prove two theorems concerning families of open sets in a space of weight $\mathfrak{m}$.

THEOREM 6. *Let a topological space X of weight $\mathfrak{m}$ and a family $\{U_s\}_{s\in S}$ of its open subsets be given. Then there exists a subset $S_1 \subset S$ such that*

$$\bigcup_{s\in S_1} U_s = \bigcup_{s\in S} U_s \quad \textit{and} \quad \overline{\overline{S}}_1 \leqslant \mathfrak{m}.$$

Proof. Let $\mathfrak{B}_0$ be a minimal base of the space X. Let us denote by $\mathfrak{B}_1$ the subset of $\mathfrak{B}_0$ consisting of those $W \in \mathfrak{B}_0$ for which there exists an $s \in S$ such that $W \subset U_s$. Let us assign an $s = s(W) \in S$ to every $W \in \mathfrak{B}_1$ in such a manner that

(6) $$W \subset U_{s(W)}.$$

Thus we have defined a function s of the set $\mathfrak{B}_1$ into the set S. Let $S_1 = s(\mathfrak{B}_1) \subset S$; we shall show that the set S_1 has the required properties.

Since $\overline{\overline{\mathfrak{B}}}_0 = \mathfrak{m}$, $\overline{\overline{S}}_1 = \overline{\overline{s(\mathfrak{B}_1)}} \leqslant \overline{\overline{\mathfrak{B}}}_1 \leqslant \overline{\overline{\mathfrak{B}}}_0 = \mathfrak{m}$ holds. Now, let an element $x \in \bigcup_{s\in S} U_s$ be given. There exists an $s \in S$ such that $x \in U_s$. By the definition of a base there exists a $W \in \mathfrak{B}_0$ such that $x \in W \subset U_s$. Therefore $W \in \mathfrak{B}_1$ and $s(W) \in S_1$. It follows from (6) that

$$x \in W \subset U_{s(W)} \subset \bigcup_{s\in S_1} U_s;$$

therefore, $\bigcup_{s\in S} U_s \subset \bigcup_{s\in S_1} U_s$. The inverse inclusion is obvious. ■

THEOREM 7. *Let a topological space X of weight $\mathfrak{m} \geqslant \aleph_0$ be given and let $\mathfrak{B}$ be its base. Then there exists a subfamily $\mathfrak{B}_1 \subset \mathfrak{B}$ which is also a base and such that $\overline{\overline{\mathfrak{B}}}_1 = \mathfrak{m}$.*

Proof. Let us consider a minimal base $\mathfrak{B}_0 = \{W_t\}_{t\in T}$ of the space X and let $\mathfrak{B} = \{U_s\}_{s\in S}$. For every $t \in T$ let

$$S(t) = \{s \in S\colon U_s \subset W_t\}.$$

Since $\mathfrak{B}$ is a base of the space X, the equality $\bigcup_{s\in S(t)} U_s = W_t$ holds. By virtue of Theorem 6, there exists a subset $S_1(t) \subset S(t)$ such that

(7) $$W_t = \bigcup_{s\in S(t)} U_s = \bigcup_{s\in S_1(t)} U_s,$$

and

(8) $$\overline{\overline{S_1(t)}} \leqslant \mathfrak{m}.$$

Let $\mathfrak{B}_1 = \{U_s\}_{s\in S_1(t), t\in T}$. Since $\overline{\overline{T}} = \mathfrak{m}$, by virtue of (8) and the equality $\mathfrak{m}^2 = \mathfrak{m}$, we have $\overline{\overline{\mathfrak{B}}}_1 \leqslant \mathfrak{m}$. We shall show that $\mathfrak{B}_1$ is a base.

Let an arbitrary point $x \in X$ and its neighbourhood U be given. Since $\mathfrak{B}_0$ is a base, there exists a $t \in T$ such that

$$x \in W_t \subset U.$$

By virtue of (7), there exists an $s \in S_1(t)$, i.e. a $U_s \in \mathfrak{B}_1$ such that

$$x \in U_s \subset W_t \subset U;$$

therefore, $\mathfrak{B}_1$ is a base and $\overline{\overline{\mathfrak{B}_1}} = \mathfrak{m}$. ■

EXERCISES

A. Show that for arbitrary subsets A and B of a topological space the following inclusions are true:

$$\overline{A \cap B} \subset \overline{A} \cap \overline{B}, \quad \text{and} \quad \overline{A} \setminus \overline{B} \subset \overline{A \setminus B}.$$

Can the inclusions in the above formulas be replaced by equalities?

B. Show that for an arbitrary sequence $A_1, A_2, \ldots,$ of subsets of a topologica space we have

$$\overline{\bigcup_{i=1}^{\infty} A_i} = \bigcup_{i=1}^{\infty} \overline{A_i} \cup \bigcap_{i=1}^{\infty} \overline{\bigcup_{j=0}^{\infty} A_{i+j}}.$$

Give an example which shows that the above formula would not be correct if we ommitted the second term on the right side.

C. A subset A of a topological space is called a *closed domain* if $A = \overline{\operatorname{Int} A}$, and an *open domain* if $A = \operatorname{Int} \overline{A}$. Show that the union of two closed domains is a closed domain and that the complement of a closed domain is an open domain.

D. Let a set X and a family $\{\mathfrak{O}_s\}_{s \in S}$ of topologies in X be given. Show that $\bigcap_{s \in S} \mathfrak{O}_s$ is also a topology in X. Is the union $\bigcup_{s \in S} \mathfrak{O}_s$ also a topology? What about the union of two topologies?

§ 2. Various methods of generating a topology. Let us suppose that a set X is given. By the *generation of a topology* in X we mean the determination of a family $\mathfrak{O}$ of subsets of X which is subject to conditions (O1)-(O3), i.e. a family $\mathfrak{O}$ such that the pair $(X, \mathfrak{O})$ is a topological space. Sometimes it is more convenient not to describe the family $\mathfrak{O}$ of open sets directly. We shall give some other methods of generating the topology in the set X; they consist in the definition of a base, a neighbourhood system, a family of closed sets, a closure operator, and an operator of interior.

THEOREM 1. *Suppose we are given a set X and a family $\mathfrak{B}$ of its subsets which satisfies conditions* (B1) *and* (B2) *of the previous paragraph. Let us denote by $\mathfrak{O}$ the family of all sets which are unions of subfamilies of the family $\mathfrak{B}$, i.e.*

$$(U \in \mathfrak{O}) \equiv \Big(U = \bigcup_{s \in S} U_s \text{ for a subfamily } \mathfrak{B}_0 = \{U_s\}_{s \in S} \text{ of the family } \mathfrak{B}\Big).$$

The family $\mathfrak{O}$ has properties (O1)-(O3). *The family $\mathfrak{B}$ is a base of the topological space $(X, \mathfrak{O})$.*

The topology $\mathfrak{O}$ is said to be *generated by the base* $\mathfrak{B}$.

Proof. Condition (O1) is satisfied, for the empty set is the union of the empty family of elements of $\mathfrak{B}$, and the union of all elements of $\mathfrak{B}$ is, by (B2), the whole set X. Let $U_1, U_2 \in \mathfrak{O}$, whence

$$U_1 = \bigcup_{s \in S} U_s, \quad U_2 = \bigcup_{t \in T} U_t, \quad \text{where } U_s, U_t \in \mathfrak{B} \text{ for } s \in S \text{ and } t \in T.$$

Since

$$U_1 \cap U_2 = \bigcup_{(s,t) \in S \times T} U_s \cap U_t,$$

to prove (O2) it is sufficient to show that $U_s \cap U_t$ is the union of sets from the family $\mathfrak{B}$. Let us consider an arbitrary point $x \in U_s \cap U_t$. By condition (B1), there exists a set $U(x) \in \mathfrak{B}$ such that

$$x \in U(x) \subset U_s \cap U_t.$$

It can easily be seen that

$$U_s \cap U_t = \bigcup_{x \in U_s \cap U_t} U(x),$$

whence condition (O2) is satisfied. In order to prove (O3) it is sufficient to use the definition of the family $\mathfrak{O}$.

The family $\mathfrak{B}$ is obviously a base of the space $(X, \mathfrak{O})$. ■

EXAMPLE 1. Let $X = R$ be the set of all real numbers. Let us define $\mathfrak{B}$ as the family of all intervals $[x, r)$, where x is an arbitrary element of the set X and r is a rational number, $x < r$. The family $\mathfrak{B}$ possesses properties (B1) and (B2). Elements of the family $\mathfrak{B}$ are open-and-closed with respect to the topology generated by the base. We shall show that the base $\mathfrak{B}$ is minimal; since $\overline{\overline{\mathfrak{B}}} = \mathfrak{c}$, this implies that $w(X) = \mathfrak{c}$. Indeed, for an arbitrary family of open sets $\mathfrak{R}$ such that $\overline{\overline{\mathfrak{R}}} < \mathfrak{c}$, a point $x_0 \in X$ can be found which is not the greatest lower bound of any set belonging to $\mathfrak{R}$. Therefore, the open set $[x_0, x_0+1)$ would not be the union of elements of the family $\mathfrak{R}$ and $\mathfrak{R}$ would not be a base. ■

THEOREM 2. *Suppose we are given a set X and a collection $\{\mathfrak{B}(x)\}_{x \in X}$ of families satisfying conditions* (BP1)-(BP3) *of the previous paragraph. Let us denote by $\mathfrak{O}$ the family of all sets which are unions of subfamilies of the family $\bigcup_{x \in X} \mathfrak{B}(x)$. Then the family $\mathfrak{O}$ has properties* (O1)-(O3) *and the collection $\{\mathfrak{B}(x)\}_{x \in X}$ is a neighbourhood system of the space $(X, \mathfrak{O})$.*

The topology $\mathfrak{O}$ is said to be *generated by the neighbourhood system* $\{\mathfrak{B}(x)\}_{x \in X}$.

The proof of Theorem 2, which is analogous to the proof of Theorem 1, is omitted. ■

EXAMPLE 2. Let X be a subset of a plane $R \times R$ defined by the condition $y \geqslant 0$, i.e. let X be the upper half-plane. Let the straight line $y = 0$

be denoted by X_1 and let $X_2 = X \setminus X_1$. Let $U(x, r)$ denote the set of all points of X_2 which lie inside the circle of radius r tangent to X_1 at the point x for every $x \in X_1$ and a real number $r > 0$; let $U_i(x) = U(x, 1/i) \cup \{x\}$ for $i = 1, 2, \ldots$ Let $U(x, r)$ denote the set of all points of X_2 which lie inside the circle with radius r and centre at x for every $x \in X_2$ and a real number $r > 0$; let $U_i(x) = U(x, 1/i)$ for $i = 1, 2, \ldots$ It can easily be verified that the collection $\{B(x)\}_{x \in X}$, where $B(x) = \{U_i(x)\}_{i=1}^{\infty}$, is subject to conditions (BP1)-(BP3). The set X_1 is closed with respect to the topology generated by the neighbourhood system $\{\mathfrak{B}(x)\}_{x \in X}$. ■

THEOREM 3. *Let us suppose that the set X and a family $\mathfrak{C}$ of its subsets which satisfiesc onditions* (C1)-(C3) *of the previous paragraph are given. Let us put*

$$\mathfrak{O} = \{X \setminus F : F \in \mathfrak{C}\}.$$

Then the family $\mathfrak{O}$ satisfies conditions (O1)-(O3) *and family $\mathfrak{C}$ is the family of all sets closed in the topological space* $(X, \mathfrak{O})$.

The topology $\mathfrak{O}$ is said to be *generated by the family $\mathfrak{C}$ of closed subsets*. ■

EXAMPLE 3. Let X be an arbitrary infinite set. Let us consider the family $\mathfrak{C}$ of subsets of X consisting of all finite subsets and of the set X. The family $\mathfrak{C}$ satisfies conditions (C1)-(C3). The sets open with respect to the topology determined by the family $\mathfrak{C}$ are complements of finite sets and the empty set. Every two non-empty open sets have a non-empty intersection. ■

THEOREM 4. *Let us suppose that we are given a set X and an operator which assigns to every set $A \subset X$ a set $\bar{A} \subset X$ in such a manner that conditions* (CO1)-(CO4) *of the previous paragraph are satisfied. Let*

$$\mathfrak{O} = \{X \setminus A : A = \bar{A} \subset X\}.$$

Then the family $\mathfrak{O}$ has properties (O1)-(O3), *and $\bar{A}$ is the closure of the set A in the space* $(X, \mathfrak{O})$.

The topology $\mathfrak{O}$ is said to be *generated by the closure operator*.

Proof. In order to prove the first part of the theorem it is sufficient to show that the family $\mathfrak{C}$ of sets satisfying the condition $A = \bar{A}$ has properties (C1)-(C3). Since $\bar{A} \subset X$ for every A, the inclusion $\bar{X} \subset X$ holds. This combined with (CO2) proves the equality $\bar{X} = X$. Furthermore, we have by (CO1) that $\bar{0} = 0$, so that the family $\mathfrak{C}$ has property (C1). Let $A_1, A_2 \in \mathfrak{C}$, i.e. let $A_1 = \bar{A}_1$, $A_2 = \bar{A}_2$. By (CO3),

$$\overline{A_1 \cup A_2} = \bar{A}_1 \cup \bar{A}_2 = A_1 \cup A_2;$$

therefore $\mathfrak{C}$ satisfies property (C2).

Let us observe that (CO3) implies the following:

(1) $$\text{if } A \subset B, \text{ then } \bar{A} \subset \bar{B}.$$

Indeed, if $A \subset B$, then $A \cup B = B$; therefore $\bar{A} \cup \bar{B} = \overline{A \cup B} = \bar{B}$, whence $\bar{A} \subset \bar{B}$.

Let us now suppose that a family $\{A_s\}_{s \in S}$ consisting of elements of $\mathfrak{C}$ is given. This means that $A_s = \bar{A}_s$ for every $s \in S$. Since $\bigcap_{s \in S} A_s \subset A_s$, we infer from (1) that $\overline{\bigcap_{s \in S} A_s} \subset \bar{A}_s = A_s$. Hence $\overline{\bigcap_{s \in S} A_s} \subset \bigcap_{s \in S} A_s$ and according to (CO2), $\overline{\bigcap_{s \in S} A_s} = \bigcap_{s \in S} A_s$, which proves that $\mathfrak{C}$ has property (C3).

Let $\tilde{A}$ denote the closure of the set A in the topological space $(X, \mathfrak{O})$. We shall show that $\tilde{A} = \bar{A}$ for every $A \subset X$. By virtue of (CO4), $\bar{A} \in \mathfrak{C}$ for every A; therefore $\tilde{A} \subset \bar{A}$. By (1), $\bar{A} \subset \bar{F} = F$ for every closed set F containing A, whence $\bar{A} \subset \tilde{A} = \bigcap_{F = \bar{F} \supset A} F$, which proves the equality $\tilde{A} = \bar{A}$. Thus the proof of our theorem is completed. ■

EXAMPLE 4. Let X be an arbitrary set containing more than one point and x_0 an arbitrary point of this set. Let us define $\bar{A} = A \cup \{x_0\}$ for every non-empty set $A \subset X$ and let $\bar{0} = 0$. The closure operator defined in this manner has properties (CO1)-(CO4). In the topology generated by this operator the only one-point closed set is x_0; other points are open but not closed. ■

THEOREM 5. *Let us suppose that we are given a set X and an operator which assigns a set* $\operatorname{Int} A$ *to every set* $A \subset X$ *in such a manner that conditions* (I1)-(I4) *of the previous paragraph are satisfied. Let*

$$\mathfrak{O} = \{A : A = \operatorname{Int} A\}.$$

Then the family $\mathfrak{O}$ *has properties* (O1)-(O3), *and the interior of the set* A *in the topological space* $(X, \mathfrak{O})$ *is the set* $\operatorname{Int} A$.

The topology $\mathfrak{O}$ is said to be *generated by the operator of interior.*

We omit the proof of Theorem 5, which is dual to the proof of Theorem 4. ■

EXAMPLE 5. Let X be an arbitrary set containing more than one point. Let us put $\operatorname{Int} A = 0$ if $A \subset X$, $A \neq X$ and $\operatorname{Int} X = X$. The operator of interior defined above has properties (I1)-(I4). In the space $(X, \mathfrak{O})$, where $\mathfrak{O}$ denotes the topology generated by the operator of interior, the only open sets are the empty set and the whole space. The topology $\mathfrak{O}$ is the weakest topology in the set X. ■

EXERCISES

A. Formulate and prove a theorem on the generation of a topology by a subbase of open sets, analogous to the theorems of this paragraph.

B. Let X be an arbitrary set and let $\mathfrak{B}_1, \mathfrak{B}_2$ denote two families of subsets of X which satisfy conditions (B1) and (B2). Show that the topologies generated in X

by the bases $\mathfrak{B}_1$ and $\mathfrak{B}_2$ are identical if and only if for an arbitrary choice of the point $x \in X$ and for every set $U \in \mathfrak{B}_1$ containing the point x there exists a set $W \in \mathfrak{B}_2$ such that $x \in W \subset U$, and for every set $U \in \mathfrak{B}_2$ containing the point x there exists a set $W \in \mathfrak{B}_1$ such that $x \in W \subset U$.

State and prove an analogous theorem for a topology generated by a neighbourhood system.

C. Show that for every topological space $(X, \mathfrak{O})$ and for a base of that space (a neighbourhood system, the family of closed sets, the closure operator, the operator of interior) the topology determined in X by that base (neighbourhood system, etc.) is identical with the initial topology in X.

§ 3. Boundary of a set and derived set. Dense sets and boundary sets. F_σ-sets and G_δ-sets. In the first paragraph we got acquainted with two operators defined on subsets of a topological space: the closure operator and the operator of interior. Also, we defined some classes of subsets of topological spaces, namely open sets and closed sets, and we examined their properties. This paragraph is a continuation of paragraph one. We further define two operators and distinguish a few classes of subsets of a topological space.

Let X be a topological space and let $A \subset X$. The set $\mathrm{Fr}A = \bar{A} \cap \overline{X \setminus A}$ is called the *boundary* of the set A.

From Theorem 1.3 follows immediately

THEOREM 1. *Let X be a topological space and let A denote an arbitrary subset of X. The point x belongs to* $\mathrm{Fr}A$ *if and only if for every element U of a certain (or, equivalently, of an arbitrary) base $\mathfrak{B}(x)$ at the point x we have that $U \cap A \neq 0 \neq U \setminus A$.* ■

Let us mention some algebraic properties of the boundary operator.

THEOREM 2. *The boundary operator has the following properties*:

(1) $\mathrm{Int}A = A \setminus \mathrm{Fr}A$.
(2) $\bar{A} = A \cup \mathrm{Fr}A$.
(3) $\mathrm{Fr}(A \cup B) \subset \mathrm{Fr}A \cup \mathrm{Fr}B$.
(4) $\mathrm{Fr}(A \cap B) \subset \mathrm{Fr}A \cup \mathrm{Fr}B$.
(5) $\mathrm{Fr}(X \setminus A) = \mathrm{Fr}A$.
(6) *If A is an open set, then* $\mathrm{Fr}A = \bar{A} \setminus A$.
(7) $\mathrm{Fr}A = 0$ *if and only if A is open-and-closed.*

Proof. The proof consists of a simple calculation. By way of example, we prove properties (1) and (3)

$$A \setminus \mathrm{Fr}A = A \setminus [\bar{A} \cap (\overline{X \setminus A})]$$
$$= (A \setminus \bar{A}) \cup (A \setminus \overline{X \setminus A}) = A \setminus (\overline{X \setminus A}) = A \cap \mathrm{Int}A = \mathrm{Int}A.$$

$$\mathrm{Fr}(A \cup B) = \overline{A \cup B} \cap [\overline{X \setminus (A \cup B)}]$$
$$= (\bar{A} \cup \bar{B}) \cap [\overline{(X \setminus A) \cap (X \setminus B)}] \subset (\bar{A} \cup \bar{B}) \cap [(\overline{X \setminus A}) \cap (\overline{X \setminus B})]$$
$$= [\bar{A} \cap (\overline{X \setminus A}) \cap (\overline{X \setminus B})] \cup [\bar{B} \cap (\overline{X \setminus A}) \cap (\overline{X \setminus B})] \subset \mathrm{Fr}A \cup \mathrm{Fr}B. \ ■$$

A point x is said to be an *accumulation point* of the set A if $x \in \overline{A \setminus \{x\}}$. The set of all accumulation points of the set A is called the *derived set* of set A and denoted by A^{d}.

THEOREM 3. *Let X be a topological space and let A denote an arbitrary subset of X. The point x belongs to A^{d} if and only if each element U of a certain (or, equivalently, of an arbitrary) base $\mathfrak{B}(x)$ at the point x contains a point of the set A different from the point x.*

Proof. Let us suppose that x is an accumulation point of the set A. Then $x \in \overline{A \setminus \{x\}}$ and for every $U \in \mathfrak{B}(x)$ we have $U \cap (A \setminus \{x\}) \neq 0$. Hence $U \cap A \setminus \{x\} \neq 0$ and U contains a point of the set A different from the point x.

If every element $U \in \mathfrak{B}(x)$, where $\mathfrak{B}(x)$ is a base at the point x, contains a point of the set A different from x, then the intersection $U \cap (A \setminus \{x\})$ is non-empty and, by Theorem 1.1, $x \in \overline{A \setminus \{x\}}$, i.e. x is an accumulation point of the set A. ■

Points of the set $A \setminus A^{\mathrm{d}}$ are called *isolated points* of the set A. The point x is an isolated point of the space X if and only if $\{x\}$ is an open set. Indeed, $\{x\}$ is an open set if and only if $\{x\} = X \setminus \overline{X \setminus \{x\}}$, i.e. if $x \notin \overline{X \setminus (x)}$.

The proof of the following theorem is left to the reader as an exercise.

THEOREM 4. *The derived set has the following properties:*

(1) $\bar{A} = A \cup A^{\mathrm{d}}$.

(2) *If* $A \subset B$, *then* $A^{\mathrm{d}} \subset B^{\mathrm{d}}$.

(3) $(A \cup B)^{\mathrm{d}} = A^{\mathrm{d}} \cup B^{\mathrm{d}}$.

(4) $\bigcup_{s \in S} A_s^{\mathrm{d}} \subset \big(\bigcup_{s \in S} A_s\big)^{\mathrm{d}}$. ■

By means of the operators, defined above, operating on subsets of a topological space the following classes of sets can be distinguished:

A set A is said to be *dense* in the space X if $\bar{A} = X$.

A set A is said to be a *boundary set* in the space X if $\operatorname{Int} A = 0$.

A set A is said to be *nowhere dense* in the space X if $\bar{A}$ is a boundary set.

A set A is said to be *dense in itself* if $A \subset A^{\mathrm{d}}$.

THEOREM 5. *The set A is dense in the space X if and only if every non--empty open set in X contains points of the set A.*

The set A is a boundary set in the space X if and only if every non-empty open set in X contains points of the complement of the set A.

The set A is nowhere dense in the space X if and only if every non--empty open set contains a non-empty open set which is disjoint with A. ■

In the sequel we will use the following two theorems.

THEOREM 6. *If D is a dense subset of the topological space X, we have*

$$\bar{U} = \overline{U \cap D}$$

for every open set $U \subset X$.

Proof. For every $x \in \overline{U}$ and for an arbitrary neighbourhood W of the point x, the set $W \cap U$ is non-empty and open in X. By virtue of the previous theorem, we have that $W \cap U \cap D \neq 0$. Hence, from Theorem 1.1, we infer that $x \in \overline{U \cap D}$. Thus we have proved the inclusion

$$\overline{U} \subset \overline{U \cap D},$$

and the inverse inclusion is obvious. ∎

THEOREM 7. *A topological space which has a base of power* $\leqslant \mathfrak{m}$ *contains a dense subset of power* $\leqslant \mathfrak{m}$.

Proof. Let $\mathfrak{B} = \{U_s\}_{s \in S}$ denote a base of the space X consisting of non-empty sets and such that $\overline{\overline{S}} \leqslant \mathfrak{m}$. For every $s \in S$ let us choose an arbitrary element $x_s \in U_s$. We shall show that the set $D = \bigcup_{s \in S} \{x_s\}$ is dense in X. Indeed, every non-empty open set in the space X contains a set $U_s \in \mathfrak{B}$, and consequently, it also contains the point $x_s \in D$. ∎

A space X which contains a countable dense subset is said to be *separable*.

Thus Theorem 7 implies the following:

COROLLARY. *Every space which satisfies the second axiom of countability is separable.* ∎

EXAMPLE 1. In the discrete space X the boundary and the derived set of every subset are empty. The set of all rational numbers is simultaneously dense and boundary in the set of all real numbers and in the space of Example 2.1. The set $X_2 \subset X$, where X is the space constructed in Example 2.2, is dense in X and the set X_1 is nowhere dense in X. The first of those sets is dense in itself while the derived set of the second one is empty.

The space X constructed in Example 1.2 has only one accumulation point — the point x_0; all other points are isolated. The set of real numbers, the segment I, and the spaces constructed in Examples 2.1 and 2.2 are separable. A discrete space X is separable if and only if $\overline{\overline{X}} \leqslant \aleph_0$. ∎

The union of a countable number of closed sets in the topological space X is called an *F_σ-set*. The intersection of a countable number of open sets is called a *G_δ-set*. It follows directly from the definition that the complement of an F_σ-set is a G_δ-set and conversely.

The intersection of two F_σ-sets is an F_σ-set. Indeed, if $E = \bigcup_{i=1}^{\infty} E_i$, $F = \bigcup_{i=1}^{\infty} F_i$, where E_i, F_i are closed sets, then evidently $E \cap F = \bigcup_{i,j=1}^{\infty} (E_i \cap F_j)$, thus $E \cap F$ is an F_σ-set. Similarly it can be proved that the union of two G_δ-sets is a G_δ-set. Of course, the union (the intersection) of a countable number of F_σ-sets (G_δ-sets) is an F_σ-set (a G_δ-set). The set of all rational numbers is an F_σ-set in the space R; that it is not a G_δ-set is not obvious (see Exercise 3.8.1 below).

EXERCISES

A. Prove that in an arbitrary topological space the union of two nowhere dense sets is a nowhere dense set and that the union of a boundary set and a nowhere dense set is a boundary set. Is the union of two boundary sets necessarily a boundary set?

B. Let n be a natural number; the *n-th derived set* $A^{(n)}$ of the set A in a topological space X is defined inductively by means of the formulas:

$$A^{(1)} = A^{\mathrm{d}}, \quad A^{(n)} = (A^{(n-1)})^{\mathrm{d}}.$$

Give an example of a set of real numbers which have three different consecutive derived sets.

C. Prove that every open subset of a space which is dense in itself is also dense in itself.

D. Generalize Theorem 6 by proving that for every open subset U of a topological space X and for every $A \subset X$ the equality

$$\overline{U \cap \overline{A}} = \overline{U \cap A}$$

holds.

Hint: Make use of the second formula from exercise 1. A and of the fact that $U = X \setminus \overline{X \setminus U}$.

§ 4. Mappings. Real-valued functions. Homeomorphisms. Let us suppose that two topological spaces $(X, \mathfrak{O})$ and $(Y, \mathfrak{O}')$ are given. The function f of the set X into Y is called a *mapping* of the space $(X, \mathfrak{O})$ into the space $(Y, \mathfrak{O}')$ if $f^{-1}(U) \in \mathfrak{O}$ for every $U \in \mathfrak{O}'$, i.e. if the inverse image of every open set in Y is open in X. Instead of writing that f is a mapping of the space X into the space Y we shall frequently write $f: X \to Y$(1).

The definition of a mapping adopted above depends on the notion of an open set. Since we will frequently generate a topology by means of one of the methods described in Paragraph 2, it will be convenient to have some criteria, formulated in suitable terms, which would allow us to ascertain whether f is a mapping. These criteria are contained in the following:

THEOREM 1. *Let X and Y be topological spaces and let f be a function of the set X into the set Y. The following conditions are equivalent:*

(i) *f is a mapping.*

(ii) *Inverse images of elements of a subbase $\mathfrak{S}$ of the space Y are open in X.*

(ii′) *Inverse images of elements of a base $\mathfrak{B}$ of the space Y are open in X.*

(iii) *If $\{\mathfrak{B}(x)\}_{x \in X}$ and $\{\mathfrak{D}(y)\}_{y \in Y}$ are systems of neighbourhoods of the spaces X and Y respectively, then for every $x \in X$ and $V \in \mathfrak{D}(f(x))$ there exists a $U \in \mathfrak{B}(x)$ such that $f(U) \subset V$.*

(iv) *The inverse image of every closed set in Y is closed in X.*

---

(1) By a mapping we understand in this book a function which satisfies an additional condition. This term is usually used as a synonym of "a function" or "a map", and the mappings which satisfy this additional condition are called *continuous* mappings or functions.

(v) $f(\bar{A}) \subset \overline{f(A)}$, *for every* $A \subset X$.
(v′) $\overline{f^{-1}(B)} \subset f^{-1}(\bar{B})$, *for every* $B \subset Y$.
(vi) $f^{-1}(\operatorname{Int} B) \subset \operatorname{Int} f^{-1}(B)$, *for every* $B \subset Y$.

Proof. The implication (i) ⇒ (ii) is obvious.

We shall show that (ii) ⇒ (ii′). Let us suppose that there is given a subbase $\mathfrak{S}$ of the space Y such that $f^{-1}(U)$ is open for every $U \in \mathfrak{S}$. Let us denote by $\mathfrak{B}$ the base of Y consisting of all intersections $U_1 \cap U_2 \cap \ldots \cap U_k$ of elements from $\mathfrak{S}$. Since

$$f^{-1}(U_1 \cap U_2 \cap \ldots \cap U_k) = f^{-1}(U_1) \cap f^{-1}(U_2) \cap \ldots \cap f^{-1}(U_k),$$

the inverse images of elements of $\mathfrak{B}$ are open in X.

Now we shall prove that (ii′) ⇒ (iii). If $V \in \mathfrak{D}(f(x))$, then there exists a $W \in \mathfrak{B}$ such that $f(x) \in W \subset V$. By assumption, $f^{-1}(W)$ is open. Since $x \in f^{-1}(W)$, there exists a $U \in \mathfrak{B}(x)$ such that $U \subset f^{-1}(W)$, whence $f(U) \subset ff^{-1}(W) \subset W \subset V$.

We shall now prove the implication (iii) ⇒ (iv). Let $A \subset Y$ and $A = \bar{A}$. Since $f^{-1}(A) = X \setminus f^{-1}(Y \setminus A)$, it is sufficient to show that the inverse image of the set $Y \setminus A$ is open. For this purpose it is sufficient to prove that every point $x \in f^{-1}(Y \setminus A)$ has a neighbourhood U_x contained in $f^{-1}(Y \setminus A)$.

Let x denote an arbitrary point of $f^{-1}(Y \setminus A)$; since $f(x) \in Y \setminus A$, there exists a $V \in \mathfrak{D}(f(x))$ such that $V \subset Y \setminus A$. The element $U_x \in \mathfrak{B}(x)$ such that $f(U_x) \subset V$, which exists by virtue of (iii), satisfies the condition

$$x \in U_x \subset f^{-1}f(U_x) \subset f^{-1}(V) \subset f^{-1}(Y \setminus A),$$

and this proves that $f^{-1}(Y \setminus A)$ is an open set.

We shall show that (iv) ⇒ (v). Indeed, $f^{-1}\left(\overline{f(A)}\right)$ is closed and contains A, therefore $\bar{A} \subset f^{-1}\left(\overline{f(A)}\right)$ and

$$f(\bar{A}) \subset ff^{-1}\left(\overline{f(A)}\right) \subset \overline{f(A)}.$$

To prove the implication (v) ⇒ (v′) we use formula (v) for the set $f^{-1}(B)$. Then we have

$$f\left(\overline{f^{-1}(B)}\right) \subset \overline{ff^{-1}(B)} \subset \bar{B}; \qquad \text{therefore} \qquad \overline{f^{-1}(B)} \subset f^{-1}(\bar{B}).$$

We shall now prove that (v′) ⇒ (vi). Indeed, making use of (v′) for the set $Y \setminus B$ we have:

$$f^{-1}(\operatorname{Int} B) = f^{-1}(Y \setminus \overline{Y \setminus B}) = X \setminus f^{-1}(\overline{Y \setminus B}) \subset X \setminus \overline{f^{-1}(Y \setminus B)}$$

$$= X \setminus \overline{X \setminus f^{-1}(B)} = \operatorname{Int} f^{-1}(B).$$

In order to complete the proof of the theorem it is sufficient to show that (vi) ⇒ (i). If B is an open set in Y, then $B = \operatorname{Int} B$ and it follows from (vi) that $f^{-1}(B) \subset \mathrm{Int} f^{-1}(B)$. Therefore $f^{-1}(B) = \mathrm{Int} f^{-1}(B)$ and the set $f^{-1}(B)$ is open. ■

Let us suppose that we have two mappings, $f: X \to Y$ and $g: Y \to Z$, and let us consider the function gf of the set X into Z defined by the formula $gf(x) = g(f(x))$. It follows from the formula $(gf)^{-1}(A) = f^{-1}(g^{-1}(A))$ that $gf: X \to Z$. The mapping gf is called the *composition* of the mappings f and g. If there exists a mapping $f: X \to Y$ onto Y, then we say that X can be *mapped onto* Y or that Y is the *continuous image* of the space X.

EXAMPLE 1. Let X denote a discrete space (Example 1.1) and let Y denote an arbitrary topological space. Every function f of the set X into Y is a mapping. ■

EXAMPLE 2. Let us suppose that in a set X there are given two topologies $\mathfrak{O}_1$ and $\mathfrak{O}_2$. Let us consider the function f of the set X into itself defined by the formula $f(x) = x$. It can easily be observed that f is a mapping of the space $(X, \mathfrak{O}_1)$ into $(X, \mathfrak{O}_2)$ if and only if the topology $\mathfrak{O}_1$ is stronger than the topology $\mathfrak{O}_2$. ■

Let us suppose that X is an arbitrary space, R is the set of all real numbers with the natural topology (Example 1.3) and I the segment $[0,1]$ with the natural topology (Example 1.4). By virtue of condition (iii), Theorem 1, a function of X into R or into I is a mapping if and only if for every $x \in X$ and an arbitrary $\varepsilon > 0$ there exists a neighbourhood U of the point x such that $|f(x) - f(x')| < \varepsilon$ for every $x' \in U$. In particular, f is a mapping of R into R if for every $x \in R$ and for an arbitrary $\varepsilon > 0$ there exists a $\delta > 0$ such that for every $x' \in E$ if $|x' - x| < \delta$, then $|f(x) - f(x')| < \varepsilon$. Mappings of a space X into R or I will be called *continuous real-valued functions*. This terminology is consistent with the terminology used in analysis.

From the above remark it follows that if $f: X \to E$, then $|f|$, where $|f|(x) = |f(x)|$, is also a continuous real-valued function, for the function $|f|$ is a composition of the function f and a continuous function which maps R into itself, namely the absolute value. It can easily be proved that if f and g are continuous real-valued functions defined on X, then $f+g$, $f \cdot g$, $\min(f, g)$, and $\max(f, g)$, where

$$[f+g](x) = f(x) + g(x), \quad [f \cdot g](x) = f(x) \cdot g(x),$$
$$[\min(f, g)](x) = \min[f(x), g(x)],$$

and

$$[\max(f, g)](x) = \max[f(x), g(x)],$$

are also continuous. If a function $f: X \to R$ differs from zero at every point of the space X, then the function $1/f$, where $(1/f)(x) = 1/f(x)$, is also continuous.

EXAMPLE 3. Let us consider the space X defined in Example 2.1. Let $[x, r)$ denote an arbitrary element of the base $\mathfrak{B}$ of this space. Since $[x, r)$ is simultaneously closed and open, the function f (the arguments of which run over the set X and the values of which lie in the segment I) defined by the formula

$$f(y) = \begin{cases} 0, & \text{if } x \leqslant y < r, \\ 1, & \text{in the contrary case} \end{cases}$$

is continuous. ■

EXAMPLE 4. Let us consider the space X constructed in Example 2.2. Let $x \in X_1$ and let $U_i(x)$ be an arbitrary element of the base $\mathfrak{B}(x)$. For every $y \in U_i(x) \setminus \overline{U}_{2i}(x)$ let us denote by $\bar{y}$ and $\bar{\bar{y}}$ those points of intersection of the straight line passing through x and y with the circumference of $U_{2i}(x)$ and $U_i(x)$ respectively which are different from x. The function f of the set X into I defined by the formula

$$f(y) = \begin{cases} 0 & \text{for} \quad y \in \overline{U}_{2i}(x), \\ 1 & \text{for} \quad y \in X \setminus U_i(x), \\ \dfrac{|y\bar{y}|}{|\bar{y}\bar{\bar{y}}|} & \text{for} \quad y \in U_i(x) \setminus \overline{U}_{2i}(x), \end{cases}$$

where $|ab|$ denotes the length of the segment joining the points a and b, is continuous. Let $x \in X_2$ and let $U_i(x)$ be an arbitrary element of the base $\mathfrak{B}(x)$. The function f of the set X into I defined by the formula

$$f(y) = \begin{cases} 1 & \text{for} \quad y \notin U_i(x), \\ |xy| \cdot i & \text{for} \quad y \in U_i(x) \end{cases}$$

is, as can easily be observed, also continuous. ■

In Paragraph 5 we will use the functions constructed in Examples 3 and 4.

Let us suppose that a topological space X and a sequence of continuous functions $\{f_n\}$ defined on X with values in R or in I are given. We say that the sequence $\{f_n\}$ is *uniformly convergent* to the function f of the set X into the set of real numbers if for every $\varepsilon > 0$ there exists an N such that for $n \geqslant N$ and for every $x \in X$ we have $|f(x) - f_n(x)| < \varepsilon$. We then write $f = \lim f_n$.

THEOREM 2. *If the sequence of continuous real-valued functions $\{f_n\}$ is uniformly convergent to the function f of the set X into the set of real numbers, then f is continuous. If every f_n maps X into the segment I, then f also maps X into I.*

Proof. We shall show that for every $x \in X$ and for an arbitrary $\varepsilon > 0$ there exists a neighbourhood U of the point x such that $|f(x)-f(x')| < \varepsilon$ for every $x' \in U$. Let us take an N such that for $n \geqslant N$ we have

$$(1) \qquad |f(x)-f_n(x)| < \varepsilon/3 \quad \text{for every } x \in X.$$

Since f_N is a continuous function, there exists a neighbourhood U of the point x such that

$$(2) \qquad |f_N(x)-f_N(x')| < \varepsilon/3 \quad \text{for every } x' \in U.$$

We shall prove that the chosen U has the required property. Let us consider an arbitrary $x' \in U$. By virtue of (1) and (2) we have

$$|f(x)-f(x')| \leqslant |f(x)-f_N(x)|+|f_N(x)-f_N(x')|+|f(x')-f_N(x')|$$
$$< \varepsilon/3+\varepsilon/3+\varepsilon/3 = \varepsilon.$$

Of course, if $f_n(X) \subset I$ for every n, then also $f(X) \subset I$. ■

There exists one more method of generating a topology. That method, which is frequently used, depends on the notion of a mapping.

THEOREM 3. *Let us suppose that we are given a set X, a family $\{Y_s\}_{s \in S}$ of topological spaces and a family $\{f_s\}_{s \in S}$, where f_s is a function of X into Y_s. In the family of all topologies for which every f_s is a mapping, there exists a weakest topology; we call it the topology generated by the family of mappings $\{f_s\}_{s \in S}$.*

The base for the topology generated by $\{f_s\}_{s \in S}$ consists of the sets of the form:

$$\bigcap_{i=1}^{k} f_{s_i}^{-1}(V_i),$$

where $s_1, \ldots, s_k \in S$ and V_i is open in Y_{s_i} for $i = 1, 2, \ldots, k$.

Proof. The above sets have properties (B1) and (B2) of Paragraph 1. By virtue of Theorem 2.1, they generate a topology $\mathfrak{O}$ in X. All functions f_s are mappings in this topology. On the other hand, each topology in X for which every function f_s is a mapping is stronger than $\mathfrak{O}$. ■

The mapping $f: X \to Y$ is said to be *closed* (*open*) if the image $f(A)$ of an arbitrary closed (open) set $A \subset X$ is closed (open) in Y.

EXAMPLE 5. The mapping $r: R \to I$ defined by the formula:

$$r(x) = \begin{cases} 0, & \text{if} \quad x \leqslant 0, \\ x, & \text{if} \quad 0 \leqslant x \leqslant 1, \\ 1, & \text{if} \quad x \geqslant 1 \end{cases}$$

is closed but not open. This mapping is called the *retraction* of R onto the segment I. ■

EXAMPLE 6. Let X be the space considered in Example 1.2.

We shall show that for every continuous function $f: X \to R$ there exists a countable subset $X_0 \subset X$ not containing x_0 and such that $f(x) = f(x_0)$ for every $x \in X \setminus X_0$.

First, we shall prove that the set $f(X) \subset R$ is countable. Indeed, if it were not, there would exist in X two sequences of different points $\{x_k\}$ and $\{x_k'\}$ such that $\lim f(x_k) = r \neq r' = \lim f(x_k')$, where $r, r' \in R$. But this situation is impossible, for if we put $\varepsilon = \frac{1}{3}|r-r'|$ and $A = f^{-1}([r-\varepsilon, r+\varepsilon])$, $A' = f^{-1}([r'-\varepsilon, r'+\varepsilon])$, we obtain two disjoint infinite sets which are closed in X.

Let $r_0 = f(x_0) \in f(X)$. It can easily be seen that the inverse image of every $r \in f(X) \setminus r_0$ is finite. It is, therefore, sufficient to set $X_0 = f^{-1}(f(X) \setminus \{r_0\})$. ∎

A one-to-one mapping $f: X \to Y$ onto the space Y is said to be a *homeomorphism* if the function f^{-1} of the space Y onto the space X is a mapping.

THEOREM 4. *For a one-to-one mapping f of the space X onto Y the following conditions are equivalent:*

(i) *f is a homeomorphism.*

(ii) *f is a closed mapping.*

(iii) *f is an open mapping.*

The proof follows from the fact that $(f^{-1})^{-1}(A) = f(A)$ for every $A \subset X$. ∎

For every space X the mapping $\mathrm{id}_X: X \to X$, defined by means of the formula $\mathrm{id}_X(x) = x$ for every $x \in X$, is a homeomorphism. We call it the *identity mapping* of the space X onto itself.

EXAMPLE 7. Let us consider the set of all real numbers with one of the following topologies: (a) the discrete topology, (b) the natural topology, (c) the topology of Example 1.2, where $x_0 = 0$, (d) the topology of Example 2.1, (e) the topology of Example 2.3, (f) the topology of Example 2.4, where $x_0 = 0$, (g) the topology of Example 2.5.

For every real number $a > 0$ the mapping $f_a: R \to R$ given by the formula: $f_a(x) = a \cdot x$ is a homeomorphism. If we consider $a < 0$, then for the topology (d) f_a is not a mapping. For the other topologies considered here f_a is a homeomorphism. ∎

The spaces X and Y will be called *homeomorphic* if there exists a homeomorphism $h: X \to Y$.

Let us suppose that X and Y are homeomorphic spaces. The homeomorphism $h: X \to Y$ establishes a one-to-on ceorrespondence between points of the set X and Y and between open sets of the two spaces. Therefore, each property of a topological space, which is defined by means of the notion of an open set and notions of set theory, belongs to the space

X if and only if it belongs to an arbitrary space Y which is homeomorphic to X. The examination of these properties, which are called *topological properties* or *invariants of homeomorphisms*, is the subject of topology. When studying a given space we try to discover which topological properties it possesses. If we develop the general theory, we study topological properties and their connections with other properties, and we try to find under which operations on topological spaces those properties are invariant. Clearly, from the topological point of view, two homeomorphic spaces may be considered as identical spaces. The property: "X is of the weight $\mathfrak{m}$" is an example of a topological property. In this book we shall study many different invariants and it may be said that throughout the whole book we shall define and examine topological properties.

EXERCISES

A. Show that the topology in the space considered in Example 2.1 can be generated by the family of mappings into a two-point discrete space.

B. Show that the space constructed in Example 2.1 can be mapped onto a discrete countable space. Can it be mapped onto a discrete space of the power $\mathfrak{c}$?

C. Give an example of an open mapping which is not closed.

§ 5. Axioms of separation. The definition of a topological space is very general. Not many theorems can be proved about such spaces. In this book we will consider various classes of topological spaces, ranging from very general to specific. Obviously, the more specific the class under consideration, the more theorems about spaces of that class may be proved. The restrictions put on topological spaces are of various nature. We have already considered axioms of countability which restrict the power of the family of open sets. In this paragraph we shall study conditions which are usually called the *axioms of separation.* They concern the separation of points and closed sets in a topological space.

A topological space X is called a T_0-*space* if for each pair of different points $x_1, x_2 \in X$ there exists an open set U which contains exactly one of these points. The space described in Example 2.5 is a topological space which is not a T_0-space. All others spaces considered are T_0-spaces.

A topological space X is called a T_1-*space* if for each pair of different points $x_1, x_2 \in X$ there exists an open set $U \subset X$ such that $x_1 \in U$ and $x_2 \notin U$.

Every T_1-space is of course a T_0-space. The space described in Example 2.4 is a T_0-space which is not a T_1-space. All the other spaces which were considered above are T_1-spaces except the space of Example 2.5 (which is not a T_0-space).

We shall show that X is a T_1-space if and only if for every $x \in X$ the set $\{x\}$ is closed. Let X be a T_1-space and let $\mathfrak{O}$ denote the family of open sets in X. For an arbitrary $x \in X$

$$\{x\} = \bigcap_{x \notin U \in \mathfrak{O}} X \setminus U,$$

whence, by (C3), the set $\{x\}$ is closed. Now let us consider a space X such that for every $x \in X$ the set $\{x\}$ is closed. We shall show that X is a T_1-space. Indeed, for each pair of different points $x_1, x_2 \in X$ the open set $U = X \setminus \{x_2\}$ contains the point x_1 but does not contain x_2.

The so called Hausdorff spaces form a narrower class. A space X is called a *Hausdorff space* or a *T_2-space* if for each pair of different points $x_1, x_2 \in X$ there exist neighbourhoods U_1 and U_2 of the points x_1 and x_2 respectively such that $U_1 \cap U_2 = 0$.

Every T_2-space is obviously a T_1-space. The space considered in Example 2.3 is an example of a T_1-space which is not a Hausdorff space. All the spaces described in Paragraph 1 and the spaces constructed in Examples 2.1 and 2.2 are T_2-spaces.

The reader can easily prove the following

THEOREM 1. *Let us suppose that we are given a set X and a collection of families $\{\mathfrak{B}(x)\}_{x \in X}$ which satisfy conditions* (BP1)-(BP3) *of Paragraph* 1 *and the following additional condition*:

(BP4) *For each pair of different points $x, y \in X$ there exist sets $U \in \mathfrak{B}(x)$ and $V \in \mathfrak{B}(y)$ such that $U \cap V = 0$.*

Then the space X with the topology generated by the neighbourhood system $\{\mathfrak{B}(x)\}_{x \in X}$ is a Hausdorff space. ■

In the following chapters we shall frequently use the following property of T_2-spaces:

THEOREM 2. *For an arbitrary pair f, g of mappings of a topological space X into a Hausdorff space Y the set*

$$\{x: f(x) = g(x)\}$$

is closed.

Proof. We shall show that the set $A = \{x: f(x) \neq g(x)\}$ is open. Let $x \in A$; then $f(x) \neq g(x)$ and in the space Y there exist neighbourhoods U_1 and U_2 of the points $f(x)$ and $g(x)$ respectively such that $U_1 \cap U_2 = 0$. The set $U = f^{-1}(U_1) \cap g^{-1}(U_2)$ is a neighbourhood of the point x. It can easily be observed that $U \subset A$. ■

A topological space X is called a *regular space* or a *T_3-space* if it is a T_1-space and if for every $x \in X$ and for every closed F such that $x \notin F$ there exist open sets U_1 and U_2 such that

$$x \in U_1, \qquad F \subset U_2, \qquad U_1 \cap U_2 = 0.$$

THEOREM 3. *A T_1-space X is regular if and only if for each point $x \in X$ and its neighbourhood V which belongs to a fixed subbase $\mathfrak{S}$, there exists in X a neighbourhood U of the point x such that $x \in U \subset \overline{U} \subset V$.*

Proof. Let us assume that X is a regular space and let $x \in V$, where $V \in \mathfrak{S}$. There exist open sets U_1 and U_2 such that

$$x \in U_1, \quad X \setminus V \subset U_2, \quad \text{and} \quad U_1 \cap U_2 = 0.$$

Therefore $U_1 \subset X \setminus U_2 \subset V$ and it follows that

$$x \in U_1 \subset \overline{U}_1 \subset \overline{X \setminus U_2} = X \setminus U_2 \subset V.$$

Now let us assume that our condition is satisfied. Let $x \in X$ and let F be an arbitrary closed subset of the space X which does not contain x. By virtue of the definition of a subbase, there exist sets $V_1, V_2, \ldots, V_k \in \mathfrak{S}$ such that $x \in \bigcap_{i=1}^{k} V_i \subset X \setminus F$. Let W_i, where $i = 1, 2, \ldots, k$, denote a neighbourhood of the point x such that $x \in W_i \subset \overline{W}_i \subset V_i$. Let us put $U_1 = \bigcap_{i=1}^{k} W_i$ and $U_2 = X \setminus \bigcap_{i=1}^{k} \overline{W}_i$. Evidently, $U_1 \cap U_2 = 0$ and $x \in U_1$; moreover,

$$F \subset X \setminus \bigcap_{i=1}^{k} V_i \subset X \setminus \bigcap_{i=1}^{k} \overline{W}_i = U_2. \blacksquare$$

Each regular space is a Hausdorff space. It is precisely to ensure this implication that we assume, in addition to the possibility of separation of points and closed sets, that X is a T_1-space. The space considered in Example 2.5 has the required property of separation but is not a T_1-space. All Hausdorff spaces considered before are also T_3-spaces.

We are now going to give an example of a Hausdorff space which is not a T_3-space.

EXAMPLE 1. Let X be the set of all real numbers. Let us denote by Z the set of reciprocals of integers which are different from zero. For every $x \in X$ let us put $O_i(x) = (x - 1/i, x + 1/i)$ and

$$\mathfrak{B}(x) = \begin{cases} \{O_i(x)\}_{i=1}^{\infty} & \text{for} \quad x \neq 0, \\ \{O_i(x) \setminus Z\}_{i=1}^{\infty} & \text{for} \quad x = 0. \end{cases}$$

It can easily be verified that the collection $\{\mathfrak{B}(x)\}_{x \in X}$ is subject to conditions (BP1)-(BP4) and therefore, by virtue of Theorem 1, the set X with the topology generated by the neighbourhood system $\{\mathfrak{B}(x)\}_{x \in X}$ is a Hausdorff space. The set Z is closed in X and $0 \notin Z$; however, for arbitrary open sets U_1 and U_2 such that $0 \in U_1$ and $Z \subset U_2$ we have $U_1 \cap U_2 \neq 0$. $\blacksquare$

Tychonoff spaces form a narrower class of spaces; they are also called *$T_{3\frac{1}{2}}$-spaces*. We say that a space X is a *Tychonoff space* if it is a a T_1-space and if for every point $x \in X$ and every closed set F not containing x there exists a continuous function $f: X \to I$ such that $f(x) = 0$ and $f(y) = 1$ for $y \in F$. Since for the open sets $U_1 = f^{-1}([0, \frac{1}{2}))$ and

$U_2 = f^{-1}((\frac{1}{2}, 1])$ we have

$$x \in U_1, \quad F \subset U_2, \quad \text{and} \quad U_1 \cap U_2 = 0,$$

every Tychonoff space is regular. The Tychonoff spaces are sometimes called *completely regular.*

THEOREM 4. *A T_1-space X is a Tychonoff space if and only if for an arbitrary point $x \in X$ and its neighbourhood V which belongs to a fixed subbase $\mathfrak{S}$ there exists a continuous function $f: X \to I$ such that $f(x) = 0$ and $f(y) = 1$ for $y \in X \setminus V$.*

Proof. Since $X \setminus V$ is a closed set not containing x, the necessity of the condition is obvious.

Let us suppose now that our condition is satisfied and that $x \notin \overline{F} = F \subset X$. By the definition of a subbase there exist sets $V_1, V_2, \ldots \ldots, V_k \in \mathfrak{S}$ such that $x \in \bigcap_{i=1}^{k} V_i \subset X \setminus F$. Let $f_i: X \to I$ be a continuous function such that $f_i(x) = 0$ and $f_i(y) = 1$ for $y \in X \setminus V_i$. It is easily verified that the value of the continuous function $f = \max(f_1, f_2, \ldots, f_k)$ is equal to 0 at the point x and equal to 1 at every point of the set F. ■

It follows from Examples 4.3 and 4.4 that the spaces constructed in Examples 2.1 and 2.2 are Tychonoff spaces. It is obvious that the spaces of Examples 1.1-1.4 are Tychonoff spaces.

Examples of regular spaces which are not Tychonoff spaces are more difficult than the examples considered before. They cannot be defined immediately, it is necessary to know some methods of constructing more complicated topological spaces from simpler ones. An example of such a space will be given in the next chapter. Also, there exist regular spaces on which every real-valued continuous function is constant; their construction, however, is complicated.

A space X is called a *normal space* or a *T_4-space* if X is a T_1-space and if for each pair A, B of disjoint and closed sets there exist in X two open sets U and V such that

$$A \subset U, \quad B \subset V, \quad \text{and} \quad U \cap V = 0. \tag{1}$$

It is evident that every T_4-space is a T_3-space. It follows from Theorem 5 proved below that every T_4-space is also a Tychonoff space. The following example shows that there exist Tychonoff spaces which are not normal.

EXAMPLE 2. As we have already stated, the space X constructed in Example 2.2 is a Tychonoff space. We shall show that it is not normal. We have already noted that the set $X_1 \subset X$ has an empty derived set. The derived set of an arbitrary set $A \subset X_1$ is also empty, whence, by Theorem 3.4, every set $A \subset X_1$ is closed in the space X. Let us denote by D the subset of X_2 consisting of points whose coordinates are both rational. The set D is obviously dense in X.

Let us suppose that X is a normal space. Consequently for every $A \subset X_1$ there exist open sets U_A and V_A such that

$$A \subset U_A, \quad X_1 \setminus A \subset V_A, \quad U_A \cap V_A = 0.$$

Let $D_A = D \cap U_A$. We shall prove that if $A, B \subset X_1$ and $A \neq B$, then $D_A \neq D_B$; this will lead to a contradiction, because X_1 contains $2^{\mathfrak{c}}$ different subsets and D contains only $\mathfrak{c}$.

Let $A \neq B$ and, by the symmetry of the assumption, let us suppose that $A \setminus B \neq 0$. Since $0 \neq A \setminus B \subset \overline{U}_A \cap V_B$ and since, by virtue of the corollary to Theorem 1.1, $\overline{U}_B \cap V_B = 0$, we have $\overline{U}_A \neq \overline{U}_B$. By virtue of Theorem 3.6, we infer that $\overline{D}_A \neq \overline{D}_B$ and $D_A \neq D_B$. ∎

The remark concerning the assumption that X is a T_1-space, which was made when we defined regular spaces, is also true for the definition of $T_{3\frac{1}{2}}$-spaces and T_4-spaces. The space defined in Example 2.5 can be considered as an illustration.

We are now going to prove the fundamental theorem on normal spaces, which is known as Urysohn's Lemma.

THEOREM 5 (Urysohn's Lemma). *Let a normal space X and a pair A, B of sets disjoint and closed in X be given. Then there exists a continuous function $f: X \to I$ such that*

$$f(x) = 0 \text{ for } x \in A \quad \text{and} \quad f(x) = 1 \text{ for } x \in B.$$

Proof. For every rational number r from the segment $[0, 1]$ we shall define an open set V_r in X subject to the following conditions:

$$\overline{V}_r \subset V_{r'} \quad \text{for} \quad r < r', \tag{2}$$

$$A \subset V_0, \quad B = X \setminus V_1. \tag{3}$$

The sets V_r are constructed inductively. Let us arrange the rational numbers of the segment $(0, 1)$ in an infinite sequence $r_3, r_4, \ldots$ and let us put $r_1 = 0, r_2 = 1$. Let

$$V_0 = U, \quad V_1 = X \setminus B,$$

where U together with some V satisfies condition (1). Of course,

$$A \subset V_0 \subset X \setminus V = \overline{X \setminus V} \subset V_1, \quad \text{whence} \quad \overline{V}_0 \subset V_1.$$

Condition (3) and the following condition

$$\overline{V}_{r_i} \subset V_{r_j} \quad \text{if} \quad r_i < r_j \quad \text{and} \quad i, j \leqslant k \tag{2_k}$$

for $k = 1$ are, therefore, satisfied.

Let us assume that the sets V_{r_i} are defined for $i \leqslant n$ and that they satisfy condition (2_n). Let us denote by r_l and r_m those, of the numbers $r_1, \ldots, r_n$, which are closest to r_{n+1} from the left and the right side respectively. We have of course $r_l < r_m$, whence by virtue of (2_n), $\overline{V}_{r_l} \subset V_{r_m}$. The sets $\overline{V}_{r_l}$ and $X \setminus V_{r_m}$ are disjoint and closed subsets of the normal space X, whence there exist open sets U and V such that

$$\overline{V}_{r_l} \subset U, \quad X \setminus V_{r_m} \subset V, \quad U \cap V = 0.$$

We infer that $U \subset X \setminus V \subset V_{r_m}$ and

$$\overline{V}_{r_l} \subset U \subset \overline{U} \subset \overline{X \setminus V} = X \setminus V \subset V_{r_m}.$$

Putting $V_{r_{n+1}} = U$ we obtain the sets $V_{r_1}, \ldots, V_{r_{n+1}}$ satisfying condition (2_{n+1}). The sequence $V_{r_1}, V_{r_2}, \ldots$ defined in this manner is subject to conditions (2) and (3).

Now let us put for $x \in X$

$$f(x) = \begin{cases} \inf\limits_{x \in V_r} r, & \text{if} \quad x \in V_1, \\ 1, & \text{if} \quad x \in X \setminus V_1. \end{cases}$$

By virtue of (3), $f(A) \subset \{0\}$ and $f(B) \subset \{1\}$. In order to complete the proof it is, therefore, sufficient to show that f is a continuous function, i.e. (cf. condition (ii) of Theorem 4.1) that the inverse images of the sets $[0, a)$ and $(b, 1]$, where $a \leqslant 1$ and $b \geqslant 0$, under the function f are open.

The inequality $f(x) < a$ is equivalent to the existence of an $r_j < a$ such that $x \in V_{r_j}$, thus the set $f^{-1}([0, a)) = \bigcup\limits_{r_j < a} V_{r_j}$ is open. On the other hand, the inequality $f(x) > b$ is equivalent to the existence of an $r_j > b$ such that $x \notin V_{r_j}$, which, by virtue of (2), is equivalent to the existence of an $r_i > b$ such that $x \notin \overline{V}_{r_i}$. Thus the set

$$f^{-1}((b, 1]) = \bigcup_{r_i > b} (X \setminus \overline{V}_{r_i}) = X \setminus \bigcap_{r_i > b} \overline{V}_{r_i}$$

is also open. ■

The subsets A and B of a topological space X are said to be *completely separated* if there exists a continuous function $f: X \to I$ such that $f(x) = 0$ for $x \in A$ and $f(x) = 1$ for $x \in B$; in this case we say that f *separates* the sets A and B. In other words, the Urysohn Lemma states that in a normal space every pair of closed and disjoint sets is completely separated. It can easily be noted that if in a T_1-space every pair of closed and disjoint sets is completely separated, then the space is normal.

It is evident that a discrete space is normal. It can easily be verified that the space of Example 1.2 is also normal. It follows from the theorem proved below that the space of real numbers and the segment I are also normal spaces. From this theorem we shall also deduce that the space described in Example 2.1 is normal.

THEOREM 6. *Every regular space X that satisfies the second axiom of countability is normal.*

Proof. Let us suppose that two sets A and B, disjoint and closed in X, are given. By virtue of Theorem 3, we infer that for every $x \in A$ there exists an open set V_x such that

$$x \in V_x \subset \overline{V}_x \subset X \setminus B.$$

Therefore, we have

$$(4) \qquad A \subset \bigcup_{x \in A} V_x \quad \text{and} \quad \overline{V}_x \cap B = 0 \quad \text{for every } x \in A.$$

Similarly, for each $y \in B$ there exists an open set U_y such that

$$(5) \qquad B \subset \bigcup_{y \in B} U_y \quad \text{and} \quad \overline{U}_y \cap A = 0.$$

By virtue of Theorem 1.6, there exist countable sets of points $\{x_1, x_2, \ldots\}$ and $\{y_1, y_2, \ldots\}$ such that

$$(6) \qquad \bigcup_{i=1}^{\infty} V_i = \bigcup_{x \in A} V_x, \quad \bigcup_{i=1}^{\infty} U_i = \bigcup_{y \in B} U_y,$$

where $V_i = V_{x_i}$ and $U_i = U_{y_i}$. Let

$$(7) \qquad G_i = V_i \setminus \bigcup_{j \leqslant i} \overline{U}_j, \quad \text{and} \quad H_i = U_i \setminus \bigcup_{j \leqslant i} \overline{V}_j.$$

The sets G_i and H_i are open. By virtue of (4), (5), and (6),

$$A \subset U = \bigcup_{i=1}^{\infty} G_i, \quad B \subset V = \bigcup_{i=1}^{\infty} H_i.$$

In order to complete the proof of our theorem it is sufficient to show that the open sets U and V are disjoint. Since by (7) $G_i \cap U_j = 0$ for $j \leqslant i$, $G_i \cap H_j = 0$ holds for $j \leqslant i$. Similarly $H_j \cap V_i = 0$, whence also $G_i \cap H_j = 0$ for $j \geqslant i$. Therefore we have

$$G_i \cap H_j = 0 \quad \text{for} \quad i, j = 1, 2, \ldots \quad \text{and} \quad U \cap V = 0. \blacksquare$$

EXAMPLE 3. We shall show that the space of Example 2.1 is normal (cf. Example 3.7.2). Let us consider a pair A_1, A_2 of closed and disjoint subsets of it and let F_i, where $i = 1, 2$, be the set of those points of $G_i = X \setminus A_i$ which are not contained in any open interval $(a, b) \subset G_i$. Since A_i is closed, we infer that for every point $x \in F_i$ there exists an interval $[x, y) \subset G_i$ and the definition of F_i implies that disjoint intervals correspond to different points. Hence the set $F = F_1 \cup F_2$ is countable.

Let D denote a subset of the real-line containing a point from every intersection of an open interval with rational end-points and the set $X \setminus F$. The set D is countable and dense in the real-line. The family $\mathfrak{B}$ consisting of intervals of the form

$$(d_1, d_2), \text{ where } d_1, d_2 \in D, \quad \text{and} \quad [x, d), \text{ where } x \in F,\ d \in D$$

satisfies conditions (B1) and (B2). Let X_0 be the real-line with the topology generated by the base $\mathfrak{B}$. It is not difficult to verify that X_0 is a regular space and, since $\overline{\overline{\mathfrak{B}}} \leqslant \aleph_0$, X_0 is normal by Theorem 6. The sets A_1 and A_2 are closed in X_0, thus there exist disjoint sets U_1, U_2 open in X_0 — i.e. also in X, because the topology of X_0 is weaker than the topology of X — and such that $A_i \subset U_i$ for $i = 1, 2$. ∎

EXERCISES

A. Prove that X is a T_0-space if and only if for each pair x, y of different points of the space X the inequality $\overline{\{x\}} \neq \overline{\{y\}}$ holds.

B. Show that in T_1-spaces the derived set operator has the following properties:

$$(A^{\mathrm{d}})^{\mathrm{d}} \subset A^{\mathrm{d}}, \quad \overline{(A^{\mathrm{d}})} = A^{\mathrm{d}} = (\bar{A})^{\mathrm{d}}.$$

Give an example which points out that these formulas are generally not true in T_0-spaces.

C. Show that if $(X, \mathfrak{O}_1)$ is a T_0-space and the topology $\mathfrak{O}_2$ is stronger than $\mathfrak{O}_1$, then $(X, \mathfrak{O}_2)$ is also a T_0-space. For what other axioms of separation is an analogous theorem true? Give suitable examples.

D. Show that for any finite family $\{A_i\}_{i=1}^{k}$ of mutually disjoint closed subsets of a normal space X there exists a family $\{U_i\}_{i=1}^{k}$ of open subsets of that space such that $A_i \subset U_i$ for $i = 1, 2, \ldots, k$ and $U_i \cap U_j = 0$ for $i \neq j$. Verify that if A_i consists of a single point, then it is sufficient to assume that X is a Hausdorff space (cf. Corollary to Theorem 2.1.6).

E. Show that a space X is normal if and only if it is a T_1-space and for each pair of open sets U and V such that $U \cup V = X$ there exists a pair of closed sets A and B such that $A \subset U$, $B \subset V$, and $A \cup B = X$.

Prove that if $f: X \to Y$ is a closed mapping of a normal space X onto an arbitrary topological space Y, then Y is normal. Is the assumption that f is closed essential?

§ 6. Nets and filters. A *net* in a topological space X is an arbitrary function of a directed set into the space X. To denote it we shall use the symbol $S = \{x_\sigma, \sigma \in \Sigma\}$, where x_σ is the point of the space X assigned to the element σ of the directed set Σ. The relation which directs the set Σ will always be denoted by $\leqslant$. For $\sigma_1, \sigma_2 \in \Sigma$ we shall often write $\sigma_1 \geqslant \sigma_2$ instead of $\sigma_2 \leqslant \sigma_1$.

Let a net $S = \{x_\sigma, \sigma \in \Sigma\}$ and a set $A \subset X$ be given. We shall say that *S is eventually in A* if there exists $\sigma_0 \in \Sigma$ such that $x_\sigma \in A$ for every $\sigma \geqslant \sigma_0$. If for every $\sigma_0 \in \Sigma$ there exists a $\sigma \geqslant \sigma_0$ such that $x_\sigma \in A$, then we say that *S is frequently in A*.

A point x is said to be a *cluster point* of a net S if S is frequently in every neighbourhood of x. A point x is called a *limit* of a net S if S is eventually in every neighbourhood of the point x; in this case we also say that the net S is *convergent* to x. A net may converge to several different points. The set of all limits of a net $S = \{x_\sigma, \sigma \in \Sigma\}$ is denoted by $\lim S$ or $\lim_{\sigma\in\Sigma} x_\sigma$. If the net $S = \{x_\sigma, \sigma \in \Sigma\}$ has a unique limit x, then we write $x = \lim S = \lim_{\sigma\in\Sigma} x_\sigma$.

A net $S' = \{x_{\sigma'}, \sigma' \in \Sigma'\}$ is said to be *finer* than a net $S = \{x_\sigma, \sigma \in \Sigma\}$ if there exists a function $\varphi\colon \Sigma' \to \Sigma$ such that

(FN1) *For every $\sigma_0 \in \Sigma$ there exists a $\sigma_0' \in \Sigma'$ such that $\varphi(\sigma') \geqslant \sigma_0$ for $\sigma' \geqslant \sigma_0'$.*
(FN2) $x_{\varphi(\sigma')} = x_{\sigma'}$ *for* $\sigma' \in \Sigma'$.

It can easily be seen that (FN1) is satisfied if $\varphi\colon \Sigma' \to \Sigma$ is monotone and $\varphi(\Sigma')$ is cofinal in Σ.

THEOREM 1. *If a point x is a cluster point of a net S' which is finer than a net S, then x is a cluster point of S. If x is a limit of the net S, then it is a limit of every finer net S'. If a point x is a cluster point of a net S, then it is a limit of a finer net S'.*

Proof. Let us suppose that x is a cluster point of the net $S' = \{x_{\sigma'}, \sigma' \in \Sigma'\}$ which is finer than the net $S = \{x_\sigma, \sigma \in \Sigma\}$. Let $\varphi\colon \Sigma' \to \Sigma$ denote function satisfying (FN1) and (FN2). Let us consider an arbitrary neighbourhood U of the point x and an arbitrary $\sigma_0 \in \Sigma$. There exists a $\sigma_0' \in \Sigma'$ such that $\varphi(\sigma') \geqslant \sigma_0$, for $\sigma' \geqslant \sigma_0'$. By virtue of the definition of a cluster point, there exists a $\sigma'' \in \Sigma'$ such that $\sigma'' \geqslant \sigma_0'$ and $x_{\sigma''} \in U$. Therefore $x_{\varphi(\sigma'')} = x_{\sigma''} \in U$ and $\varphi(\sigma'') \geqslant \sigma_0$ which proves that x is a cluster point of the net S.

Let us assume that x is a limit of the net S. Let $S' = \{x_{\sigma'}, \sigma' \in \Sigma'\}$ be an arbitrary net finer than S and let $\varphi\colon \Sigma' \to \Sigma$ denote the corresponding function. Let us consider an arbitrary neighbourhood U of the point x. There exists a $\sigma_0 \in \Sigma$ such that $x_\sigma \in U$ for $\sigma \geqslant \sigma_0$. Let us consider $\sigma_0' \in \Sigma'$ such that $\varphi(\sigma') \geqslant \sigma_0$ for $\sigma' \geqslant \sigma_0'$. Of course, $x_{\sigma'} \in U$ for $\sigma' \geqslant \sigma_0'$, whence $x \in \lim_{\sigma'\in\Sigma'} x_{\sigma'}$.

Let x be a cluster point of a net $S = \{x_\sigma, \sigma \in \Sigma\}$. Let us consider the set Σ' of ordered pairs (σ, U), where $\sigma \in \Sigma$, U is a neighbourhood of the point x, and $x_\sigma \in U$. Let us write $(\sigma_1, U_1) \leqslant (\sigma_2, U_2)$ if $\sigma_1 \leqslant \sigma_2$ and $U_1 \supset U_2$. It can easily be verified that the set Σ' is directed by the relation $\leqslant$. The net $S' = \{x_{\sigma'}, \sigma' \in \Sigma'\}$, where $x_{\sigma'} = x_\sigma$ for $\sigma' = (\sigma, U)$, is finer than the net S, for the function $\varphi\colon \Sigma' \to \Sigma$ defined by means of the formula $\varphi((\sigma, U)) = \sigma$ is monotone and maps Σ' onto Σ. For an arbitrary neighbourhood U of the point x there exists a $\sigma \in \Sigma$ such that $x_\sigma \in U$. Since for $\sigma' \geqslant (\sigma, U) \in \Sigma'$ we have $x_{\sigma'} \in U$, it follows that $x \in \lim_{\sigma'\in\Sigma'} x_{\sigma'}$, holds. ∎

EXAMPLE 1. Let Σ denote the set of all rational numbers less than zero directed by the relation $\leqslant$ and let us suppose that $x_r = r$ for each $r \in \Sigma$. Of course, $S = \{x_r, r \in \Sigma\}$ is a net (in the space R) convergent to the real number 0. Let us note that the set consisting of all the elements of this net and its limit is not closed in R.

Let Σ' denote the set of all natural numbers directed by the relation $\leqslant$ and let $\varphi(n) = -1/n$ for $n \in \Sigma'$. The function φ is monotone and the set of its values is cofinal in the set Σ. The net $S' = \{x_n, n \in \Sigma'\}$, where $x_n = -1/n$, is finer than the net S. According to Theorem 1 the net S' is also convergent to 0. ■

THEOREM 2. *Let a subset A of a topological space X and a point $x \in X$ be given. The point x belongs to the closure of the set A if and only if there exists a net consisting of elements of A and convergent to x.*

Proof. It is evident that the condition is sufficient. In order to prove that it is also necessary, let us assume that $x \in \bar{A}$ and let $\mathfrak{U}$ be the set of all neighbourhoods of the point x directed by the relation $\supset$. In other words, let us assume that $U_1 \leqslant U_2$ if $U_1 \supset U_2$. For every $U \in \mathfrak{U}$ let x_U denote an arbitrary element of the intersection $U \cap A$. One can easily verify that $x \in \lim\limits_{U \in \mathfrak{U}} x_U$. ■

COROLLARY 1. *A set $A \subset X$ is closed if and only if, together with every convergent net, it contains all limits of that net.* ■

COROLLARY 2. *The point x is an accumulation point of a set A if and only if it is the limit of a net, $S = \{x_\sigma, \sigma \in \Sigma\}$, where $x_\sigma \in A$ and $x_\sigma \neq x$ for each $\sigma \in \Sigma$.* ■

Nets have many properties analogous to the properties of ordinary infinite sequences. It is for that reason that they are often considered to be a good tool for examining topological spaces. The reader is sure to have observed that the theorems we have just proved are similar to the well-known theorems on infinite sequences, but where the notion of a subsequence has been replaced by the notion of a finer net. One can define various notions in topology in terms of nets. In Problem V at the end of this chapter it is shown how one can generate a topology in an arbitrary set from a definition of a class of convergent nets. Now we shall show how to use nets to define a mapping and to formulate the axiom of separation which has been used to define a Hausdorff space.

THEOREM 3. *Let two topological spaces X and Y be given. A function f of the set X into Y is a mapping if and only if*

$$f(\lim_{\sigma \in \Sigma} x_\sigma) \subset \lim_{\sigma \in \Sigma} f(x_\sigma)$$

for every net $\{x_\sigma, \sigma \in \Sigma\}$ in the space X.

Proof. Let us suppose that $f: X \to Y$ and $x \in \lim_{\sigma\in\Sigma} x_\sigma$. Let us take an arbitrary neighbourhood V of the point $f(x)$. By virtue of condition (iii), Theorem 4.1, there exists a neighbourhood U of the point x such that $f(U) \subset V$. Since $x \in \lim_{\sigma\in\Sigma} x_\sigma$, there exists a $\sigma_0 \in \Sigma$ such that $x_\sigma \in U$ for $\sigma \geqslant \sigma_0$. It follows that $f(x_\sigma) \in V$ for $\sigma \geqslant \sigma_0$ and hence $f(x) \in \lim_{\sigma\in\Sigma} f(x_\sigma)$ and $f(\lim_{\sigma\in\Sigma} x_\sigma) \subset \lim_{\sigma\in\Sigma} f(x_\sigma)$.

Let us now suppose that the function f satisfies the condition of our theorem. In order to prove that $f: X \to Y$ it is sufficient, by virtue of Theorem 4.1, to prove that for every $A \subset X, f(\bar{A}) \subset \overline{f(A)}$ holds. But it follows from Theorem 2 that under our assumption the above inclusion is valid. ■

THEOREM 4. *A space X is a Hausdorff space if and only if every net in X has at most one limit.*

Proof. Let X be a Hausdorff space and let $S = \{x_\sigma, \sigma \in \Sigma\}$ denote a net in X. Let us suppose that $x_1, x_2 \in \lim_{\sigma\in\Sigma} x_\sigma$. If we had $x_1 \neq x_2$, then there would exist disjoint neighbourhoods U_1 and U_2 of the points x_1 and x_2, respectively. Since the net S is eventually in both neighbourhoods, and since the set Σ is directed, S is eventually in $U_1 \cap U_2$. Therefore this intersection cannot be empty and we have $x_1 = x_2$.

Let us now suppose that X is not a Hausdorff space. In X there exist, therefore, two different points x_1 and x_2 such that for their arbitrary neighbourhoods U_1 and U_2 we have $U_1 \cap U_2 \neq 0$. Sets of the form $U_1 \cap U_2$ constitute a set Σ directed by inclusion. For every $\sigma = U_1 \cap U_2 \in \Sigma$ let us consider an arbitrary point $x_\sigma \in U_1 \cap U_2$. It is easy to verify that $x_1, x_2 \in \lim_{\sigma\in\Sigma} x_\sigma$. ■

The theory of filters is another equivalent approach to convergence in general topological spaces. In this paragraph we shall give only the basic definitions in the theory of filters, the formulation in terms of filters of a few theorems proved before, and an outline of the equivalence of the two theories.

A *filter* in a topological space X is a non-empty family $\mathfrak{F}$ of subsets of X which satisfies the following conditions:

(F1) *If $A \in \mathfrak{F}$ and $A \subset A_1$, then $A_1 \in \mathfrak{F}$.*

(F2) *If $A_1 \in \mathfrak{F}$ and $A_2 \in \mathfrak{F}$, then $A_1 \cap A_2 \in \mathfrak{F}$.*

(F3) $0 \notin \mathfrak{F}$.

A *filter-base* in X is a non-empty family $\mathfrak{H}$ of subsets of X which satisfies (F3), $\mathfrak{F}$ being replaced with $\mathfrak{H}$, and the following condition:

(F2′) *If* $A_1 \in \mathfrak{H}$ *and* $A_2 \in \mathfrak{H}$, *then there exists an* $A_3 \in \mathfrak{H}$ *such that* $A_3 \subset A_1 \cap A_2$.

It can easily be verified that for every filter-base $\mathfrak{H}$ the family

$$\mathfrak{F}_{\mathfrak{H}} = \{A \subset X\colon \text{there exists a } B \in \mathfrak{H} \text{ such that } B \subset A\}$$

is a filter.

A point x is called a *limit* of the filter $\mathfrak{F}$ if every neighbourhood of x belongs to $\mathfrak{F}$. We then say that the filter $\mathfrak{F}$ is *convergent* to x and we write $x \in \lim \mathfrak{F}$. A point x is called a *limit* of a filter-base $\mathfrak{H}$ if $x \in \lim \mathfrak{F}_{\mathfrak{H}}$. We then say that the filter-base $\mathfrak{H}$ is *convergent* to x and write $x \in \lim \mathfrak{H}$. It can easily be verified that $x \in \lim \mathfrak{H}$ if and only if each neighbourhood U of the point x contains an element of the filter-base $\mathfrak{H}$.

A point x is called a *cluster point* of a filter $\mathfrak{F}$ (a filter-base $\mathfrak{H}$) if x belongs to the closure of every element of the filter $\mathfrak{F}$ (the filter-base $\mathfrak{H}$). Evidently, x is a cluster point of a filter (a filter-base) if and only if every element of that filter (filter-base) intersects an arbitrary neighbourhood U of the point x.

We say that a filter $\mathfrak{F}_1$ is *finer* than a filter $\mathfrak{F}_2$ if $\mathfrak{F}_1 \supset \mathfrak{F}_2$.

THEOREM 1F. *If a point* x *is a cluster point of a filter* $\mathfrak{F}'$ *which is finer than a filter* $\mathfrak{F}$, *then* x *is a cluster point of* $\mathfrak{F}$. *If* x *is a limit of the filter* $\mathfrak{F}$, *then it is also a limit of every finer filter* $\mathfrak{F}'$. *If a point* x *is a cluster point of a filter* $\mathfrak{F}$, *then it is a limit of a finer filter* $\mathfrak{F}'$. ■

THEOREM 2F. *Let a subset* A *of a topological space* X *and a point* $x \in X$ *be given. The point* x *belongs to the closure of the set* A *if and only if there exists a filter-base consisting of subsets of* A *and convergent to* x. ■

THEOREM 3F. *Let two topological spaces* X *and* Y *be given. A function* f *of the set* X *into* Y *is a mapping if and only if*

$$f(\lim \mathfrak{H}) \subset \lim f(\mathfrak{H})$$

for every filter base $\mathfrak{H}$ *in* X *and the filter base* $f(\mathfrak{H}) = \{f(A)\}_{A \in \mathfrak{H}}$ *in* Y. ■

THEOREM 4F. *A space* X *is a Hausdorff space if and only if every filter in* X *has at most one limit.* ■

We are now going to show how filters correspond to nets.

THEOREM 5. *Let* S *be a net in a space* X. *The family* $\mathfrak{F}(S)$ *of all sets which the net* S *is eventually in, is a filter in the space* X. *Moreover, we have the equality*

$$\lim S = \lim \mathfrak{F}(S).$$

If a net S' *is finer than the net* S, *then the filter* $\mathfrak{F}(S')$ *is finer than the filter* $\mathfrak{F}(S)$. ■

THEOREM 6. *Let* $\mathfrak{F}$ *be a filter. Let us denote by* Σ *the set of all pairs* (x, A), *where* $x \in A \in \mathfrak{F}$. *Let us assume that* $(x_1, A_1) \leqslant (x_2, A_2)$ *when* $A_2 \subset A_1$.

The set Σ is directed. The formula $x_\sigma = x$, where $\sigma = (x, A) \in \Sigma$, defines a net $S(\mathfrak{F}) = \{x_\sigma, \sigma \in \Sigma\}$ in the space X. Furthermore, we have $\mathfrak{F} = \mathfrak{F}(S(\mathfrak{F}))$, and thus

$$\lim \mathfrak{F} = \lim S(\mathfrak{F}). \blacksquare$$

EXERCISES

A. Let $S = \{x_\sigma, \sigma \in \Sigma\}$ be a net in a space X and let $S(\sigma_0) = \{x_\sigma : \sigma \geqslant \sigma_0\}$ for $\sigma_0 \in \Sigma$. Show that a point x is a cluster point of the net S if and only if $x \in \overline{S(\sigma_0)}$ for every $\sigma_0 \in \Sigma$.

B. Let Ξ be a directed set and let Σ_ξ be a directed set for every $\xi \in \Xi$. The product $\Sigma = \Xi \times \boldsymbol{P}_{\xi \in \Xi} \Sigma_\xi$ is directed by assuming that $(\xi_0, f_0) \leqslant (\xi_1, f_1)$ if $\xi_0 \leqslant \xi_1$ and $f_0(\xi) \leqslant f_1(\xi)$ for every $\xi \in \Xi$.

Let us suppose that for every $\xi \in \Xi$ a net $S = \{x_\sigma^{(\xi)}, \sigma \in \Sigma_\xi\}$ in the space X is given. Show that if $x_\xi \in \lim S_\xi$ for every $\xi \in \Xi$ and $x \in \lim_{\xi \in \Xi} x_\xi$, then x is also a limit of the net $\{x_\sigma, \sigma \in \Sigma\}$, where $x_\sigma = x_{f(\xi)}^{(\xi)}$ for $\sigma = (\xi, f)$.

C. Infinite sequences are a particular case of nets; the sequence $x_1, x_2, \ldots$ is a net $\{x_n, n \in N\}$, where N is the set of natural numbers directed by the ordinary relation $\leqslant$.

Show that an arbitrary subsequence $x_{k_1}, x_{k_2}, \ldots$ of the sequence $x_1, x_2, \ldots$ is finer than $x_1, x_2, \ldots$ Verify that Theorem 1 remains true after replacing the term "net" by the term "sequence" and the term "finer net" by the term "subsequence".

Verify that for spaces which satisfy the first axiom of countability Theorems 2-4 remain true if we replace the term "net" by the term "sequence" and the term "finer net" by the term "subsequence". Show by means of a modification of the space of Example 1.2 that the modified theorems are not valid in arbitrary topological spaces.

HISTORICAL REMARKS AND BIBLIOGRAPHIC NOTES

The concept of a topological space was defined in a sufficiently general manner by F. Hausdorff in [1914]. He defined T_2-spaces as sets given with a neighbourhood system satisfying conditions (BP1)-(BP4). Definitions of abstract spaces based on the concept of a convergent sequence and a derived set were given earlier by M. Fréchet in [1906] (see also M. Fréchet [1926]) and F. Riesz in [1907] and [1908], but these definitions were not satisfactory. The concept of a topological space as considered in this book was introduced by K. Kuratowski in [1922a]. He defined the topology in a set X by means of the closure operator satisfying conditions (CO1)-(CO4). A study of subsets of topological spaces which is the subject of the first and third paragraph of this chapter was made earlier (about 1880) by G. Cantor for the particular case of subsets of the straight line. Accordingly, G. Cantor is considered to be one of originators of general topology. The axioms of countability were formulated in F. Hausdorff's book [1914]. The axiom T_0 was introduced by A. Kolmogoroff (see P. Alexandroff and H. Hopf [1935], p. 58), axiom T_1 — by F. Riesz in [1907], axiom T_3 — by L. Vietoris in [1921], and axiom $T_{3\frac{1}{2}}$ — by A. Tychonoff in [1930]. An example of a regular space on which every continuous real-valued function is constant is given in the papers of E. Hewitt [1946] and J. Novák [1948]. The axiom of normality was formulated by H. Tietze in [1923], and independently by P. Alexandroff and P. Urysohn in [1929]; the property of normality was also considered by L. Vietoris in [1921]. The Urysohn Lemma was proved in P. Urysohn's paper [1925]. Theorem 5.6 was proved by A. Tychonoff in [1925]. The theory of nets was constructed by E. H. Moore and H. L. Smith in [1922] and by E. H. Moore in [1939]. The concept of a filter was introduced by H. Cartan in [1937]; N. Bourbaki exploits this concept intensively in his book [1961]. The space of Example 2.1 was constructed by P. Alexandroff and P. Urysohn in [1929]. The space of Example 2.2 was defined by V. Niemytzki (see P. Alexandroff and H. Hopf [1935], p. 35), and our proof that the space it is not normal makes use of F. B. Jones [1937].

PROBLEMS

A (K. Kuratowski [1922a]). Let X be a topological space. We shall denote the closure of the set $A \subset X$ by A^- and its complement by A'. Prove that by applying the operation of closure and complement to the fixed set $A \subset X$ one can obtain at most 14 different sets.

Hint: Prove the equality $A^{-'-'-'-} = A^{-'-}$.

B. Let X be a set partially ordered by the relation $\leqslant$ and let $L(x) = \{y : y \leqslant x\}$ for every $x \in X$. The topology generated by the neighbourhood system $\{L(x)\}_{x \in X}$ is called the *left topology* in the set X induced by the relation $\leqslant$.

(1) Prove that, under this topology, the intersection of an arbitrary number of open sets is an open set.

(2) Prove that X is a T_0-space.

(3) For which points $x \in X$ is the set $\{x\}$ closed, open, open-and-closed?

(4) What is the form of the closure of the set $\{x\}$?

(5) Define the right topology in a set X.

C. Let X be a space satisfying conditions (1) and (2) of the previous problem. Show that the set X can be partially ordered in such a manner that the topology in X is the left topology induced by this partial ordering.

D. Let X be a set ordered by a relation $<$ and containing more than one element. For arbitrary $a, b \in X$ such that $a < b$ let us write

$$(a, b) = \{x: a < x < b\}, \quad L(a) = \{x: x < a\}, \quad R(a) = \{x: a < x\}.$$

Verify that the family $\mathfrak{B}$ consisting of all sets described above has properties (B1) and (B2); the topology generated in the set X by the base $\mathfrak{B}$ is called the *order topology* induced by the ordering $<$. Show that topological spaces obtained in this manner are T_3-spaces.

E. Give an example of a set of real numbers which has infinitely many different derived sets.

F. Prove that if a Hausdorff space X contains a dense subset of power $\leqslant \mathfrak{m}$, then the power of X does not exceed $2^{2^{\mathfrak{m}}}$ (cf. Lemmas 1 and 2 to Theorem 3.4.3). Show that the assumption that X is a Hausdorff space cannot be replaced by the assumption that X is a T_1-space.

G (E. Čech [1932], N. Vedenissoff [1936] and [1940]). A space X is called *perfectly normal* if it is normal and if every closed subset is a G_δ-set (or equivalently — every open subset is an F_σ-set). Show that for T_1-spaces the following conditions are equivalent:

(i) The space X is perfectly normal.

(ii) For each pair of closed and disjoint sets $A, B \subset X$ there exists a continuous function $f: X \to I$ such that $A = f^{-1}(0)$ and $B = f^{-1}(1)$.

(iii) For every closed set $A \subset X$ there exists a continuous function $f: X \to I$ such that $f^{-1}(0) = A$.

Give an example of a normal space which is not perfectly normal. Prove that the space defined in Example 2.1 is perfectly normal.

Hint: To prove implication (i) $\Rightarrow$ (ii) make use of Theorem 4.2. To prove implication (ii) $\Rightarrow$ (iii) consider a pair A, B of closed and disjoint subsets of the space X, and functions $f, g: X \to I$ which vanish only on A and B, respectively; then consider the function $|f| - |g|$.

H. Let X be a perfectly normal space and let Y denote an arbitrary topological space. Show that if $f: X \to Y$ is a closed mapping onto the space Y, then Y is perfectly normal.

Hint: Use Exercise 5.E.

I. Give an example of a Tychonoff space which is not normal and is such that every closed subset is a G_δ-set.

J (Yu. M. Smirnov [1948]). Show that a T_1-space X is normal if and only if it is subject to the following two conditions:

(1) Every closed subset which is a G_δ-set is of the form $f^{-1}(0)$, where $f: X \to I$.

(2) For every closed set F and every open set G which contains F, there exists in X a closed G_δ-set M such that $F \subset M \subset G$.

K (Yu. M. Smirnov [1951c]). We say that the set A is *normally placed* in the space X if for an arbitrary open set U containing A there exists in X an F_σ-set H such that $A \subset H \subset U$.

(a) Show that for a normal space X one can equivalently define normally placed sets by the condition that H is an open F_σ-set.

(b) Prove that a normal space X is perfectly normal if and only if each subset $A \subset X$ is normally placed.

L (P. Urysohn [1925]). We say that a space X is a *Urysohn space* if for each two points $x_1, x_2 \in X$ there exist neighbourhoods U_1 and U_2 such that $\overline{U}_1 \cap \overline{U}_2 = 0$. Show that every regular space is a Urysohn space. Give an example of a T_2-space which is not a Urysohn space.

M (M. H. Stone [1937]). We say that a T_2-space is *semi-regular* if open domains constitute a base of this space. Prove that every regular space is semi-regular. Give an example of a T_2-space which is not semi-regular.

N. Study the relation between Urysohn spaces and semi-regular spaces.

O. Show that the union of sets, of which each one is dense in itself, is dense in itself.

Deduce that every T_1-space is the union of two disjoint sets of which one is closed and dense in itself (such a set is called *perfect*) and the other contains no non-empty set dense in itself (such a set is called *scattered*).

P. A point x of a topological space X is called a *condensation point* of the set $A \subset X$ if an arbitrary neighbourhood of the point x contains an uncountable subset of this set. The set of the condensation points of a set A is denoted by A^0.

Show that

$$A^0 \subset A^d, \quad A^0 = \overline{A^0}, \quad \text{and} \quad (A \cup B)^0 = A^0 \cup B^0;$$

show that, under the assumption that the space considered satisfies the second axiom of countability, the set $A \setminus A^0$ is countable and $(A^0)^0 = A^0$.

Deduce that an arbitrary T_1-space which satisfies the second axiom of countability is the union of two disjoint sets of which one is countable and the other is perfect.

Q. Let us consider the following properties of a topological space X:

(B) The space X satisfies the second axiom of countability.

(D) The space X is separable.

(I) Every subset $A \subset X$ consisting of isolated points is countable.

(Š) Each uncountable family of non-empty open subsets of X contains an uncountable subfamily with a non-empty intersection.

(S) Each family of non-empty disjoint and open subsets of X is countable.

Show that the following diagram contains all implications between the properties under consideration:

$$\begin{array}{ccccccc} (B) & \Rightarrow & (D) & \Rightarrow & (\check{S}) & \Rightarrow & (S) \\ & & \searrow & & \nearrow & & \\ & & & (I) & & & \end{array}$$

Examine the conditions obtained by replacing the number $\aleph_0$ by an arbitrary cardinal number $\mathfrak{m} \geqslant \aleph_0$ in conditions (B)-(S).

Hint: A space satisfying (I) but not (Š) can be obtained from an arbitrary set X of real numbers, where $\overline{\overline{X}} = \omega_1$, in which we define a base as a family of sets of the form $X \cap (a, b) \setminus A$, where $\overline{\overline{A}} = \aleph_0$ (make use of the previous problem). A space satisfying (S) but not (Š) and a space satisfying (Š) but not (D) can be obtained by a modification of Example 2.3. Tychonoff spaces with those properties can be constructed by means of Theorem 2.3.10 and Problems 2.K and 2.O.

R. Let us suppose that a mapping $f: X \to Y$ onto the space Y is given. Which of the properties (B)-(S) of the preceding problem belong to the space Y under the assumption that they belong to the space X?

S. A set X is said to be an $\mathscr{L}^*$ *space* if certain (countable) sequences of its elements are regarded as convergent and if to every convergent sequence $\{x_n\}$ an element $\lim x_n$ of the space X, called a *limit* of the sequence $\{x_n\}$, is assigned in such a way that

(L*1) If $x_n = x$ for every n, then $\lim x_n = x$.

(L*2) If $\lim x_n = x$, then for every subsequence $\{x_{k_n}\}$ of the sequence $\{x_n\}$ we have $\lim x_{k_n} = x$.

(L*3) If a sequence $\{x_n\}$ is not convergent to the point x, then it contains a subsequence containing no subsequences convergent to x.

In na $\mathscr{L}^*$ space one can define the closure operator by assuming that $x \in \overline{A}$ if and only if there exists a sequence $x_1, x_2, \ldots$ in A such that $x = \lim x_n$.

Show that the closure operator defined in this manner satisfies properties (CO1)-(CO3) but may fail to satisfy property (CO4).

T. Show that if in an $\mathscr{L}^*$ space the following condition is satisfied:

(L*4) If $x = \lim x_n$, and $x_n = \lim x_k^{(n)}$, then there exists such a sequence $k_1, k_2, \ldots$ that $x = \lim x_{k_n}^{(n)}$,

then the operation of closure defined in Problem S satisfies property (CO4).

The topology generated by this closure operator is called a *topology induced by convergent sequences*.

U. Give an example of a Hausdorff space whose topology cannot be induced by convergent sequences.

V (J. L. Kelley [1950]). State and prove analogues of conditions (L*1)-(L*3) of Problem S for nets. Generate a topology by a closure operator in a set, in which a class of convergent nets satisfying these analogues and the theorem on iterated limit of Exercise 6.B, is distinguished. Show that every topology can be *generated by convergent nets*, i.e. in the manner described above.

CHAPTER 2

OPERATIONS ON TOPOLOGICAL SPACES

The present chapter is devoted to the description of operations on topological spaces. These operations lead from simpler spaces to more complicated ones. The theorems on the universality of the Tychonoff cube for Tychonoff spaces, and on the universality of the Alexandroff cube for T_0-spaces, which are proved in Paragraph 3, show that by using only two operations one can obtain all spaces belonging to the classes mentioned above. Chapter 2 is, in a sense, the central chapter of the whole book. In subsequent chapters we shall define some classes of topological here spaces and study their behaviour under the operations described. The chapter consists of six paragraphs corresponding to the six operations under consideration.

Paragraph 1 is devoted to subspaces. After defining the notion of a subspace we shall study the problem of extending a real-valued function (the Tietze-Urysohn Theorem), and we shall examine the heredity of certain properties and combinations of mappings.

Paragraph 2 is devoted to the sum of topological spaces. We define here the notion of an additive property.

Paragraph 3 which is the longest, deals with Cartesian products. After giving the definition of the Tychonoff topology and proving some elementary theorems we introduce the notion of a multiplicative property and prove that separation properties (normality excepted) are multiplicative, and that separability is $\mathfrak{c}$-multiplicative. At the end of the paragraph we prove the theorems on universality mentioned before.

In Paragraph 4 we study quotient spaces. It is only a preliminary examination of that operation. More interesting results will be obtained for compact spaces in Chapter 3.

Paragraph 5 is devoted to inverse systems and their limits and to mappings of inverse systems. We show there that the limit of an inverse system is a generalization of the Cartesian product.

In the last paragraph we consider spaces of real-valued continuous functions with the topology of uniform convergence, and spaces of mappings with the topology of pointwise convergence. Another, more interesting topology, called the compact-open topology of mapping spaces, will be considered in Chapter 3.

§ 1. Subspaces. Let a topological space X and its subset M be given. Let us consider in M a family of sets of the form $M \cap U$, where U is an open subset of X. We shall show that this family satisfies conditions (O1)-(O3). Condition (O1) is satisfied because $0 = M \cap 0$ and $M = M \cap X$; it follows from the formulas:

$$(M \cap U_1) \cap (M \cap U_2) = M \cap (U_1 \cap U_2) \quad \text{and} \quad \bigcup_{s \in S} (M \cap U_s) = M \cap \bigcup_{s \in S} U_s$$

that conditions (O2) and (O3) are also satisfied. If we regard the family under consideration as a family of open subsets in M, the set M assumes the character of a topological space. The set M with its topology defined in this manner is called a *subspace* of the space X, and the topology in M is called a *topology induced* by the topology in X.

THEOREM 1. *Let X be a topological space and let M denote its subspace. A set $A \cap M$ is closed in M if and only if $A = M \cap F$, where $F = \overline{F} \subset X$. The closure $\tilde{A}$ of the set $A \subset M$ in the space M and its closure $\overline{A}$ in the space X are linked by means of the formula $\tilde{A} = \overline{A} \cap M$.*

Proof. If $A = M \cap F$, where $F = \overline{F} \subset X$, then $M \setminus A = M \cap (X \setminus F)$ and A is closed in M because its complement is open. If A is a closed set in M, then $M \setminus A = M \cap U$, where U is an open set in X. Thus we have $A = M \setminus (M \setminus A) = M \setminus (M \cap U) = M \cap (X \setminus U)$ and $A = M \cap F$, where $F = X \setminus U$ is a closed set in X.

By the definition of closure, $\tilde{A}$ is the intersection of all sets closed in M and containing A, i.e. sets of the form $M \cap F$, where $F = \overline{F}$ and $A \subset F$. It follows immediately that $\tilde{A} = M \cap \overline{A}$. ■

For every topological space X and subspace M the formula $i_M(x) = x$ defines a function i_M of the set M into X. Since $i_M^{-1}(U) = M \cap U$ for every $U \subset X$, $i_M: M \to X$. The mapping i_M is called the *embedding* of the subspace M in the space X. Let us suppose that two topological spaces, X and X_1, are given. If for a subspace $M \subset X$ there exists a homeomorphism $f: X_1 \to M$, then we call the space X_1 *embeddable* in X and the mapping $i_M f: X_1 \to X$ a *homeomorphic embedding* of X_1 into X.

A subspace M of the space X is said to be *closed* if M is a closed subset of X. If M is a closed subspace of the space X, then $A \subset M$ is closed in M if and only if it is closed in X; therefore $\tilde{A} = \overline{A}$ for every $A \subset M$. The notions of an *open* subspace and a *dense* subspace are defined analogously. It is easy to see that if M is an open (dense) subspace of a space X, then a set $A \subset M$ is open (dense) in M if and only if it is open (dense) in X.

Example 1. The segment I with its natural topology is a closed subspace of the space R of real numbers with its natural topology. By the natural topology of a segment we understand the topology induced by the natural topology of the real-line. Henceforth, when speaking about the segment and the set of real numbers (or the real-line), we shall always mean that these spaces have the natural topology. It can easily be verified that every two closed segments (non-reducing to a single point), just as every two open segments and every two segments with one end--point, are homeomorphic. A discrete space of power $\mathfrak{c}$ is embeddable in the space X considered in Example 1.2.2: it is homeomorphic to the closed subspace X_1. The real-line R is embeddable in the segment $J = [-1, 1]$: it is homeomorphic to the segment $(-1, 1)$. The homeomorphic embedding $f: R \to J$ is defined by means of the formula: $f(x) = x/(1+|x|)$. ■

We say that a property $\mathfrak{W}$ of topological spaces is *hereditary* (*hereditary with respect to closed subsets*) if any subspace (any closed subspace) of a space possessing property $\mathfrak{W}$ also possesses that property. Possessing a base of power $\leqslant \mathfrak{m}$ and possessing a base of power $\leqslant \mathfrak{m}$ at every point, in particular, satisfying the second and the first axiom of countability, is an example of a hereditary property. Possessing a dense countable subset is not a hereditary property, as is shown by Example 1.2.2.

Theorem 2. *Every subspace of a T_i-space is a T_i-space for $i \leqslant 3\frac{1}{2}$. Normality is a hereditary property with respect to closed subsets.*

Proof. We shall prove, for example, that a subspace M of a regular space X is regular. Proofs of the remaining parts of the theorem are analogous.

Suppose we are given a point $x \in M$ and a set A closed in M and such that $x \notin A$. By virtue of Theorem 1, $A = M \cap \bar{A}$, whence $x \notin \bar{A}$. There exist, therefore, sets U_1 and V_1, open in X and such that $x \in U_1$, $\bar{A} \subset V_1$, and $U_1 \cap V_1 = 0$. Assuming that $U = M \cap U_1$, $V = M \cap V_1$ we obtain open sets in M such that $x \in U$, $A \subset V$ and $U \cap V = 0$. The space M is, therefore, regular. ■

Example 3.3 given below shows that normality is not hereditary.

Let X be a topological space and let M denote a subspace of X. Let us consider a mapping $f: X \to Y$ into an arbitrary space Y. The function $f|M$ which assigns the point $f(x) \in Y$ to every point $x \in M$ is, as we see from the formula: $(f|M)^{-1}(U) = M \cap f^{-1}(U)$, a mapping, and $f|M: M \to Y$. We call this mapping a *restriction* of f to M. If for some $f: M \to Y$ there exists an $F: X \to Y$ such that $F|M = f$, then the mapping f is called *extendable* over X and F is called an *extension* of f over X. Not every mapping defined on a subspace is extendable; in fact, few mappings have this property. Theorems which give some conditions under which mappings can be extended over the whole space are very important in topology and are usually rather difficult. Let us note that the Urysohn Lemma can be formulated as a theorem on the existence of an extension. In fact, the Lemma states that if a subspace M of a normal space X is the union of two subsets A and B disjoint and closed in X, then the function $f\colon M \to I$ defined by means of the formulas: $f(x) = 0$ for $x \in A$, $f(x) = 1$ for $x \in B$, is extendable over X.

We can see that the following, more general theorem is true.

THEOREM 3 (Tietze-Urysohn). *Let X be a normal space and M its closed subspace. Every continuous function defined on M with values in I or in R is extendable over X.*

Proof. First we shall prove that the theorem is valid for a function with values in I. To simplify the proof, instead of I we shall consider the homeomorphic segment $J = [-1, 1]$ and a continuous function $f\colon M \to J$.

Let us observe, to begin with, that for an arbitrary $f_0\colon M \to R$ such that $|f_0(x)| \leqslant c$ for $x \in M$, there exists a $g\colon X \to R$ such that

$$(1) \qquad |g(x)| \leqslant \tfrac{1}{3}c \quad \text{for} \quad x \in X$$

and

$$(2) \qquad |f_0(x) - g(x)| \leqslant \tfrac{2}{3}c \quad \text{for} \quad x \in M.$$

Indeed, since the sets $A = f_0^{-1}([-c, -\tfrac{1}{3}c])$ and $B = f_0^{-1}([\tfrac{1}{3}c, c])$ are disjoint and closed in M, they are closed in X and, by the Urysohn Lemma, there exists a function $k\colon X \to I$ such that $k(x) = 0$ for $x \in A$ and $k(x) = 1$ for $x \in B$. It is easy to verify that putting $g(x) = \tfrac{2}{3}c\big(k(x) - \tfrac{1}{2}\big)$ we obtain a continuous function satisfying (1) and (2).

We are now going to define inductively a sequence $g_1, g_2, \ldots$ of functions continuous on X such that

$$(3) \qquad |g_n(x)| \leqslant \tfrac{1}{3}(\tfrac{2}{3})^{n-1} \quad \text{for} \quad x \in X$$

and

$$(4) \qquad \Big|f(x) - \sum_{i=1}^{n} g_i(x)\Big| \leqslant (\tfrac{2}{3})^n \quad \text{for} \quad x \in M.$$

The existence of the function g_1 follows from the above remark. Let us suppose that the functions $g_1, g_2, \ldots, g_n$ are already defined. Putting in our remark $f - \big(\sum_{i=1}^{n} g_i\big)\big| M$ instead of f_0 and $(\tfrac{2}{3})^n$ instead of c, we obtain a function $g = g_{n+1}$ which satisfies (3) and (4), where n is replaced by $n+1$.

By virtue of (3), the series $\sum_{n=1}^{\infty} g_n$ is uniformly convergent. From Theorem 1.4.2 and from formula (3) it follows that its limit F is a continuous function of X into J. By condition (4) we infer that $F(x)=f(x)$ for $x \in M$; therefore F is an extension of $f: M \to R$.

Let us now consider a continuous function $f: M \to R$. Let us denote by $i: R \to J$ the homeomorphic embedding described in Example 1. By the part of the theorem which is already proved, there exists an extension $F_1: X \to J$ of the function $if: M \to J$. Evidently $N = F_1^{-1}(\{-1, 1\})$ is a closed subset of X disjoint with M. Let $k: X \to I$ be a function such that $k(x) = 1$ for $x \in M$ and $k(x) = 0$ for $x \in N$. It can easily be verified that $F_2: X \to J$ defined by means of the formula: $F_2(x) = F_1(x) \cdot k(x)$ for $x \in X$, is also an extension of the function $if: M \to J$ and that $F_2(X) \subset i(E)$. The function $F: X \to R$ defined by means of the formula: $F(x) = i^{-1}F_2(x)$ is the required extension of f. ■

Let us observe that the property of extendability described in the above theorem in the class of T_1-spaces belongs to normal spaces only. Indeed, if X is a non-normal T_1-space, then there exist in X two closed and disjoint sets A and B which cannot be separated by open sets. Hence it follows that the function $f: A \cup B \to I$, defined by means of the formulas: $f(x) = 0$ for $x \in A$ and $f(x) = 1$ for $x \in B$, is not extendable over X.

We shall prove one more theorem on extending of mappings.

THEOREM 4. *Let X be a topological space X and D its dense subspace. Let $f: D \to Y$ denote an arbitrary mapping of D into a Hausdorff space Y. There is at most one way of extending f over X.*

Proof. Let us suppose that $F_i: X \to Y$ is an extension of f for $i = 1, 2$. Let us consider the set:

$$T = \{x: F_1(x) = F_2(x)\}.$$

By virtue of Theorem 1.5.2, the set T is closed. Since $D \subset T$, $\bar{D} = X \subset T$ holds, hence $T = X$. ■

EXAMPLE 2. We shall show how it can be deduced from the above theorems that the space X constructed in Example 1.2.2 is not normal (see also Example 1.5.2). We have already learned that X contains a closed subspace X_1 which is homeomorphic to the discrete space of power $\mathfrak{c}$ and a dense countable subset D. By Theorem 4, there exist at most $\mathfrak{c}^{\aleph_0} = \mathfrak{c}$ different continuous real-valued functions on X. If the space X were normal, then, by Theorem 3, each of $2^{\mathfrak{c}}$ continuous functions defined on X_1 could be extended over the whole X, which is impossible because of the inequality $2^{\mathfrak{c}} > \mathfrak{c}$. Therefore X is not a normal space. ■

To define a mapping f of a space X into Y it is sometimes convenient to split X into subspaces and to define f separately (for instance by different formulas) on each of those subspaces (cf. Examples 1.4.3 and 1.4.4). We should, therefore, have some criteria for verifying whether the function defined in this manner is a mapping. We now give two theorems of this type.

Suppose we are given topological spaces X and Y, a family $\{A_s\}_{s\in S}$ of subspaces of X, and a family of mappings $\{f_s\}_{s\in S}$, where $f_s\colon A_s \to Y$. We shall say that the mappings $\{f_s\}_{s\in S}$ are *compatible* if

$$f_{s_1}|A_{s_1} \cap A_{s_2} = f_{s_2}|A_{s_1} \cap A_{s_2},$$

for every $s_1, s_2 \in S$.

If the mappings are compatible and $\bigcup_{s\in S} A_s = X$, then the formula

$$f(x) = f_s(x) \quad \text{for} \quad x \in A_s$$

defines a function f of the space X into the space Y, called the *combination of mappings* $\{f_s\}_{s\in S}$.

THEOREM 5. *Suppose we are given topological spaces X and Y, a family $\{U_s\}_{s\in S}$ of open subspaces of X such that $\bigcup_{s\in S} U_s = X$, and a family of compatible mappings $\{f_s\}_{s\in S}$, where $f_s\colon U_s \to Y$. The combination f of the mappings $\{f_s\}_{s\in S}$ is a mapping of the space X into the space Y.*

Proof. For an arbitrary U which is open in Y we have

$$f^{-1}(U) = \bigcup_{s\in S} f_s^{-1}(U).$$

The set $f_s^{-1}(U)$ is open in U_s, whence also in X. It follows that $f^{-1}(U)$ is open in X. ∎

Theorem 5 implies the following:

COROLLARY. *Suppose we are given topological spaces X and Y, and a function f defined on X with values in Y. In order that f be a mapping, it is necessary and sufficient that each point $x \in X$ have a neighbourhood U_x such that $f|U_x$ is a mapping.* ∎

THEOREM 6. *Suppose we are given topological spaces X and Y, a finite family $\{A_i\}_{i=1}^k$ of closed subspaces of X such that $\bigcup_{i=1}^k A_i = X$, and a family $\{f_i\}_{i=1}^k$ of compatible mappings, where $f_i\colon A_i \to Y$ for $i = 1, 2, \ldots, k$. Then the combination f of mappings $\{f_i\}_{i=1}^k$ is a mapping of the space X into the space Y.*

Proof. For every A closed in Y we have

$$f^{-1}(A) = f_1^{-1}(A) \cup f_2^{-1}(A) \cup \ldots \cup f_k^{-1}(A).$$

The set $f_i^{-1}(A)$ is closed in A_i; therefore it is closed in X. Hence it follows that $f^{-1}(A)$ is closed in X. ∎

COROLLARY. *For an arbitrary finite family $\{A_i\}_{i=1}^k$ of mutually disjoint closed subsets of a normal space X there exists a family $\{U_i\}_{i=1}^k$ of open* *subsets of that space such that $F_i \subset U_i$ for $i = 1, 2, \ldots, k$ and $\overline{U}_i \cap \overline{U}_j = 0$ for $i \neq j$.*

Proof. Let $M = \bigcup_{i=1}^{k} A_i$. The combination $f: M \to R$ of mappings $\{f_i\}_{i=1}^{k}$, where $f_i: A_i \to R$ and $f_i(x) = i$ for $x \in A_i$, has, by virtue of Theorem 3, an extension $F: X \to R$. It can easily be verified that the sets $U_i = F^{-1}\big((i-\frac{1}{3}, i+\frac{1}{3})\big)$ have the required properties. ∎

EXERCISES

A. Let X be a topological space and let M denote its subspace. Verify that the interior and the boundary of a set A in the space M are given by the formulas:

$$M\setminus\overline{M\setminus A} \quad \text{and} \quad M \cap \bar{A} \cap \overline{M\setminus A},$$

respectively, where the dash denotes the closure in the space X.

B. Show that if a subspace $M \subset X$ is an F_σ-set (a G_δ-set) in X then a set $A \subset M$ is an F_σ-set (a G_δ-set) in M if and only if it is an F_σ-set (a G_δ-set) in X.

C. Let X denote a regular space and let A be its dense subspace. Verify that for an arbitrary point $x \in A$ the weight of the space X at the point x is equal to the weight of the space A at the point x.

D. Show that Theorem 6 is not true if we omit the assumption that the family of subspaces under consideration is finite.

§ 2. Sum of spaces. Let $\{X_s\}_{s \in S}$ be a family of disjoint topological spaces, i.e. let $X_s \cap X_{s'} = 0$ for $s \neq s'$. Let us consider the set $X = \bigcup_{s \in S} X_s$ and let us assume that sets $U \subset X$, such that the intersection $U \cap X_s$ is open in X_s for every $s \in S$, are open in X. Evidently, the open sets defined in this manner have properties (O1)-(O3); therefore a topology has been defined in X. The set X with this topology is called the *sum* of spaces $\{X_s\}_{s \in S}$ and is denoted by the symbol $\bigoplus_{s \in S} X_s$ or $X_1 \oplus X_2 \oplus \ldots \oplus X_k$ if $S = \{1, 2, \ldots, k\}$.

THEOREM 1. *The set $F \subset \bigoplus_{s \in S} X_s$ is closed if and only if the intersection $F \cap X_s$ is closed in X for every $s \in S$.*

Proof. The set F is closed if and only if $\bigoplus_{s \in S} X_s \setminus F$ is an open set. Thus the theorem follows from the formula

$$\Big(\bigoplus_{s \in S} X_s \setminus F\Big) \cap X_s = X_s \setminus (F \cap X_s). \; ∎$$

COROLLARY 1. *Each set X_s is open-and-closed in $\bigoplus_{s \in S} X_s$.* ∎

COROLLARY 2. *Each space X_s is a subspace of the space $\bigoplus_{s \in S} X_s$. Therefore the formula $i_s(x) = x$ defines an embedding of the space X_s into $\bigoplus_{s \in S} X_s$ for every $s \in S$.* ∎

THEOREM 2. *Let X be a topological space. If $X = \bigcup_{s \in S} X_s$, and X_s is an open subset of X for every $s \in S$, and $X_s \cap X_{s'} = 0$ for $s \neq s'$, then $X = \bigoplus_{s \in S} X_s$, where X_s is considerded with the topology of a subspace of X.*

Proof. The spaces X and $\bigoplus_{s \in S} X_s$ consist of the same points; it is, therefore, sufficient to show that the same families of open subsets are distinguished in those two spaces. If U is open in X, then for every $s \in S$ the intersection $U \cap X_s$ is open in X_s; therefore U is open in $\bigoplus_{s \in S} X_s$. If U is open in $\bigoplus_{s \in S} X_s$, then for every $s \in S$ the set $U \cap X_s$ is open in X_s, whence also in X, for X_s is open in X. The set $U = \bigcup_{s \in S} U \cap X_s$ is, therefore, open in X. ■

COROLLARY. *Let a family of disjoint topological spaces $\{X_s\}_{s \in S}$ be given. If $S = \bigcup_{t \in T} S_t$ and $S_t \cap S_{t'} = 0$ for $t \neq t'$, then $\bigoplus_{s \in S} X_s = \bigoplus_{t \in T} (\bigoplus_{s \in S_t} X_s)$. The operation of the sum of spaces is, therefore, associative.* ■

THEOREM 3. *A function f of the space $\bigoplus_{s \in S} X_s$ into Y is a mapping if and only if for every $s \in S$ the composition fi_s is a mapping, $fi_s: X_s \to Y$.*

Proof. If $f: \bigoplus_{s \in S} X_s \to Y$, then for every $s \in S$ we have $fi_s: X_s \to Y$, for fi_s is the composition of two mappings. Suppose we are given a function f of the space $\bigoplus_{s \in S} X_s$ into Y such that $fi_s: X_s \to Y$ for every $s \in S$. The function f is the combination of the mappings $\{fi_s\}_{s \in S}$; it follows from Theorem 1.5 that f is a mapping. ■

A property $\mathfrak{W}$ of topological spaces is said to be *additive* ($\mathfrak{m}$-*additive*) if for every family of disjoint spaces $\{X_s\}_{s \in S}$ (where $\overline{\overline{S}} \leqslant \mathfrak{m}$) which have this property the sum $\bigoplus_{s \in S} X_s$ also has this property.

THEOREM 4. *The property "X is a T_i-space" is additive for $i \leqslant 4$.*

Proof. We shall prove, for example, that normality is an additive property. Let us consider a family $\{X_s\}_{s \in S}$ of disjoint normal spaces. Suppose that A and B are disjoint and closed in $\bigoplus_{s \in S} X_s$. By virtue of Theorem 1, for every s the sets $A \cap X_s$ and $B \cap X_s$ are disjoint and closed in X_s. By the normality of X_s, for every $s \in S$ there exist sets U_s and V_s open in X_s and such that

$$A \cap X_s \subset U_s, \quad B \cap X_s \subset V_s, \quad \text{and} \quad U_s \cap V_s = 0.$$

It can easily be observed that

$$A \subset U = \bigcup_{s \in S} U_s, \quad B \subset V = \bigcup_{s \in S} V_s, \quad U \cap V = 0,$$

and that U and V are open in $\bigoplus_{s\in S} X_s$. The space $\bigoplus_{s\in S} X_s$ is, therefore, normal. ■

The property "X is of weight $\leqslant \mathfrak{m}$" is $\mathfrak{m}$-additive for $\mathfrak{m} \geqslant \aleph_0$ but is not additive.

EXAMPLE 1. The discrete space of power $\mathfrak{m}$ is the sum of $\mathfrak{m}$ one-point spaces.

Let X denote the space of Example 1.2.1. For every $x \in X$ and for its arbitrary neighbourhood U the space X can be represented in the form of a sum $X_1 \oplus X_2$, where $x \in X_1 \subset U$. In fact, we can assume that X_1 is a set of the form $[x, r)$ contained in U and put $X_2 = X \setminus X_1$. Since X_1 is open-and-closed in X, by Theorem 2, we have that $X = X_1 \oplus X_2$.

The space R of real numbers cannot be represented in the form of the sum $X_1 \oplus X_2$ of its non-empty subsets X_1 and X_2. Indeed, let us suppose that $R = X_1 \oplus X_2$ and $X_1 \neq 0 \neq X_2$, i.e. that there exist points $x_1 \in X_1$ and $x_2 \in X_2$. Let us suppose that $x_1 < x_2$. The set $X_1 \cap [x_1, x_2]$ is bounded; therefore it has the least upper bound x_0. Since the set X_1 is closed, $x_0 \in X_1$ and $x_0 < x_2$. The set X_1 is also open, whence there exists an $\varepsilon > 0$ such that $(x_0 - \varepsilon, x_0 + \varepsilon) \subset X_1$, i.e. $X_1 \cap (x_0, x_2) \neq 0$, contrary to the definition of the least upper bound. ■

The sum $\bigoplus_{s\in S} X_s$ can also be defined for a family of spaces which does not satisfy the condition $X_s \cap X_{s'} = 0$ for $s \neq s'$. For this purpose it is necessary to find a family $\{X'_s\}_{s\in S}$ such that X'_s is homeomorphic to X_s and $X'_s \cap X'_{s'} = 0$ for $s \neq s'$ and then put $\bigoplus_{s\in S} X_s = \bigoplus_{s\in S} X'_s$. The reader can verify that the spaces obtained in this manner are homeomorphic irrespective of the choice of the family $\{X'_s\}_{s\in S}$. Lastly, let us note that there always exists a family $\{X'_s\}_{s\in S}$ which has the required property. It is sufficient to put $X'_s = X_s \times \{s\}$ and to assume that those sets U are open in X'_s for which the set $\{x: (x, s) \in U\}$ is open in X_s.

EXERCISES

A. Show that if a space X is a continuous image of the real-line R, then it cannot be represented in the form of the sum $X_1 \oplus X_2$, where $X_1 \neq 0 \neq X_2$. How can one strengthen this result?

B. Prove that "X is a discrete space" is an additive property.

C. Show that a space X is homeomorphic to the sum $\bigoplus_{s\in S} X_s$ if and only if there exists a family of mappings $\{i_s\}_{s\in S}$, where $i_s: X_s \to X$, and the following conditions are satisfied:

(1) For every space Y and a pair f, g of mappings of X into Y if $fi_s = gi_s$ for every $s \in S$, then $f = g$.

(2) For every space Y and a family of mappings $\{f_s\}_{s\in S}$, where $f_s: X_s \to Y$, there exists a mapping $f: X \to Y$ such that $fi_s = f_s$ for every $s \in S$.

§ 3. Cartesian product. Let a family $\{X_s\}_{s\in S}$ of topological spaces be given. Let us consider the product $X = \underset{s\in S}{\boldsymbol{P}} X_s$ of spaces of that family. The point f of the set X, i.e. a function of the set S into $\bigcup_{s\in S} X_s$ such that $f(s)\in X_s$, will be denoted by the symbol $x = \{x_s\}$, where $x_s = f(s)$. Therefore, if $x = \{x_s\}\in \underset{s\in S}{\boldsymbol{P}} X_s$, then we have $x_s\in X_s$ for every $s\in S$. The point x_s is called the s-th *coordinate* of the point x. The assigning to a point $x\in X$ of its s-th coordinate defines a function of the product $\underset{s\in S}{\boldsymbol{P}} X_s$ into the topological space X_s; we denote it by the symbol p_s and call the *projection* on the s-th axis X_s. The set $\underset{s\in S}{\boldsymbol{P}} X_s$ with the topology generated by the family of mappings $\{p_s\}_{s\in S}$ is called the *Cartesian product* of spaces from the family $\{X_s\}_{s\in S}$. The topology in the product $\underset{s\in S}{\boldsymbol{P}} X_s$ described above is called the *Tychonoff topology*.

For an arbitrary family $\{X_s\}_{s\in S}$ of topological spaces, $\underset{s\in S}{\boldsymbol{P}} X_s$ will always denote the topological space defined above, i.e. a set of points — the product $\underset{s\in S}{\boldsymbol{P}} X_s$ — and a family of open sets — the Tychonoff topology. For a finite set of indices $S = \{1, 2, \ldots, k\}$ we shall use the symbol $X_1\times\times X_2\times\ldots\times X_k$ to denote the Cartesian product of spaces $\{X_i\}_{i=1}^{k}$; if $X_s = X$ for $s\in S$ and $\overline{\overline{S}} = \mathfrak{m}$, then we shall also write $X^{\mathfrak{m}}$ for $\underset{s\in S}{\boldsymbol{P}} X_s$.

THEOREM 1. *The base of the Cartesian product* $\underset{s\in S}{\boldsymbol{P}} X_s$ *consists of sets of the form* $\underset{s\in S}{\boldsymbol{P}} W_s$, *where* W_s *is an open subset of the space* X_s *and* $W_s \neq X_s$ *only for a finite number of elements of the set* S. *Furthermore, if for every* $s\in S$ *a base* $\mathfrak{B}_s$ *in the space* X_s *is given, then we can assume that* $W_s\in\mathfrak{B}_s$ *for* $W_s \neq X_s$.

Proof. By virtue of Theorem 1.4.3, the base is composed of the sets of the form:

$$\bigcap_{i=1}^{k} p_{s_i}^{-1}(W_i),\text{ where } s_1, \ldots, s_k\in S \text{ and } W_i \text{ is open in } X_{s_i} \text{ for } i = 1, \ldots, k.$$

In order to prove the first part of our theorem it is, therefore, sufficient to note that $p_s^{-1}(W_s) = \underset{s\in S}{\boldsymbol{P}} W_s$, where $W_{s'} = X_{s'}$ for $s' \neq s$, and that $\underset{s\in S}{\boldsymbol{P}} W_s \cap \underset{s\in S}{\boldsymbol{P}} W'_s = \underset{s\in S}{\boldsymbol{P}}(W_s \cap W'_s)$. It follows immediately from the definition of a base that the second part of the theorem is also valid. ■

Sets of the form $\underset{s\in S}{\boldsymbol{P}} W_s$, where W_s is an open subset of the space X_s and $W_s \neq X_s$ for only one $s\in S$, form a subbase of the space $\underset{s\in S}{\boldsymbol{P}} X_s$.

THEOREM 2. *Let $\{X_s\}_{s\in S}$ denote an arbitrary family of spaces. For an arbitrary family $\{A_s\}_{s\in S}$, where $A_s \subset X_s$, the following formula holds true:*

$$(1) \qquad \overline{\underset{s\in S}{\boldsymbol{P}} A_s} = \underset{s\in S}{\boldsymbol{P}} \bar{A}_s.$$

Proof. In virtue of Theorem 1.1.1, $x \in \overline{\underset{s\in S}{\boldsymbol{P}} A_s}$ if and only if for each element $\underset{s\in S}{\boldsymbol{P}} W_s$ of the base which contains x we have the inequality $\underset{s\in S}{\boldsymbol{P}} W_s \cap \underset{s\in S}{\boldsymbol{P}} A_s = \underset{s\in S}{\boldsymbol{P}} W_s \cap A_s \neq 0$, i.e. if for every $s \in S$ and an arbitrary neighbourhood W_s of the s-th coordinate of the point x the inequality $W_s \cap A_s \neq 0$ holds. The last condition is satisfied if and only if $x \in \underset{s\in S}{\boldsymbol{P}} \bar{A}_s$. ∎

COROLLARY 1. *If $A_s = \bar{A}_s \subset X_s$ for every $s \in S$, then the set $\underset{s\in S}{\boldsymbol{P}} A_s$ is closed in the Cartesian product $\underset{s\in S}{\boldsymbol{P}} X_s$.* ∎

COROLLARY 2. *If for every $s \in S$ the set A_s is dense in X_s, then the set $\underset{s\in S}{\boldsymbol{P}} A_s$ is dense in the Cartesian product $\underset{s\in S}{\boldsymbol{P}} X_s$.* ∎

It is worth noting that the topology in the Cartesian product cannot be generated by the closure operator given by formula (1). Indeed, not every subset of $\underset{s\in S}{\boldsymbol{P}} X_s$ is of the form $\underset{s\in S}{\boldsymbol{P}} A_s$.

THEOREM 3. *A function f of a space Y into the Cartesian product $\underset{s\in S}{\boldsymbol{P}} X_s$ is a mapping if and only if for every $s \in S$ the composition $p_s f$ is a mapping, i.e. $p_s f\colon Y \to X_s$.*

Proof. If $f\colon Y \to \underset{s\in S}{\boldsymbol{P}} X_s$, then $p_s f$ is a mapping, for it is the composition of two mappings. Let us suppose that $p_s f\colon Y \to X_s$ for every $s \in S$. Let us consider an arbitrary element $\underset{s\in S}{\boldsymbol{P}} W_s$ of the subbase of the Cartesian product under consideration where $W_{s_0} \subset X_{s_0}$ is an open set and $W_s = X_s$ for $s \neq s_0$. By virtue of Theorem 1.4.1 (condition (ii)), it is sufficient to show that $f^{-1}\big(\underset{s\in S}{\boldsymbol{P}} W_s\big)$ is open. We have, however,

$$f^{-1}\big(\underset{s\in S}{\boldsymbol{P}} W_s\big) = f^{-1}\big(p_{s_0}^{-1}(W_{s_0})\big) = (p_{s_0} f)^{-1}(W_{s_0}). \ \blacksquare$$

THEOREM 4. *Let $\{X_s\}_{s\in S}$ be a family of topological spaces, where $S = \bigcup_{t\in T} S_t$ and $S_t \cap S_{t'} = 0$ for $t \neq t'$. The spaces $\underset{s\in S}{\boldsymbol{P}} X_s$ and $\underset{t\in T}{\boldsymbol{P}}\big(\underset{s\in S_t}{\boldsymbol{P}} X_s\big)$ are homeomorphic. The operation of Cartesian product is, therefore, associative.*

Proof. Let us assign the point $f(x) = \{x_t\}$ of the space $\underset{t\in T}{\boldsymbol{P}}\big(\underset{s\in S_t}{\boldsymbol{P}} X_s\big)$, where $x_t = \{x_s\} \in \underset{s\in S_t}{\boldsymbol{P}} X_s$, to the point $x = \{x_s\}$ of the product $\underset{s\in S}{\boldsymbol{P}} X_s$. The function defined in this manner is one-to-one and onto the space

$\underset{t\in T}{\boldsymbol{P}}\big(\underset{s\in S_t}{\boldsymbol{P}} X_s\big)$. By applying Theorem 3, one can easily show that f and f^{-1} are mappings. ■

THEOREM 5. *Suppose we are given a family $\{X_s\}_{s\in S}$ of topological spaces such that $X_s \cap X_{s'} = 0$ for $s \neq s'$, and a topological space X. Then the following equality holds:*

$$(\bigoplus_{s\in S} X_s)\times X = \bigoplus_{s\in S}(X_s\times X),$$

i.e. the Cartesian product is distributive with respect to the sum. ■

The projection $p_s\colon \underset{s\in S}{\boldsymbol{P}} X_s \to X_s$ is an important example of an open mapping. Since in order to prove that a mapping is open it is sufficient to show that the images of elements of a base are open, the openness of p_s follows from the formula $p_s\big(\underset{s\in S}{\boldsymbol{P}} W_s\big) = W_s$.

Suppose we are given two families of topological spaces, $\{X_s\}_{s\in S}$ and $\{Y_s\}_{s\in S}$, and a family of mappings $\{f_s\}_{s\in S}$, where $f_s\colon X_s \to Y_s$ for every $s\in S$. The function which assigns the point $\{f_s(x_s)\}\in \underset{s\in S}{\boldsymbol{P}} Y_s$ to the point $x = \{x_s\}\in \underset{s\in S}{\boldsymbol{P}} X_s$ is a mapping, as follows from Theorem 3. We call it the *Cartesian product* of the mappings $\{f_s\}_{s\in S}$ and denote it by the symbol $\underset{s\in S}{\boldsymbol{P}} f_s$ or $f_1\times f_2\times \ldots \times f_k$ if $S = \{1, 2, \ldots, k\}$. Let us observe that if $f = \underset{s\in S}{\boldsymbol{P}} f_s$, then $f\big(\underset{s\in S}{\boldsymbol{P}} X_s\big) = \underset{s\in S}{\boldsymbol{P}} f_s(X_s)$.

Suppose we are given a topological space X, a family $\{Y_s\}_{s\in S}$ of topological spaces, and a family of mappings $\{f_s\}_{s\in S}$, where $f_s\colon X \to Y_s$ for every $s\in S$. The function which assigns the point $\{f_s(x)\}\in \underset{s\in S}{\boldsymbol{P}} Y_s$ to every point $x\in X$ is, according to Theorem 3, a mapping. We call it the *diagonal* of the mappings $\{f_s\}_{s\in S}$ and denote it by $\underset{s\in S}{\triangle} f_s$ or by $f_1 \triangle f_2 \triangle \ldots \triangle f_k$ in the case $S = \{1, 2, \ldots, k\}$.

EXAMPLE 1. The Cartesian product R^m of m copies (m is finite) of the set of real numbers is called the *m-dimensional Euclidean space*. The product I^m of m copies (m is finite) of the segment I is called an *m-dimensional cube*. Let us suppose that $m > n$ and let us consider the subset of the space R^m consisting of points whose last $m-n$ coordinates are equal to zero. It is easy to observe that this subset is homeomorphic to R^n; the space R^n is, therefore, embeddable in R^m for $m > n$. The subset of the space R^{n+1} consisting of points $(x_1, \ldots, x_{n+1})$ whose coordinates satisfy the condition $x_1^2+x_2^2+\ldots+x_{n+1}^2 = 1$ is called an *n-dimensional sphere* and denoted by the symbol S^n. Replacing the sign of equality in the condition which characterizes the sphere S^{n-1} by the sign $\leqslant$ we obtain a subset of the space E^n called an *n-dimensional ball* and denoted by Q^n.

The sphere S^1 is also called a *circle*; the product $S^1 \times S^1$ is called a *torus* and denoted by T^2. ■

A property $\mathfrak{W}$ of topological spaces is said to be *multiplicative* ($\mathfrak{m}$-*multiplicative*) if for every family of spaces $\{X_s\}_{s \in S}$ (where $S \leqslant \mathfrak{m}$) which have this property the Cartesian product $\underset{s \in S}{\boldsymbol{P}} X_s$ also has this property.

THEOREM 6. *The Cartesian product of T_i-spaces is a T_i-space for $i \leqslant 3\frac{1}{2}$. If the Cartesian product $\underset{s \in S}{\boldsymbol{P}} X_s$ is a non-empty T_i-space for $i \leqslant 4$, then X_s is a T_i-space for every $s \in S$.*

Proof. It follows from Theorem 2 that the property "X is a T_1-space" is multiplicative. The proofs of the multiplicativity of the remaining properties are similar; we shall prove for example that the property "X is a Tychonoff space" is multiplicative.

Let us suppose that the spaces $\{X_s\}_{s \in S}$ are Tychonoff spaces. By virtue of Theorem 1.5.4, it is sufficient to show that for an arbitrary point $x = \{x_s\} \in \underset{s \in S}{\boldsymbol{P}} X_s$ and a neighbourhood V of the form $p_s^{-1}(W_s)$, where W_s is an open set in X_s and $x_s \in W_s$, there exists a continuous function $f\colon \underset{s \in S}{\boldsymbol{P}} X_s \to I$ such that $f(x) = 0$ and $f(y) = 1$ for $y \in \underset{s \in S}{\boldsymbol{P}} X_s \setminus V$. Let $f_s\colon X_s \to I$ be a function such that $f_s(x_s) = 0$ and $f_s(y) = 1$ for $y \in X_s \setminus W_s$. The reader can easily verify that the function $f_s p_s$ has the required properties.

Let us now consider the Cartesian product $\underset{s \in S}{\boldsymbol{P}} X_s$ of the non-empty spaces $\{X_s\}_{s \in S}$. For every $s \in S$ let us choose an arbitrary point $x_s^* \in X_s$. Let us assume that $X_{s_0}^* = \underset{s \in S}{\boldsymbol{P}} A_s$, where $A_s = \{x_s^*\}$ for $s \neq s_0$ and $A_{s_0} = X_{s_0}$. If the product $\underset{s \in S}{\boldsymbol{P}} X_s$ is a T_i-space for $i \geqslant 1$, then $X_{s_0}^*$ is its closed subspace for every $s_0 \in S$. It is easy to see that the mapping $i_{s_0}\colon X_{s_0} \to X_{s_0}^*$ defined by means of the formula $i_{s_0}(x) = \{x_s\}$, where $x_s = x_s^*$ for $s \neq s_0$, and $x_{s_0} = x$, is a homeomorphism. The space X_{s_0} is, therefore, embeddable in the Cartesian product $\underset{s \in S}{\boldsymbol{P}} X_s$ (as a closed subspace if this product is a T_i-space for $i \geqslant 1$). By Theorem 1.2, we infer that if the product $\underset{s \in S}{\boldsymbol{P}} X_s$ is a T_i-space for $i \leqslant 4$, then each factor also satisfies the corresponding axiom of separation. ■

We shall now give an example which shows that normality is not a multiplicative property.

EXAMPLE 2. In Example 1.5.3 we proved that the space X defined in Example 1.2.1 is normal. The Cartesian product $X \times X$ contains a closed subset $\{(x, y)\colon y = -x\}$ homeomorphic to the discrete space of power $\mathfrak{c}$, and a countable dense subset. By the same reasoning as in Example 1.5.2 or 1.2 we infer that $X \times X$ is not normal. ■

THEOREM 7. *Separability is a* $\mathfrak{c}$*-multiplicative property.*

Proof. Let $\{X_s\}_{s \in S}$ be a family of separable spaces, where $\overline{\overline{S}} \leqslant \mathfrak{c}$. It may be assumed without loss of generality that S is the set of real numbers, i.e. that $S = R$. Let D_s be a countable dense set in X_s for every $s \in R$ and let f_s denote a mapping of the set of natural numbers N (the discrete space of power $\aleph_0$) onto D_s. Let us consider the Cartesian product $\underset{s \in R}{\boldsymbol{P}} N_s$, where $N_s = N$ for $s \in R$, and the mapping $f = \underset{s \in R}{\boldsymbol{P}} f_s$ of $\underset{s \in R}{\boldsymbol{P}} N_s$ into the space $\underset{s \in R}{\boldsymbol{P}} X_s$. In order to prove our theorem it is sufficient to show that there exists in $\underset{s \in R}{\boldsymbol{P}} N_s$ a countable dense subset D. Indeed, then the theorem will follow from the formula $f(\overline{D}) \subset \overline{f(D)}$.

Let us denote by $\mathfrak{W}$ the class of all finite families $\{P_1, P_2, \ldots, P_k\}$ of disjoint closed intervals in R with rational end-points.

Let D denote the set of all functions f of R into N which satisfy the following condition:

There exists a family $\{P_1, P_2, \ldots, P_k\} \in \mathfrak{W}$ such that f is constant on the intervals $P_1, P_2, \ldots, P_k$, and its value is equal to 1 outside the union of these intervals.

Since the class $\mathfrak{W}$ is countable, the set D is obviously also countable. We shall show that D is dense in $\underset{s \in R}{\boldsymbol{P}} N_s$, i.e. that $D \cap V \neq 0$ for an arbitrary non-empty open set $V \subset \underset{s \in R}{\boldsymbol{P}} N_s$. We can of course assume that $V = \underset{s \in R}{\boldsymbol{P}} W_s$, where W_s is an open non-empty subset of N_s and $W_s \neq N_s$ only for $s \in \{s_1, s_2, \ldots, s_k\} \subset R$. Let $P_1, P_2, \ldots, P_k$ denote disjoint closed intervals with rational end-points which contain the points $s_1, s_2, \ldots, s_k$ respectively. Let $n_i \in W_{s_i}$ for every $i = 1, 2, \ldots, k$. The function f of the set R into N defined by means of the formula

$$f(s) = \begin{cases} n_i & \text{for } s \in P_i,\ i = 1, 2, \ldots, k, \\ 1 & \text{for } s \in R \setminus (P_1 \cup P_2 \cup \ldots \cup P_k) \end{cases}$$

belongs simultaneously to D and to V. ∎

We shall now consider the problem of embedding topological spaces in Cartesian products. Suppose we are given a topological space X, a family of topological spaces $\{Y_s\}_{s \in S}$ and a family of mappings $\mathfrak{f} = \{f_s\}_{s \in S}$, where $f_s \colon X \to Y_s$. We say that the family $\mathfrak{f}$ *separates points* of the space X if for each pair $x, y \in X$ of distinct points there exists a mapping $f_s \in \mathfrak{f}$ such that $f_s(x) \neq f_s(y)$. We say that the family $\mathfrak{f}$ *separates points from closed sets* if for each point $x \in X$ and a closed set $F \subset X$ which does not contain x there exists a mapping $f_s \in \mathfrak{f}$ such that $f_s(x) \notin \overline{f_s(F)}$. If X is a T_1-space, then each family separating points from closed sets also separates points of the space X.

The proof of the two theorems which are given below is based on the following lemma.

THE DIAGONAL LEMMA. *Suppose we are given a topological space X, a family of topological spaces $\{Y_s\}_{s\in S}$ and a family of mappings $\mathfrak{f} = \{f_s\}_{s\in S}$, where $f_s\colon X \to Y_s$. Let us consider the diagonal $F = \mathop{\triangle}_{s\in S} f_s\colon X \to \mathop{\boldsymbol{P}}_{s\in S} Y_s$. If the family $\mathfrak{f}$ separates points, then F is one-to-one. If, furthermore, the family $\mathfrak{f}$ separates points from closed sets, then F is a homeomorphic embedding.*

In particular, if f_s is a homeomorphic embedding for some $s\in S$, then F is a homeomorphic embedding.

Proof. Let us suppose that the family $\mathfrak{f}$ separates points of the space X. Let us consider two distinct points $x, y \in X$. There exists $f_s \in \mathfrak{f}$ such that $f_s(x) \neq f_s(y)$; therefore $F(x) \neq F(y)$.

Let us assume moreover that the family $\mathfrak{f}$ separates points from closed sets. By virtue of Theorem 1.4.4, in order to prove our theorem it is sufficient to show that the mapping $F : X \to F(X)$ is open.

Let U be an arbitrary open set in X and let us assume that $y \in F(U)$; therefore $y = F(x)$ for some $x \in U$. In order to prove our lemma it is sufficient to show that the set $F(U)$ contains a neighbourhood of the point $F(x)$ in $F(X)$, i.e. the intersection of a neighbourhood V of the point $F(x)$ in $\mathop{\boldsymbol{P}}_{s\in S} Y_s$ with $F(X)$. Let us consider a function f_s such that $f_s(x) \notin \overline{f_s(X\setminus U)}$ and let us take $V = p_s^{-1}\big(Y_s \setminus \overline{f_s(X\setminus U)}\big)$. Obviously $F(x) \in V$ holds. We shall show that

$$V \cap F(X) \subset F(U). \tag{2}$$

Let us assume that $F(y) \in V$ for some $y \in X$. In order to prove (2) it is sufficient to show that $y \in U$. Suppose the contrary; thus $y \in X\setminus U$ and $f_s(y) \in f_s(X\setminus U)$; on the other hand $f_s(y) \in Y_s \setminus \overline{f_s(X\setminus U)}$ because $F(y) \in V$. This contradiction shows that $y \in U$. ■

Let a property $\mathfrak{W}$ of topological spaces be given. We say that a space X is *universal* for spaces having the property $\mathfrak{W}$ if X has the property $\mathfrak{W}$, and every space which has this property is embeddable in X.

We call the reader's attention to the fact that theorems on the existence of universal spaces are very important. Indeed, instead of examining the whole class of spaces with the property $\mathfrak{W}$, which is often defined in a rather abstract manner, we can restrict our study to subspaces of a fixed space. This can be done because we make no distinctions between homeomorphic spaces, as we have already stated at the end of Paragraph 1.4.

The space $I^{\mathfrak{m}} = \mathop{\boldsymbol{P}}_{s\in S} I_s$, where $I_s = I$ for every $s \in S$ and $\overline{\overline{S}} = \mathfrak{m} \geqslant \aleph_0$, is called the *Tychonoff cube* of weight $\mathfrak{m}$. The Tychonoff cube $I^{\aleph_0}$ is called *the Hilbert cube.* We can immediately note that if $\mathfrak{n} \leqslant \mathfrak{m}$, then the cube $I^{\mathfrak{n}}$ is embeddable in $I^{\mathfrak{m}}$.

THEOREM 8. *For every $\mathfrak{m} \geqslant \aleph_0$ the Tychonoff cube $I^{\mathfrak{m}}$ is a universal space for Tychonoff spaces of weight $\mathfrak{m}$.*

Proof. By Theorem 6, the cube $I^{\mathfrak{m}}$ is a Tychonoff space. It follows from Theorem 1 that there exists in $I^{\mathfrak{m}}$ a base of power $\mathfrak{m}$, namely, the base $\mathfrak{B}_0$ consisting of the sets $\mathop{\boldsymbol{P}}_{s\in S} W_s$, where $W_s \subset I_s$ is a segment with rational end-points and $W_s \neq I_s$ only for s belonging to a finite subset $S_1 \subset S$. The elements of the set S_1 will be called the *distinguished indices* of the given element of the base $\mathfrak{B}_0$. The weight of the space $I^{\mathfrak{m}}$ is thus not greater than $\mathfrak{m}$; let us suppose that it is equal to $\mathfrak{n} < \mathfrak{m}$. The weight of the space $I^{\mathfrak{m}}$ at the point $x = \{x_s\}$, where $x_s = 0$ for $s \in S$, is therefore not greater than $\mathfrak{n}$. Let $\mathfrak{B}(x) \subset \mathfrak{B}_0$ be a base at the point x which satisfies the condition $\overline{\overline{\mathfrak{B}(x)}} \leqslant \mathfrak{n}$. Hence the power of the set of distinguished indices of all elements of the base $\mathfrak{B}(x)$ does not exceed $\mathfrak{n}$. Therefore there exists an index $s_0 \in S$ which is not distinguished for any element of the base $\mathfrak{B}(x)$. It is easy to see that the neighbourhood $\mathop{\boldsymbol{P}}_{s\in S} W_s$ of x, where $W_s = I_s$ for $s \neq s_0$ and $W_{s_0} = [0, \frac{1}{2})$, does not contain any element of $\mathfrak{B}(x)$.

The assumption that the weight of $I^{\mathfrak{m}}$ is less than $\mathfrak{m}$ leads to a contradiction; the weight of $I^{\mathfrak{m}}$ is thus equal to $\mathfrak{m}$.

Let X be a Tychonoff space of weight $\mathfrak{m} \geqslant \aleph_0$. We shall show that X is embeddable in the cube $I^{\mathfrak{m}}$. Let us denote by $\mathfrak{B}_0$ an arbitrary minimal base of the space X. A pair (U_1, U_2) of elements of $\mathfrak{B}_0$ will be called *distinguished* if there exists a continuous function

(3) $\quad f: X \to I$ such that $f(x) = 1$ for $x \in X \setminus U_2$ and $f(x) < \frac{1}{2}$ for $x \in U_1$.

To begin with, let us observe that for each point $x \in X$ and a neighbourhood $U_2 \in \mathfrak{B}_0$ of x there exists a $U_1 \in \mathfrak{B}_0$ such that $x \in U_1$ and the pair (U_1, U_2) is distinguished. Indeed, since X is a Tychonoff space, there exists a function $f: X \to I$ such that $f(x) = 0$ and $f(y) = 1$ for $y \in X \setminus U_2$. The set $f^{-1}([0, \frac{1}{2}))$ is a neighbourhood of the point x; therefore there exists a set $U_1 \in \mathfrak{B}_0$ such that $x \in U_1 \subset f^{-1}([0, \frac{1}{2})) \subset U_2$. The pair (U_1, U_2) is distinguished.

We assign a function satisfying (3) to every distinguished pair and let us denote by $\mathfrak{f}$ the family obtained in this manner. Since the set of all distinguished pairs is of power $\mathfrak{m}$, $\overline{\overline{\mathfrak{f}}} \leqslant \mathfrak{m}$ holds. In order to complete the proof by virtue of the Diagonal Lemma and the fact that X is a T_1-space, it is sufficient to show that the family $\mathfrak{f}$ separates points from closed sets. Let us consider a point $x \in X$ and a set $F = \overline{F} \subset X$ which does not contain x. There exists a $U_2 \in \mathfrak{B}_0$ such that $x \in U_2 \subset X \setminus F$. By the above remark, there exists a $U_1 \in \mathfrak{B}_0$ such that the pair (U_1, U_2) is distinguished. The function $f \in \mathfrak{f}$ satisfying (3) for the pair (U_1, U_2) separates the point x from the set F, because

$$f(x) < \tfrac{1}{2} \quad \text{and} \quad \overline{f(F)} \subset \overline{f(X \setminus U_2)} \subset \overline{\{1\}} = \{1\}. \ ■$$

We shall now state a theorem on the existence of a universal space for all T_0-spaces of a given weight. Let us denote by F the topological space consisting of two points, 0 and 1, where the only open sets are the empty set, $\{0\}$, and $\{0,1\} = F$. It is easy to note that F is a T_0-space.

The space $F^{\mathfrak{m}} = \underset{s \in S}{\boldsymbol{P}} F_s$, where $F_s = F$ for every $s \in S$ and $\overline{\overline{S}} = \mathfrak{m} \geqslant \aleph_0$, is called the *Alexandroff cube* of weight $\mathfrak{m}$.

THEOREM 9. *For every $\mathfrak{m} \geqslant \aleph_0$ the Alexandroff cube $F^{\mathfrak{m}}$ is a universal space for T_0-spaces of weight $\mathfrak{m}$.*

The proof of Theorem 9, which is analogous to the proof of Theorem 8, is left to the reader. ■

The Cartesian product of $\mathfrak{m} \geqslant \aleph_0$ copies of the discrete two-point space $D = \{0,1\}$ is called the *Cantor cube* of weight $\mathfrak{m}$. The Cantor cube of weight $\mathfrak{m}$ is denoted by the symbol $D^{\mathfrak{m}}$; we have therefore $D^{\mathfrak{m}} = \underset{s \in S}{\boldsymbol{P}} D_s$, where $D_s = D$ for every $s \in S$ and $\overline{\overline{S}} = \mathfrak{m}$. The Cantor cube of weight $\aleph_0$ is called the *Cantor set*. We leave to the reader the verification that $D^{\mathfrak{m}}$ is indeed of weight $\mathfrak{m}$.

THEOREM 10. *In the Cartesian product of an arbitrary family of separable spaces every family of mutually disjoint non-empty open sets is countable.*

Proof. Let us consider the Cartesian product $\underset{s \in S}{\boldsymbol{P}} X_s$ of the family $\{X_s\}_{s \in S}$ of separable spaces and a family $\{U_t\}_{t \in T}$ of non-empty, open and mutually disjoint subsets of this product. We can assume, without loss of generality, that the family $\{U_t\}_{t \in T}$ consists of elements of the base of the space $\underset{s \in S}{\boldsymbol{P}} X_s$ which was described in Theorem 1, i.e. that for every $t \in T$ there exist a finite set $S_t \subset S$ and a family of sets $\{W_s^t\}_{s \in S}$, where W_s^t is an open subset of the space X_s and $W_s^t = X_s$ for $s \notin S_t$, such that $U_t = \underset{s \in S}{\boldsymbol{P}} W_s^t$.

Let T_0 denote an arbitrary subset of the set T whose power does not exceed $\mathfrak{c}$. The set $S_0 = \bigcup_{t \in T_0} S_t$ is also of power not greater than $\mathfrak{c}$. Let us consider the Cartesian product $\underset{s \in S_0}{\boldsymbol{P}} X_s$. The family $\{\underset{s \in S_0}{\boldsymbol{P}} W_s^t\}_{t \in T_0}$ consists of non-empty and, as we easily see from the form of the sets U_t, mutually disjoint open subsets of $\underset{s \in S_0}{\boldsymbol{P}} X_s$. We infer from Theorem 7 that $\overline{\overline{T_0}} \leqslant \aleph_0$, since each set of the family in question contains an element of a countable dense subset of $\underset{s \in S_0}{\boldsymbol{P}} X_s$. Therefore an arbitrary subset of the set T, which has power not exceeding $\mathfrak{c}$, is countable, i.e. the set T is countable. ■

THEOREM 11. *A net $T = \{x_\sigma, \sigma \in \Sigma\}$ in the Cartesian product $\underset{s \in S}{\boldsymbol{P}} X_s$ is convergent to a point $x \in \underset{s \in S}{\boldsymbol{P}} X_s$ if and only if for every $s \in S$ the net $T_s = \{p_s(x_\sigma), \sigma \in \Sigma\}$ is convergent to $p_s(x)$.*

Proof. If $x \in \lim T$, then by virtue of Theorem 1.6.3, $p_s(x) \in \lim T_s$ for every $s \in S$.

Let us now suppose that for some $x \in \underset{s \in S}{\boldsymbol{P}} X_s$, $p_s(x) \in \lim T_s$ holds for every $s \in S$. Let us consider an arbitrary neighbourhood W of the point x. There exist elements $s_1, s_2, \ldots, s_k \in S$ and open sets $U_i \subset X_{s_i}$ for $i = 1, 2, \ldots, k$ such that $x \in p_{s_1}^{-1}(U_1) \cap p_{s_2}^{-1}(U_2) \cap \ldots \cap p_{s_k}^{-1}(U_k) \subset W$. By hypothesis there exist elements $\sigma_1, \sigma_2, \ldots, \sigma_k \in \Sigma$ such that $p_{s_i}(x_\sigma) \in U_i$ for $\sigma \geqslant \sigma_i$. Let σ_0 denote an element of the set Σ_0 such that $\sigma_i \leqslant \sigma_0$ for $i = 1, 2, \ldots, k$. For $\sigma \geqslant \sigma_0$ we have

$$x_\sigma \in p_{s_1}^{-1}(U_1) \cap p_{s_2}^{-1}(U_2) \cap \ldots \cap p_{s_k}^{-1}(U_k) \subset W,$$

whence $x \in \lim T$. ∎

Here is an analogous theorem for filters:

THEOREM 11F. *Let $\mathfrak{F}$ be a filter in the Cartesian product $\underset{s \in S}{\boldsymbol{P}} X_s$. For every $s \in S$ the family $\mathfrak{F}_s = \{p_s(F): F \in \mathfrak{F}\}$ is a filter in the space X_s. The filter $\mathfrak{F}$ is convergent to the point $x \in \underset{s \in S}{\boldsymbol{P}} X_s$ if and only if for every $s \in S$ the filter $\mathfrak{F}_s$ is convergent to the point $p_s(x)$.* ∎

EXAMPLE 3. We shall show here that normality is not a hereditary property. Let us consider two copies, X and Y, of the space considered in Example 1.1.2, where $\overline{\overline{X}} = \mathfrak{m}$, $\overline{\overline{Y}} = \mathfrak{n}$ and $\aleph_0 < \mathfrak{m} < \mathfrak{n}$. Let x_0 and y_0 denote the distinguished points of the spaces X and Y.

The Cartesian product $X \times Y$ is a normal space. This follows from the fact that for every pair of disjoint sets closed in $X \times Y$ there exists an open-and-closed set $V \times W$, which contains the point (x_0, y_0), and is disjoint with at least one of the sets under consideration, and also from the normality of the subspace $X \times Y \setminus (V \times W)$, which is a consequence of Theorem 2.2 and 2.4 (cf. Example 3.2.1).

Let us assume that $Z = X \times Y \setminus (x_0, y_0)$. We shall show that for every continuous real-valued function $f: Z \to R$ there exist a number $r \in R$ and subsets $X_0 \subset X \setminus \{x_0\}$, $Y_0 \subset Y \setminus \{y_0\}$ such that $\overline{\overline{X_0}} \leqslant \aleph_0$, $\overline{\overline{Y_0}} \leqslant \mathfrak{m}$ and

(4) $\quad f(x, y) = r$ for $(x, y) \in Z \setminus Z_0$, where $Z_0 = X_0 \times Y \cup X \times Y_0$.

Let us consider an arbitrary $x \in X \setminus \{x_0\}$. We put

(5) $$Y_0(x) = \{y: f(x, y) \neq f(x, y_0)\}, \qquad Y_0 = \bigcup_{x \in X \setminus \{x_0\}} Y_0(x).$$

By the property of the space $\{x\}\times Y$ proved in Example 1.4.6, we infer that $\overline{\overline{Y_0(x)}} \leqslant \aleph_0$; therefore $\overline{\overline{Y}}_0 \leqslant \mathfrak{m}$ and $y_0 \notin Y_0$.

Let us consider an arbitrary $\bar{y} \in Y\setminus(Y_0 \cup \{y_0\})$ and let us put

$$X_0 = \{x: f(x, \bar{y}) \neq f(x_0, \bar{y})\}. \tag{6}$$

Then $\overline{\overline{X}}_0 \leqslant \aleph_0$ and $x_0 \notin X_0$. Let $r = f(x_1, y_1)$, where $(x_1, y_1) \in Z\setminus Z_0$. Let us consider an arbitrary point $(x, y) \in Z\setminus Z_0$; by virtue of (5) and (6)

$$f(x, y) = f(x, y_0) = f(x, \bar{y}) = f(x_0, \bar{y}) = f(x_1, \bar{y})$$
$$= f(x_1, y_0) = f(x_1, y_1) = r;$$

thus condition (4) is proved.

We shall now prove that the space Z is not normal. Indeed, the sets $A = (X\setminus\{x_0\})\times\{y_0\}$ and $B = \{x_0\}\times(Y_0\setminus\{y_0\})$ are disjoint and closed in Z, and $A\setminus Z_0 \neq 0 \neq B\setminus Z_0$ for an arbitrary Z_0 of the form given in (4). By virtue of (4), a continuous real-valued function defined on Z and equal to 0 on A and to 1 on B does not exist. ■

EXERCISES

A. Let $\{X_s\}_{s\in S}$ denote an arbitrary family of topological spaces and let $A_s \subset X_s$ for every $s \in S$. Two topologies can be considered in the product $\underset{s\in S}{\boldsymbol{P}} A_s$: the topology of the Cartesian product of subspaces and the topology of a subspace of the Cartesian product $\underset{s\in S}{\boldsymbol{P}} X_s$. Show that the two topologies coincide.

B. Suppose we are given two families of disjoint topological spaces $\{X_s\}_{s\in S}$ and $\{Y_t\}_{t\in T}$. Show that

$$(\bigoplus_{s\in S} X_s)\times(\bigoplus_{t\in T} Y_t) = \bigoplus_{(s,t)\in S\times T} (X_s\times Y_t).$$

C (K. Kuratowski [1921]). Let X be a discrete space of power $\aleph_0$ and let X_1, X_2 denote subspaces of the segment I defined by means of the conditions

$$X_1 = \{x: 0 < x < 1\}, \quad X_2 = \{x: 0 \leqslant x < 1\}.$$

Let $Y_1 = X\oplus(X\times X_1)$, $Y_2 = Y_1\oplus X_2$. Show that the spaces Y_1 and Y_2 are not homeomorphic and that each of them can be one-to-one mapped on the other.

Hint: In order to prove that Y_1 and Y_2 are not homeomorphic make use of the fact that the set $X_2\setminus\{0\}$ cannot be represented in the form of the sum of two subspaces.

D. Prove that for the Cartesian product $X\times Y$ of topological spaces X and Y and for $A\subset X, B\subset Y$, we have

$$\operatorname{Int}(A\times B) = \operatorname{Int}A\times\operatorname{Int}B,$$

$$\operatorname{Fr}(A\times B) = \bar{A}\times\operatorname{Fr}B \cup \operatorname{Fr}A\times\bar{B}.$$

E. The set $\Delta = \{(x, x): x \in X\}$ is called the *diagonal* of the Cartesian product $X\times X$. Show that X is a Hausdorff space if and only if the diagonal Δ is a closed subset of $X\times X$.

F. Show that a space X is homeomorphic to the Cartesian product $\underset{s\in S}{\boldsymbol{P}} X_s$ if and only if there exists a family of mappings $\{p_s\}_{s\in S}$, where $p_s: X \to X_s$, and the following conditions are satisfied:

(1) For every space Y and a pair f, g of mappings of Y into X if $p_s f = p_s g$ for every $s \in S$, then $f = g$.

(2) For each space Y and a family of mappings $\{f_s\}_{s\in S}$, where $f_s: Y \to X_s$, there exists a mapping $f: Y \to X$ such that $p_s f = f_s$ for every $s \in S$.

§ 4. Quotient spaces. Let X be a topological space and R an equivalence relation in the set X. We denote the set of equivalence classes of the relation R by the symbol X/R. Let us assign to every element $x \in X$ the equivalence class $[x]$ which contains it; thus a function φ is defined, where $\varphi(x) = [x] \in X/R$ for every $x \in X$.

We want to introduce a topology in the set X/R. It is reasonable to require that φ be a mapping of X onto X/R. If we assume that the only open sets in X/R are the empty set and the whole space then φ is obviously a mapping. This topology is too meager however, and it does not depend on the topology in X, so that it cannot be considered as a suitable topology in the set X/R. On the other hand the number of open sets in X/R cannot be too large since the inverse image under the function φ of every open set in X/R must be open in X. The best way out of this difficulty is to assume that those and only those sets U are open in X/R for which $\varphi^{-1}(U)$ is open in X. The verification that the open sets defined in this manner have properties (O1)-(O3) is left to the reader. It can easily be noted that the topology in the set X/R defined above is the strongest topology under which φ is a mapping. This topology is called the *quotient topology*, the set X/R with this topology the *quotient space*, and $\varphi: X \to X/R$ the *natural mapping*.

THEOREM 1. *Let X be a topological space and let R denote an equivalence relation in X. A set F is closed in the quotient space X/R if and only if $\varphi^{-1}(F)$ is a closed subset of X.*

Proof. The proof follows from the formula

$$\varphi^{-1}(X/R \setminus F) = X \setminus \varphi^{-1}(F). \blacksquare$$

THEOREM 2. *Let X and Y be topological spaces and let R denote an equivalence relation in X. A function f of the space X/R into Y is a mapping if and only if the composition $f\varphi$, where φ is the natural mapping, is a mapping.*

Proof. The necessity of the condition is obvious. In order to prove its sufficiency let us observe that for an arbitrary $U \subset Y$ the set $(f\varphi)^{-1}(U) = \varphi^{-1}(f^{-1}(U))$ is open in X, i.e. that $f^{-1}(U)$ is open in X/R. $\blacksquare$

Unlike the operations considered before, the operation of taking a quotient space preserves very few topological properties. For example, it is easy to see that X/R is a T_1-space if and only if all equivalence classes are closed in X.

EXAMPLE 1. Let X be a regular space which is not normal (see Example 1.5.2). Then X must contain two closed and disjoint sets A and B for which there exist no open sets U and V such that $A \subset U, B \subset V$, and $U \cap V = 0$. Let R denote the equivalence relation in X determined by the decomposition of X into the sets A, B and single points of the set $X \setminus (A \cup B)$. It can easily be seen that X/R is a T_1-space but is not a Hausdorff space. ■

Let X be an arbitrary topological space and f a mapping of the space X onto Y. Let us consider in X the equivalence relation $R(f)$ determined by the decomposition into classes $\{f^{-1}(y)\}_{y \in Y}$. The mapping $f: X \to Y$ can be represented in the form of the composition $f'\varphi$, where $\varphi: X \to X/R$ and f' is a function of the quotient space $X/R(f)$ onto Y defined by means of the formula $f'(f^{-1}(y)) = y$. By virtue of Theorem 2, the function f' is a mapping. Of course f' is a one-to-one mapping but the spaces $X/R(f)$ and Y need not be homeomorphic; the topology in $X/R(f)$ is in general stronger than the topology in Y. In some particular cases the two topologies are identical.

THEOREM 3. *If $f: X \to Y$ is a closed mapping or an open mapping of X onto Y, then the space $X/R(f)$ is homeomorphic to Y.*

Proof. As we have already stated, $f = f'\varphi$, where $\varphi: X \to X/R(f)$ and $f': X/R(f) \to Y$, where f' is a one-to-one mapping. By virtue of Theorem 1.4.4 it is sufficient to prove that $f'(U)$ is open for an open set $U \subset X/R(f)$, or that $f'(F)$ is closed for a closed set $F \subset X/R(f)$. Let us note that $f'(A) = f\varphi^{-1}(A)$ for $A \subset X/R(f)$. Since φ is a mapping, in the case of open f, the image $f'(U) = f\varphi^{-1}(U)$ is open for an arbitrary open set U, and in the case of closed f, the image $f'(F) = f\varphi^{-1}(F)$ is closed for an arbitrary closed set F. ■

EXAMPLE 2. Let X be a discrete space of power $\mathfrak{c}$ and let $f: X \to I$ denote a one-to-one mapping of X onto the segment I. The space $X/R(f)$ is homeomorphic to X; it is therefore discrete and not homeomorphic to I. ■

Finally let us mention two classes of equivalence relations in topological spaces. We say that a relation R is *closed* (*open*) if for every closed (open) set A the union of equivalence classes of the relation R which intersect A is a closed (an open) set. It follows from the definition that equivalence classes of a closed equivalence relation in a T_1-space are closed.

THEOREM 4. *Let R be an equivalence relation in a topological space X. The following conditions are equivalent*:

(i) *R is closed* (*open*).

(ii) *For every set A open* (*closed*) *in X the union of equivalence classes of the relation R which are contained in A is an open* (*a closed*) *set in X.*

(iii) *$\varphi: X \to X/R$ is a closed* (*open*) *mapping.*

Proof. The equivalence of conditions (i) and (ii) follows from the de Morgan formulas; the equivalence of (i) and (iii) follows from Theorem 1 and from the definition of open sets in X/R. ■

THEOREM 5. *If X is a normal space and R denotes a closed equivalence relation in X, then the space X/R is also normal.*

Proof. Since the equivalence classes of the relation R are closed, X/R is a T_1-space. Let us assume that $A, B \subset X/R$ are disjoint and closed in X/R. The sets $\varphi^{-1}(A)$ and $\varphi^{-1}(B)$ are closed in X and disjoint; by the normality of X, there exist two open sets U_1 and U_2 in X such that

$$\varphi^{-1}(A) \subset U_1, \quad \varphi^{-1}(B) \subset U_2, \quad \text{and} \quad U_1 \cap U_2 = 0.$$

Let V_i for $i = 1, 2$ denote the union of the equivalence classes of the relation R which are contained in U_i. By virtue of Theorem 4, V_1 and V_2 are open in X. Since $V_i = \varphi^{-1}\varphi(V_i)$, $\varphi(V_1)$ and $\varphi(V_2)$ are sets open in X/R and such that

$$A \subset \varphi(V_1), \quad B \subset \varphi(V_2), \quad \text{and} \quad \varphi(V_1) \cap \varphi(V_2) = 0. \; ■$$

EXAMPLE 3. Let us consider the segment I and the mapping $f: I \to S^1$ defined by means of the formula $f(x) = (\cos 2\pi x, \sin 2\pi x)$. It can easily be verified that f is a closed mapping. By virtue of Theorem 3, the space $I/R(f)$ is homeomorphic to the circle S^1. The equivalence classes of the relation $R(f)$ are sets $\{x\}$ for $0 < x < 1$ and the set $\{0, 1\}$. The quotient space S^1 is therefore obtained by *identification* of the ends of the segment I. Considering the Cartesian products $I^2 = I \times I$ and $T^2 = S^1 \times S^1$, we can define the mapping $f \times f: I^2 \to T^2$. The reader can easily find what identifications should be made in the square in order to obtain the torus. ■

EXAMPLE 4. We shall give here an example of a regular space which is not a Tychonoff space. Let Z be the space defined in Example 3.3. The subsets $A, B \subset Z$, defined there, will be called the *axes* of Z.

For every natural number n, let $Z_n = Z \times \{n\}$ and

$$Z^* = \bigoplus_{n=1}^{\infty} Z_n,$$

and let $i_n: Z_n \to Z^*$ denote the embedding of Z_n into Z^*.

Let us consider a point $z \notin Z^*$ and put $T^* = Z^* \cup \{z\}$. We generate a topology in T^* by means of the neighbourhood system $\{\mathfrak{B}(x)\}_{x \in T^*}$, where $\mathfrak{B}(x)$ for $x \in Z^*$ is the family of all open sets in Z^* which contain x, and $\mathfrak{B}(z) = \{O_n(z)\}_{n=1}^{\infty}$, where $O_n(z) = T^* \setminus \bigcup_{i=1}^{n} Z_i$. The reader can easily verify that T^* is a regular space and that the identity $i: Z^* \to T^*$ is an embedding of Z^* into T^*.

We define an equivalence relation R in T^*, assuming that $t_1 R t_2$, if one of the following conditions is satisfied:

(1) $t_1 = t_2$.
(2) $t_1 = (a, n)$, $t_2 = (a, n+1)$ for $a \in A$ and an odd number n.
(3) $t_1 = (b, n)$, $t_2 = (b, n+1)$ for $b \in B$ and an even number n.

Let $T = T^*/R$ and $\varphi: T^* \to T$. The space T is thus obtained by identifying, in T, axis A with numbers n and $n+1$, where n is odd, and axis B with numbers n and $n+1$, where n is even.

The space T is the required space. Since the equivalence classes of the relation R are closed, T is a T_1-space. The verification that T is a regular space is left to the reader. Let $t = \varphi(z)$ and $F = \varphi i i_1(A \times \{1\})$; evidently $F = \overline{F}$. We shall show that for each function $f: T \to I$ such that $f(F) = \{1\}$, we have $f(t) = 1$, and it will follow that T is not a Tychonoff space.

Let us put $f_n = f\varphi i i_n: Z_n \to I$ for every $n = 1, 2, \ldots$ By virtue of the property of the space Z proved in Example 3.3, there exist subsets $X_0^n \subset X \setminus \{x_0\}$ and $Y_0^n \subset Y \setminus \{y_0\}$ such that $\overline{\overline{X_0^n}} \leqslant \aleph_0$, $\overline{\overline{Y_0^n}} \leqslant \mathfrak{m}$, and

$$f_n(x, y, n) = r_n \text{ for } (x, y) \in Z \setminus Z_0^n, \text{ where } Z_0^n = X_0^n \times Y \cup X \times Y_0^n,$$

r_n being a fixed number from the segment I. Let us set $X_0^* = \bigcup_{n=1}^{\infty} X_0^n$, $Y_0^* = \bigcup_{n=1}^{\infty} Y_0^n$, and $Z_0^* = X_0^* \times Y \cup X \times Y_0^*$. We then have

(4) $$f_n(x, y, n) = r_n \quad \text{for } (x, y) \in Z \setminus Z_0^* \text{ and } n = 1, 2, \ldots$$

and

(5) $$A \setminus Z_0^* \neq 0 \neq B \setminus Z_0^*.$$

However, on account of the identification which has already been done

$$f_n(a, n) = f_{n+1}(a, n+1) \quad \text{for } a \in A \text{ and odd numbers } n,$$

and

$$f_n(b, n) = f_{n+1}(b, n+1) \quad \text{for } b \in B \text{ and even numbers } n.$$

It follows from (4) and (5) that $r_{n+1} = r_n$ for $n = 1, 2, \ldots$ Thus $r_n = 1$ for $n = 1, 2, \ldots$, because $f_1(A \times \{1\}) = f(F) = 1$. Since $t \in \overline{M}$, where $M = \{\varphi i i_n(x, y, n): (x, y) \in Z \setminus Z_0^*, \ n = 1, 2, \ldots\}$, we have $f(t) = 1$. ∎

EXERCISES

A. Let a family $\{X_s\}_{s \in S}$ of disjoint topological spaces be given and for every $s \in S$ let R_s denote an equivalence relation in the space X_s. Let us define a relation R_S in the sum $\bigoplus_{s \in S} X_s$ by taking $x R_S y$ if and only if $x R_s y$ for some $s \in S$. Verify that R_S is an equivalence relation and show that the spaces $(\bigoplus_{s \in S} X_s)/R_S$ and $\bigoplus_{s \in S} (X_s/R_s)$ are homeomorphic. Is it true that if all the relations R_s are closed (open), then the relation R_S must be closed (open)?

B. Let X be a topological space. Let us assume that xRy for $x, y \in X$ if $\overline{\{x\}} = \overline{\{y\}}$. Show that R is an equivalence relation in X and that X/R is a T_0-space. Let R' denote an equivalence relation in X such that X/R' is a T_0-space. What is the connection between the relations R' and R?

C. Give examples of topological spaces X and equivalence relations R such that
(a) The relation R is closed (open) but R is not a closed (open) subset of $X \times X$.
(b) R is closed (open) subset of $X \times X$, but the relation R is not closed (open).

§ 5. Limits of inverse systems. An *inverse system* of topological spaces is a family $\boldsymbol{S} = \{X_\sigma, \pi_\varrho^\sigma, \Sigma\}$, where Σ is a set directed by the relation $\leqslant$, X_σ is a topological space for every $\sigma \in \Sigma$, and π_ϱ^σ is a mapping of X_σ into X_ϱ for each pair $\sigma, \varrho \in \Sigma$ such that $\varrho \leqslant \sigma$. To complete the definition we require that for each three elements σ, ϱ, τ of the set Σ such that $\tau \leqslant \varrho \leqslant \sigma$ the condition $\pi_\tau^\varrho \pi_\varrho^\sigma = \pi_\sigma^\tau$ should hold, and that $\pi_\sigma^\sigma = \mathrm{id}_{X_\sigma}$ for every $\sigma \in \Sigma$.

Let an inverse system $\boldsymbol{S} = \{X_\sigma, \pi_\varrho^\sigma, \Sigma\}$ be given. Let us consider the Cartesian product $\underset{\sigma\in\Sigma}{\boldsymbol{P}} X_\sigma$; the element $\{x_\sigma\}$ of this product is called a *thread* of our system if for each pair σ, ϱ of elements of the set Σ such that $\varrho \leqslant \sigma$ we have $\pi_\varrho^\sigma(x_\sigma) = x_\varrho$. The subspace of the product $\underset{\sigma\in\Sigma}{\boldsymbol{P}} X_\sigma$ consisting of all threads of the inverse system $\boldsymbol{S} = \{X_\sigma, \pi_\varrho^\sigma, \Sigma\}$ is called the *limit of the inverse system* $\boldsymbol{S}$ and is denoted by the symbol $\underleftarrow{\lim}\, \boldsymbol{S}$ or $\underleftarrow{\lim}\, \{X_\sigma, \pi_\varrho^\sigma, \Sigma\}$.

THEOREM 1. *The limit of an inverse system $\boldsymbol{S} = \{X_\sigma, \pi_\varrho^\sigma, \Sigma\}$ of Hausdorff spaces is a closed subset of the Cartesian product of those spaces.*

Proof. Let us suppose that for $\sigma, \varrho \in \Sigma$, where $\varrho \leqslant \sigma$,

$$M_{\sigma\varrho} = \{x: \pi_\varrho^\sigma p_\sigma(x) = p_\varrho(x)\},$$

i.e. $x = \{x_\sigma\} \in M_{\sigma\varrho}$ if $\pi_\varrho^\sigma(x_\sigma) = x_\varrho$. By virtue of Theorem 1.5.2, the set $M_{\sigma\varrho}$ is closed. Since $\underleftarrow{\lim}\, \boldsymbol{S} = \bigcap_{\varrho\leqslant\sigma} M_{\sigma\varrho}$, $\underleftarrow{\lim}\, \boldsymbol{S}$ is a closed subset of the Cartesian product. ■

Theorem 1.2 and Theorem 3.6 imply

THEOREM 2. *The limit of an inverse system of T_i-spaces is a T_i-space for $i \leqslant 3\frac{1}{2}$.* ■

On the other hand, the limit of an inverse system of normal spaces is not necessarily normal (cf. Example 1 and Exercise 3.1.F).

EXAMPLE 1. Let $\{X_s\}_{s\in S}$ be a family of topological spaces. Let us denote by Σ the family of all finite subsets of the set S. The family Σ is partially ordered by inclusion (we put $\varrho \leqslant \sigma$ if $\varrho \subset \sigma$) and directed. Let us put $X_\sigma = \underset{s\in\sigma}{\boldsymbol{P}} X_s$ and let us consider two elements $\sigma, \varrho \in \Sigma$ such that

$\varrho \leqslant \sigma$. We thus have $\sigma = \{s_1, \ldots, s_k\}$, $\varrho = \{s_1, \ldots, s_l\}$, where $l \leqslant k$ and $X_\sigma = X_{s_1} \times \ldots \times X_{s_k}$, $X_\varrho = X_{s_1} \times \ldots \times X_{s_l}$. Let us define a mapping $\pi_\varrho^\sigma: X_\sigma \to X_\varrho$ by means of the formula $\pi_\varrho^\sigma(x_1, \ldots, x_k) = (x_1, \ldots, x_l)$. Since obviously $\pi_\tau^\varrho \pi_\varrho^\sigma = \pi_\tau^\sigma$ for $\tau \leqslant \varrho \leqslant \sigma$ and $\pi_\sigma^\sigma = \mathrm{id}_{X_\sigma}$, $\boldsymbol{S} = \{X_\sigma, \pi_\varrho^\sigma, \Sigma\}$ is an inverse system. For every $s \in S$ let us denote by σ_s the subset $\{s\} \in \Sigma$. Let us assume that an element $\{x_\sigma\} \in \varprojlim \boldsymbol{S}$ is given and let us assign to it the element $\{x_{\sigma_s}\} \in \boldsymbol{P}_{s \in S} X_s$. It is easy to verify that the mapping defined above is a homeomorphism of the space $\varprojlim \boldsymbol{S}$ onto the Cartesian product $\boldsymbol{P}_{s \in S} X_s$. The operation of the limit of an inverse system is therefore a generalization of the Cartesian product. ■

EXAMPLE 2. Let X be a T_1-space and let $A \subset X$ denote an arbitrary subset of X. Let us consider the family Σ of all open subsets containing A. Let us put $U_2 \leqslant U_1$ if $U_1, U_2 \in \Sigma$ and $U_1 \subset U_2$. The family Σ is directed by the relation $\leqslant$. Let us define $\pi_{U_2}^{U_1}: U_1 \to U_2$ for $U_2 \leqslant U_1$ to be the embedding of U_1 in U_2. The limit of the inverse system $\boldsymbol{S} = \{U, \pi_{U_2}^{U_1}, \Sigma\}$, where the space assigned to the element U is U itself, is homeomorphic to the intersection $\bigcap_{A \subset U} U$. Since X is a T_1-space, the limit $\varprojlim \boldsymbol{S}$ is homeomorphic to A. ■

EXAMPLE 3. Let an arbitrary directed set Σ and a space X be given. Let us put $X_\sigma = X$ for every $\sigma \in \Sigma$ and $\pi_\varrho^\sigma = \mathrm{id}_X$ for $\varrho \leqslant \sigma$. It can easily be verified that $\boldsymbol{S} = \{X_\sigma, \pi_\varrho^\sigma, \Sigma\}$ is an inverse system and that the limit $\varprojlim \boldsymbol{S}$ is homeomorphic to X. ■

Let us consider an inverse system $\boldsymbol{S} = \{X_\sigma, \pi_\varrho^\sigma, \Sigma\}$ and let $X = \varprojlim \boldsymbol{S}$. For every $\sigma \in \Sigma$ a mapping $\pi_\sigma: X \to X_\sigma$ is defined which is the restriction of the projection $p_\sigma: \boldsymbol{P}_{\sigma \in \Sigma} X_\sigma \to X_\sigma$ onto the σ-th axis. Since the limit of an inverse system is the set of threads, $\pi_\varrho = \pi_\varrho^\sigma \pi_\sigma$ for $\varrho \leqslant \sigma$.

THEOREM 3. *Let $\boldsymbol{S} = \{X_\sigma, \pi_\varrho^\sigma, \Sigma\}$ be an inverse system. Then the family $\mathfrak{B}$ of all sets of the form $\pi_\sigma^{-1}(U_\sigma)$, where σ runs over an arbitrary set Σ' cofinal in Σ and U_σ are open subsets of the space X_σ, is a base of the space $X = \varprojlim \boldsymbol{S}$.*

Proof. Since all π_σ are mappings, every set described above is open. We shall show that every open set $U \subset X$ is the union of sets from $\mathfrak{B}$. Let us consider an arbitrary point $x = \{x_\sigma\} \in U$; it is sufficient to show that there exist $\sigma \in \Sigma'$ and a set U_σ open in X_σ such that $x \in \pi_\sigma^{-1}(U_\sigma) \subset U$. By virtue of the definition of a subspace, there exists a set V open in $\boldsymbol{P}_{\sigma \in \Sigma} X_\sigma$ and such that $U = X \cap V$. It follows from Theorem 3.1 that there exist elements $\sigma_1, \sigma_2, \ldots, \sigma_k \in \Sigma$ and sets U_i open in X_{σ_i} for $i = 1, 2, \ldots, k$

such that

$$x \in p_{\sigma_1}^{-1}(U_1) \cap \ldots \cap p_{\sigma_k}^{-1}(U_k) \subset V. \tag{1}$$

Since Σ is a directed set and Σ' is cofinal in Σ, there exists a $\sigma \in \Sigma'$ such that $\sigma_i \leqslant \sigma$ for $i = 1, 2, \ldots, k$. The sets $(\pi_{\sigma_i}^{\sigma})^{-1}(U_i)$ and the set $U_\sigma = \bigcap_{i=1}^{k} (\pi_{\sigma_i}^{\sigma})^{-1}(U_i)$ are open in X_σ. Since $\pi_{\sigma_i}^{\sigma}(x_\sigma) = x_{\sigma_i}$, we have that

$$x_\sigma \in U_\sigma. \tag{2}$$

Let us further note that

$$\pi_\sigma^{-1}(\pi_{\sigma_i}^{\sigma})^{-1}(U_i) = (\pi_{\sigma_i})^{-1}(U_i) = p_{\sigma_i}^{-1}(U_i) \cap X. \tag{3}$$

Then from (2), (3), and (1) we have that

$$x \in \pi_\sigma^{-1}(U_\sigma) = \pi_\sigma^{-1}\Big(\bigcap_{i=1}^{k} (\pi_{\sigma_i}^{\sigma})^{-1}(U_i)\Big) = \bigcap_{i=1}^{k} \pi_\sigma^{-1}(\pi_{\sigma_i}^{\sigma})^{-1}(U_i)$$

$$= X \cap \bigcap_{i=1}^{k} p_{\sigma_i}^{-1}(U_i) \subset V \cap X = U. \quad \blacksquare$$

Suppose we are given two inverse systems $\boldsymbol{S} = \{X_\sigma, \pi_\varrho^\sigma, \Sigma\}$ and $\boldsymbol{S}' = \{Y_{\sigma'}, \pi_{\varrho'}^{\sigma'}, \Sigma'\}$. A *mapping* of the system $\boldsymbol{S}$ into the system $\boldsymbol{S}'$ is a family $\{\varphi, f_{\sigma'}\}$ consisting of a monotone function of the set Σ' into Σ and of mappings $f_{\sigma'}\colon X_{\varphi(\sigma')} \to Y_{\sigma'}$ defined for every $\sigma' \in \Sigma'$ and such that

$$\pi_{\varrho'}^{\sigma'} f_{\sigma'} = f_{\varrho'} \pi_{\varphi(\varrho')}^{\varphi(\sigma')}, \tag{4}$$

i.e. such that the diagram

$$\begin{array}{ccc} X_{\varphi(\sigma')} & \xrightarrow{f_{\sigma'}} & Y_{\sigma'} \\ \big\downarrow \pi_{\varphi(\varrho')}^{\varphi(\sigma')} & & \big\downarrow \pi_{\varrho'}^{\sigma'} \\ X_{\varphi(\varrho')} & \xrightarrow{f_{\varrho'}} & Y_{\varrho'} \end{array}$$

is commutative for each pair σ', ϱ' of elements from Σ', where $\varrho' \leqslant \sigma'$.

Every mapping of an inverse system $\boldsymbol{S}$ into a system $\boldsymbol{S}'$ induces a mapping of the limit of $\boldsymbol{S}$ into the limit of $\boldsymbol{S}'$. To show this suppose that $X = \varprojlim \boldsymbol{S}$ and $Y = \varprojlim \boldsymbol{S}'$ and that we are given a thread $x = \{x_\sigma\} \in X$. Let us consider an arbitrary element $\sigma' \in \Sigma'$ and let us put

$$y_{\sigma'} = f_{\sigma'}(x_{\varphi(\sigma')}). \tag{5}$$

The element $\{y_{\sigma'}\} \in \boldsymbol{P}_{\sigma' \in \Sigma'} Y_{\sigma'}$ defined in this manner is a thread. Indeed, for every $\sigma', \varrho' \in \Sigma'$ such that $\varrho' \leqslant \sigma'$, by virtue of (5), (4), and since $x = \{x_\sigma\}$ is a thread, we have

$$\pi_{\varrho'}^{\sigma'}(y_{\sigma'}) = \pi_{\varrho'}^{\sigma'} f_{\sigma'}(x_{\varphi(\sigma')}) = f_{\varrho'} \pi_{\varphi(\varrho')}^{\varphi(\sigma')}(x_{\varphi(\sigma')}) = f_{\varrho'}(x_{\varphi(\varrho')}) = y_{\varrho'}.$$

Let us denote the function obtained in this manner by f. We shall show that f is a mapping. Let us consider an arbitrary set of the shape $\pi_{\sigma'}^{-1}(U_{\sigma'})$, where $\sigma' \in \Sigma'$ and $U_{\sigma'}$ is an open subset of $Y_{\sigma'}$. Since, by virtue of Theorem 3, sets of this shape form a base of the space Y, it is sufficient to show that the inverse image of each of them is open. By virtue of (5),

$$\pi_{\sigma'}f(x) = f_{\sigma'}(x_{\varphi(\sigma')}) = f_{\sigma'}\pi_{\varphi(\sigma')}(x) \tag{6}$$

for $x = \{x_\sigma\} \in X$, so that $f^{-1}\pi_{\sigma'}^{-1}(U_{\sigma'}) = \pi_{\varphi(\sigma')}^{-1}f_{\sigma'}^{-1}(U_{\sigma'})$ and is an open set because $f_{\sigma'}$ and $\pi_{\varphi(\sigma')}$ are mappings. The mapping $f\colon X \to Y$ is called the *limit mapping* induced by $\{\varphi, f_{\sigma'}\}$.

THEOREM 4. *Let* $\mathbf{S} = \{X_\sigma, \pi_\varrho^\sigma, \Sigma\}$ *and* $\mathbf{S}' = \{Y_{\sigma'}, \pi_{\varrho'}^{\sigma'}, \Sigma'\}$ *be two inverse systems and let us suppose that* $\{\varphi, f_{\sigma'}\}$ *is a mapping of the system* $\mathbf{S}$ *into* $\mathbf{S}'$. *If* $\varphi(\Sigma')$ *is cofinal in* Σ *and* $f_{\sigma'}\colon X_{\varphi(\sigma')} \to Y_{\sigma'}$ *is a homeomorphism for every* $\sigma' \in \Sigma'$, *then the limit mapping* $f\colon \varprojlim \mathbf{S} \to \varprojlim \mathbf{S}'$ *is a homeomorphism.*

Proof. It is sufficient to prove that

(a) f is one-to-one.

(b) f is a mapping onto $\varprojlim \mathbf{S}'$.

(c) f is an open mapping.

Let $x = \{x_\sigma\}$ and $\bar{x} = \{\bar{x}_\sigma\}$ be two different elements of the space $X = \varprojlim \mathbf{S}$. Then there exists a $\sigma_0 \in \Sigma$ such that $x_{\sigma_0} \neq \bar{x}_{\sigma_0}$ and a $\sigma' \in \Sigma'$ such that $\sigma_0 \leqslant \varphi(\sigma')$. Evidently $x_{\varphi(\sigma')} \neq \bar{x}_{\varphi(\sigma')}$, whence, $f_{\sigma'}$ being a homeomorphism, $f_{\sigma'}(x_{\varphi(\sigma')}) \neq f_{\sigma'}(\bar{x}_{\varphi(\sigma')})$ and $f(x) \neq f(\bar{x})$. Thus we have proved (a).

Suppose we are given a point $y = \{y_{\sigma'}\} \in Y = \varprojlim \mathbf{S}'$. It is easy to verify that if $\varphi(\sigma') = \varphi(\sigma'')$, then $f_{\sigma'}^{-1}(y_{\sigma'}) = f_{\sigma''}^{-1}(y_{\sigma''})$. Therefore for every $\varphi(\sigma') \in \varphi(\Sigma')$ the formula

$$x_{\varphi(\sigma')} = f_{\sigma'}^{-1}(y_{\sigma'})$$

defines exactly one point of the space $X_{\varphi(\sigma')}$. For an arbitrary $\sigma \in \Sigma$ let us set

$$x_\sigma = \pi_\sigma^{\varphi(\sigma')}(x_{\varphi(\sigma')}),$$

where σ' is an element of the set Σ' satisfying the condition $\sigma \leqslant \varphi(\sigma')$, which always exists because of the confinality of $\varphi(\Sigma')$ in Σ. It can easily be verified that x_σ does not depend on the choice of σ', that $x = \{x_\sigma\}$ is a thread, and that $f(x) = y$. Thus we have proved (b).

In order to prove (c) it is sufficient, by virtue of Theorem 3, to show that the set $f\pi_{\varphi(\sigma')}^{-1}(U)$ is open in Y, for $\sigma' \in \Sigma'$ and an open subset U of $X_{\varphi(\sigma')}$. We infer from (6) that $\pi_{\varphi(\sigma')}^{-1}f_{\sigma'}^{-1}(A) = f^{-1}\pi_{\sigma'}^{-1}(A)$ for $A \subset Y_{\sigma'}$. Making use of the fact that $f_{\sigma'}$ is a one-to-one mapping onto $Y_{\sigma'}$, we have for $A = f_{\sigma'}(U)$ that

$$\pi_{\varphi(\sigma')}^{-1}(U) = \pi_{\varphi(\sigma')}^{-1}f_{\sigma'}^{-1}f_{\sigma'}(U) = f^{-1}\pi_{\sigma'}^{-1}f_{\sigma'}(U).$$

Hence, for (b) we have

$$f\pi_{\varphi(\sigma')}^{-1}(U) = ff^{-1}\pi_{\sigma'}^{-1}f_{\sigma'}(U) = \pi_{\sigma'}^{-1}f_{\sigma'}(U)$$

and (c) follows from the openness of $f_{\sigma'}$. ■

COROLLARY 1. *Let* $\mathbf{S} = \{X_\sigma, \pi^\sigma_\varrho, \Sigma\}$ *be an inverse system and let* Σ' *be cofinal in* Σ. *Then the restriction of threads from* $X = \varprojlim \mathbf{S}$ *to the set* Σ' *is a homeomorphism of* X *onto* $X' = \varprojlim \mathbf{S}'$, *where* $\mathbf{S}' = \{X_{\sigma'}, \pi^{\sigma'}_{\varrho'}, \Sigma'\}$. ∎

COROLLARY 2. *Let* $\mathbf{S} = \{X_\sigma, \pi^\sigma_\varrho, \Sigma\}$ *denote an inverse system. If the set* Σ *has the last element* σ_0, *then the limit* $\varprojlim \mathbf{S}$ *is homeomorphic to the space* X_{σ_0}. ∎

EXERCISES

A. Give an example of an inverse system $\mathbf{S} = \{X_n, \pi^n_m, N\}$, where N denotes the set of natural numbers, such that $X_n \neq 0$ for every $n \in N$ but $\varprojlim \mathbf{S} = 0$.

B. Given an inverse system $\mathbf{S} = \{X_\sigma, \pi^\sigma_\varrho, \Sigma\}$, a topological space Y, and a family of mappings $\{f_\sigma\}_{\sigma\in\Sigma}$, where $f_\sigma: Y \to X_\sigma$, show that if $\pi^\sigma_\varrho f_\sigma = f_\varrho$ for each pair σ, ϱ of elements from Σ such that $\varrho \leqslant \sigma$, then there exists a mapping $f: Y \to X = \varprojlim \mathbf{S}$ which satisfies the condition $\pi_\varrho f = f_\sigma$ for every $\sigma \in \Sigma$.

C. Give a characterization of the limit of an inverse system analogous to the characterization of the Cartesian product given in Exercise 3.F.

§ 6. Function spaces: the topology of uniform convergence. Mapping spaces: the topology of pointwise convergence. Let us consider two topological spaces, X and Y. The set of all mappings of the space X into the space Y will be denoted by the symbol Y^X. We will define a topology in this set.

Let us begin with the introduction of a topology in the set R^X, i.e. in the set of all real-valued continuous functions defined on X. Since $I^X \subset R^X$, the introduction of a topology in R^X determines automatically the topology of a subspace in I^X.

Let us assume that for $A \subset R^X$ and $f \in R^X$

(1) $$(f \in \bar{A}) \equiv (f = \lim f_i, \text{ where } f_i \in A \text{ for } i = 1, 2, \ldots).$$

As in Paragraph 1.4, the equality $f = \lim f_i$ denotes that the sequence $f_1, f_2, \ldots$ is uniformly convergent to f.

THEOREM 1. *Formula* (1) *defines a closure operator with properties* (CO1)-(CO4) *in the set* R^X.

Proof. The closure operator defined by means of formula (1) evidently satisfies property (CO1). Since $f = \lim f_i$ for $f_i = f$, $i = 1, 2, \ldots$, condition (CO2) is also satisfied. From (1) it follows immediately that

(2) $$\text{if } A \subset B, \text{ then } \bar{A} \subset \bar{B};$$

therefore, in order to prove (CO3) it is sufficient to prove the inclusion

(3) $$\overline{A \cup B} \subset \bar{A} \cup \bar{B}.$$

Let us suppose that $f \in \overline{A \cup B}$. Then there exists a sequence $f_1, f_2, \ldots$ of functions belonging to $A \cup B$ such that $f = \lim f_i$ i.e. that the sequence

$f_1, f_2, \ldots$ is uniformly convergent to f. Infinitely many terms of our sequence, i.e. a subsequence $f_{k_1}, f_{k_2}, \ldots$, must be contained in one of the sets A and B — say in A. By virtue of the definition of uniform convergence $f = \lim f_{k_i}$ and so $f \in \bar{A}$. Thus inclusion (3) has been proved.

By virtue of (2), $\bar{A} \subset \overline{(\bar{A})}$. In order to prove (CO4) it is therefore sufficient to show that

$$\overline{(\bar{A})} \subset \bar{A}. \tag{4}$$

Let us suppose that $f \in \overline{(\bar{A})}$ and $f = \lim f_i$, where $f_i \in \bar{A}$. For every natural number m let us denote by $i(m)$ such an index that

$$|f(x) - f_{i(m)}(x)| \leqslant \frac{1}{2m} \quad \text{for} \quad x \in X. \tag{5}$$

Since $f_{i(m)} \in \bar{A}$, $f_{i(m)} = \lim g_k^m$ holds, where $g_k^m \in A$ for $k = 1, 2, \ldots$ In particular, for some $k = k(m)$ we have

$$|g_{k(m)}^m(x) - f_{i(m)}(x)| \leqslant \frac{1}{2m} \quad \text{for} \quad x \in X. \tag{6}$$

Let us assume that $g_m = g_{k(m)}^m$; then $g_m \in A$ for $m = 1, 2, \ldots$ and, by virtue of (5) and (6), $f = \lim g_m$, whence $f \in \bar{A}$. Thus the proof of (4) is completed. ∎

The topology generated by the closure operator defined by (1) in the sets R^X and I^X is called the *topology of uniform convergence*. We are not going to study this topology now; many of its properties will follow from Theorem 4.2.8.

We note only that Theorem 1.4.2 implies

THEOREM 2. *For every topological space X the set I^X is a closed subspace of the space R^X.* ∎

Let X and Y be arbitrary topological spaces. For $A \subset X$ and $B \subset Y$ let

$$M(A, B) = \{f \in Y^X : f(A) \subset B\}. \tag{7}$$

Let us denote by $\mathfrak{S}$ the family of finite subsets of the space X, and the family of open subsets of the space Y by $\mathfrak{O}$. The family of sets of the form $\bigcap_{i=1}^{k} M(A_i, B_i)$, where $A_i \in \mathfrak{S}$, $B_i \in \mathfrak{O}$ for $i = 1, 2, \ldots, k$, is, according to Theorem 1.2.1, a base for a topology in the set Y^X. This topology will be called the *topology of pointwise convergence* or the *pointwise topology* in Y^X.

THEOREM 3. *The topology of pointwise convergence in the set Y^X is the same as the topology of a subspace of the Cartesian product $\mathbf{P}_{x \in X} Y_x$, where $Y_x = Y$ for every $x \in X$.*

Proof. Every open subset of the space Y^X considered as a subspace of the Cartesian product is the union of sets of the form

$$Y^X \cap p_{x_1}^{-1}(U_1) \cap p_{x_2}^{-1}(U_2) \cap \ldots \cap p_{x_k}^{-1}(U_k), \tag{8}$$

where $U_i \in \mathfrak{O}$ and $x_i \in X$ for $i = 1, 2, \ldots, k$. However,

$$Y^X \cap p_x^{-1}(U) = M(\{x\}, U); \tag{9}$$

thus all sets of form (8) and all sets open in Y^X with respect to the topology of a subspace of the Cartesian product are open with respect to the topology of pointwise convergence.

Conversely, it follows from (9) that

$$M(A, U) = Y^X \cap p_{x_1}^{-1}(U) \cap p_{x_2}^{-1}(U) \cap \ldots \cap p_{x_k}^{-1}(U),$$

for $A = \{x_1, x_2, \ldots, x_k\} \in \mathfrak{S}$ and $U \in \mathfrak{O}$; hence every set open with respect to the pointwise topology is open with respect to the topology of a subspace of the Cartesian product in Y^X. ∎

Theorems 3, 1.2, and 3.6 imply the following

COROLLARY. *If Y is a T_i-space, where $i \leqslant 3\frac{1}{2}$, then the space Y^X with the pointwise topology is also a T_i-space.* ∎

Theorem 3 and Theorem 3.11 imply:

THEOREM 4. *A net $\{f_\sigma, \sigma \in \Sigma\}$ in the space Y^X with the pointwise topology is convergent to the mapping $f \in Y^X$ if and only if for every $x \in X$ the net $\{f_\sigma(x), \sigma \in \Sigma\}$ is convergent to $f(x)$.* ∎

EXAMPLE 1. Let Y be the space of Example 1.2.1 and let X be a two--point discrete space. We infer, by Theorem 3 and Example 3.2, that the space Y^X with the pointwise topology is not necessarily normal for a normal space Y. ∎

The pointwise topology in Y^X can be defined directly as the topology of a subspace of the Cartesian product. We have used here an apparently less natural method because in Chapter 3 we shall analogously define one more topology which is considerably more useful and more interesting in the set Y^X. Instead of the family $\mathfrak{S}$, we shall use in this case another family $\mathfrak{Z}$ of subsets of the space X.

EXAMPLE 2. Let X denote a discrete space of weight $\aleph_0$. The pointwise topology and the topology of uniform convergence in I^X are different. Indeed, let $A \subset I^X$ be the set of functions which assume the value 1 at a finite number of points of the space X and the value 0 at the remaining points, and let f denote the function assuming the value 1 at every point of the space X. It can easily be verified that f belongs to the closure of the set A with respect to the pointwise topology, but does not belong to the closure of this set with respect to the topology of uniform convergence. ∎

THEOREM 5. *For every topological space X the topology of uniform convergence in R^X is stronger than the pointwise topology.*

Proof. Let $\mathfrak{S}$ be the family of all finite subsets of the space X. For every $S \in \mathfrak{S}$ the formula $j_S(f) = f|S$ defines a function of R^X into R^S. If we consider the sets R^S with the pointwise topology, then a family of functions $\{j_S\}_{S \in \mathfrak{S}}$ into topological spaces is defined on R^X. It can easily be verified that the pointwise topology in R^X is the topology generated by that family of mappings. It is, therefore, sufficient to show that for every $S \in \mathfrak{S}$ the function j_S is a mapping of the space R^X with the topology of uniform convergence into the space R^S with the pointwise topology. This follows, however, from the fact that the pointwise topology and the topology of uniform convergence coincide in R^S. ■

EXERCISES

A. Show that the sets

$$U_n(f) = \{g \in R^X : |f(x) - g(x)| < a < 1/n \text{ for every } x \in X\},$$

where $f \in R^X$ and n is a natural number, form a base for the topology of uniform convergence in the space R^X.

B. Let us consider the space Y^X with the topology of pointwise convergence. Show that the function φ of the Cartesian product $Y^X \times X$ into Y which assigns the point $\varphi(f, x) = f(x)$ to the pair (f, x) is not necessarily a mapping.

HISTORICAL REMARKS AND BIBLIOGRAPHIC NOTES

The Tietze-Urysohn Theorem originated in the paper of P. Urysohn [1925]; a particular case was proved by H. Tietze in [1915]. A simple proof that the space constructed in Example 1.2.2 is not normal was given by M. Katětov in [1950]. A. Tychonoff defined the topology in the Cartesian product of topological spaces and proved Theorem 3.8 in [1930]. Theorem 3.7 has been proved independently in the papers of E. S. Pondiczery [1944], E. Hewitt [1946a] and E. Marczewski [1947]. P. Alexandroff proved Theorem 3.9 in [1936]. Theorem 3.10 was proved by E. Marczewski in [1947] (a special case in [1941]). Example 3.2 was given by R. H. Sorgenfrey in [1947].The notion of the limit of an inverse system has been introduced (in a slightly different form) by P. Alexandroff in [1929]. The notion of the sum of spaces and of the quotient space for general topological spaces appears explicitly in the first edition of the book N. Bourbaki [1961]. Example 4.4 is a combination of examples considered in the papers of J. Novák [1948] and A. Tychonoff [1930].

PROBLEMS

A. Verify whether the properties "X is a Urysohn space" and "X is a semi-regular space", are hereditary and multiplicative.

B (P. Urysohn [1925]). Show that for an arbitrary space X the following conditions are equivalent:

(i) The space X is hereditarily normal (i.e. every subspace of the space X is normal).

(ii) Every open subspace of the space X is normal.

(iii) For every pair of subsets $A, B \subset X$, which are such that $\bar{A} \cap B = 0 = A \cap \bar{B}$, i.e. which are disjoint and closed in their union, there exist sets U and V which are open in X and satisfy the conditions $A \subset U, B \subset V$, and $U \cap V = 0$.

C (P. Urysohn [1925]). (a) Show that an arbitrary subspace of a normal space which is an F_σ-set is normal.

Hint: Let X be a normal space, $F_1, F_2, \ldots$ a sequence of closed subsets of X, and A, B a pair of disjoint and closed subsets of the space $M = \bigcup_{i=1}^{\infty} F_i$. Construct sequences $U_1, U_2, \ldots$ and $V_1, V_2, \ldots$ of open subsets of the space X such that

$$\bar{U}_{i-1} \cup (A \cap F_i) \subset U_i, \quad \bar{U}_i \cap (B \cup \bar{V}_{i-1}) = 0$$

and

$$\bar{V}_{i-1} \cup (B \cap F_i) \subset V_i, \quad \bar{V}_i \cap (A \cup \bar{U}_i) = 0.$$

(b) Deduce that every perfectly normal space is hereditarily normal and that perfect normality is a hereditary property. Give an example of a hereditarily normal space which is not perfectly normal.

D. Show that hereditary normality is invariant under closed mappings.

Hint: Make use of Exercise 1.5.E.

E (M. Katětov [1948]). Show that if the Cartesian product $X \times Y$ is a hereditarily normal space, then either every countable subset of the space X is closed or Y is perfectly normal.

Hint: Assume that there exist a countable set $M \subset X$ such that $\bar{M} \setminus M \neq 0$ and a closed set $N \subset Y$ which is not a G_δ-set. Consider the sets

$$A = M \times N \quad \text{and} \quad B = \{x\} \times (Y \setminus N),$$

where $x \in \bar{M} \setminus M$.

F (M. Katětov [1948]). Let $\{X_i\}_{i=1}^{\infty}$ be an arbitrary countable family of topological spaces.

(a) Show that the Cartesian product $\mathop{\boldsymbol{P}}\limits_{i=1}^{\infty} X_i$ is perfectly normal if and only if every finite product $X_1 \times X_2 \times \ldots \times X_n$ is perfectly normal (Example 3.2 and Problem 1.G show that the Cartesian product of two perfectly normal spaces need not even be normal).

(b) Prove that the perfect normality of the product $\mathop{\boldsymbol{P}}\limits_{i=1}^{\infty} X_i$ is equivalent to its hereditary normality.

G (Yu. M. Smirnov [1951c]). Prove the following properties of normally placed sets:

(a) If the set A_i is normally placed in X for every $i = 1, 2, \ldots$, then $\bigcup\limits_{i=1}^{\infty} A_i$ is also normally placed in X.

(b) If A is normally placed in X then every subset $B \subset A$, which is an F_σ-set in the space A, is normally placed in X.

(c) If A is normally placed in X then every subset $B \subset A$, which is normally placed in A, is normally placed in X.

Deduce that if X is a normal space then every subset $A \subset X$ normally placed in X is a normal space.

H (K. Kuratowski and W. Sierpiński [1921a]). A subset A of a topological space X is said to be *locally closed* provided every point $x \in A$ has a neighbourhood U in X such that the intersection $A \cap U$ is closed in U. Show that for a subset A of the space X the following conditions are equivalent:

(i) The set A is locally closed.
(ii) $\bar{A} \setminus A$ is a closed set.
(iii) The set A is the intersection of a closed set and an open set.

I. Let X and Y be Hausdorff spaces. Show that the *graph* of the mapping $f: X \to Y$, i.e. the set of pairs $(x, f(x))$, is closed in the Cartesian product $X \times Y$. Let the graph of a function of X into Y be closed; does this imply that the function is a mapping?

J. Prove that the weight of the Cartesian product $\mathop{\boldsymbol{P}}\limits_{s \in S} X_s$, where $w(X_s) = \mathfrak{m} \geqslant \aleph_0$ for $s \in S$, is equal to the greater of the numbers $\overline{\overline{S}}$ and $\mathfrak{m}$.

K (E. S. Pondiczery [1944], E. Marczewski [1947]). Prove that the Cartesian product of more than $\mathfrak{c}$ T_2-spaces which do not reduce to single points is not separable.

L (E. S. Pondiczery [1944], E. Hewitt [1946a]). Making use of the fact that for an arbitrary cardinal number $\mathfrak{m} \geqslant \aleph_0$ the Tychonoff cube of weight $\mathfrak{m}$ is of power $2^{\mathfrak{m}}$, show that if $\overline{\overline{S}} = 2^{\mathfrak{m}}$ and if each of the spaces X_s contains a dense subset of power $\leqslant \mathfrak{m}$ for $s \in S$, then the product $\mathop{\boldsymbol{P}}\limits_{s \in S} X_s$ contains a dense subset of power $\leqslant \mathfrak{m}$.

M (N. A. Šanin [1944], S. Mrówka [1956]). Prove that for a T_0-space Y the following conditions are equivalent:

(i) The space Y is embeddable in the Cartesian product of a number of copies of a space X.

(ii) The family of sets of the form $f^{-1}(U)$, where $f: X \to Y$ and U is open in X, is a subbase in the space Y.

(iii) The topology of the space Y can be generated by a family of mappings into a space X.

(iv) For every closed subset $A \subset Y$ and a point $y \notin A$ there exists a mapping f of the space Y into the Cartesian product of a finite number of copies of a space X such that $f(y) \notin \overline{f(A)}$.

N (S. Mrówka [1956]). (a) Making use of the preceding exercise prove that there exists no T_1-space X such that every T_1-space could be embedded in the Cartesian product of a certain number of copies of the space X.

(b) Let us denote by $L_{\mathfrak{m}}$ the space constructed in Example 1.2.3, where $\overline{\overline{X}} = \mathfrak{m}$. Prove that every T_1-space of power $\mathfrak{m}$ can be embedded in the Cartesian product of $\mathfrak{m}$ copies of the space $L_{\mathfrak{m}}$.

O. (a) (N. A. Šanin [1948]) Prove that the Cartesian product of any number of spaces which have property (Š) of Problem 1.Q also has that property.

Hint: Prove the above for a finite product and reduce the problem to the following:

(b) Prove that for any family $\{S_t\}_{t \in T}$ of sets of power $\leqslant k < \aleph_0$, where $\overline{\overline{T}} \geqslant \aleph_0$, there exist a set Z and an uncountable set $T_0 \subset T$ such that $S_t \cap S_{t'} = Z$ for distinct $t, t' \in T_0$.

Hint (S. Mazur [1952]): Show that for any family $\{A_t\}_{t \in T'}$ of countable sets, where $\overline{\overline{T'}} \geqslant \aleph_0$ and $\bigcap_{t \in T''} A_t = 0$ for an uncountable $T'' \subset T'$, there exists an uncountable set $T_0 \subset T'$ such that $A_t \cap A_{t'} = 0$ for distinct $t, t' \in T_0$. Then consider the greatest natural number l such that there exists a set Z consisting of l elements and an uncountable set $T' \subset T$ such that $Z \subset S_t$ for $t \in T'$. Define $A_t = S_t \setminus Z$.

(c) Show that the property obtained from condition (Š) by replacing the number $\aleph_0$ with an arbitrary regular cardinal number $\mathfrak{m} \geqslant \aleph_0$ (i.e. such a number that $\sum_{s \in S} \mathfrak{m}_s < \mathfrak{m}$ if $\overline{\overline{S}} < \mathfrak{m}$ and $\mathfrak{m}_s < \mathfrak{m}$ for $s \in S$) is multiplicative.

(d) Verify that property (I) of Problem 1.Q is not multiplicative. The problem on whether the property (S) is multiplicative is unsolved.

P (K. A. Ross and A. H. Stone [1964]). Let $\{X_s\}_{s\in S}$ be a family of separable spaces. Show that the closure of every open set $U \subset \boldsymbol{P}_{s\in S} X_s$ depends on countably many coordinates, i.e. that there exists a countable subset $S_0 \subset S$ suchthat if $\{x_s\} \in \overline{U}$, $\{y_s\} \in \boldsymbol{P}_{s\in S} X_s$ and $x_s = y_s$ for $s \in S_0$, then $\{y_s\} \in \overline{U}$.

Hint: Consider the maximal family of disjoint and non-empty elements of the base of $\boldsymbol{P}_{s\in S} X_s$ which are contained in U. Make use of Theorem 3.10.

Q (M. Bockstein [1948], K. A. Ross and A. H. Stone [1964]). Making use of the preceding problem show that for every two open and disjoint sets $U, W \subset \boldsymbol{P}_{s\in S} X_s$, where X_s is separable for every $s \in S$, there exists a countable set $S_0 \subset S$ such that the projections of U and W onto $\boldsymbol{P}_{s\in S_0} X_s$ are disjoint. If, moreover, the spaces X_s satisfy the second axiom of countability, then there exist sets V_1 and V_2 which are the unions of countably many elements of the base of the space $\boldsymbol{P}_{s\in S} X_s$ and are such that

$$U \subset V_1, \quad W \subset V_2, \quad \text{and} \quad V_1 \cap V_2 = 0.$$

R (H. H. Corson [1959], H. H. Corson and J. R. Isbell [1960], K. A. Ross and A. H. Stone [1964]). Suppose we are given a topological space Y, a family of spaces $\{X_s\}_{s\in S}$ and a mapping $f\colon \boldsymbol{P}_{s\in S} X_s \to Y$. If there exists a countable subset $S_0 \subset S$ such that $f(x) = f(y)$ for each pair $x = \{x_s\}$ and $y = \{y_s\}$ where $x_s = y_s$ for $s \in S_0$, then we say that f *depends only on a countable number of coordinates.*

Making use of the preceding problem show that if Y is a T_2-space which satisfies the second axiom of countability, and $\{X_s\}_{s\in S}$ denotes an arbitrary family of separable spaces, then $f\colon \boldsymbol{P}_{s\in S} X_s \to Y$ depends only on a countable number of coordinates (cf. Exercise 3.2.F).

S (H. H. Corson [1959]). Let $\{X_s\}_{s\in S}$ and Y be spaces which satisfy the assumptions of the preceding problem and let us assume that $a_s \in X_s$ denotes a fixed point for every $s \in S$. Let us denote by X the subset of the product $\boldsymbol{P}_{s\in S} X_s$ consisting of points $\{x_s\}$, where $x_s \neq a_s$ for at most countably many $s \in S$. Show that every mapping $f\colon X \to Y$ can be extended over $\boldsymbol{P}_{s\in S} X_s$.

Hint: Show that the conclusion of Problem Q remains true after replacing $\boldsymbol{P}_{s\in S} X_s$ by X.

T (A. H. Stone [1948]). Let $\{X_s\}_{s \in S}$ be an uncountable family of discrete spaces of power $\aleph_0$. Prove that the Cartesian product $\underset{s \in S}{\boldsymbol{P}} X_s$ is not a normal space.

Hint: Assume that X_s is the set of natural numbers for $s \in S$. Consider the sets A_1 and A_2, where A_i is the set of those points $\{x_s\}$ for which, for an arbitrary number $j \neq i$, the equality $x_s = j$ holds for at most one $s \in S$. Show that the sets A_1 and A_2 are closed and disjoint and further, making use of Problem Q, that for arbitrary open sets V_1 and V_2 such that $A_1 \subset V_1$ and $A_2 \subset V_2$, $V_1 \cap V_2 \neq 0$ holds.

U (B. Pospíšil [1937 a]). Show that the Cartesian product of an uncountable family of spaces not reduced to a single point is not a hereditarily normal space.

Hint: Make use of the preceding problem.

V. Let X be a topological space and let R denote an equivalence relation in X. Show that if X/R is a Hausdorff space, then R is a closed subset of $X \times X$. If R is a closed subset of $X \times X$ and $\varphi: X \to X/R$ is an open mapping, then X/R is a Hausdorff space.

W. Let R be an equivalence relation in the space X, and let S be an equivalence relation in the space Y. Let us define the relation $R \times S$ in the product $X \times Y$, assumming that $(x_1, y_2)(R \times S)(x_2, y_2)$ if and only if $x_1 R x_2$ and $y_1 S y_2$. Prove that $R \times S$ is an equivalence relation in the space $X \times Y$. Are the spaces $X \times Y/R \times S$ and $X/R \times Y/S$ homeomorphic? Are they homeomorphic under the additional assumption that R and S are open relations?

X. Let $S = \{X_\sigma, \pi_\varrho^\sigma, \Sigma\}$ be an inverse system. Let us suppose that π_ϱ^σ is a one-to-one mapping for each pair σ, ϱ of elements from the set Σ, where $\varrho \leqslant \sigma$. Show that π_σ is also a one-to-one mapping for every $\sigma \in \Sigma$. If, furthermore, π_ϱ^σ are mappings onto the space X_ϱ, then π_σ is also a mapping onto X_σ.

CHAPTER 3

COMPACT SPACES

Compact spaces, the investigation of which is the main object of this chapter, form one of the most important classes of topological spaces. By definition, X is a compact space if it possesses a property analogous to the property of the segment discovered by Borel and Lebesgue; namely, if every family of open sets covering X contains a finite subfamily which also covers X. The class of compact spaces contains the class of all closed segments and also the class of closed and bounded subsets of Euclidean spaces of arbitrary dimension. It turns out that many properties of this class belong also to compact spaces. At the end of the chapter we consider two other classes of spaces defined by means of some properties which in the case of subsets of Euclidean spaces are equivalent to compactness. The examination of those classes along with the classes of Lindelöf spaces and real-compact spaces gives us a better understanding of the significance of the notion of compactness and its position in general topology.

In Paragraph 1 we give the definition of a compact space and prove some important properties of spaces of this class. We introduce the notion of a grid (which is weaker than the notion of a base) and prove, by means of it, some theorems on the power of compact spaces and on the behavior of the weight of compact spaces under mappings.

Paragraph 2 is devoted to operations on compact spaces. We prove in it a theorem on extending of mappings, Tychonoff's Theorem on the multiplicativity of compactness, Alexandroff's Theorem giving a characterization of quotient spaces, and two theorems on inverse systems of compact spaces. The paragraph ends with a proof of the Stone-Weierstrass Theorem.

In Paragraph 3 we give the definition of the compact-open topology in the space of mappings and study basic properties of this topology.

In Paragraph 4 we define the notion of compactification of a topological space X, introduce a partial order in the set $\mathfrak{C}(X)$ of all compactifications of the space X, and prove that $\mathfrak{C}(X)$ is a complete semi-lattice with respect to that order.

Paragraph 5 is devoted to the greatest element of the set $\mathfrak{C}(X)$ called the Čech-Stone compactification of the space X.

Locally compact spaces are considered in Paragraph 6. In this paragraph we prove that locally compact spaces have the least compactification, which can be obtained by adding a single point.

Paragraph 7 is devoted to Lindelöf spaces.

The last three paragraphs concern more specific problems. Paragraph 8 concerns spaces, complete in the sense of Čech. In this paragraph we prove that for spaces complete in the sense of Čech, thus in particular for compact and locally compact spaces, Baire's Theorem is valid. Paragraph 9 is devoted to the examination of two classes of spaces (countably compact and pseudo-compact spaces) which are similar to compact spaces. We give a few examples constructed by means of the Čech-Stone compactification which show that neither of those classes is as well behaved with respect to operations as the class of compact spaces. In particular, the Cartesian product of two countably compact (pseudo-compact) spaces is not necessarily a countably compact (pseudo-compact) space. The class of real-compact spaces, recently discovered but important, is considered in Paragraph 10.

§ 1. Compact spaces. A family $\{A_s\}_{s\in S}$ of subsets of a set X such that $\bigcup_{s\in S} A_s = X$ is called a *covering* of X. Suppose we are given two coverings $\mathfrak{A} = \{A_s\}_{s\in S}$ and $\mathfrak{B} = \{B_t\}_{t\in T}$; we say that $\mathfrak{A}$ is a *refinement* of $\mathfrak{B}$ if for every $s \in S$ there exists a $t_s \in T$ such that $A_s \subset B_{t_s}$. A covering $\mathfrak{A}' = \{A'_s\}_{s\in S'}$ of the set X is called a *subcovering* of the covering $\mathfrak{A} = \{A_s\}_{s\in S}$ of the set X if $S' \subset S$ and $A_{s'} = A_s$ for $s \in S'$. A subcovering $\mathfrak{A}'$ of a covering $\mathfrak{A}$ is therefore its refinement. Let us now suppose that X is a topological space. A covering $\{A_s\}_{s\in S}$ of the space X is said to be *open* (*closed*) if all sets A_s are open (closed) in X.

A topological space X is said to be *compact* if it is a Hausdorff space and if every open covering $\{U_s\}_{s\in S}$ of the space X has a finite subcovering, i.e. if for every open covering $\{U_s\}_{s\in S}$ of the space X there exists a finite set $\{s_1, s_2, \ldots, s_k\} \subset S$ such that $X = U_{s_1} \cup U_{s_2} \cup \ldots \cup U_{s_k}$.

It can easily be noted that a Hausdorff space is compact if and only if every open covering of it has a finite refinement. Since every open covering of a topological space always has a refinement consisting of elements of a fixed base of the space, a Hausdorff space X is compact if and only if every covering of the space X consisting of elements of a fixed base has a finite refinement.

We say that a family $\mathfrak{F} = \{F_s\}_{s\in S}$ of subsets of the set X has the *finite intersection property* provided that $\mathfrak{F} \neq 0$ and $F_{s_1} \cap F_{s_2} \cap \ldots \cap F_{s_k} \neq 0$ for every finite system $s_1, s_2, \ldots, s_k \in S$. If for every countable subset $S_1 \subset S$, $\bigcap_{s\in S_1} F_s \neq 0$ holds, then we say that the family $\{F_s\}_{s\in S}$ has the *countable intersection property*.

THEOREM 1. *A Hausdorff space X is compact if and only if every family of closed sets which possesses the finite intersection property has the non-empty intersection.*

Proof. Let us suppose that X is a compact space and let $\{F_s\}_{s\in S}$ be the family of closed subsets of X such that $\bigcap_{s\in S} F_s = 0$. Let us consider the open sets $U_s = X\setminus F_s$; since

$$\bigcup_{s\in S} U_s = \bigcup_{s\in S} (X\setminus F_s) = X\setminus \bigcap_{s\in S} F_s = X,$$

the family $\{U_s\}_{s\in S}$ is an open covering of the space X. By the compactness of X, the covering $\{U_s\}_{s\in S}$ has a finite subcovering $\{U_{s_1}, U_{s_2}, \ldots, U_{s_k}\}$. Therefore

$$X = \bigcup_{i=1}^{k} U_{s_i} = \bigcup_{i=1}^{k} (X\setminus F_{s_i}) = X\setminus \bigcap_{i=1}^{k} F_{s_i},$$

whence $\bigcap_{i=1}^{k} F_{s_i} = 0$. Thus, if the family $\{F_s\}_{s\in S}$ of closed subsets of the space X has the finite intersection property, then $\bigcap_{s\in S} F_s \neq 0$.

We leave it to the reader to prove that if in a Hausdorff space every family of closed sets possessing the finite intersection property has a non-empty intersection, then the space is compact. ■

Theorem 1 immediately implies

THEOREM 2. *A closed subspace of a compact space is compact.* ■

We shall now prove some theorems concerning compact subspaces of a topological space.

The definition of a subspace immediately implies

THEOREM 3. *If a subspace A of a topological space X is compact, then for every family $\{U_s\}_{s\in S}$ of open subsets of X such that $A \subset \bigcup_{s\in S} U_s$ there exists a finite set $\{s_1, s_2, \ldots, s_k\} \subset S$ such that $A \subset \bigcup_{i=1}^{k} U_{s_i}$.* ■

Theorems 2 and 3 imply

COROLLARY 1. *Let X be a Hausdorff space and $\{F_1, F_2, \ldots, F_k\}$ a family of closed subsets of X. In order that $F = \bigcup_{i=1}^{k} F_i$ be compact it is necessary and sufficient that the spaces F_i be compact for $i = 1, 2, \ldots, k$.* ■

COROLLARY 2. *Let U be an open subset of a topological space X. If a family $\{F_s\}_{s\in S}$ of closed subsets of X contains at least one compact set, in particular if X is compact, and if $\bigcap_{s\in S} F_s \subset U$, then there exists a finite set $\{s_1, s_2, \ldots, s_k\} \subset S$ such that $F_{s_1} \cap F_{s_2} \cap \ldots \cap F_{s_k} \subset U$.*

Proof. Let F_{s_0} be a compact subspace of X. Replacing X by F_{s_0}, U by $U \cap F_{s_0}$ and the family $\{F_s\}_{s\in S}$ by the family $\{F_{s_0} \cap F_s\}_{s\in S}$, we reduce the problem to the case of a compact X. In this case we put $A = X\setminus U$ and $U_s = X\setminus F_s$ in the theorem and obtain the set $\{s_1, s_2, \ldots, s_k\}$ which satisfies the conclusion of the corollary. ∎

THEOREM 4. *Let A be a compact subspace of a regular space X. For every closed set $B \subset X\setminus A$ there exist sets U, V open in X and such that $A \subset U, B \subset V$, and $U \cap V = 0$.*

If B is compact it is sufficient to assume that X is a Hausdorff space.

Proof. By virtue of the regularity of X, for every point $x \in A$ there exist open sets U_x, V_x such that

$$(1) \qquad x \in U_x, \quad B \subset V_x, \quad \text{and} \quad U_x \cap V_x = 0.$$

Since $A \subset \bigcup_{x\in A} U_x$, there exists, by Theorem 3, a finite number of points $x_1, x_2, \ldots, x_k \in A$ such that $A \subset \bigcup_{i=1}^{k} U_{x_i}$. It is easy to verify that the sets $U = \bigcup_{i=1}^{k} U_{x_i}$ and $V = \bigcap_{i=1}^{k} V_{x_i}$ satisfy the conclusion of the theorem.

Let us note that if the set B consists of only a single point, then in the proof of the first part of the theorem it is sufficient to use the fact that X is a Hausdorff space. If B is compact and X is a Hausdorff space, then for every $x \in A$, by replacing A by B and B by x in the proved part of the theorem and by making use of the above remark, we also get the sets U_x, V_x which satisfy (1). ∎

THEOREM 5. *Let A be a compact subspace of a Tychonoff space X. For every closed subset $B \subset X\setminus A$ there exists a continuous function $f\colon X \to I$ such that $f(x) = 0$ for $x \in A$ and $f(x) = 1$ for $x \in B$.*

Proof. For every point $x \in A$ there exists a function $f_x\colon X \to I$ such that $f_x(x) = 0$ and $f_x(B) \subset \{1\}$, Since $A \subset \bigcup_{x\in A} f_x^{-1}([0, \frac{1}{2}))$, by virtue of Theorem 3, there exists a finite number of points $x_1, x_2, \ldots, x_k \in A$ such that $A \subset \bigcup_{i=1}^{k} f_{x_i}^{-1}([0, \frac{1}{2}))$. For the function $g\colon X \to I$ defined by the formula

$$g(x) = \min\big(f_{x_1}(x), f_{x_2}(x), \ldots, f_{x_k}(x)\big)$$

we have

$$A \subset g^{-1}([0, \tfrac{1}{2})) \quad \text{and} \quad g(B) \subset \{1\}.$$

It can easily be verified that the function $f\colon X \to I$ defined by $f(x) = 2\max\big(g(x) - \frac{1}{2}, 0\big)$ has the required properties. ∎

THEOREM 6. *Every compact subspace of a Hausdorff space X is a closed subset of X.*

Proof. Let A be a compact subspace of X. Replacing the set B in the second part of Theorem 4 by an arbitrary point $x \in X \setminus A$, we infer that there exist open sets U, V such that $A \subset U, x \in V$ and $U \cap V = 0$. Since $\overline{U} \cap V = 0$, we have $x \notin \overline{U}$ and $x \notin \overline{A}$, so that $A = \overline{A}$. ■

The second part of Theorem 4 and Theorem 2 imply

THEOREM 7. *Every compact space is normal.* ■

We shall now prove three theorems on mappings of compact spaces.

THEOREM 8. *Let X be a compact space and Y a Hausdorff space. If there exists a mapping f of the space X onto the space Y, then the space Y is also compact. In other words, the continuous image of a compact space is compact provided that it is a Hausdorff space.*

Proof. Let us consider an arbitrary open covering $\{U_s\}_{s \in S}$ of the space Y. The sets $\{f^{-1}(U_s)\}_{s \in S}$ form an open covering of the space X; therefore, there exists a finite number of indices $s_1, s_2, \ldots, s_k \in S$ such that

$$f^{-1}(U_{s_1}) \cup f^{-1}(U_{s_2}) \cup \ldots \cup f^{-1}(U_{s_k}) = X.$$

Considering the image of both sides of this equality we infer that $U_{s_1} \cup \cup U_{s_2} \cup \ldots \cup U_{s_k} = Y$. ■

COROLLARY. *If X is a compact space and f denotes a mapping of X into a Hausdorff space Y, then $\overline{f(A)} = f(\overline{A})$ for every $A \subset X$.*

Indeed, by condition (v) of Theorem 1.4.1, it is sufficient to note that the definition of closure and Theorems 2, 8, and 6 imply the inclusion $\overline{f(A)} \subset f(\overline{A})$. ■

The corollary implies

THEOREM 9. *Every mapping of a compact space into a Hausdorff space is closed.* ■

Theorems 9 and 1.4.4 imply the following important theorem:

THEOREM 10. *If X is a compact space and $f: X \to Y$ is a one-to-one mapping of X onto a Hausdorff space Y, then f is a homeomorphism.* ■

COROLLARY. *Let us suppose that in a set X two topologies, $\mathfrak{O}_1$ and $\mathfrak{O}_2$, are defined such that $\mathfrak{O}_1 \supset \mathfrak{O}_2$. If the space $(X, \mathfrak{O}_1)$ is compact and the space $(X, \mathfrak{O}_2)$ is a Hausdorff space, then $\mathfrak{O}_1 = \mathfrak{O}_2$. In other words, the compact topologies are minimal among Hausdorff topologies.*

In fact, the identity is a one-to-one mapping of the space $(X, \mathfrak{O}_1)$ onto $(X, \mathfrak{O}_2)$; therefore, by Theorem 10, it must be a homeomorphism. ■

We shall now introduce the notion of a grid in a topological space. We define it at this point because this notion is particularly useful for examining compact spaces.

A family $\mathfrak{N}$ of subsets of a topological space X is called a *grid* in the space X if for every point $x \in X$ with a neighbourhood U there exists an $N \in \mathfrak{N}$ such that $x \in N \subset U$. The base is therefore a special case of the grid: namely, it is a grid whose elements are open. The family of all sets consisting of a single point is another example of a grid.

The following theorem is fundamental for grids.

THEOREM 11. *If in the compact space X there exists a grid $\mathfrak{N}$ of power $\mathfrak{m}$, then there exists in X a base of power $\leqslant \mathfrak{m}$. The weight of a compact space is, therefore, equal to the minimal power of a grid.*

Proof. It is easy to verify that if $\mathfrak{m}$ is a finite number, then X is a discrete space of power $\leqslant \mathfrak{m}$; therefore it has a base of power $\leqslant \mathfrak{m}$. We can, therefore, assume that $\mathfrak{m} \geqslant \aleph_0$. Let $\mathfrak{O}_1$ be a topology of the space X. Let us consider pairs of elements M, N of the grid $\mathfrak{N}$ for which there exist disjoint sets $U, V \in \mathfrak{O}_1$ containing M and N respectively and for each of the pairs let us choose a pair U, V of sets satisfying the above conditions. Let $\mathfrak{B}$ denote the family of sets obtained in this manner. The family $\mathfrak{B}_0$ of all finite intersections of elements of the family $\mathfrak{B}$ has properties (B1)-(B2). From the definition of a grid and from the fact that $(X, \mathfrak{O}_1)$ is a Hausdorff space, we infer that the set X with the topology $\mathfrak{O}_2$ generated by $\mathfrak{B}_0$ is also a Hausdorff space. Since evidently $\mathfrak{O}_2 \subset \mathfrak{O}_1$, we infer from the corollary to Theorem 10 that $\mathfrak{O}_1 = \mathfrak{O}_2$. Thus, by the evident inequality $\overline{\overline{\mathfrak{B}}}_0 \leqslant \mathfrak{m}$, the proof has been completed. ■

The family of all one-point subsets of the space X is a grid. Thus we obtain

COROLLARY 1. *The weight of a compact space is not greater than its power.* ■

COROLLARY 2. *Let X and Y be topological spaces. If Y is compact and if there exists a mapping $f: X \to Y$ onto Y, then the weight of Y does not exceed the weight of X. In other words, the weight cannot be increased under a mapping onto a compact space.*

In fact, it follows from Theorem 1.4.1 that the family $\{f(U)\}_{U \in \mathfrak{B}}$, where $\mathfrak{B}$ denotes a base of the space X, is a grid in the space Y. ■

The following theorem characterizes compact spaces in terms of nets.

THEOREM 12. *A Hausdorff space X is compact if and only if every net in this space has a cluster point.*

Proof. Let X be a compact space and let $S = \{x_\sigma, \sigma \in \Sigma\}$ denote an arbitrary net in the space X. The family $\{F_\sigma\}_{\sigma \in \Sigma}$, where

$$F_{\sigma_0} = \overline{\{x_\sigma: \sigma_0 \leqslant \sigma\}},$$

consists of closed sets and has the finite intersection property because $F_{\sigma_1} \subset F_{\sigma_2}$ for $\sigma_1 \geqslant \sigma_2$. The point $x \in \bigcap_{\sigma \in \Sigma} F_\sigma$, which exists by Theorem 1, is the cluster point of the net S. Indeed, if it were not, there would exist a neighbourhood U of the point x and an element σ_0 of the set Σ such that

$$U \cap \{x_\sigma: \sigma_0 \leqslant \sigma\} = 0,$$

i.e. we would have $x \notin F_{\sigma_0}$, contrary to the definition of the point x.

Let us now consider a Hausdorff space X in which every net has a cluster point and let $\mathfrak{F}$ denote a family of closed subsets of the space X which has the finite intersection property. Let us denote by Σ the set of all finite subfamilies $\{F_1, F_2, \ldots, F_k\}$ of the family $\mathfrak{F}$. For $\sigma = \{F_1, F_2, \ldots, F_k\}$ and $\sigma' = \{F_1', F_2', \ldots, F_l'\}$ belonging to Σ let us assume that $\sigma \leqslant \sigma'$ provided that $F_1 \cap F_2 \cap \ldots \cap F_k \supset F_1' \cap F_2' \cap \ldots \cap F_l'$. The set Σ is directed by the relation $\leqslant$ and $S = \{x_\sigma, \sigma \in \Sigma\}$, where x_σ is an arbitrary point of the set $F_1 \cap F_2 \cap \ldots \cap F_k$ for $\sigma = \{F_1, F_2, \ldots, F_k\}$, is a net in the space X. In order to complete the proof it is sufficient to show that the cluster point x of the net S, which exists by our assumption, belongs to every element of the family $\mathfrak{F}$.

Let F_0 be an arbitrary element of the family $\mathfrak{F}$. For an arbitrary neighbourhood U of the point x there exists a $\sigma = \{F_1, F_2, \ldots, F_k\} \geqslant \sigma_0 = \{F_0\}$ such that $x_\sigma \in U$. Since $x_\sigma \in F_1 \cap F_2 \cap \ldots \cap F_k \subset F_0$, $F_0 \cap U \neq 0$ holds, and since the set F_0 is closed, this proves that $x \in F_0$. ■

Theorem 12 can be stated in terms of filters as follows:

THEOREM 12F. *A Hausdorff space X is compact if and only if every filter in this space has a cluster point.* ■

Beside compact spaces a larger class of quasi-compact spaces is considered. A topological space X is said to be *quasi-compact* if each open covering of it contains a finite subcovering. Compact spaces can thus be defined as quasi-compact Hausdorff spaces. The reader can verify without any difficulty that Theorems 1, 2, 3, 8, 12, and 12F in the present paragraph and Theorems 3, 4, and 8 in Paragraph 2, along with their proofs, remain valid after replacing the term "compact" by the term "quasi-compact" and the term "Hausdorff space" by the term "topological space".

EXAMPLE 1. A discrete space is compact if and only if it is finite.

The real-line and the space considered in Example 1.2.1 are not compact; in fact, the covering $\{(-n, n)\}_{n=1}^{\infty}$ does not contain any finite subcovering.

We shall show that the space of Example 1.1.2, i.e. the space with only one accumulation point x_0, is compact. Let us consider an arbitrary open covering $\{U_s\}_{s \in S}$ of the space X. There exists an $s_0 \in S$ such that $x_0 \in U_{s_0}$. By virtue of the definition of the topology in the space X, the set $X \setminus U_{s_0}$ is finite. Let us assume that $X \setminus U_{s_0} = \{x_1, x_2, \ldots, x_k\}$ and let U_{s_i} be an arbitrary set of our covering which contains the point x_i for $i = 1, 2, \ldots, k$. The family $\{U_{s_i}\}_{i=0}^{k}$ is a finite subcovering of the covering $\{U_s\}_{s \in S}$. Since X is a Hausdorff space, X is indeed compact.

Every open covering of the space considered in Example 1.2.3 contains a finite subcovering. But since this space is not a T_2-space, it is not compact.

The closed segment $J = [a, b] \subset R$ is compact. In order to prove this it is sufficient to show that for an arbitrary open covering $\{U_s\}_{s \in S}$ of the space J the point b belongs to the set A consisting of those $c \in [a, b]$ for which the segment $[a, c]$ is contained in a finite number of elements of the covering $\{U_s\}_{s \in S}$. The set A is a non-empty set (because it contains the point a) and is a bounded set of real numbers; therefore it has a least upper bound, $d \in [a, b]$. One can easily verify that the set A is closed; it is therefore sufficient to show that $d = b$. Let us assume that $d < b$ and let us choose an arbitrary element U_{s_0} of the covering which contains the point d. There exists an $\varepsilon > 0$ such that $(d-\varepsilon, d+\varepsilon) \subset U_{s_0}$ and since $d-\varepsilon/2 \in A$, $[a, d-\varepsilon/2] \subset \bigcup_{i=1}^{k} U_{s_i}$ holds, where $s_1, s_2, \ldots, s_k \in S$. This implies, however, that $[a, d+\varepsilon/2] \subset \bigcup_{i=0}^{k} U_{s_i}$, contrary to the definition of d. ■

EXAMPLE 2. Let us consider two segments $C_i = \{(x, y) : y = i, 0 \leqslant x \leqslant 1\}$ for $i = 1, 2$ in the plane R^2 and their union $X = C_1 \cup C_2$. We generate the topology of a compact space in the set X by means of a neighbourhood system. Namely, let $\mathfrak{B}(z) = \{\{z\}\}$ if $z \in C_2$ and $\mathfrak{B}(z) = \{U_k(z)\}_{k=1}^{\infty}$, where

$$U_k(z) = \{(x', y') \in X : 0 < |x-x'| < 1/k\} \cup \{z\},$$

if $z = (x, 1) \in C_1$. It can easily be verified that the family $\{\mathfrak{B}(z)\}_{z \in X}$ satisfies conditions (BP1)-(BP4); therefore, by virtue of Theorem 1.5.1, the space X is a Hausdorff space.

The subspace C_2 is a discrete space of power $\mathfrak{c}$ and it is open and dense in X. The subspace C_1 is homeomorphic to the segment I with the natural topology, and it is closed in the space X.

We shall now prove that the space X is compact. Let us suppose that $\{U_s\}_{s \in S}$ is an open covering of the space X. We can assume without loss of generality that the sets U_s belong to the neighbourhood system described above. By the compactness of the space C_1, there exists a finite subfamily $\{U_{s_1}, U_{s_2}, \ldots, U_{s_k}\}$ of the covering such that

$$C_1 \subset U_{s_1} \cup U_{s_2} \cup \ldots \cup U_{s_k}. \tag{2}$$

We can eliminate all sets U_{s_i} consisting of a single point and the inclusion (2) still remains valid. It can thus be assumed that $U_{s_i} = U_{k_i}(z_i)$, where $z_i = (x_i, 1)$ for $i = 1, 2, \ldots, k$. It is easy to note that

$$X \setminus \bigcup_{i=1}^{k} \{(x_i, 2)\} \subset U_{s_1} \cup U_{s_2} \cup \ldots \cup U_{s_k}.$$

Adding to the family $\{U_{s_i}\}_{i=1}^{k}$ arbitrary elements $U_{s_{k+1}}, U_{s_{k+2}}, \ldots, U_{s_{2k}}$ of the covering which contain the points $(x_1, 2), (x_2, 2), \ldots, (x_k, 2)$

respectively, we obtain the finite subcovering $\{U_{s_i}\}_{i=1}^{2k}$ of the covering $\{U_s\}_{s\in S}$.

The space X satisfies the first axiom of countability but does not satisfy the second one, and is not separable.

It should be mentioned we do not as yet know whether there exist compact spaces which satisfy the first axiom of countability and have a power greater than $\mathfrak{c}$.

It is not difficult to verify that there exists a mapping of the space X onto a space of power $\mathfrak{c}$ with only one accumulation point: C_2 is one-to-one mapped onto the set of isolated points of that space and C_1 is mapped onto the accumulation point. The above remark shows that an equivalent of Corollary 2 to Theorem 11, for the weight at a point, is not neccesarily true. ■

EXAMPLE 3. We shall now show that the Cantor set $D^{\aleph_0}$ is homeomorphic to a subspace of the real-line. Let us consider the set C of all real numbers of the segment I which have a tryadic expansion in which number 1 does not occur, i.e. the set of all numbers of the form $x = \sum_{i=1}^{\infty} \frac{2x_i}{3^i}$, where $x_i = 0$ or 1 for $i = 1, 2, \ldots$ Numbers of the set C are representable in that form uniquely. Thus the formula $f(x) = \{x_i\}$ defines a one-to-one function of C onto $D^{\aleph_0}$. Theorem 2.3.3 implies that f is a mapping provided that C is considered as a subspace of the real-line. In order to prove that f is a homeomorphism it is sufficient, by Theorem 10, to show that C is compact. This follows, however, from the fact that $C = \bigcap_{i=1}^{\infty} F_i$, where F_i is the subset (closed) of the segment I consisting of the numbers which have a tryadic expansion in which the number 1 does not occur as the i-th term. It is easy to see that the set F_1 can be obtained from the segment I by removing the "middle" interval $(\frac{1}{3}, \frac{2}{3})$; the set F_2 can be obtained from the set F_1 by removing the "middle" intervals, $(\frac{1}{9}, \frac{2}{9})$ and $(\frac{7}{9}, \frac{8}{9})$, from the two segments constituting F_2, and so on.

From the fact proved above we infer that the Cantor set $D^{\aleph_0}$ is compact. In the next paragraph we shall prove that the Cantor cube $D^{\mathfrak{m}}$ is compact for every $\mathfrak{m} \geqslant \aleph_0$ (cf. Theorem 2.4). ■

EXAMPLE 4. We shall give here an example of a countable space X which does not satisfy the first axiom of countability at any point, so that it may be seen that the property of compact spaces which was stated in Corollary 1 to Theorem 11 does not apply to arbitrary topological spaces. Considering the one-to-one mapping of the discrete countable space onto the space X, we infer that also in Corollary 2 to Theorem 11 the assumption that the space Y is compact is essential.

Let us consider the Cartesian product $N^{\mathfrak{c}} = \mathop{\boldsymbol{P}}_{t \in R} N_t$, where N_t is identical with the set of all natural numbers N for every $t \in R$ (i.e., N_t is the discrete space of power $\aleph_0$). By virtue of Theorem 2.3.7, the space $N^{\mathfrak{c}}$ contains a dense countable subset X. We shall show that the subspace X of the space $N^{\mathfrak{c}}$ has the required property. For this purpose it is sufficient to show that for an arbitrary point $x \in X$ and an arbitrary countable family $\{V_i\}_{i=1}^{\infty}$ of its neighbourhoods there exists a neighbourhood U of this point such that

(3) $$V_i \cap (X \setminus U) \neq 0 \quad \text{for} \quad i = 1, 2, \ldots$$

Let $x = \{x_t\} \in X$ and let $\{V_i\}_{i=1}^{\infty}$ be a family of its neighbourhoods. For every natural number i there exist a finite subset $S_i \subset R$ and a family $\{W_t^i\}_{t \in R}$ consisting of open subsets of the space N such that $W_t^i = N_t$ for $t \in R \setminus S_i$ and

(4) $$x \in X \cap \mathop{\boldsymbol{P}}_{t \in R} W_t^i \subset V_i.$$

Since the set R is uncountable, there exists a point $t_0 \in R \setminus \bigcup_{i=1}^{\infty} S_i$. The set $U = p_{t_0}^{-1}(x_{t_0})$ is a neighbourhood of the point $x = \{x_t\}$, and the set $(\mathop{\boldsymbol{P}}_{t \in R} W_t^i) \setminus U$ is non-empty and open in $N^{\mathfrak{c}}$ for $i = 1, 2, \ldots$ Since X is dense in $N^{\mathfrak{c}}$, we infer that $\mathop{\boldsymbol{P}}_{t \in R} W_t^i \cap (X \setminus U) \neq 0$; hence from (4), formula (3) follows. ■

EXERCISES

A. Show by means of examples that Corollary 1 to Theorem 3, and Theorems 6 and 8 are not true if we replace the term "Hausdorff space" by the term "topological space".

B. Give an example of a separable space which has no countable grid.

C (R. Arens [1950]). Let X be a subset of the plane consisting of those points for which both coordinates are integers. Let us assume that the base of the space X consists of the sets of the form $\{(m, n)\}$ for $(m, n) \neq (0, 0)$ and of the sets which remain after removing at most a finite number of straight lines parallel to the axis $y = 0$ and a finite number of points on each of the remaining lines parallel to the axis $y = 0$.

Show that every compact subset of the space X is finite and that X is not a discrete space.

Verify that X is a normal space and that it has no countable base at the point $(0, 0)$.

D. Let X be a countable space without any countable base at the point x_0. Show that the subspace of the Cartesian product $X^{\aleph_0}$ consisting of the points $\{x_i\}$ for which there exists a natural number j such that $x_i = x_0$ for $i > j$ is countable and has no countable base at any point.

E. Let X be a compact space and let $X_i = X \times \{i\}$ for $i = 1, 2$, $A(X) = X_1 \cup X_2$. Following Example 2, generate a topology of a compact space in $A(X)$ in such a manner that X_1 is homeomorphic to the space X and X_2 is a discrete space. Verify that for any set $M \subset X$ the subspace $X_1 \cup M_2 \subset A(X)$, where $M_2 = M \times \{2\} \subset X_2$, is compact and, under the additional assumption that M is dense in X and X is dense in itself, M_2 is a dense subset of it.

F. Show that a discrete space of power $\mathfrak{c}$ is embeddable as a closed subset in the Cartesian product of $\mathfrak{c}$ copies of the discrete space of power $\aleph_0$. Deduce that the product is not normal (cf. Problem 2.T).

Hint: Let X_0 be the space $A(D^{\aleph_0})$ defined in the preceding exercise, $X = D_2^{\aleph_0} \subset X_0$ its discrete subspace of power $\mathfrak{c}$, and $Y = D_1^{\aleph_0} \subset X_0$ a subspace homeomorphic to the Cantor set. Verify that for every $x \in Y$ there exists a mapping $f_x: X_0 \to Z$, where Z is the subspace of the real-line consisting of number zero and reciprocals of natural numbers, such that $f_x^{-1}(0) = \{x\}$. Consider the mapping $i_X \triangle (\mathop{\triangle}_{x \in Y} f_x|X): X \to X_0 \times (Z \setminus \{0\})^{\mathfrak{c}}$, where i_X is the embedding of X into X_0. Making use of the Diagonal Lemma show that X_0 is embeddable in the Cartesian product of $\mathfrak{c}$ copies of the discrete space of power $\aleph_0$.

§ 2. Operations on compact spaces. Theorems 1.2 and 1.6 imply that compactness is a hereditary property only with respect to closed subsets.

The following theorem, concerning extensions of mappings with values in a compact space, is valid.

THEOREM 1. *Let A be a dense subset of a topological space X and let f denote a mapping of A into a compact space Y. The mapping f can then be extended over X if and only if for each two subsets B_1, B_2 which are closed in Y and disjoint, the closures of the inverse images $f^{-1}(B_1), f^{-1}(B_2)$ in X are disjoint.*

Proof. Let $F: X \to Y$ be an extension of f. If $B_i = \overline{B_i} \subset Y$ for $i = 1, 2$ and $B_1 \cap B_2 = 0$, then $F^{-1}(B_i) = \overline{F^{-1}(B_i)}$ for $i = 1, 2$ and $F^{-1}(B_1) \cap F^{-1}(B_2) = 0$. Hence we infer that

$$\overline{f^{-1}(B_1)} \cap \overline{f^{-1}(B_2)} \subset F^{-1}(B_1) \cap F^{-1}(B_2) = 0;$$

thus the condition is necessary. We shall show that it is also sufficient.

Let x be an arbitrary point of the space X. Let $\mathfrak{B}(x)$ denote the family of all neighbourhoods of the point x in the space X and let us consider the family $\{\overline{f(A \cap U)}\}_{U \in \mathfrak{B}(x)}$. Since for $U_1, U_2, \ldots, U_k \in \mathfrak{B}(x)$

$$(1) \quad \overline{f(A \cap U_1 \cap U_2 \cap \ldots \cap U_k)} \subset \overline{f(A \cap U_1)} \cap \overline{f(A \cap U_2)} \cap \ldots \cap \overline{f(A \cap U_k)}$$

holds, $\mathfrak{F}_x = \{\overline{f(A \cap U)}\}_{U \in \mathfrak{B}(x)}$ has the finite intersection property; moreover it consists of closed subsets of the space Y. Let $F(x)$ denote the intersection of all elements of the family $\mathfrak{F}_x$. Then by virtue of Theorem 1.1 $F(x) \neq 0$ holds.

We shall show that $F(x)$ contains only one element. In fact, if $y_1, y_2 \in F(x)$ and $y_1 \neq y_2$, then there exist neighbourhoods V_1 and V_2

of the points y_1 and y_2 in Y such that $\overline{V}_1 \cap \overline{V}_2 = 0$. By our assumption, $\overline{f^{-1}(V_1)} \cap \overline{f^{-1}(V_2)} = 0$ and therefore

$$X = W_1 \cup W_2, \quad \text{where } W_i = X \setminus \overline{f^{-1}(V_i)} \text{ for } i = 1, 2.$$

It follows that $x \in W_{i_0}$ for i_0 equal to 1 or to 2. Since for an arbitrary set V which is open in Y the equality $V \cap f\big(A \setminus \overline{f^{-1}(V)}\big) = 0$ holds, we have

$$V \cap \overline{f\big(A \setminus \overline{f^{-1}(V)}\big)} = 0$$

and

$$y_{i_0} \notin \overline{f\big(A \setminus \overline{f^{-1}(V_{i_0})}\big)} = \overline{f(A \cap W_{i_0})} \in \mathfrak{F}_x,$$

which is contrary to our assumption. Thus we have shown that $F(x)$ contains only one point and, in particular, it follows that $F(x) = f(x)$ for $x \in A$.

We have thus defined a function F of the space X into Y which is an extension of f. We shall show that F is subject to condition (iii) of Theorem 1.4.1, i.e. that F is a mapping.

Let V be an arbitrary neighbourhood of the point $F(x) \in Y$. Since $\{F(x)\} = \bigcap_{U \in \mathfrak{B}(x)} \overline{f(A \cap U)} \subset V$, we infer by Corollary 2 to Theorem 1.3 that there exist a finite number of sets $U_1, U_2, \ldots, U_k \in \mathfrak{B}(x)$ such that

$$\overline{f(A \cap U_1)} \cap \overline{f(A \cap U_2)} \cap \ldots \cap \overline{f(A \cap U_k)} \subset V. \tag{2}$$

Evidently $U_1 \cap U_2 \cap \ldots \cap U_k = U \in \mathfrak{B}(x)$, and in view of (1) and (2) we have for every $x' \in U$ that $F(x') \in \overline{f(A \cap U)} \subset V$, i.e. $F(U) \subset V$. ■

Theorem 1 implies

THEOREM 2. *Every compact space of weight* $\mathfrak{m} \geqslant \aleph_0$ *is a continuous image of a closed subspace of the Cantor cube* $D^{\mathfrak{m}}$.

Proof. Let Y be a compact space of weight $\mathfrak{m}$. By virtue of Theorem 2.3.9, Y is homeomorphic to a subset of the Alexandroff cube $F^{\mathfrak{m}} = \boldsymbol{P}_{s \in S} F_s$, where $\overline{\overline{S}} = \mathfrak{m}$. We shall simply assume that $Y \subset F^{\mathfrak{m}}$. Let us denote by $\mathfrak{B}$ the base of the space $F^{\mathfrak{m}}$ consisting of sets of the form $\bigcap_{i=1}^{k} p_{s_i}^{-1}(0)$, where $p_s \colon F^{\mathfrak{m}} \to F_s$ is the projection onto the s-th axis. The spaces $D^{\mathfrak{m}}$ and $F^{\mathfrak{m}}$ considered as sets of points are identical. The elements of the base $\mathfrak{B}$ are open-and-closed in the space $D^{\mathfrak{m}}$. Thus the topology in $D^{\mathfrak{m}}$ is stronger and the identity function h of the space $D^{\mathfrak{m}}$ onto $F^{\mathfrak{m}}$ is a mapping.

We shall show that the assumptions of Theorem 1 are satisfied for $A = h^{-1}(Y)$, $X = \overline{A} \subset D^{\mathfrak{m}}$, and $f = h|A \colon A \to Y$.

Let B_1 and B_2 be closed and disjoint subsets of the space Y. There exist closed subsets $K_1, K_2 \subset F^{\mathfrak{m}}$ such that $B_i = Y \cap K_i$ for $i = 1, 2$. Since $B_1 \cap B_2 = 0$, $Y \subset F^{\mathfrak{m}} \setminus (K_1 \cap K_2)$ holds. This set is open; therefore, for every $x \in Y$ there exists a $U_x \in \mathfrak{B}$ such that $x \in U_x \subset F^{\mathfrak{m}} \setminus (K_1 \cap K_2)$. By virtue of Theorem 1.3, there exists a finite set $\{x_1, x_2, \ldots, x_k\} \subset Y$ such that

$$Y \subset U = U_{x_1} \cup U_{x_2} \cup \ldots \cup U_{x_k} \subset F^{\mathfrak{m}} \setminus (K_1 \cap K_2).$$

The set U is open-and-closed in the space $D^{\mathfrak{m}}$ and it contains A, whence

$$X = \bar{A} \subset U \subset D^{\mathfrak{m}} \setminus (K_1 \cap K_2).$$

Since $f^{-1}(B_i) = A \cap K_i \subset \bar{A} \cap K_i$ for $i = 1, 2$, $\overline{f^{-1}(B_1)} \cap \overline{f^{-1}(B_2)} \subset \bar{A} \cap K_1 \cap K_2 \subset [D^{\mathfrak{m}} \setminus (K_1 \cap K_2)] \cap K_1 \cap K_2 = 0$ holds.

By virtue of Theorem 1, there exists an extension $F: X \to Y$ of the mapping f and since $f(A) = Y$, Y is the continuous image of the closed set $X \subset D^{\mathfrak{m}}$. ∎

We shall proceed now to the sum of compact spaces.

THEOREM 3. *The sum* $\bigoplus_{s \in S} X_s$ *of disjoint and non-empty spaces* $\{X_s\}_{s \in S}$ *is compact if and only if the set* S *is finite and for every* $s \in S$ *the space* X_s *is compact.*

Proof. If the sum $\bigoplus_{s \in S} X_s$ is compact, then the set S must be finite, for otherwise, the open covering $\{X_s\}_{s \in S}$ would not contain any finite subcovering; since X_s is a closed subspace of the sum $\bigoplus_{s \in S} X_s$, it is compact.

By virtue of Theorem 2.2.4, the space $X = \bigoplus_{i=1}^{k} X_i$, where X_i are disjoint compact spaces, is a Hausdorff space. Its compactness follows therefore from Corollary 1 to Theorem 1.3. ∎

We shall now consider properties of the Cartesian product of compact spaces. The following theorem is basic in this subject and fundamental for general topology:

THEOREM 4 (Tychonoff). *The Cartesian product* $\boldsymbol{P}_{s \in S} X_s$ *of a family* $\{X_s\}_{s \in S}$ *of non-empty topological spaces is compact if and only if* X_s *is a compact space for every* $s \in S$.

Proof. If $\boldsymbol{P}_{s \in S} X_s$ is a compact space, then we infer from Theorem 2.3.6 that X_s is a Hausdorff space for every $s \in S$, and it follows from Theorem 1.8 that X_s is compact because $p_s: \boldsymbol{P}_{s \in S} X_s \to X_s$ is a mapping onto the space X_s.

Let us now assume that $\{X_s\}_{s \in S}$ is a family of compact spaces. By virtue of Theorem 2.3.6, the Cartesian product $\boldsymbol{P}_{s \in S} X_s$ is a Hausdorff space. Let us consider an arbitrary family $\mathfrak{F}_0$ of closed subsets of the product $\boldsymbol{P}_{s \in S} X_s$ which has the finite intersection property. Since the finite intersection property is of finite character, it follows from Tukey's Lemma that the family $\mathfrak{F}_0$ is contained in a maximal family $\mathfrak{F}$ which has the finite intersection property.

In order to prove that the intersection of all elements of the family $\mathfrak{F}_0$ is non-empty it suffices to show that there exists a point $x \in \underset{s\in S}{\boldsymbol{P}} X_s$ such that

(3) $$x \in \bar{A} \quad \text{for every } A \in \mathfrak{F}.$$

By the maximality of $\mathfrak{F}$,

(4) $$\text{if } A_1, A_2, \ldots, A_k \in \mathfrak{F}, \text{ then } A_1 \cap A_2 \cap \ldots \cap A_k \in \mathfrak{F}$$

and

(5) $$\text{if } A_0 \subset \underset{s\in S}{\boldsymbol{P}} X_s \text{ and } A_0 \cap A \neq 0 \text{ for every } A \in \mathfrak{F}, \text{ then } A_0 \in \mathfrak{F}.$$

Since $\mathfrak{F}$ has the finite intersection property, the family $\mathfrak{F}_s = \{\overline{p_s(A)}\}_{A\in\mathfrak{F}}$ of closed subsets of the space X_s also has this property for every $s \in S$. For every $s \in S$ there exists therefore a point $x_s \in X_s$ such that

$$x_s \in \bigcap_{A\in\mathfrak{F}} \overline{p_s(A)}.$$

Let W_s be an arbitrary neighbourhood of the point x_s in the space X_s. By the above formula $W_s \cap p_s(A) \neq 0$ holds for every $A \in \mathfrak{F}$, i.e.

$$p_s^{-1}(W_s) \cap A \neq 0 \quad \text{for every } A \in \mathfrak{F}.$$

By virtue of (5), we have $p_s^{-1}(W_s) \in \mathfrak{F}$ and we infer from (4) that every set of the form

$$\underset{s\in S}{\boldsymbol{P}} W_s = \bigcap_{s\in S} p_s^{-1}(W_s),$$

where $W_s \subset X_s$ is an open set containing x_s for every $s \in S$ and $W_s \neq X_s$ only for a finite number of $s \in S$, also belongs to the family $\mathfrak{F}$. It follows from (5) that an arbitrary neighbourhood of the point $x = \{x_s\}$ in the space $\underset{s\in S}{\boldsymbol{P}} X_s$ belongs to $\mathfrak{F}$, whence it intersects every set $A \in \mathfrak{F}$. Thus we conclude that (3) is valid. ■

Theorems 4 and 2.3.8 yield the following two theorems:

THEOREM 5. *For every $\mathfrak{m} \geqslant \aleph_0$ the Tychonoff cube $I^{\mathfrak{m}}$ is a universal space for compact spaces of weight $\mathfrak{m}$.* ■

THEOREM 6. *A space X is a Tychonoff space if and only if it is embeddable in a compact space.* ■

EXAMPLE 1. From Theorem 4 and 1.7 it follows that the space considered in Example 2.3.3 is normal. At the same time another example of a non-normal subspace of a normal space follows from Theorem 4 and Theorem 2.3.8. Namely, the Tychonoff cube $I^{\mathfrak{c}}$ contains a space homeomorphic to the non-normal Tychonoff space considered in Example 1.2.2. ■

A subset A of the Euclidean space R^n is said to be *bounded* provided that there exists a closed segment $J = [a, b] \subset R$ such that $A \subset J^n \subset R^n$. A continuous real-valued function $f: X \to R$ defined on a topological space X is said to be *bounded* if $f(X)$ is a bounded subset of R.

We are now able to characterize compact subspaces of Euclidean spaces.

THEOREM 7. *A subspace A of the Euclidean space R^n is compact if and only if the set A is closed and bounded.*

Proof. Let A be a compact subspace of R^n. The set A is closed by Theorem 1.6. Since $A \subset \bigcup_{i=1}^{\infty} K_i^n$, where $K_i = (-i, i)$, and since $K_i^n \subset K_j^n$ for $i \leqslant j$, there exists a natural number i_0 such that $A \subset K_{i_0}^n$. Hence it follows that $A \subset J^n$, where $J = [-i_0, i_0]$, i.e. A is a bounded set. A closed and bounded set is compact by Theorem 1.2, because it follows from the Tychonoff Theorem that the space J^n, where $J = [a, b]$, is compact. ■

COROLLARY. *Every real-valued continuous function $f: X \to R$ defined on a compact space X is bounded and the set of its values contains its bounds.* ■

We shall prove one more theorem connected with the Cartesian product of compact spaces.

THEOREM 8. *Let X be a compact space and let Y denote an arbitrary topological space. The projection $p: X \times Y \to Y$ is a closed mapping; in other words, the projection parallel to a compact axis is closed.*

Proof. Let $F = \overline{F} \subset X \times Y$. We have to show that $p(F)$ is a closed set.

Let us assume that $y_0 \in \overline{p(F)}$. Now for every neighbourhood V of the point y_0, $V \cap p(F) \neq 0$ holds, so that the set

$$A_V = \{x \in X: (x, y) \in F \text{ for some } y \in V\}$$

is non-empty. The family $\{\overline{A}_V\}_{V \in \mathfrak{B}}$, where $\mathfrak{B}$ is the family of all neighbourhoods of the point y_0, has the finite intersection property because $A_{V_1 \cap V_2} \subset A_{V_1} \cap A_{V_2}$, and consists of closed subsets of the space X. Let us denote by x_0 the point which belongs to all sets $\overline{A}_V$. For arbitrary neighbourhoods U, V of the points x_0 and y_0 respectively, we have $A_V \cap U \neq 0$. Hence $(U \times V) \cap F \neq 0$ holds, and since the set F is closed, $(x_0, y_0) \in F$ and $y_0 \in p(F)$. ■

We shall now examine the quotient spaces of compact spaces. Here is the basic theorem concerning this subject:

THEOREM 9 (Alexandroff). *For every closed equivalence relation R in a compact space X there exist: exactly one (up to a homeomorphism) compact space Y and a mapping $f: X \to Y$ onto Y such that $R = R(f)$, namely, the quotient space X/R and the natural mapping $\varphi: X \to X/R$.*

In other words, every closed equivalence relation in a compact space is determined by a mapping.

Conversely, the relation $R(f)$ is closed for every mapping $f: X \to Y$ onto a Hausdorff space Y.

Proof. It follows from Theorems 1.8 and 2.4.5 that X/R is compact, and the equality $R = R(\varphi)$ is obvious. Let us now assume that $f: X \to Y$ is a mapping onto a compact space and that $R = R(f)$. By Theorems 1.9 and 2.4.3, the space Y is homeomorphic to the space $X/R(f) = X/R$.

On the other hand, if $f: X \to Y$ is an arbitrary mapping onto a Hausdorff space Y, then by virtue of the same theorems, the natural mapping $\varphi: X \to X/R(f)$ is closed and we infer from Theorem 2.4.4 that the relation $R(f)$ is closed. ■

EXAMPLE 2. Let R^2 denote the Euclidean plane and let $f: R^2 \to R$ be the projection onto the first axis. The relation $R(f)$ is not closed, because the union of all equivalence classes which intersect the closed set $F = \{(x, y): xy = 1\}$, is not closed.

It follows from Corollary 2 to Theorem 1.11 that if X is a compact space and S denotes a closed equivalence relation in X, then the weight of the space X/S does not exceed the weight of the space X. We shall now show that the assumption that X is compact is essential.

Let us consider in the plane R^2 the relation S determined by the decomposition of R^2 into the set $A = \{(x, 0): x \in R\}$ and individual points of the set $R^2 \setminus A$. It can easily be observed that S is a closed relation.

Let $a \in X = R^2/S$ be the equivalence class corresponding to the set A. We shall show that the space X has no countable base at the point a.

For every open set $V \subset R^2$ such that $A \subset V$ the equality $\varphi^{-1}\varphi(V) = V$ holds, hence $\varphi(V)$ is a neighbourhood of the point $a \in X$. Let $\{U_i\}_{i=1}^{\infty}$ be a countable family of neighbourhoods of the point $a \in X$. From each of the sets $\varphi^{-1}(U_i) \setminus A$ let us choose a point $a_i = (x_i, y_i)$ satisfying the condition $x_i \geqslant i$. The set $V = R^2 \setminus \bigcup_{i=1}^{\infty} \{a_i\}$ is an open set containing A and the set $\varphi(V)$ is a neighbourhood of the point a which does not contain any of the sets U_i. Thus the space X does not possess any countable base at the point a. Hence the weight of the space X is greater than the weight of the plane, which is equal to $\aleph_0$. ■

We shall now consider inverse systems of compact spaces. We shall prove two theorems.

THEOREM 10. *The limit of an inverse system $\boldsymbol{S} = \{X_\sigma, \pi_\varrho^\sigma, \Sigma\}$ of compact spaces is compact. If $X_\sigma \neq 0$ for every $\sigma \in \Sigma$, then $\underleftarrow{\lim} \boldsymbol{S} \neq 0$.*

Proof. The first part of the theorem follows directly from Theorems 2.5.1, 1.2, and the Tychonoff Theorem.

Let us now assume that $X_\sigma \neq 0$ for every $\sigma \in \Sigma$. Let

$$Z_\varrho = \Big\{\{x_\sigma\} \in \mathop{\boldsymbol{P}}_{\sigma\in\Sigma} X_\sigma \colon \pi^\varrho_\sigma(x_\varrho) = x_\sigma \text{ for } \sigma \leqslant \varrho\Big\}.$$

We shall prove that $Z_\varrho \neq 0$ for every $\varrho \in \Sigma$. Let us consider an arbitrary point $y_\varrho \in X_\varrho \neq 0$, let $y_\varrho = \pi^\varrho_\sigma(y_\varrho)$ for $\sigma \leqslant \varrho$, and let y_σ be an arbitrary element of X_σ for the remaining $\sigma \in \Sigma$. It can easily be observed that $\{y_\sigma\} \in Z_\varrho$, so that $Z_\varrho \neq 0$. It follows from Theorem 1.5.2 that Z_ϱ is a closed subset of $\mathop{\boldsymbol{P}}_{\sigma\in\Sigma} X_\sigma$. Furthermore, it is evident that

$$Z_{\varrho_1} \subset Z_{\varrho_2} \quad \text{for} \quad \varrho_2 \leqslant \varrho_1 .$$

The family $\{Z_\varrho\}_{\varrho\in\Sigma}$ consists of closed subsets of the Cartesian product $\mathop{\boldsymbol{P}}_{\sigma\in\Sigma} X_\sigma$ and, since the set Σ is directed, it has the finite intersection property. Therefore by the Tychonoff Theorem, $\bigcap_{\varrho\in\Sigma} Z_\varrho \neq 0$, which in view of the obvious equality $\varprojlim \boldsymbol{S} = \bigcap_{\varrho\in\Sigma} Z_\varrho$, completes the proof of our theorem. ■

THEOREM 11. *If for an inverse system $\boldsymbol{S} = \{X_\sigma, \pi^\sigma_\varrho, \Sigma\}$ of compact spaces the equality $\pi^\sigma_\varrho(X_\sigma) = X_\varrho$ holds for all $\sigma, \varrho \in \Sigma$ such that $\varrho \leqslant \sigma$, then for every $\varrho \in \Sigma$ we have $\pi_\varrho(X) = X_\varrho$, where $X = \varprojlim \boldsymbol{S}$ is the limit of the system and π_ϱ denotes its projection onto X_ϱ.*

Proof. Let us suppose that for some $\varrho \in \Sigma$ there exists a point $y_\varrho \in X_\varrho \setminus \pi_\varrho(X)$. Let $\Sigma' = \{\sigma \in \Sigma \colon \varrho \leqslant \sigma\}$ and $Y_\sigma = (\pi^\sigma_\varrho)^{-1}(y_\varrho)$ for every $\sigma \in \Sigma'$. Since $\pi^\sigma_\tau(Y_\sigma) = Y_\tau$ for $\sigma, \tau \in \Sigma'$ such that $\tau \leqslant \sigma$, we infer that $\{Y_\sigma, \pi^\sigma_\tau | Y_\sigma, \Sigma'\}$ is an inverse system of non-empty compact spaces. By virtue of Theorem 10, the limit Y' of the system is non-empty. It can easily be noted that $Y' \subset X' = \varprojlim \boldsymbol{S}'$, where $\boldsymbol{S}' = \{X_\sigma, \pi^\sigma_\varrho, \Sigma'\}$; thus, in particular, $y_\varrho \in \pi_\varrho(Y') \subset \pi_\varrho(X')$. According to Corollary 1 to Theorem 2.5.4, the mapping $f\colon X \to X'$ defined as the restriction of threads from X to the set Σ' is a homeomorphism. Since $\varrho \in \Sigma'$, we obtain $\pi_\varrho(X') = \pi_\varrho(X)$ and $y_\varrho \in \pi_\varrho(X)$, contrary to the assumption. ■

To complete this paragraph we shall prove an important theorem on the space of real-valued continuous functions defined on a compact space. The study of the mapping space is included into the next paragraph.

A family $P \subset R^X$ or real-valued continuous functions defined on the topological space X is called a *ring of functions* provided that for every $f, g \in P$ the functions $f+g, f-g$, and $f\cdot g$ also belong to P.

The considerations of Paragraph 1.4 imply that the family R^X is a ring of functions. It follows from Theorem 1.4.2 that this family is closed with respect to uniform convergence. Furthermore, if X is a Tychonoff space, then the family R^X separates points of the space X, i.e.

for every pair of distinct points $p, q \in X$ there exists an $f \in R^X$ such that $f(p) \neq f(q)$. Moreover, R^X contains all constant functions. For compact spaces the inverse theorem is valid, i.e. every ring of real-valued continuous functions defined on a compact space X which satisfies the above conditions coincides with R^X. The proof of this theorem follows from three lemmas. Lemma 2 is a well-known theorem of analysis. It is included here in order to make the book complete. Lemma 1 is used only in the proof of Lemma 2.

LEMMA 1. *Let X be a compact space and let $\{f_i\}$ be a sequence of real-valued continuous functions defined on X and satisfying the condition $f_i(x) \leqslant f_{i+1}(x)$ for $x \in X$ and $i = 1, 2, \ldots$ If for a function $f \in R^X$ we have $f(x) = \lim f_i(x)$ for every $x \in X$, then $f = \lim f_i$, i.e. the sequence $f_1, f_2, \ldots$ is uniformly convergent to the function f.*

Proof. Let ε be a positive number. For every $a \in X$ there exists a natural number $i(a)$ such that

$$0 \leqslant f(a) - f_{i(a)}(a) \leqslant \varepsilon/3 .$$

By the continuity of the functions $f_{i(a)}$ and f, there exists a neighbourhood U_a of the point a such that

$$|f_{i(a)}(x) - f_{i(a)}(a)| < \varepsilon/3 \quad \text{and} \quad |f(x) - f(a)| < \varepsilon/3 \quad \text{for} \quad x \in U_a .$$

Thus for $x \in U_a$ we have $0 \leqslant f(x) - f_{i(a)}(x) < \varepsilon$. Let us choose a finite covering $\{U_{a_j}\}_{j=1}^{k}$ from the covering $\{U_a\}_{a \in X}$ of the space X and let $i_0 = \max\big(i(a_1), i(a_2), \ldots, i(a_k)\big)$. Let us consider an $i \geqslant i_0$ and a point $x \in X$. There exists a $j \leqslant k$ such that $x \in U_{a_j}$. Making use of the inequality $f_{i(a_j)}(x) \leqslant f_{i_0}(x) \leqslant f_i(x)$ we have

$$0 \leqslant f(x) - f_i(x) \leqslant f(x) - f_{i(a_j)}(x) < \varepsilon .$$

Thus the proof is completed. ∎

LEMMA 2. *There exists a sequence $\{w_i\}$ of polynomials which is uniformly convergent on the segment I to the function $\sqrt{t}$.*

Proof. We define the sequence $\{w_i\}$ by the inductive formulas:

$$(6) \qquad w_1(t) = 0, \qquad w_{i+1}(t) = w_i(t) + \tfrac{1}{2}\big(t - w_i^2(t)\big) \quad \text{for} \quad i \geqslant 1,\ t \in I .$$

We shall prove, by means of induction, that

$$(7) \qquad w_i(t) \leqslant \sqrt{t} \quad \text{for} \quad t \in I \text{ and } i = 1, 2, \ldots$$

Inequality (7) is valid for $i = 0$. Let us assume that $w_n(t) \leqslant \sqrt{t}$. Since

$$\sqrt{t} - w_{n+1}(t) = \sqrt{t} - w_n(t) - \tfrac{1}{2}\big(t - w_n^2(t)\big) = \big(\sqrt{t} - w_n(t)\big) \cdot \big(1 - \tfrac{1}{2}(\sqrt{t} + w_n(t))\big),$$

from the inductive assumption and the inequality $t \leqslant 1$ we obtain

$$\sqrt{t}-w_{n+1}(t) \geqslant \big(\sqrt{t}-w_n(t)\big)\cdot(1-\tfrac{1}{2}2\sqrt{t}) \geqslant 0,$$

and the proof of (7) is completed.

Formulas (6) and (7) imply that $w_i(t) \leqslant w_{i+1}(t)$ for $t \in I$ and $i = 1, 2, \ldots$ Making use of (7) we infer that for every $t \in I$ there exists a limit $f(t)$ of the sequence $w_i(t)$. Assuming that $i \to \infty$ in the second formula of (6) we infer that $f(t) = \sqrt{t}$ for $t \in I$. Lemma 1 implies that $f = \lim w_i$. ■

LEMMA 3. *Let P be a ring of real-valued continuous and bounded functions defined on the topological space X. If P contains all constant functions and is closed with respect to uniform convergence, then for arbitrary functions $f, g \in P$ the functions $|f|$, $\max(f, g)$, and $\min(f, g)$ also belong to P.*

Proof. Since

$$\min(f, g) = \tfrac{1}{2}(f+g-|f-g|), \quad \text{and} \quad \max(f, g) = \tfrac{1}{2}(f+g+|f-g|),$$

it is sufficient to prove that if $f \in P$, then $|f| \in P$. Let $f \in P$ and let c denote a real number such that $|f(x)| \leqslant c$ for all $x \in X$. Since it is sufficient to show that $(1/c)\cdot|f| \in P$, we can assume that $|f(x)| \leqslant 1$ for $x \in X$. Making use of Lemma 2 we infer that the function $|f| = \sqrt{f^2}$ is a limit of a uniformly convergent sequence $f_1, f_2, \ldots$ of functions belonging to P, where $f_i(x) = w_i\big(f^2(x)\big)$. ■

THEOREM 12 (Stone-Weierstrass). *If X is a compact space, then an arbitrary ring P of real-valued continuous functions defined on X which contains constant functions, separates points of the space X, is closed with respect to the uniform convergence (i.e. closed in the space R^X with the topology of uniform convergence), and is identical with the ring of all real-valued continuous functions defined on X.*

Proof. It is sufficient to prove that for each real-valued continuous function f defined on X and for every $\varepsilon > 0$ there exists a function $f_\varepsilon \in P$ such that $|f(x)-f_\varepsilon(x)| < \varepsilon$ for every $x \in X$.

For every pair $a, b \in X$ one can find a function $h \in P$ such that $h(a) \neq h(b)$. The function g defined by means of the formula $g(x) = \big(h(x)-h(a)\big)\cdot\big(h(b)-h(a)\big)^{-1}$ belongs to P and $g(a) = 0$, $g(b) = 1$. For real numbers r_1 and r_2 the function $(r_2-r_1)g+r_1$, which assumes the value r_1 at the point a and the value r_2 at the point b, belongs to P.

For every pair of points $a, b \in X$ there exists, therefore, a function $f_{a,b} \in P$ such that

$$|f(a)-f_{a,b}(a)| < \varepsilon \quad \text{and} \quad |f(b)-f_{a,b}(b)| < \varepsilon.$$

Let us now consider the neighbourhoods

$$U_{a,b} = \{x: f_{a,b}(x) < f(x)+\varepsilon\} \quad \text{and} \quad V_{a,b} = \{x: f_{a,b}(x) > f(x)-\varepsilon\}$$

of the points a and b.

For a fixed $b \in X$ let us choose a finite subcovering $\{U_{a_i,b}\}_{i=1}^k$ from the covering $\{U_{a,b}\}_{a \in X}$. Let us denote by f_b the minimum of the functions of the family $\{f_{a_i,b}\}_{i=1}^k$. By Lemma 3, $f_b \in P$. Furthermore, $f_b(x) < f(x)+\varepsilon$ for $x \in X$ and $f_b(x) > f(x)-\varepsilon$ for $x \in V_b = \bigcap_{i=1}^{k} V_{a_i,b}$.

The set V_b is a neighbourhood of the point $b \in X$. From the covering $\{V_b\}_{b \in X}$ of the space X a finite subcovering $\{V_{b_i}\}_{i=1}^l$ can be chosen. Let us denote by f_ε the maximum of the functions of the family $\{f_{b_i}\}_{i=1}^l$. It can easily be verified that

$$f_\varepsilon \in P \quad \text{and} \quad |f_\varepsilon(x)-f(x)| < \varepsilon \quad \text{for} \quad x \in X. \ \blacksquare$$

The importance of the Stone-Weierstrass Theorem lies in the fact, that it implies the method of uniform approximation of real-valued continuous functions defined on a compact space X. Namely, every real-valued continuous function defined on X can be approximated with arbitrary accuracy by polynomials (in many variables) of functions from an arbitrary family which separates points of the space X. Since the function $f: J \to R$, where $f(x) = x$, separates points of every closed segment $J \subset R$, Theorem 12 implies the classical theorem of Weierstrass, which states that every continuous function on J is the limit of a uniformly convergent sequence of polynomials.

EXAMPLE 3. We shall show here that the assumption of the compactness of the space X in Theorem 12 is essential. In fact, it is easy to observe that the ring P, which is the closure in R^R with the topology of uniform convergence of the set of functions defined on the real-line and constant outside a bounded segment, satisfies all the assumptions of Theorem 12. Since the function $f(x) = \sin x$ does not belong to P, P is not the ring of all continuous functions defined on P. $\blacksquare$

EXERCISES

A (S. Eilenberg and N. Steenrod [1952]). Prove the following theorem, dual to Theorem 1:

Let A be a dense subset of the space X and let f denote a mapping of A into a compact space Y. The mapping f can be extended over X if and only if for every finite open covering $\{V_i\}_{i=1}^k$ of the space Y there exists a finite open covering $\{U_i\}_{i=1}^l$ of the space X such that the covering $\{U_i \cap A\}_{i=1}^l$ is a refinement of the covering $\{f^{-1}(V_i)\}_{i=1}^k$.

B. Show that the formula

$$f(\{x_i\}) = \sum_{i=1}^{\infty} \frac{x_i}{2^i}$$

defines a mapping of the Cantor set $D^{\aleph_0}$ onto the segment I. Verify that there exists a countable set $A \subset I$ such that the inverse image of every point from A contains exactly two points of the Cantor set, and the inverse image of every point from the set $I\setminus A$ contains exactly one point.

Note that Theorem 2 follows from the existence of a mapping of the Cantor set onto a segment.

C. The set of points of the form $(1-t)x+ty$, where $x, y\in R^n$, $0\leqslant t\leqslant 1$ and where addition of points and multiplication by a number are defined as on page 296, is called the *segment* with *end-points* x and y. The set of points of the form $(1-t)x+ty$, where $t>0$ and $x\neq y$ is called the *ray* starting at the point x and passing through the point y. A subset A of the space R^n is said to be *convex* if for every $x, y\in A$ the segment with the end-points x, y is contained in A.

Show that every compact and convex subset $A\subset R^n$ such that $\operatorname{Int}A\neq 0$, is homeomorphic to the ball Q^n, while its boundary $\operatorname{Fr}A$ is homeomorphic to the sphere S^{n-1}. In particular, it follows that the spaces I^n and Q^n are homeomorphic. The same holds for the spaces $\operatorname{Fr}I^n$ and S^{n-1}, $n = 1, 2, \ldots$

Hint: Let $x\in\operatorname{Int}A$ and show that every ray starting from the point x intersects the set $\operatorname{Fr}A$ exactly at one point.

D. Making use of Theorem 8, show that a function f of the space X into a compact space Y is a mapping if and only if its graph, i.e. the set $\{(x, f(x)) : x\in X\}$, is closed in $X\times Y$.

E. Show that if X is a compact space, then an equivalence relation R in the space X is closed if and only if R is a closed subset of $X\times X$.

F. (a) (Y. Mibu [1944]) Let $\{X_s\}_{s\in S}$ be a family of compact spaces. Making use of the Stone-Weierstrass Theorem, show that every continuous function $f\colon \mathbf{P}_{s\in S} X_s\to R$ depends only on a countable number of coordinates (see Problem 2.R).

(b) Let T be the discrete space of power $\mathfrak{c}$. Define a mapping, depending on uncountably many coordinates, of the Cartesian product $X = T\times \mathbf{P}_{t\in T} D_t$, where $D_t = D = \{0, 1\}$ is the discrete two-point space for every $t\in T$, into D.

Hint: Consider the decomposition of the space X into open-and-closed sets $A_{t,i} = \{x\in X : p(x) = t \text{ and } p_t(x) = i\}$, where $t\in T$, $i\in D$, p is the projection of X onto T, and p_t is the projection onto D_t.

G. Show that for a Tychonoff space X each of the following conditions is a consequence of the preceding one, and that for a compact space X all the conditions are equivalent:

(i) The space R^X with the topology of uniform convergence contains a dense subset of power $\leqslant\mathfrak{m}$.

(ii) X has a base of power $\leqslant\mathfrak{m}$.

(iii) R^X contains a subset of power $\leqslant\mathfrak{m}$ which separates points of X.

Deduce Corollary 1 to Theorem 1.11 and Corollary 2 to that theorem under the additional assumption that X is compact.

Hint: When deducing the second corollary, note that if there exists a mapping f of X onto Y, then R^Y is embeddable in R^X and, making use of Exercise 2.6.A, verify that if R^X contains a dense subset of power $\leqslant\mathfrak{m}$, it also has a base of power $\leqslant\mathfrak{m}$.

H (M. H. Stone [1947]). Making use of the Stone-Weierstrass Theorem, show that if X is a Tychonoff space and A a compact subspace of it, then every real-valued function $f\colon A\to R$ is extendable over X. Further show that if $f(A)\subset J$, where J is a closed interval, then there exists an extension F of the function f such that $F(X)\subset J$.

§ 3. Mapping spaces: the compact-open topology. Let X and Y be arbitrary topological spaces. We denote the set of all mappings of the space X into Y by Y^X. In Chapter 2 we have defined the topology of pointwise convergence in the set Y^X assuming that the base consists of the intersections $\bigcap_{i=1}^{k} M(S_i, U_i)$, where

$$M(A, B) = \{f \in Y^X : f(A) \subset B\},$$

$S_i \subset X$ is finite, and $U_i \subset Y$ is open for $i = 1, 2, \ldots, k$.

The topology generated by the base consisting of the sets of the form $\bigcap_{i=1}^{k} M(Z_i, U_i)$, where $Z_i \subset X$ is a compact subspace of the space X and $U_i \subset Y$ is an open subset of Y for $i = 1, 2, \ldots, k$, is called the *compact-open topology* in the set Y^X. Since the space consisting of a single point is compact, and for every finite $S = \{x_1, x_2, \ldots, x_n\} \subset X$ the equality $M(S, U) = \bigcap_{i=1}^{k} M(\{x_i\}, U)$ holds, every set open with respect to the topology of pointwise convergence is also open with respect to the compact-open topology. The compact-open topology is therefore stronger than the pointwise topology. It follows from the corollary to Theorem 2.6.3, that if Y is a T_i-space for $i \leqslant 2$, then Y^X with the compact-open topology is also a T_i-space. We shall now show that an analogous theorem is valid for regular and Tychonoff spaces.

LEMMA. *Let X and Y be arbitrary topological spaces. For every set $A \subset X$ and a closed set $B \subset Y$ the set $M(A, B)$ is closed in the space Y^X with the compact-open topology.*

Proof. Evidently

$$M(A, B) = \bigcap_{x \in A} M(\{x\}, B)$$

holds; since $M(\{x\}, B) = Y^X \setminus M(\{x\}, Y \setminus B)$ is closed for every $x \in A$, the set $M(A, B)$ is also closed. ■

THEOREM 1. *If Y is a regular space, then the space Y^X with the compact-open topology is also regular.*

Proof. Let $f: X \to Y$ be an arbitrary mapping. By virtue of Theorem 1.5.3, it is sufficient to show that for every set $P(Z, U)$ containing f, where Z is a compact subset of X and U is an open subset of Y, there exists a set V open in Y and such that

(1) $$f \in M(Z, V) \subset \overline{M(Z, V)} \subset M(Z, U).$$

Theorems 1.8 and 1.4 imply that there exists an open set $V \subset Y$ such that

(2) $$f(Z) \subset V \subset \overline{V} \subset U.$$

Furthermore, $\overline{M(Z, V)} \subset M(Z, \overline{V})$ holds, because $M(Z, \overline{V})$ is closed by the lemma. Thus (1) follows from (2). ■

LEMMA 1. *Let X be a topological space and let $Z \subset X$ denote a compact subspace. For each function $f \in R^X$ let us define $\Phi(f) = \sup_{x \in Z} f(x)$. The function Φ is continuous with respect to the compact-open topology in R^X, i.e. $\Phi\colon R^X \to R$.*

Proof. Suppose that $(a, b) \subset R$ is an arbitrary open segment. We shall show that $\Phi^{-1}\big((a, b)\big)$ is open in R^X. Since open segments form a base in R, this will imply the conclusion of the lemma. From the Corollary to Theorem 2.7 it follows that $\sup_{x \in Z} f(x) < b$ if and only if $f(x) < b$ for every $x \in Z$. We thus have

$$\Phi^{-1}\big((a, b)\big) = \big(R^X \setminus M(Z, A)\big) \cap M(Z, B),$$

where $A = \{x \in R\colon x \leqslant a\}$ and $B = \{x \in R\colon x < b\}$. By virtue of the Lemma to Theorem 1, $\Phi^{-1}\big((a, b)\big)$ is open. ■

LEMMA 2. *Let X, Y, and T be topological spaces, and let $g\colon Y \to T$ denote a fixed mapping. Let us consider the spaces Y^X and T^X with the compact-open topology. Let $\Phi(f) = gf$ for every $f \in Y^X$. The function Φ is a mapping, $\Phi\colon Y^X \to T^X$.*

The proof follows from the equalities:

$$\Phi^{-1}\big(M(Z, U)\big) = \{f\colon gf(Z) \subset U\} = \{f\colon f(Z) \subset g^{-1}(U)\} = M\big(Z, g^{-1}(U)\big). \ ■$$

THEOREM 2. *If Y is a Tychonoff space, then the space Y^X with the compact-open topology is also a Tychonoff space.*

Proof. Let us consider an arbitrary $Z \subset X$, an open set $U \subset Y$, and $f \in M(Z, U)$. The set $A = f(Z)$ is compact and contained in the open set U, so that by Theorem 1.5, there exists a continuous function $g\colon Y \to I$ such that $g(A) \subset \{0\}$ and $g(y) = 1$ for $y \in Y \setminus U$. For every $h \in Y^X$ let us assume that

$$G(h) = \sup_{x \in Z} gh(x).$$

It follows from Lemmas 1 and 2 that G is a mapping; namely, $G\colon Y^X \to I$. Evidently $G(f) = 0$ holds, but $G(h) = 1$ for every $h \notin M(Z, U)$. Indeed, there exists a point $x \in Z$ such that $h(x) \in Y \setminus U$, whence $gh(x) = 1$. In order to complete the proof it is sufficient to make use of Theorem 1.5.4. ■

It can be easily seen that the space Y^X with the compact-open topology is, for a discrete space X, homeomorphic to the Cartesian product $\boldsymbol{P}_{x \in X} Y_x$, where $Y_x = Y$ for every $x \in X$. Since there exists a normal space whose Cartesian product by itself is not normal, the space Y^X is not necessarily normal for a normal space Y.

A topological space X is said to be a *k-space* provided that it is a Hausdorff space and a set $A \subset X$ is closed if and only if the intersection $A \cap Z$ is closed for every compact $Z \subset X$.

Every compact space is evidently a k-space.

THEOREM 3. *Every Hausdorff space X which satisfies the first axiom of countability is a k-space.*

Proof. Let us suppose that $A \neq \bar{A}$ for $A \subset X$. We shall show that there exists a compact subspace $Z \subset X$ such that the intersection $A \cap Z$ is not closed. Let $x_0 \in \bar{A} \setminus A$ and let $\{V_i\}_{i=1}^{\infty}$ denote a countable base at the point x_0. Since $x_0 \in \bar{A}$, there exists an $x_i \in \bigcap_{j=1}^{i} V_j \cap A$ for every $i = 1, 2, \ldots$ Let us suppose that $Z = \{x_0, x_1, x_2, \ldots\}$. Since $x_0 \in \overline{A \cap Z} \setminus A \cap Z$, it is sufficient to note that Z is a compact space; but this is obvious, because Z is homeomorphic to the space of power $\aleph_0$ which has one accumulation point (see Example 1.1.2). ∎

Another class of k-spaces will be considered in Paragraph 6.

THEOREM 4. *Let X be a k-space and let f denote a function of the space X into an arbitrary space Y. If, for each compact $Z \subset X$, the restriction $f|Z$ is a mapping, then f is a mapping.*

Proof. Let A be a closed subset of the space Y. For every compact $Z \subset X$ the set $f^{-1}(A) \cap Z = (f|Z)^{-1}(A)$ is closed, from which we have that $f^{-1}(A)$ is also closed. ∎

Let $\mathfrak{Z}(X)$ denote the family of all compact subsets of a Hausdorff space X. The family $\mathfrak{Z}(X)$ is partially ordered by the relation $\leqslant$, which is defined by means of the condition:

$$Z_2 \leqslant Z_1 \text{ if and only if } Z_2 \subset Z_1.$$

Moreover, the family $\mathfrak{Z}(X)$ is directed, because in a Hausdorff space the union of two compact subspaces is compact. The mapping $\pi_{Z_2}^{Z_1}\colon Y^{Z_1} \to Y^{Z_2}$, where $\pi_{Z_2}^{Z_1}(f) = f|Z_2$ for $f \in Y^{Z_1}$, is defined for $Z_2 \leqslant Z_1$ and for arbitrary Y.

THEOREM 5. *If X is a k-space, then for every Y the space Y^X with the compact-open (pointwise) topology is homeomorphic to the limit of the inverse system $\{Y^Z, \pi_{Z_2}^{Z_1}, \mathfrak{Z}(X)\}$ of the spaces Y^Z with the compact-open (pointwise) topology.*

Proof. Let $f = \{f_Z\}_{Z \in \mathfrak{Z}(X)}$ be an element of the limit of our system. Let us assign to it the function $\varphi(f) = f'$ of the space X into Y, where $f'(x) = f_{\{x\}}(x)$. Evidently $f'|Z = f_Z$ holds for every $Z \in \mathfrak{Z}(X)$; thus by virtue of Theorem 4, $f' \in Y^X$. It can easily be verified that φ is a one-to-one function onto Y^X. Since, for $Z \in \mathfrak{Z}(X)$ and $A \subset Z$, we have that

$$\varphi(f) \in M(A, U) \text{ if and only if } f_Z \in M(A, U),$$

we conclude by virtue of Theorem 2.5.3, that φ is a homeomorphism. ∎

Let us suppose that topological spaces X and Y are given. A function φ which assigns the point $\varphi(f, x) = f(x) \in Y$ to every element $f \in Y^X$ and point $x \in X$, is defined in a natural way. Considering the various topologies in the mapping space, we may ask for which of them φ is a mapping of the Cartesian product $Y^X \times X$ into Y. It is evident that if we consider Y^X with the discrete topology, then $\varphi: Y^X \times X \to Y$. On the other hand, simple examples show that the function φ is not necessarily a mapping with respect to the pointwise topology. If φ is a mapping with respect to a topology $\mathfrak{O}_1$ in Y^X, then it is also a mapping with respect to every topology $\mathfrak{O}_2$ which is stronger than $\mathfrak{O}_1$. The problem of the weakest topologies under which φ is still a mapping can thus be raised. In this paragraph we are only able to prove the following theorem (cf. Theorem 6.11).

THEOREM 6. *If for a topology $\mathfrak{O}$ in the space Y^X the function φ of the Cartesian product $Y^X \times X$ into the space Y defined by means of the formula $\varphi(f, x) = f(x)$ is a mapping, then the topology $\mathfrak{O}$ is stronger than the compact-open topology.*

Proof. It is sufficient to show that the sets $M(Z, U)$, where $Z \subset X$ is compact and $U \subset Y$ is open, are open with respect to the topology $\mathfrak{O}$. Let $f \in M(Z, U)$. For every $x \in Z$ let V_x and $W_x \in \mathfrak{O}$ be neighbourhoods of the points $x \in X$ and $f \in Y^X$, such that $\varphi(W_x \times V_x) \subset U$. Let us choose a finite number of points $x_1, x_2, \ldots, x_k \in Z$ such that $Z \subset V_{x_1} \cup V_{x_2} \cup \ldots \cup X_{x_k}$. Let us assume that $W = \bigcap_{i=1}^{k} W_{x_i}$. It is easy to note that $f \in W \in \mathfrak{O}$ and $W \subset M(Z, U)$. Since f is an arbitrary point of $M(Z, U)$, it follows that $M(Z, U) \in \mathfrak{O}$. ∎

EXERCISES

A. Show that in the set I^I the compact-open topology is different from the pointwise topology.

B. Making use of the property of the space considered in Exercise 1.C show that Theorem 4 is not valid without the assumption that X is a k-space.

C. From the fact that the space considered in Exercise 1.C is normal deduce that a subset of a k-space is not necessarily a k-space. Show that a closed subset of a k-space is a k-space.

D. Prove that if X is a compact space, then the function φ of the space $Y^X \times X$ into Y defined by means of the formula $\varphi(f, x) = f(x)$ is a mapping with respect to the compact-open topology.

E (A. H. Stone [1963]). Verify that the space of mappings of the segment I into the Tychonoff cube I^c with the compact-open topology is not normal (cf. Exercise 7.E).

Hint: Show that for any space X and a family of spaces $\{Y_s\}_{s \in S}$ the spaces $(\boldsymbol{P}_{s \in S} Y_s)^X$ and $\boldsymbol{P}_{s \in S} (Y_s^X)$ are homeomorphic. Note that the space I^I contains a discrete space of power $\aleph_0$ as a closed subset and make use of Exercise 1.F.

§ 4. Compactifications. Let a topological space X be given. A pair (Y, c), where Y is a compact space and $c: X \to Y$ is a homeomorphic embedding of the space X into Y such that $\overline{c(X)} = Y$, is called a *compactification* of the space Y.

If the space X is embeddable in a compact space Y, i.e., if there exists a homeomorphism $f: X \to f(X) \subset Y$, then the pair $(\overline{f(X)}, f)$ is clearly a compactification of the space X. It follows, in particular, that spaces embeddable in compact spaces have compactifications.

Theorems 2.6 and 2.3.8 imply the following theorems:

THEOREM 1. *A topological space has a compactification if and only if it is a Tychonoff space.* ∎

THEOREM 2. *Every Tychonoff space X has a compactification (Y, c) such that $w(X) = w(Y)$.* ∎

In the sequel by a compactification we will understand the space Y itself in which X can be embedded as a dense subset (this is not exactly correct but convenient). Compactifications of the space X will be frequently denoted by the symbols cX, c_iX, aX, etc.; c, c_i, a denote simultaneously the homeomorphic embeddings into the correspondent compactification. Thus, when considering a compactification as a space, we shall always know which homeomorphism has been used to embed the space X in this compactification. Therefore, for a compactification cX of the space X we have

$c: X \to c(X) \subset cX$, where c is a homeomorphism and $\overline{c(X)} = cX$.

Compatifications c_1X and c_2X are said to be *equivalent* provided that there exists a homeomorphism $f: c_1X \to c_2X$ such that the diagram

$$\begin{array}{ccc} c_1X & \xrightarrow{f} & c_2X \\ {\scriptstyle c_1}\uparrow & \mathrm{id}_X & \uparrow{\scriptstyle c_2} \\ X & \longrightarrow & X \end{array}$$

is commutative, i.e. $fc_1(x) = c_2(x)$ for every $x \in X$.

Thus two compactifications are equivalent if they are homeomorphic and if the space X is embedded in them in the same manner. The reader can easily verify that the equivalence of compactifications is an equivalence relation.

It follows from the definition that every two compactifications of a compact space X are equivalent, whence every compactification of a compact space X is equivalent to X, i.e. X is clearly its own compactification. For, if cX is a compactification of a compact space X, then since $c(X)$ is closed and dense in cX, we have $c(X) = cX$ and c is a homeomorphism of X onto cX. For two given compactifications c_1X and c_2X of a compact space X we can assume that f is equal to $c_2c_1^{-1}$.

In the sequel we shall identify equivalent compactifications. We shall speak about the class of equivalent compactifications instead of individual compactifications, and this class will be denoted by the symbol cX, where cX is an arbitrary compactification belonging to the class.

We shall now estimate the weight and the power of a compactification of a given space X.

LEMMA 1. *A regular space X containing a dense subset X_0 of power $\mathfrak{m}$ has a base of power $\leqslant 2^{\mathfrak{m}}$.*

Proof. Let $\{U_s\}_{s\in S}$ be a base of the space X and let

$$V_s = \operatorname{Int}(\overline{U_s \cap X_0}). \tag{1}$$

We infer from Theorem 1.3.6 that $U_s \subset \operatorname{Int}(\overline{U_s \cap X_0}) \subset \overline{U}_s$, and since the space X is regular, the family $\{V_s\}_{s\in S}$ is also its base. It follows from (1) that the number of different sets V_s does not exceed the number of subsets of the set X_0, i.e. the number $2^{\mathfrak{m}}$. ■

LEMMA 2. *If a T_0-space X has a base of power $\leqslant \mathfrak{m}$, then $\overline{\overline{X}} \leqslant 2^{\mathfrak{m}}$.*

Proof. Every point of a T_0-space is determined by the family of the elements of a base which contain it. ■

The above lemmas along with Theorem 1.3.7 imply

THEOREM 3. *For every compactification Y of a space X we have $\overline{\overline{Y}} \leqslant 2^{2^{\mathfrak{m}}}$ and $w(Y) \leqslant 2^{\mathfrak{m}}$, where $\mathfrak{m}$ is the smallest cardinality of dense subsets of X.* ■

All compactifications (up to equivalence) of the space X are, by Theorem 3 and 2.5, subspaces of a Tychonoff cube. It follows that one can consider the family $\mathfrak{C}(X)$ of all compactifications of a given Tychonoff space X. Strictly speaking $\mathfrak{C}(X)$ is the family of classes consisting of equivalent compactifications of the space X which are subspaces of the Tychonoff cube $I^{2^{w(X)}}$.

A partial ordering can be defined in the family $\mathfrak{C}(X)$. That is, we say that c_1X is *not less* than c_2X (and write $c_2X \leqslant c_1X$) if and only if there exists a mapping $f: c_1X \to c_2X$ such that $fc_1 = c_2$, i.e. if c_1X can be mapped onto c_2X in such a manner that every point of the set X (considered as the subset of c_1X and c_2X) is mapped onto itself. The verification that if $c_1X \leqslant c_2X$ and $c_2X \leqslant c_3X$, then $c_1X \leqslant c_3X$, is left to the reader. In order to show that $\leqslant$ is a partial ordering it is sufficient to prove

THEOREM 4. *Compactifications c_1X and c_2X of a space X are equivalent if and only if $c_1X \leqslant c_2X$ and $c_2X \leqslant c_1X$.*

Proof. It follows from the definition that if compactifications c_1X and c_2X are equivalent, then $c_1X \leqslant c_2X$ and $c_2X \leqslant c_1X$.

Let us now assume that $c_1X \leqslant c_2X$, $c_2X \leqslant c_1X$ and let $f_1: c_1X \to c_2X$, $f_2: c_2X \to c_1X$ denote such mappings that $f_1c_1 = c_2$ and $f_2c_2 = c_1$. In order to prove that f_1 is a homeomorphism, i.e. that the compactifications are equivalent, it is sufficient, by Theorem 1.10, to prove that

$$f_2f_1(x) = x \quad \text{for} \quad x \in c_1X. \tag{2}$$

Let us note that $f_2f_1: c_1X \to c_1X$ and $f_2f_1c_1 = c_1$. Thus for every $x \in c_1(X) \subset c_1X$, $f_2f_1(x) = x$ holds. The restriction of the mapping f_2f_1 to the dense subset $c_1(X)$ is equal to the restriction of the identity mapping, from which by virtue of Theorem 2.1.4, (2) follows. ■

The following theorem gives a necessary and sufficient condition for the equivalence of two compactifications.

THEOREM 5. *In order that two compactifications c_1X and c_2X of a space X be equivalent it is necessary and sufficient that for every pair of closed subsets A, B of the space X the following equivalence hold:*

$$\left(\overline{c_1(A)} \cap \overline{c_1(B)} = 0\right) \equiv \left(\overline{c_2(A)} \cap \overline{c_2(B)} = 0\right). \tag{3}$$

Proof. The necessity of the condition follows from the definition of equivalence. Let us assume that (3) holds for compactifications c_1X and c_2X. By Theorem 2.1, the mappings

$$c_1c_2^{-1}: c_2(X) \to c_1X \quad \text{and} \quad c_2c_1^{-1}: c_1(X) \to c_2X$$

can be extended to the mappings

$$C_2: c_2X \to c_1X \quad \text{and} \quad C_1: c_1X \to c_2X,$$

which satisfy the conditions $C_2c_2 = c_1$ and $C_1c_1 = c_2$. Thus the equivalence of c_1X and c_2X follows from Theorem 4. ■

We shall now prove an important theorem concerning the family $\mathfrak{C}(X)$.

THEOREM 6. *For every subfamily $\mathfrak{C}_0 \subset \mathfrak{C}(X)$ there exists in $\mathfrak{C}(X)$ a least upper bound with respect to the partial ordering $\leqslant$, i.e. $\mathfrak{C}(X)$ is a complete semi-lattice with respect to $\leqslant$.*

Proof. Let a family $\mathfrak{C}_0 = \{c_sX\}_{s\in S} \subset \mathfrak{C}(X)$ be given. Let us consider the Cartesian product $\underset{s\in S}{\boldsymbol{P}}\, c_sX$ and the mapping $c_S = \underset{s\in S}{\triangle}\, c_s: X \to \underset{s\in S}{\boldsymbol{P}}\, c_sX$. By the Diagonal Lemma, c_S is a homeomorphic embedding; let us assume that $c_SX = \overline{c_S(X)} \subset \underset{s\in S}{\boldsymbol{P}}\, c_sX$.

We shall show that c_SX is the required compactification of the space X. Since $p_sc_S = c_s$, where p_s denotes the projection onto the s-th axis, $c_s X \leqslant c_S X$ holds for every $s \in S$. Let us suppose that for a compactification cX there exist mappings $f_s: cX \to c_s X$ such that $f_s c = c_s$ for every $s \in S$. It is easy to verify that for $F = \triangle_{s \in S} f_s$ we have $F: cX \to c_S X$ and $Fc = c_S$. Thus $c_S X \leqslant cX$. ∎

COROLLARY. *For every Tychonoff space X there exists a greatest element in the set $\mathfrak{C}(X)$ called the maximal compactification of the space X.* ∎

The next paragraph is devoted to an examination of this compactification.

Let us consider a compactification cX of a Tychonoff space X. The set $cX \setminus c(X)$, i.e. the set of the points which are added to the space X, is called the *remainder* of the compactification X. We need the following lemma in order to prove the fundamental property of the remainder.

LEMMA. *Let D be a dense subset of a Hausdorff space X and let $f: X \to Y$ denote a mapping of X into an arbitrary space Y. If $f|D: D \to f(D) \subset Y$ is a homeomorphism, then $f(X \setminus D) \cap f(D) = 0$.*

Proof. Let $X_1 = f^{-1}f(D)$. Clearly, it is sufficient to show that $X_1 = D$. Since $D \subset X_1 \subset X$, X_1 is a Hausdorff space and D is a dense subset of X_1. Let us denote the mapping inverse to $f|D: D \to f(D)$ by $g: f(D) \to D$. The restriction of the composition $g_1 = g(f|X_1)$ to the set D is the identity mapping; it is therefore equal to the restriction of the mapping $\mathrm{id}_{X_1}: X_1 \to X_1$. It follows from Theorem 2.1.4 that $\mathrm{id}_{X_1} = g_1$. But since $g_1(X_1) \subset D$, $X_1 = D$ holds. ∎

THEOREM 7. *Let $c_1 X$ and $c_2 X$ be compactifications of a space X and let $f: c_1 X \to c_2 X$ denote a mapping such that $fc_1 = c_2$. Then*

$$f(c_1(X)) = c_2(X) \quad \textit{and} \quad f(c_1 X \setminus c_1(X)) = c_2 X \setminus c_2(X).$$

Proof. The first equality follows directly from the formula $fc_1 = c_2$. Since $f(c_1 X)$ is closed in $c_2 X$ and contains a subset $c_2(X)$ dense in $c_2 X$, the equality $f(c_1 X) = c_2 X$ holds. The second equality follows from the first one and from the lemma. ∎

EXAMPLE 1. The circle S^1 and the closed segment are compactifications of the open segment. It follows from Example 2.4.3 that the closed segment is a greater compactification than the circle. ∎

EXAMPLE 2. The space X considered in Example 1.2 is a compactification of the discrete space of power $\mathfrak{c}$. ∎

EXERCISES

A. Verify that in Lemma 1 to Theorem 3 the assumption that X is regular cannot be replaced by the assumption that it is a T_2-space. Verify also that in Lemma 2 to that theorem the assumption that X is a T_0-space cannot be omitted (cf. Problem 1.F).

B. Show that if $c_s X_s$ is a compactification of the space X_s for every $s \in S$, then $\boldsymbol{P}_{s \in S} c_s X_s$ is a compactification of the product $\boldsymbol{P}_{s \in S} X_s$.

C. Give an example of a compactification of a discrete space of power $\mathfrak{c}$ which is not equivalent to the compactification described in Example 2.

D. Show that the limit of an inverse system $\{c_\sigma X, \pi_\varrho^\sigma, \Sigma\}$ of compactifications of a topological space X, where $c_\varrho = \pi_\varrho^\sigma c_\sigma$ for every pair σ, ϱ of elements of the set Σ such that $\varrho \leqslant \sigma$, is itself a compactification of the space X.

E. Let cX be an arbitrary compactification of a space X and let R denote a closed equivalence relation in cX. Show that if individual points of $c(X)$ are the equivalence classes of the relation R, then cX/R is also a compactification of the space X.

§ 5. The Čech-Stone compactification. The greatest (with respect to the partial order $\leqslant$) compactification of a Tychonoff space X, the existence of which follows from Theorem 4.6, is called the *Čech-Stone compactification* of X and is denoted by βX.

In this paragraph we shall identify the space X with the subspace $c(X) \subset cX$ (homeomorphic to X) of a compactification cX of the space X. In other words, we shall regard the space X as the subspace of each of its compactifications. This convention enables us to examine extendability of mappings defined on a Tychonoff space over compactifications of this space.

THEOREM 1. *Every mapping $f: X \to Z$ of a Tychonoff space X into a compact space Z is extendable to a mapping $F: \beta X \to Z$.*

If every mapping defined on X with values in a compact space can be extended over a compactification aX of the space X, then aX is equivalent to the Čech-Stone compactification of X.

Proof. Let us consider the mapping $c = \beta \triangle f: X \to \beta X \times Z$. The Diagonal Lemma implies that c is a homeomorphic embedding; thus $cX = \overline{c(X)} \subset \beta X \times Z$ is a compactification of X. By the maximality of βX, there exists a mapping $g: \beta X \to cX$ such that $g\beta = c$. Let $p: \beta X \times Z \to Z$ denote the projection onto the second axis and let us define $F = pg: \beta X \to Z$. Since $F\beta = pg\beta = pc = f$, F is an extension of the mapping f.

If the compactification aX has the property described in the theorem, then there exists an extension $B: aX \to \beta X$ of the mapping $\beta: X \to \beta X$. Hence $Ba = \beta$, and $\beta X \leqslant aX$, which proves that aX and βX are equivalent. ∎

COROLLARY 1. *Let X be a Tychonoff space. Then every pair of sets which are completely separated in X have disjoint closures in βX.*

If a compactification aX of a space X is such that closures of every two completely separated subsets of the space X in aX are disjoint, then aX is equivalent to the Čech-Stone compactification of the space X.

Proof. Let us suppose that the function $f: X \to I$ separates the sets A and B. By virtue of the theorem, f can be extended to the function $F: \beta X \to I$. Therefore $\bar{A} \cap \bar{B} = 0$, because $\bar{A} \subset F^{-1}(0)$ and $\bar{B} \subset F^{-1}(1)$.

If aX has the above property, then by virtue of Theorems 1.5.5 and 1.7, only completely separated sets have disjoint closures in aX. The same holds true for the compactification βX, so that the equivalence of aX and βX follows from Theorem 4.5. ■

COROLLARY 2. *Every continuous function defined on a Tychonoff space X with values in the segment I can be extended over βX.*

If every continuous function defined on X with values in the segment I can be extended over a compactification aX of the space X, then aX is equivalent to the Čech-Stone compactification of the space X. ■

COROLLARY 3. *Let A and B be disjoint closed subsets of a normal space X. The closures $\bar{A}$ and $\bar{B}$ in the compactification βX are disjoint.*

If a space X has a compactification aX such that closures in aX of every two disjoint and closed subsets of the space X are disjoint, then X is a normal space and aX is a compactification equivalent to the Čech-Stone compactification of the space X. ■

COROLLARY 4. *For every open-and-closed subset A of a Tychonoff space X, the closure $\bar{A}$ of the set A in βX is open-and-closed.* ■

COROLLARY 5. *Let X and Y be Tychonoff spaces. Each mapping $f: X \to Y$ has an extension $F: \beta X \to \beta Y$.* ■

COROLLARY 6. *Let M denote a subspace of a Tychonoff space X such that every continuous function $f: M \to I$ can be extended over X. The closure $\bar{M}$ of the set M in βX is equivalent to βM.* ■

Corollary 6 and Theorem 2.1.3 imply

COROLLARY 7. *Let M be a closed subset of a normal space X. The closure $\bar{M}$ of the set M in βX is a compactification of M which is equivalent to βM.* ■

COROLLARY 8. *Let X denote a Tychonoff space. For each subspace T of βX satisfying the condition $X \subset T \subset \beta X$, $\beta T = \beta X$ holds.*

Proof. For every continuous function $f: T \to I$ there exists an extension $F: \beta X \to I$ of the function $f|X$. It follows from Theorem 2.1.4 that F is an extension of f; thus by Corollary 2, we infer that $\beta T = \beta X$. ■

EXAMPLE 1. Let X denote the set of all ordinal numbers not greater than the first uncountable ordinal number ω_1. The set X is well ordered by the relation of inequality for ordinal numbers which will be denoted by the symbol $<$. Let us introduce in X a topology, assuming that the intervals $(y, x] = \{z: y < z \leqslant x\}$, where $y < x \leqslant \omega_1$, and the set $\{0\}$, where 0 denotes the order type of the empty set, form a base. It can easily be verified that X is a Hausdorff space. We shall show that X is a compact space.

Let $\{U_s\}_{s\in S}$ denote an arbitrary open covering of the space X. Without any loss of generality we can assume that the sets U_s belong to the base described before. Let A denote the set of those $x \in X$ for which the set $[0, x] = \{z: 0 \leqslant z \leqslant x\}$ is contained in the union of finitely many elements of the covering in question. In order to complete the proof it is sufficient to show that the set $X \setminus A$ is empty.

Let us suppose that $X \setminus A \neq 0$ and let us denote by x_0 the first element of this set. Let U_{s_0} denote an arbitrary element of the covering which contains the point x_0. Since $0 < x_0$, we have $U_{s_0} = (y, x]$, where $y < x_0 \leqslant x$. By the assumption $y \in A$, we have that $[0, y] \subset \bigcup_{i=1}^{k} U_{s_i}$ and it follows that $[0, x_0] \subset \bigcup_{i=0}^{k} U_{s_i}$, which contradicts the definition of the point x_0.

Let us now consider the subspace $X_0 = X \setminus \{\omega_1\}$ of the space X. The space X_0 is normal. Moreover, for every two disjoint and closed subsets A and B of the space X, the closures $\bar{A}$ and $\bar{B}$ of the sets A and B in the space X are disjoint. This follows from the fact that only one of the sets A and B can be cofinal in X_0. Indeed, if A and B were both cofinal in X_0, then there would exist two sequences $\{a_i\}$ and $\{b_i\}$ consisting of points of the space X_0 and satisfying the conditions:

$$a_i < b_i < a_{i+1} \quad \text{and} \quad a_i \in A,\ b_i \in B \quad \text{for } i = 1, 2, \ldots$$

Since there is no countable and cofinal subset in X_0, the set C consisting of those elements of X_0 which are greater than any of the terms of the two sequences is non-empty. It can easily be verified that the first element of the set C would belong to $A \cap B$.

From the above property and from Corollary 3 to Theorem 1 it follows that X is the Čech-Stone compactification of the space X_0. It can be seen that we may also prove that for every continuous function $f: X_0 \to I$ there exists an ordinal number $x_0 < \omega_1$ such that $f(x) = f(x_0)$ for every $x \geqslant x_0$, i.e. that the function f is constant beyond an initial interval.

It is sufficient to prove that for every natural number n there exists an $x_n \in X_0$ such that $|f(x) - f(x_n)| < 1/n$ for every $x \geqslant x_n$. Indeed, then there exists an element $x_0 \in X_0$ which is greater than each x_n for $n = 1, 2, \ldots$ and it can easily be verified that it possesses the required property.

Let us therefore suppose that for some n and every $x \in X_0$ one can choose $x' \in X_0$ such that $x' > x$ and $|f(x) - f(x')| \geqslant 1/n$. Two sequences $\{a_i\}$ and $\{b_i\}$ of elements of the space X_0 such that $|f(a_i) - f(b_i)| \geqslant 1/n$ and $a_i < b_i < a_{i+1}$ for $i = 1, 2, \ldots$, can now be defined inductively, but the existence of such sequences contradicts the definition of a mapping. In fact, let us denote by c the least ordinal number which is greater than all numbers a_i and b_i; every neighbourhood of the point c contains all the points of the two sequences with the exception perhaps of a finite number. On the other hand, the set $f^{-1}\big((f(c)-1/2n, f(c)+1/2n)\big)$ contains at most one of the numbers a_i, b_i for $i = 1, 2, \dots$ ∎

We shall now examine in more detail the Čech-Stone compactification of the space of natural numbers N with the discrete topology.

THEOREM 2. *The Čech-Stone compactification βN is of power $2^{\mathfrak{c}}$ and of weight $\mathfrak{c}$.*

Proof. By the Tychonoff Theorem and Theorem 2.3.7, the Tychonoff cube $I^{\mathfrak{c}}$ is a compact space of power $2^{\mathfrak{c}}$ and weight $\mathfrak{c}$ which contains a dense countable subset $\{x_1, x_2, \dots\}$. Let us consider the mapping $f: N \to I^{\mathfrak{c}}$ defined by means of the formula $f(i) = x_i$ for $i \in N$. By virtue of Theorem 1, it has an extension $F: \beta N \to I^{\mathfrak{c}}$ which maps βN onto the space $I^{\mathfrak{c}}$, since the image $F(\beta N)$ is closed and contains a dense subset of $I^{\mathfrak{c}}$. By the well-known set-theorethical theorem, $\overline{\overline{\beta N}} \geqslant \overline{\overline{I^{\mathfrak{c}}}} = 2^{\mathfrak{c}}$, and by virtue of Corollary 2 to Theorem 1.11, $w(\beta N) \geqslant w(I^{\mathfrak{c}}) = \mathfrak{c}$. The conclusion of our theorem follows from Theorem 4.3 and the Cantor-Bernstein Theorem. ∎

THEOREM 3. *For every point $p \in \beta N$ and its neighbourhood V there exists an open-and-closed set W such that $p \in W \subset V$, i.e. the space βN has a base consisting of open-and-closed sets.*

Proof. Let U be a neighbourhood of the point p such that $p \in U \subset \overline{U} \subset V$, and let $M = U \cap N$ and $W = \overline{M}$. By virtue of Corollary 4 to Theorem 1, W is open-and-closed. It follows from Theorem 1.3.6 that $W = \overline{U \cap N} = \overline{U}$. ∎

The following theorem, the last in this paragraph, is a considerable generalization of Theorem 2.

THEOREM 4. *Every closed and infinite set $F \subset \beta N$ contains a subset homeomorphic to βN; thus $\overline{\overline{F}} = 2^{\mathfrak{c}}$.*

Proof. A sequence of points $a_1, a_2, \dots$ and a sequence of open sets $V_1, V_2, \dots$ such that

$$a_i \in V_i, \quad V_i \cap V_j = 0 \text{ for } i \neq j, \quad \text{and} \quad A = \bigcup_{i=1}^{\infty} \{a_i\} \subset F$$

can be defined inductively.

Let $g: A \to I$ denote an arbitrary continuous function. The function $G: N \to I$, defined by means of the formula:

$$G(n) = \begin{cases} g(a_i) & \text{for} \quad n \in N \cap V_i, \\ 0 & \text{for} \quad n \in N \setminus \bigcup\limits_{i=1}^{\infty} V_i, \end{cases}$$

has an extension $G^*\colon \beta N \to I$. Since N is dense in βN, we have $G^*(x) = g(a_i)$ for $x \in \overline{V}_i = \overline{N \cap V_i}$, whence $G^*|A = g$. For every function $g\colon A \to I$ there exists, therefore, an extension $G^*\colon \beta N \to I$. Hence, by Corollary 6 to Theorem 1, $\overline{A} = \beta A$.

The space A is discrete, and has the power $\aleph_0$, thus it is homeomorphic to N. Hence $\beta A = \overline{A} \subset F$ is homeomorphic to βN. ∎

EXAMPLE 2. The remainder $\beta N \setminus N$ of the Čech-Stone compactification of the space of natural numbers contains a family of power $\mathfrak{c}$ consisting of disjoint open-and-closed and non-empty sets.

Let us first observe that in the set N there exists a family of infinite subsets $\{N_t\}_{t\in I}$ such that for every two different numbers $t, t' \in I$ the intersection $N_t \cap N_{t'}$ is finite. In order to verify this property, it is sufficient to set all rational numbers of the segment I into an infinite sequence $r_1, r_2, \ldots$ and assume that $N_t = \{n_1, n_2, \ldots\}$ for every $t \in I$, where $r_{n_1}, r_{n_2}, \ldots$ is a subsequence of the sequence $r_1, r_2, \ldots$ convergent to t and consisting of distinct rational numbers.

Let us now define $U_t = (\beta N \setminus N) \cap \overline{N}_t$ for every $t \in I$. The family $\{U_t\}_{t\in I}$ is of power $\mathfrak{c}$ and, according to Corollary 4 to Theorem 1, consists of sets which are open-and-closed in $\beta N \setminus N$ and obviously are non-empty. For every two different numbers $t, t' \in I$ we have $N_{t'} = S_t \cup M_t$, where S_t is a finite set and $M_t \cap N_t = 0$. Since evidently $\overline{S}_t = S_t \subset N$, and since it follows from Corollary 3 to Theorem 1 that $\overline{M}_t \cap \overline{N}_t = 0$, we have the equality

$$U_t \cap U_{t'} = (\beta N \setminus N) \cap \overline{N}_t \cap \overline{N}_{t'} = (\beta N \setminus N) \cap \overline{N}_t \cap (\overline{S}_t \cup \overline{M}_t)$$

$$= (\beta N \setminus N) \cap [(\overline{N}_t \cap \overline{S}_t) \cup (\overline{N}_t \cap \overline{M}_t)] \subset (\beta N \setminus N) \cap N = 0. \blacksquare$$

EXAMPLE 3. By means of the family $\{U_t\}_{t\in I}$ constructed in Example 2, we can define an interesting non-normal Tychonoff space whose properties will be used in Chapter 6.

Let us choose a point $x_t \in U_t$ for every $t \in I$ and let $X = N \cup \bigcup_{t\in I} \{x_t\}$. The space X contains a dense countable subset, namely N. Since by Corollary 4 to Theorem 1, for every $n \in N$ the set $\overline{\{n\}} = \{n\}$ is open in βN, $N = \bigcup_{n=1}^{\infty} \{n\}$ is open in βN, hence also in X. The set $X \setminus N$ is therefore closed in X, and since it contains only isolated points, it is homeomorphic to the discrete space of power $\mathfrak{c}$. By the same reasoning as in Example 1.5.2 or 2.1.2 we infer that X is not normal. ∎

From Theorems 2 and 2.3.8 it follows that the space βN can be embedded in the Tychonoff cube $I^{\mathfrak{c}}$. We shall now describe directly a subspace of the cube $I^{\mathfrak{c}}$ homeomorphic to βN.

EXAMPLE 4. We shall regard the Tychonoff cube $I^{\mathfrak{c}} = \underset{t\in I}{\boldsymbol{P}} I_t$, where $I_t = I$ for every $t \in I$, as the set of all functions (not necessarily continuous) of the segment I into itself. For every number $t \in I$ let $d_i(t)$ denote the i-th number of the dyadic expansion of t, with the additional assumption that if t has two expansions, then we consider the one which contains infinitely many zeros. Since

$$S \cap \{d \in I^{\mathfrak{c}}: d(1/2^i) \in (0,1]\} = \{d_i\} \quad \text{for every } i,$$

the functions d_i belong to the cube $I^{\mathfrak{c}}$ and the subspace $S = \bigcup_{i=1}^{\infty} \{d_i\} \subset I^{\mathfrak{c}}$ is discrete. The space S can therefore be identified with the space N of natural numbers and its closure $\overline{S} \subset I^{\mathfrak{c}}$ can be considered as a compactification of the space N. We shall show that the compactification $\overline{S}$ is equivalent to the Čech-Stone compactification βN.

In view of Corollary 1 to Theorem 1 it is sufficient for this purpose to note that every mapping $f: S \to D = \{0,1\}$ has an extension $F: I^{\mathfrak{c}} \to I$. We can clearly assume that the sequence $f(d_1), f(d_2), \ldots$ contains infinitely many zeros, for otherwise, the existence of the required extension follows from the Urysohn Lemma. But it is easy to verify that under this additional assumption the projection $p_{t_0}: I^{\mathfrak{c}} = \underset{t\in I}{\boldsymbol{P}} I_t \to I_{t_0}$, where $t_0 = \sum_{i=1}^{\infty} \frac{f(d_i)}{2^i}$, is the required extension. ■

The space βN is also used for the construction of many other interesting examples of topological spaces. Some of them will be given in the next paragraphs.

EXERCISES

A (I. I. Parovičenko [1957]). Verify that the relation R between points of the remainder $\beta N \setminus N$, defined by means of the condition:

xRy if and only if the spaces $N \cup \{x\}$ and $N \cup \{y\}$ are homeomorphic,

is an equivalence relation. Prove that equivalence classes of this relation are of power $\leqslant \mathfrak{c}$ and deduce that there exists a countable space which does not satisfy the first axiom of countability (cf. Example 1.4 and Exercises 1.C, 1.D, and F).

Hint: Estimate the number of topologies with countable bases in a countable set.

B. Let Y be the discrete space of power $\mathfrak{c}$. Define a function $f: Y \to I$ which cannot be extended over the compactification described in Examples 1.2 and 4.2.

C. Verify that the Čech-Stone compactification of a Tychonoff space X can also be obtained as the closure of the image of the space X under the mapping $\underset{f\in\mathfrak{f}}{\triangle} f$ into $\underset{f\in\mathfrak{f}}{\boldsymbol{P}} I_f$, where $\mathfrak{f}$ is the family of all continuous functions defined on X with values in I and $I_f = I$ for $f \in \mathfrak{f}$.

D (M. H. Stone [1948]). Prove Corollary 7 to Theorem 1 by means of Corollary 3 to that theorem. Then, making use of Exercise 2.H, deduce the Tietze-Urysohn Theorem.

E. Deduce from Exercise 2.F that the space $\beta X \times \beta Y$ which is a compactification of the space $X \times Y$ is not necessarily its Čech-Stone compactification (even under the assumption of compactness of Y).

The equality $\beta \mathop{\boldsymbol{P}}_{s \in S} X_s = \mathop{\boldsymbol{P}}_{s \in S} \beta X_s$ holds if and only if either $\mathop{\boldsymbol{P}}_{s \in S \setminus \{s_0\}} X_s$ is finite for some $s_0 \in S$ or the product $\mathop{\boldsymbol{P}}_{s \in S} X_s$ is pseudo-compact (cf. Paragraph 9). The proof of this fact is not included in the book.

F. Show that for an arbitrary Tychonoff space X no point $x \in \beta X \setminus X$ is a G_δ-set in βX (cf. Problem M).

Hint: Assume that $x \in \beta X \setminus X$ is a G_δ-set and define, by means of Theorem 1.4.2, a function $f: \beta X \to I$ which vanishes only at the point x (see Problem 1.G). Define in X two completely separated sets A and B such that $x \in \overline{A} \cap \overline{B}$.

§ 6. Locally compact spaces. A space X is said to be *locally compact* provided for every $x \in X$ there exists a neighbourhood U of the point x such that $\overline{U}$ is compact.

Since the compact space $\overline{U}$ is a T_1-space, the set $\{x\}$ is closed in $\overline{U}$, and thus also in X. We deduce that locally compact spaces are T_1-spaces. The following stronger theorem can be proved.

THEOREM 1. *Every locally compact space is a Tychonoff space.*

Proof. Let us consider a closed subset F of a locally compact space X and a point $x \in X \setminus F$. Let U be a neighbourhood of the point x such that $\overline{U}$ is compact. The set $F_1 = (\overline{U} \setminus U) \cup (\overline{U} \cap F)$ is a closed subset of the space $\overline{U}$ and it does not contain the point x. Hence there exists a function $f_1: \overline{U} \to I$ such that $f_1(x) = 0$ and $f_1(F_1) \subset \{1\}$. Since $\overline{U} \cap (X \setminus U) = \overline{U} \setminus U \subset F_1$, the combination f of the function f_1 and the function $f_2: X \setminus U \to I$, where $f_2(y) = 1$ for $y \in X \setminus U$, is, by Theorem 2.1.6, continuous. It can easily be verified that $f(x) = 0$ and $f(F) \subset \{1\}$. ∎

THEOREM 2. *For any compact subspace A of a locally compact space X and an open set $V \subset X$ containing A, there exists an open set U such that $A \subset U \subset \overline{U} \subset V$ and $\overline{U}$ is compact.*

Proof. For every $x \in A$ let us choose neighbourhoods V_x, such that $\overline{V}_x \subset V$, and W_x, such that $\overline{W}_x$ is compact. The set $\overline{U}_x$, where $U_x = V_x \cap W_x$, being a closed subset of the compact space $\overline{W}_x$, is itself compact. By virtue of Theorem 1.3, there exists a finite number of points $x_1, x_2, \ldots, x_k \in A$ such that $A \subset U = U_{x_1} \cup U_{x_2} \cup \ldots \cup U_{x_k}$. The set $\overline{U} = \overline{U}_{x_1} \cup \overline{U}_{x_2} \cup \ldots \cup \overline{U}_{x_k}$ is compact by Corollary 1 to Theorem 1.3. Moreover,

$$\overline{U} = \overline{U}_{x_1} \cup \overline{U}_{x_2} \cup \ldots \cup \overline{U}_{x_k} \subset \overline{V}_{x_1} \cup \overline{V}_{x_2} \cup \ldots \cup \overline{V}_{x_k} \subset \overline{V}. \ ∎$$

COROLLARY. *For every point x of a locally compact space and its neighborhood V there exists a neighborhood U of this point such that $x \in U \subset \overline{U} \subset V$ and such that $\overline{U}$ is compact.* ∎

We shall now prove some theorems concerning operations on locally compact spaces.

THEOREM 3. *Closed subspaces and open subspaces of a locally compact space are locally compact.*

Proof. Let M be a closed subspace of a locally compact space X. For every $x \in M$ there exists a neighbourhood U of the point x in X such that $\overline{U}$ is compact. The set $M \cap U$ is a neighbourhood of the point x in M and by Theorem 2.1.1, the set $\overline{M \cap U} \cap M$ is its closure. This set, however, is compact as a closed subset of the compact space $\overline{U}$.

The second part of the theorem follows from the corollary to Theorem 2. ∎

Since a compact space is obviously locally compact, Theorem 3 implies the following

COROLLARY. *An open subspace of a compact space is locally compact.* ∎

THEOREM 4. *Let $\{X_s\}_{s \in S}$ denote a family of disjoint topological spaces. The sum $\bigoplus_{s \in S} X_s$ is locally compact if and only if X_s is locally compact for every $s \in S$.*

Proof. The local compactness of each of the spaces X_s follows, by Theorem 3 and Corollary 1 to Theorem 2.2.1, from the local compactness of the sum.

Let us suppose that all spaces X_s are locally compact. Let us consider an arbitrary point $x \in \bigoplus_{s \in S} X_s$; then $x \in X_{s_0}$ for some $s_0 \in S$. Since X_{s_0} is locally compact, there exists a neighbourhood U of the point x in X_{s_0} such that $\overline{U}$ (the closure in X_{s_0}) is compact. But X_{s_0} is open-and-closed in the sum $\bigoplus_{s \in S} X_s$, whence U is a neighbourhood of x and $\overline{U}$ is the closure of U in the sum $\bigoplus_{s \in S} X_s$. ∎

THEOREM 5. *The Cartesian product $\boldsymbol{P}_{s \in S} X_s$ is a non-empty locally compact space if and only if X_s is a non-empty and locally compact space for every $s \in S$, and all X_s, with the exception perhaps of a finite number, are compact.*

Proof. In order to prove that the condition is satisfactory it is sufficient, by the Tychonoff Theorem and Theorem 2.3.4, to show that the product of a finite number of locally compact spaces is locally compact. Let X_i be a locally compact space for $i = 1, 2, \ldots, k$ and let $x = (x_1, x_2, \ldots, x_k) \in X = X_1 \times X_2 \times \ldots \times X_k$. There exists a neighbourhood V_i of the point x_i in X_i such that $\overline{V}_i$ is compact. It follows from Theorem 2.3.1 that $V = V_1 \times V_2 \times \ldots \times V_k$ is a neighbourhood of the point x. By virtue of Theorem 2.3.2 and the Tychonoff Theorem, $\overline{V}$ is compact.

Let us now assume that $\boldsymbol{P}_{s \in S} X_s$ is a non-empty, locally compact space. A point $x \in \boldsymbol{P}_{s \in S} X_s$ has a neighbourhood U such that $\overline{U}$ is compact.

By virtue of Theorem 2.3.1, there exists a set $\underset{s \in S}{\boldsymbol{P}} W_s$, where $W_s \neq X_s$ for only a finite number of indices $s \in S$, such that $x \in \underset{s \in S}{\boldsymbol{P}} W_s \subset U$. We infer from Theorem 1.2 that $\underset{s \in S}{\boldsymbol{P}} \overline{W}_s = \overline{\underset{s \in S}{\boldsymbol{P}} W_s} \subset \overline{U}$ is a compact space. Hence, in view of the Tychonoff Theorem, it follows that for all $s \in S$, with the exception perhaps of a finite number, the space X_s is compact. The proof of the local compactness of each X_s is left to the reader. ∎

EXAMPLE 1. The discrete space is clearly locally compact. The real-line is locally compact, for it is homeomorphic to the open subset $\{x: -1 < x < 1\}$ of the segment $J = [-1, 1]$. From the preceding theorem it follows therefore that for every n, the Euclidean space R^n is locally compact.

Example 2.3.3 shows that there exist locally compact spaces which are not normal. Other examples of this type will be given below. ∎

THEOREM 6. *Let X be a Tychonoff space. The following conditions are equivalent*:

(i) *X is a locally compact space.*
(ii) *The remainder of every compactification of X is closed.*
(iii) *The remainder $\beta X \setminus \beta(X)$ is closed.*
(iv) *The remainder $cX \setminus c(X)$ is closed for a compactification cX of the space X.*

Proof. Implications (ii) ⇒ (iii) ⇒ (iv) ⇒ (i) are obvious. In order to prove our theorem it is therefore sufficient to show that (i) ⇒ (ii).

Let cX be an arbitrary compactification of a locally compact space X. Since the local compactness is a topological invariant, $c(X)$ is also locally compact. We shall show that $c(X)$ is open in cX. The closure of the set $A \subset c(X)$ in the space $c(X)$ will be denoted by $\tilde{A}$, and in the space cX by $\overline{A}$.

If we let $x \in c(X)$; it suffices to show that there exists a set V, open in cX, such that $x \in V \subset c(X)$. By the local compactness of $c(X)$, there exists a neighbourhood U of the point x in $c(X)$ such that $\tilde{U}$ is compact. It follows from the definition of the topology in a subspace that there exists a V open in cX and such that $U = c(X) \cap V$. From Theorem 1.3.6 it follows that $\overline{V} = \overline{V \cap c(X)}$. Thus

$$x \in V \subset \overline{V} = \overline{V \cap c(X)} = \overline{U} \subset \tilde{U} \subset c(X),$$

because $\tilde{U}$ is a closed set in cX containing U. ∎

THEOREM 7 (Alexandroff). *Every locally compact but non-compact space X has a compactification ωX with the remainder consisting of one point. This compactification is the least element of the family $\mathfrak{C}(X)$ and its weight is equal to the weight of the space X.*

Proof. Let us consider an arbitrary point $\Omega \notin X$ and let us put $\omega X = X \cup \{\Omega\}$. Let us define sets open in ωX as sets of the form $\{\Omega\} \cup (X \setminus F)$, where F is a compact subspace of X, together with sets which are open in X. It can easily be verified that ωX together with the family of open subsets thus defined is a Hausdorff space, and that $\omega: X \to \omega X$, defined by means of the formula $\omega(x) = x$, is a homeomorphism onto the subset $\omega(X)$ dense in ωX. We shall show that ωX is compact. Let $\{U_s\}_{s \in S}$ denote an open covering of the space ωX. For some $s_0 \in S$ we have $\Omega \in U_{s_0}$ so that by the definition of neighbourhoods of the point Ω, the set $F = X \setminus U_{s_0}$ is compact. Theorem 1.3 implies that there exists a finite set $\{s_1, s_2, \ldots, s_k\} \subset S$ such that $F \subset U_{s_1} \cup U_{s_2} \cup \ldots \cup U_{s_k}$, whence from the given covering of the space ωX a finite covering $\{U_{s_i}\}_{i=0}^{k}$ can be chosen.

We shall show now that for an arbitrary compactification cX of the space X we have $cX \geqslant \omega X$. Indeed, the function f defined by means of the formula

$$f(x) = \begin{cases} \omega c^{-1}(x) & \text{for} \quad x \in c(X), \\ \Omega & \text{for} \quad x \in cX \setminus c(X), \end{cases}$$

is, according to Theorem 6, a mapping, $f: cX \to \omega X$ for the inverse image of every open set in ωX, as an open subset in the open subspace $c(X)$ or as the complement of a compact subset of cX, is open in cX. Furthermore, we have that $fc = \omega$.

The remaining part of the conclusion follows from Theorem 4.2 and Corollary 2 to Theorem 1.11. ■

The minimal compactification of a locally compact space constructed above is called the *Alexandroff compactification*. One can say that it is obtained by adding "the point at infinity" to the space X.

THEOREM 8. *Let X be an arbitrary non-compact Tychonoff space. If in the family $\mathfrak{C}(X)$ of all compactifications of the space X there exists an element cX which is the least with respect to the relation $\leqslant$, then X is locally compact and cX is a compactification equivalent to the Alexandroff compactification ωX.*

Proof. In order to prove the theorem it is sufficient to show that the remainder $cX \setminus c(X)$ consists of a single point. This will imply the local compactness of X and, by virtue of Theorem 7 and 4.4, the equivalence of cX and ωX.

Let us assume that the remainder $cX \setminus c(X)$ contains two different points x_1 and x_2. The space $X_1 = cX \setminus \{x_1, x_2\}$ is locally compact and its Alexandroff compactification ωX_1 is also a compactification of the space X, $\omega X_1 = c_1 X$. Thus $cX \leqslant c_1 X$, i.e. there exists a mapping $f: c_1 X \to cX$ which is the identity on $c(X)$. Theorem 2.1.4 implies that $f|X_1$ is also the identity. Hence, by virtue of Theorem 4.7, which can be applied to the compactifications c_1X and cX of the space X_1, we infer that $f(\{\Omega\}) = \{x_1, x_2\}$, which is impossible. ■

THEOREM 9. *If in a locally compact space there exists a grid with power* $\leqslant \mathfrak{m}$, *then* $w(X) \leqslant \mathfrak{m}$.

Proof. We can assume of course that X is not compact; then $\mathfrak{m} \geqslant \aleph_0$. It is easy to note that by adding the set $\{\Omega\}$, where $\Omega \in \omega X \setminus \omega(X)$, to an arbitrary grid in X, we obtain a grid in the compactification ωX. The theorem now follows from Theorem 1.11. ■

EXAMPLE 2. It can easily be seen that the circle S^1 is the Alexandroff compactification of the real-line. The Alexandroff compactification of the discrete space has only one accumulation point and is the frequently used space of Example 1.1.2. ■

EXAMPLE 3. We shall give here an example of a space X for which $\omega X = \beta X$. A space X satisfying this condition has evidently only one compactification.

We can assume that X is the space of all ordinal numbers less than ω_1 with the topology defined in Example 5.1. Indeed, we have shown there that $\beta X = X \cup \{\omega_1\}$. Since ωX is obtained by the identification of the remainder in βX to a point, we have $\omega X = \beta X$.

More generally, for every Tychonoff space Y, the space $X = \beta Y \setminus \{x\}$, where $x \in \beta Y \setminus \beta(Y)$, has exactly one compactification. Indeed, by virtue of Corollary 8 to Theorem 5.1, $\beta X = \beta Y = X \cup \{x\}$ i.e. $\omega X = \beta X$. ■

To complete this paragraph we shall prove two theorems connected with mapping spaces.

THEOREM 10. *Every locally compact space X is a k-space.*

Proof. Let $A \neq \bar{A} \subset X$. We have to show that there exists a compact subset $Z \subset X$ such that $A \cap Z$ is not closed. The reader can verify without any difficulty that one can take for Z the compact closure of a neighbourhood of an arbitrary point $a \in \bar{A} \setminus A$. ■

THEOREM 11. *Let X be a locally compact space, let Y denote an arbitrary topological space, and let Y^X denote the space of all mappings of X into Y with the compact-open topology. Then the function φ of the product $Y^X \times X$ into the space Y defined by means of the formula $\varphi(f, x) = f(x)$ is a mapping*, i.e. $\varphi\colon Y^X \times X \to Y$.

Proof. Let $f \in Y^X$, $x \in X$, and let V denote a neighbourhood of the point $f(x) \in Y$. Let us denote by U_1 such a neighbourhood of the point $x \in X$ that $\bar{U}_1$ is compact. There exists a neighbourhood $U_2 \subset U_1$ of the point x such that $f(U_2) \subset V$. Since the space X is regular, we can choose an open subset $U \subset X$ such that $x \in U \subset \bar{U} \subset U_2$. $Z = \bar{U}$ is clearly compact. It is easy to verify that $f \in M(Z, V)$ and $\varphi\big(M(Z, V) \times U\big) \subset V$. ■

For locally compact spaces the compact-open topology in the space Y^X can therefore be defined, according to Theorem 3.6, as the weakest topology of the mapping space under which the function φ of the product $Y^X \times X$ into Y, defined above, is a mapping.

EXERCISES

A. Making use of the method used in the proof of Theorem 6, show that every locally compact subspace of a T_2-space X is the intersection of two subsets of the space X, one of which is closed and the other open.

B. Generalize Theorem 3 proving that in a locally compact space the intersection of a closed subset with an open subset is locally compact.

C. Show that the family $\mathfrak{C}(X)$ of all compactifications of a locally compact space X is a complete lattice, i.e. that every family of compactifications has also the greatest lower bound.

§ 7. Lindelöf spaces. We say that a topological space X is a *Lindelöf space*, or that it has the *Lindelöf property*, if X is regular and if from every open covering $\{U_s\}_{s\in S}$ of the space X a countable subcovering $\{U_{s_i}\}_{i=1}^{\infty}$ can be chosen. As for compact spaces, one can show that a space X is a Lindelöf space if and only if every open covering of X has a countable refinement. Of course, every compact space is a Lindelöf space. Theorem 1.1.6 implies

THEOREM 1. *Every regular space X which satisfies the second axiom of countability is a Lindelöf space.* ■

THEOREM 2. *Every Lindelöf space is normal.*

The proof of this theorem is almost identical with the proof of Theorem 1.5.6. In order to obtain the coverings of the space X one must add open sets $X\setminus A$ and $X\setminus B$, respectively, to the families of open sets $\{V_x\}_{x\in A}$ and $\{U_y\}_{y\in B}$ considered there. ■

The following theorems can be proved analogously to Theorems 1.1-1.3 and 1.8.

THEOREM 3. *A regular space X is a Lindelöf space if and only if every family of closed sets which possesses the countable intersection property has the non-empty intersection.* ■

THEOREM 4. *A closed subspace of a Lindelöf space is a Lindelöf space.* ■

THEOREM 5. *If a subspace A of a topological space X has the Lindelöf property, then from every family $\{U_s\}_{s\in S}$ of open subsets of X such that $A \subset \bigcup_{s\in S} U_s$, we can choose a countable family $\{U_{s_i}\}_{i=1}^{\infty}$ such that $A \subset \bigcup_{i=1}^{\infty} U_{s_i}$.* ■

THEOREM 6. *Let X be a Lindelöf space and Y a regular space. If there exists a mapping f of the space X onto the space Y, then Y is also a Lindelöf* *space. In other words, the continuous image of a Lindelöf space is a Lindelöf space, provided that it is regular.* ∎

We leave the proof of the following theorem to the reader.

THEOREM 7. *The sum* $\bigoplus_{s\in S} X_s$ *of disjoint and non-empty spaces is a Lindelöf space if and only if* $\overline{\overline{S}} \leqslant \aleph_0$ *and* X_s *is a Lindelöf space for every* $s \in S$. ∎

EXAMPLE 1. The space considered in Example 1.4 is a Lindelöf space, since it is easy to verify that every countable regular space is a Lindelöf space. This space is an example of a Lindelöf space which does not satisfy the first (neither the second) axiom of countability. ∎

EXAMPLE 2. We shall show that the space X considered in Example 1.2.1 is a Lindelöf space. Let $\{U_s\}_{s\in S}$ be an open covering of the space X. For every U_s let us denote by V_s the interior of the set U_s with respect to the natural topology of the real-line. We shall now show that the set $K = X \setminus \bigcup_{s\in S} V_s$ is at most countable. Indeed, for every point $x \in K$ there exist an $s(x) \in S$ and a real number $r(x) > x$ such that $[x, r(x)) \subset U_{s(x)}$. By the definition of the set K, disjoint intervals correspond to different points. Hence $\overline{\overline{K}} \leqslant \aleph_0$.

The set $X \setminus K$ with the topology of the subspace of the real-line has a countable base. The family $\{V_s\}_{s\in S}$ is its open covering. Hence, by Theorem 1, it contains a countable subcovering $\{V_{s_i}\}_{i=1}^{\infty}$. It is easy to verify that $\{U_{s(x)}\}_{x\in K} \cup \{U_{s_i}\}_{i=1}^{\infty}$ is a countable subcovering of the covering $\{U_s\}_{s\in S}$. Thus X is a Lindelöf space. It is a separable Lindelöf space which satisfies the first axiom of countability but does not satisfy the second one. ∎

EXAMPLE 3. In Example 2.3.2 we showed that the Cartesian product of the space considered in Example 2 with itself is not normal. Making use of Theorem 2 we infer that the Cartesian product of two Lindelöf spaces is not necessarily a Lindelöf space. ∎

EXERCISES

A. Let X be a regular space and let $\{A_i\}_{i=1}^{\infty}$ denote a family of its subspaces such that $\bigcup_{i=1}^{\infty} A_i = X$. Show that if A_i is a Lindelöf space for $i = 1, 2, \ldots$, then X is also a Lindelöf space. Deduce that a subset of a Lindelöf space which is an F_σ-set is also a Lindelöf space.

B. We say that X is a *hereditarily Lindelöf space* if every subspace $M \subset X$ is a Lindelöf space.

Show that X is a hereditarily Lindelöf space if and only if every open subspace $M \subset X$ is a Lindelöf space. Prove that every open subset of a hereditarily Lindelöf space is an F_σ-set.

Give an example of a non-hereditarily Lindelöf space and show that the space considered in Example 2 is a hereditarily Lindelöf space.

C. Prove that for a locally compact space X the following conditions are equivalent:

(i) X is a Lindelöf space.

(ii) $X = \bigcup_{i=1}^{\infty} A_i$, where $A_i \subset \operatorname{Int} A_{i+1}$ and A_i is compact for $i = 1, 2, \ldots$

(iii) X is compact or ωX has a countable base at the point Ω.

D. Making use of Theorem 2.8, prove that the Cartesian product of a Lindelöf space by a compact space, is a Lindelöf space.

E. (M. E. Rudin and V. L. Klee, jr. [1956], E. Michael [1961]). Show that if X and Y are spaces satisfying the second axiom of countability and Y is regular, then the space Y^X with the pointwise topology and with the compact-open topology is *hereditarily separable* (i.e. every subset of it is separable) and hereditarily Lindelöf. Thus it is hereditarily normal.

Hint: Let $\mathfrak{B}$ and $\mathfrak{D}$ be countable bases in X and Y, respectively. Consider a topology in Y^X generated by a base consisting of the sets of the form $\bigcap_{i=1}^{k} M(U_i, V_i)$, where $U_i \in \mathfrak{B}$, $V_i \in \mathfrak{D}$ for $i = 1, 2, \ldots, k$, and make use of Theorem 3.6.

§ 8. Spaces complete in the sense of Čech. We shall prove a theorem analogous to Theorem 6.6.

THEOREM 1. *For every Tychonoff space X the following conditions are equivalent*:

(i) *For every compactification cX of the space X the remainder $cX \setminus c(X)$ is an F_σ-set in cX.*

(ii) *The remainder $\beta X \setminus \beta(X)$ is an F_σ-set in βX.*

(iii) *There exists a compactification cX of the space X such that the remainder $cX \setminus c(X)$ is an F_σ-set in cX.*

Proof. Implications (i) $\Rightarrow$ (ii) $\Rightarrow$ (iii) are obvious. In order to prove our theorem it is therefore sufficient to show that (iii) $\Rightarrow$ (i).

First, let us note that (iii) $\Rightarrow$ (ii). By the maximality of βX, there exists $f\colon \beta X \to cX$ such that $f\beta = c$. By virtue of Theorem 4.7, we infer that $f^{-1}(cX \setminus c(X)) = \beta X \setminus \beta(X)$. Since $cX \setminus c(X) = \bigcup_{i=1}^{\infty} F_i$, where $F_i = \overline{F}_i$, the equality $\beta X \setminus \beta(X) = \bigcup_{i=1}^{\infty} f^{-1}(F_i)$ holds, and the remainder $\beta X \setminus \beta(X)$ is an F_σ-set.

We shall now show that (ii) $\Rightarrow$ (i). In fact, if $\beta X \setminus \beta(X) = \bigcup_{i=1}^{\infty} F_i$, where $F_i = \overline{F}_i$, then by Theorem 4.7, $cX \setminus c(X) = \bigcup_{i=1}^{\infty} f(F_i)$, where $f\colon \beta X \to cX$ is a mapping such that $f\beta = c$. Since $f(F_i)$ is a closed subset of cX, $cX \setminus c(X)$ is an F_σ-set. ■

A topological space X is said to be *complete in the sense of Čech* if X is a Tychonoff space and satisfies one of the equivalent conditions (i), (ii), (iii) of Theorem 1 (and hence all the conditions).

Let us observe that every compact space is complete in the sense of Čech. Indeed, if X is compact, then the remainder of its unique compactification is empty, whence it is an F_σ-set.

Locally compact spaces are also complete in the sense of Čech, for every locally compact but non-compact space X has the compactification ωX with a single-point remainder which is evidently closed.

The definition of spaces complete in the sense of Čech adopted above is extrinsic, that is, it characterizes the spaces complete in the sense of Čech by their relations to other topological spaces, namely their compactifications. Now we shall give an intrinsic characterization of these spaces.

To begin with, we shall introduce the following notion. We say that the *diameter* of a subset M of a topological space X *is less* than a covering $\mathfrak{A} = \{A_s\}_{s\in S}$ of this space and we write $\delta(M) < \mathfrak{A}$, provided that there exists an $s \in S$ such that $M \subset A_s$.

THEOREM 2. *A Tychonoff space X is complete in the sense of Čech if and only if there exists a countable family $\{\mathfrak{A}_i\}_{i=1}^\infty$ of open coverings of the space X such that for every family of closed sets $\{F_s\}_{s\in S}$ which has the finite intersection property and contains sets of diameters less than $\mathfrak{A}_i$ for $i = 1, 2, \ldots$, the inequality $\bigcap_{s\in S} F_s \neq 0$ holds.*

Proof. Let us suppose that there exists in $X \subset \beta X$ a family $\{\mathfrak{A}_i\}_{i=1}^\infty$ consisting of open coverings which has the required property. Let $\mathfrak{A}_i = \{U_s^{(i)}\}_{s\in S_i}$ for $i = 1, 2, \ldots$ and let $V_s^{(i)}$ denote such an open set in βX that $U_s^{(i)} = V_s^{(i)} \cap X$ for $s \in S_i$ and $i = 1, 2, \ldots$ Evidently

$$X \subset \bigcap_{i=1}^{\infty} \Big(\bigcup_{s\in S_i} V_s^{(i)} \Big).$$

In order to prove that the condition is satisfactory it is sufficient to show that the converse inclusion also holds.

Let x be an arbitrary point of the set $\bigcap_{i=1}^{\infty} \big(\bigcup_{s\in S_i} V_s^{(i)} \big)$, and let $\mathfrak{B}(x)$ denote the family of all its neighbourhoods in the space βX. The family $\mathfrak{F} = \{\overline{V} \cap X\}_{V\in\mathfrak{B}(x)}$, where $\overline{A}$ denotes the closure of the set A in the space βX, consists of closed subsets of the space X and has the finite intersection property. Since for every i there exists an $s \in S_i$ such that $x \in V_s^{(i)}$, and since the space βX is regular, the family $\mathfrak{F}$ contains a set of diameter less than $\mathfrak{A}_i$ for $i = 1, 2, \ldots$ By assumption, $X \cap \bigcap_{V\in\mathfrak{B}(x)} \overline{V} \neq 0$, and since $\bigcap_{V\in\mathfrak{B}(x)} \overline{V} = \{x\}$, we have $x \in X$.

Let us now assume that X is a G_δ-set in βX, i.e. that there exists a family $\{G_i\}_{i=1}^\infty$ of sets open in βX such that $X = \bigcap_{i=1}^{\infty} G_i$. For every

$x \in X$ and $i = 1, 2, \dots$ let $V_x^{(i)}$ denote an open set in βX such that $x \in V_x^{(i)} \subset \overline{V_x^{(i)}} \subset G_i$. We shall show that the family $\{\mathfrak{A}_i\}_{i=1}^{\infty}$ of open coverings of the space X, where $\mathfrak{A}_i = \{X \cap V_x^{(i)}{}_{x \in X}\}$, has the required property.

Let $\{F_s\}_{s \in S}$ denote a family of closed subsets of X which has the finite intersection property and contains a set of diameter less than $\mathfrak{A}_i$ for $i = 1, 2, \dots$ The family $\{\overline{F}_s\}_{s \in S}$ has the finite intersection property and consists of closed subsets of the space βX. Hence there exists a point $x \in \bigcap_{s \in S} \overline{F}_s$. Since $F_s = X \cap \overline{F}_s$, in order to prove that $x \in \bigcap_{s \in S} F_s$ it is sufficient to show that $x \in X$.

For every natural number i let us choose $s_i \in S$ such that $\delta(F_{s_i}) < \mathfrak{A}_i$. For some $x_i \in X$ we thus have $F_{s_i} \subset X \cap V_{x_i}^{(i)}$. Since

$$x \in \overline{F}_{s_i} \subset \overline{X \cap V_{x_i}^{(i)}} \subset \overline{V_{x_i}^{(i)}} \subset G_i$$

for $i = 1, 2, \dots$, $x \in X = \bigcap_{i=1}^{\infty} G_i$ holds. ■

THEOREM 3. *Completeness in the sense of Čech is a hereditary property with respect to closed subspaces and subspaces which are G_δ-sets.*

Proof. Let X be a space complete in the sense of Čech and let $M \subset X$ denote a closed subspace. Let us consider an arbitrary compactification cX of the space X. Clearly $cX \setminus c(X) = \bigcup_{i=1}^{\infty} F_i$, where F_i is a closed subset of cX for $i = 1, 2, \dots$ Since M is closed in the space X, we infer from Theorem 2.1.1 that $c(M) = c(X) \cap \overline{c(M)}$, whence $\overline{c(M)} \setminus c(M) = \overline{c(M)} \cap (cX \setminus c(X))$ and $\overline{c(M)} \setminus c(M) = \bigcup_{i=1}^{\infty} \overline{c(M)} \cap F_i$. But $\overline{c(M)} \subset cX$ is a compactification of the space M, so we have that M is complete in the sense of Čech.

Let X be a space complete in the sense of Čech and let $M \subset X$ denote a subspace which is a G_δ-set. Let us consider an arbitrary compactification cX of the space X. The set $c(X)$ is a G_δ-set in cX, so that $c(M)$ is also a G_δ-set in cX and also in the set $\overline{c(M)}$ which is a compactification of M. The set $\overline{c(M)} \setminus c(M)$ is therefore an F_σ-set. ■

THEOREM 4. *The sum $\bigoplus_{s \in S} X_s$ of a family $\{X_s\}_{s \in S}$ consisting of disjoint topological spaces is complete in the sense of Čech if and only if for every $s \in S$ the space X_s is complete in the sense of Čech.*

Proof. If $\bigoplus_{s \in S} X_s$ is complete in the sense of Čech, then all spaces X_s, being closed in $\bigoplus_{s \in S} X_s$, are complete in the sense of Čech.

Let us now assume that all the spaces of the family $\{X_s\}_{s \in S}$ are complete in the sense of Čech. Let cX_s denote an arbitrary compactification of the space X_s; thus $cX_s \setminus c(X_s) = \bigcup_{i=1}^{\infty} F_i^{(s)}$, where $F_i^{(s)}$ is a closed subset of cX_s. By virtue of Theorem 6.4, the space $X = \bigoplus_{s \in S} cX_s$ is locally compact, therefore complete in the sense of Čech. Since $X \setminus \bigoplus_{s \in S} X_s = \bigcup_{i=1}^{\infty} \big(\bigcup_{s \in S} F_i^{(s)}\big)$, and since by Theorem 2.2.1, the sets $\bigcup_{s \in S} F_i^{(s)}$ are closed in X, $\bigoplus_{s \in S} X_s$ is, by Theorem 3, complete in the sense of Čech. ■

THEOREM 5. *The Cartesian product of a countable number of spaces complete in the sense of Čech is complete in the sense of Čech.*

Proof. Let $\{X_i\}_{i=1}^{\infty}$ denote a family of spaces which are complete in the sense of Čech. Let us consider an arbitrary compactification $c_i X_i$ of the space X_i, for $i = 1, 2, \ldots$ The remainder $c_i X_i \setminus c_i(X_i)$ is an F_σ-set in $c_i X_i$ for $i = 1, 2, \ldots$

By Corollary 2 to Theorem 2.3.2, the space $cX = \mathop{\boldsymbol{P}}_{i=1}^{\infty} c_i X_i$ is a compactification of the product $X = \mathop{\boldsymbol{P}}_{i=1}^{\infty} X_i$, for the mapping $c = \mathop{\boldsymbol{P}}_{i=1}^{\infty} c_i$ is a homeomorphic embedding, $c\colon X \to cX$. The set $F_j = \mathop{\boldsymbol{P}}_{i=1}^{\infty} A_{i,j}$, where $A_{j,j} = c_j X_j \setminus c_j(X_j)$ and $A_{i,j} = c_i X_i$ for $i \neq j$, is an F_σ-set in cX. Since $cX \setminus c(X) = \bigcup_{j=1}^{\infty} F_j$, $X = \mathop{\boldsymbol{P}}_{i=1}^{\infty} X_i$ is complete in the sense of Čech. ■

The following theorem is fundamental for spaces complete in the sense of Čech.

THEOREM 6 (Baire). *Let X be a space complete in the sense of Čech and let $N_1, N_2, \ldots$ be a sequence of nowhere dense sets in X. The union $N = \bigcup_{i=1}^{\infty} N_i$ is a boundary set in X.*

Proof. It is sufficient to show that the set $G \setminus N$ is non-empty for every non-empty open subset $G \subset X$.

Let $\{\mathfrak{A}_i\}_{i=1}^{\infty}$ denote a family of open coverings of the space X such that every family of closed subsets of the space X, which has the finite intersection property and contains sets of diameter less than $\mathfrak{A}_i$ for $i = 1, 2, \ldots$, has a non-empty intersection.

Since the set N_1 is nowhere dense, there exist a point $x \in G \setminus \overline{N}_1$ and a neighbourhood G_1 of x such that

$$0 \neq \overline{G}_1 \subset G \setminus \overline{N}_1 \quad \text{and} \quad \delta(\overline{G}_1) < \mathfrak{A}_1.$$

Similarly, since $G_1 \setminus \overline{N}_2$ is a non-empty, open set, there exists a non-empty open set G_2 such that

$$0 \neq \overline{G}_2 \subset G_1 \setminus \overline{N}_2 \quad \text{and} \quad \delta(\overline{G}_2) < \mathfrak{A}_2.$$

We define inductively a sequence $G_1, G_2, \ldots$ of non-empty, open subsets of the space X in such a manner that

$$G \supset \bar{G}_1 \supset \bar{G}_2 \supset \ldots, \quad \bar{G}_i \cap N_i = 0 \quad \text{and} \quad \delta(\bar{G}_i) < \mathfrak{A}_i.$$

It is easy to verify that $0 \neq \bigcap_{i=1}^{\infty} \bar{G}_i \subset G \setminus N$. ■

The following corollary is another frequently used formulation of the Baire Theorem.

COROLLARY. *The intersection of a countable number of dense and open subsets of a space X complete in the sense of Čech, is dense in X.* ■

EXERCISES

A. Prove that the space of rational numbers considered as a subspace of the real-line is not complete in the sense of Čech. Deduce that the set of irrational numbers is not an F_σ-set.

B. Prove that if a space X, which is complete in the sense of Čech, is a subspace of a Tychonoff space Y, then there exists a G_δ-set Z in Y such that $X = \bar{X} \cap Z$.

§ 9. Countably compact spaces. Pseudo-compact spaces. A topological space X is said to be *countably compact* if X is a Hausdorff space and every open, countable covering $\{U_i\}_{i=1}^{\infty}$ contains a finite subcovering $\{U_{i_j}\}_{j=1}^{k}$. Every compact space is obviously countably compact. We shall learn further that there exist countably compact spaces which are not compact.

THEOREM 1. *In order that a space X be compact it is necessary and sufficient that X be countably compact and have the Lindelöf property.*

Proof. Every compact space is evidently a countably compact Lindelöf space. If X is a countably compact Lindelöf space, then every open covering of it has a countable subcovering, and this subcovering has a finite subcovering. ■

The following four theorems are analogous to Theorems 1.1-1.3 and 1.8. The proofs are also analogous.

THEOREM 2. *A Hausdorff space X is countably compact if and only if every countable family of closed subsets $\{F_i\}_{i=1}^{\infty}$ which possesses the finite intersection property has the non-empty intersection.* ■

THEOREM 3. *A closed subspace of a countably compact space is countably compact.* ■

THEOREM 4. *If a subspace A of a topological space X is countably compact, then from every countable family $\{U_i\}_{i=1}^{\infty}$ of open subsets of X such that $A \subset \bigcup_{i=1}^{\infty} U_i$, we can choose a finite family $\{U_{i_1}, U_{i_2}, \ldots, U_{i_k}\}$ such that $A \subset \bigcup_{j=1}^{k} U_{i_j}$.* ■

THEOREM 5. *Let X be a countably compact space and Y a Hausdorff space. If there exists a mapping f of the space X onto the space Y, then the space Y is also countably compact.* ■

The countable compactness of a space does not imply its normality. What is more, there exist countably compact spaces which are not even regular (see Problem O).

We shall give one more condition equivalent to countable compactness, which is frequently used.

THEOREM 6. *A Hausdorff space X is countably compact if and only if every infinite countable subset $A \subset X$ has an accumulation point, i.e. if $A^{d} \neq 0$ for every $A \subset X$ such that $\overline{\overline{A}} = \aleph_0$.*

Proof. Let us suppose that X is a countably compact space. Let $A = \{x_1, x_2, \ldots\}$ be an arbitrary infinite countable subset of X such that $x_i \neq x_j$ for $i \neq j$. Let us assume that $F_n = \overline{\{x_n, x_{n+1}, \ldots\}} \subset \overline{A}$. By virtue of Theorem 2, there exists an $x \in \bigcap_{n=1}^{\infty} F_n$. It can easily be verified that x is an accumulation point of the set A.

Let us now assume that the Hausdorff space X is not countably compact. By Theorem 2, there exists a family $\{F_i\}_{i=1}^{\infty}$ of closed subsets of X which has the finite intersection property and is such that $\bigcap_{i=1}^{\infty} F_i = 0$. Let us choose a point $x_n \in F_1 \cap F_2 \cap \ldots \cap F_n$ for every n and let $A = \{x_1, x_2, \ldots\}$. The set A is infinite, for otherwise one of the points of A would belong to infinitely many of the sets $F_1 \cap F_2 \cap \ldots \cap F_n$ and $\bigcap_{i=1}^{\infty} F_i \neq 0$ would hold. We shall show that $A^{d} = 0$. Indeed, by formulas (2) and (3) of Theorem 1.3.4, for $i = 1, 2, \ldots$ we have

$$A^{d} \subset (F_i \cup \{x_1, x_2, \ldots, x_{i-1}\})^{d} = F_i^{d} \cup \{x_1, x_2, \ldots, x_{i-1}\}^{d}$$
$$= F_i^{d} \subset \overline{F}_i = F_i,$$

because in a T_1-space the derived set of a finite set is empty. Hence it follows that $A^{d} \subset \bigcap_{i=1}^{\infty} F_i = 0$. ■

From Theorem 6 the following corollary can easily be deduced.

COROLLARY. *A Hausdorff space X is countably compact if and only if for every infinite $A \subset X$ we have $A^{d} \neq 0$.* ■

Every subspace of the real-line R satisfies the second axiom of countability. Hence every countably compact subspace of R is compact according to Theorems 7.1 and 1. Theorem 2.7 implies

THEOREM 7. *Every real-valued continuous function defined on a countably compact space is bounded.* ■

We leave to the reader the proof of the following

THEOREM 8. *The sum* $\bigoplus_{s \in S} X_s$ *of the family* $\{X_s\}_{s \in S}$ *consisting of disjoint and non-empty topological spaces is countably compact if and only if the set* S *is finite and for every* $s \in S$ *the space* X_s *is countably compact.* ■

Countably compact spaces were defined earlier than compact spaces. For a time they were even considered to be more important than compact spaces. The reason was that for the broad and important class of metrizable spaces the definitions were equivalent. At that time countably compact spaces were called compact while compact spaces were called *bicompact*, but now the terminology adopted in this book is generally used. Compact spaces are more important than countably compact spaces because the class of compact spaces is closed with respect to the Cartesian product. As we are going to show in Example 4, the property of countable compactness is not multiplicative.

EXAMPLE 1. The space X_0 of all ordinal numbers less than ω_1 is an example of a countably compact space which is not compact. The space X_0 is not compact, for it is different from its closure in the space $X = \beta X_0 = X_0 \cup \{\omega_1\}$. For every countable subset $A \subset X_0$ there exists a point $x_0 < \omega_1$ such that $A \subset X_1 = [0, x_0]$. Since X_1 is a closed subset of the compact space X, we have $A^{\mathrm{d}} \neq 0$, which proves that the space X_0 is countably compact. ■

EXAMPLE 2. We shall give one more example of a countably compact space which is not compact. Let us consider the Tychonoff cube $I^{\mathfrak{c}} = \boldsymbol{P}_{r \in R} I_r$, where R denotes the set of all real numbers and $I_r = I$ for $r \in R$. Let us denote by X the subspace of $I^{\mathfrak{c}}$ consisting of those points which have at most countably many coordinates different from zero. Since X is dense in $I^{\mathfrak{c}}$ and different from $I^{\mathfrak{c}}$, it is not compact. We shall show that X is countably compact. By virtue of Theorem 6, it is sufficient to show that for every infinite countable subset A of X we have the inequality $A^{\mathrm{d}} \neq 0$. Let $A \subset X$ be an infinite countable subset. There exists a countable subset $R_0 \subset R$ such that for every $x \in A$ and $r \in R \setminus R_0$ we have $p_r(x) = 0$, where p_r denotes the projection onto the r-th axis. The set A is therefore a subset of the product $\boldsymbol{P}_{r \in R} X_r$, where $X_r = I_r$ for $r \in R_0$ and $X_r = \{0\}$ for $r \in R \setminus R_0$. This product is compact by virtue of the Tychonoff Theorem, whence it is countably compact. By Theorem 6, the set A has an accumulation point in $\boldsymbol{P}_{r \in R} X_r$. Since $\boldsymbol{P}_{r \in R} X_r \subset X$, A has an accumulation point in X, so that $A^{\mathrm{d}} \neq 0$. ■

EXAMPLE 3. The space $X = \beta N \setminus \{x\}$, where $x \in \beta N \setminus N$, is another example of a non-compact but countably compact space. In fact, for every countable infinite subset $A \subset X \subset \beta N$, $\overline{\overline{(\overline{A})}} = 2^{\mathfrak{c}}$ according to

Theorem 5.4. Hence it follows that $\overline{\overline{A^d}} = 2^{\mathfrak{c}}$ and $A^d \cap X \neq 0$. Thus the set A has accumulation points in the space X. On the other hand, X is not compact, for it contains a dense subset of the space βN and is different from βN. ■

EXAMPLE 4. We shall define here two countably compact spaces, X and Y, whose Cartesian product is not countably compact. They are subspaces of the space βN such that $X \cup Y = \beta N$ and $X \cap Y = N$.

Let us denote by $\mathfrak{P}(M)$ the family of all infinite countable subsets of the set $M \subset \beta N$. Let us assume that the function f assigns to every element $S \in \mathfrak{P}(\beta N)$ an accumulation point of the set S in βN.

We shall define a sequence of sets $X_0, X_1, \ldots, X_\alpha, \ldots, \alpha < \omega_1$ by means of transfinite induction. Let $X_0 = N$ and

$$X_\alpha = \bigcup_{\gamma<\alpha} X_\gamma \cup f[\mathfrak{P}(\bigcup_{\gamma<\alpha} X_\gamma)] \quad \text{for} \quad \alpha < \omega_1.$$

The space $X = \bigcup_{\alpha<\omega_1} X_\alpha$ is countably compact, because every set $S \in \mathfrak{P}(X)$ is contained in some X_α for $\alpha < \omega_1$, whence it has an accumulation point in $X_{\alpha+1}$ (and thus in X). By transfinite induction it can be proved that $\overline{\overline{X}}_\alpha \leqslant \mathfrak{c}\cdot\mathfrak{c} + (\mathfrak{c}\cdot\mathfrak{c})^{\aleph_0} = \mathfrak{c}$, whence $\overline{\overline{X}} \leqslant \mathfrak{c}\cdot\mathfrak{c} = \mathfrak{c}$. Let us set $Y = N \cup (\beta N \setminus X)$. Since, by virtue of Theorem 5.4, $\overline{\overline{(\overline{S})}} = 2^{\mathfrak{c}}$ for every $S \in \mathfrak{P}(Y)$, we have $0 \neq S^d \cap (\beta N \setminus X) \subset S^d \cap Y$. Thus the space Y contains accumulation points of every countable set $S \subset Y$ and is countably compact.

It can be seen that the Cartesian product of the spaces X, Y constructed above is not countably compact. Indeed, the set $\Delta_1 = \{(n, n)\}_{n=1}^{\infty} \subset X \times Y$ is an infinite subset of the product $X \times Y$ which has no accumulation point in $X \times Y$, for $\overline{\Delta}_1 \subset \Delta$ and $\Delta \cap (X \times Y) = \Delta_1$, where $\Delta = \{(x, x) : x \in \beta N\}$. ■

We shall now study the other class of spaces closely connected with compact spaces.

A topological space X is called *pseudo-compact* if X is a Tychonoff space and every real-valued continuous function defined on X is bounded. Theorem 7 implies

THEOREM 9. *Every countably compact Tychonoff space is pseudo-compact.* ■

For normal spaces the converse theorem is valid.

THEOREM 10. *If a normal space is pseudo-compact, then it is countably compact.*

Proof. Let us suppose that the normal space X is not countably compact, i.e. that there exists a subset $A = \{x_1, x_2, \ldots\} \subset X$ such that $x_i \neq y_i$ for $i \neq j$ and $A^d = 0$. Evidently $A = \overline{A}$. Hence by the Tietze-Urysohn Theorem the function $f: A \to R$, defined by means of the formula

$f(x_i) = i$ for $i = 1, 2, \ldots$, is extendable over X. The space X is not pseudo-compact, hovewer, for f is not bounded. ∎

The proofs of the following two theorems are left to the reader.

THEOREM 11. *If X is a pseudo-compact space and $f: X \to Y$ is a mapping onto a Tychonoff space Y, then Y is also a pseudo-compact space.* ∎

THEOREM 12. *The sum $\bigoplus_{s \in S} X_s$ of the family $\{X_s\}_{s \in S}$ of disjoint and non-empty topological spaces is pseudo-compact if and only if the set S is finite and for every $s \in S$ the space X_s is pseudo-compact.* ∎

We shall now give an example of a pseudo-compact space which is not countably compact.

EXAMPLE 5. Let R be the set of all real numbers and let $N \subset R$ be the set of natural numbers. By virtue of Corollary 7 to Theorem 5.1, βN is a subset of the space βR. The space $X = \beta R \setminus (\beta N \setminus N)$ is not countably compact, for the set N has no accumulation point in X. Let us consider an arbitrary continuous function $f: X \to R$ and let us assume that the image $f(X)$ is not bounded. The set $R \setminus N$ is dense in X, whence there exists a sequence $x_1, x_2, \ldots$ of points belonging to $R \setminus N$ such that $|f(x_n)| \geqslant n$. Since the function f is continuous, the set $A = \bigcup_{n=1}^{\infty} \{x_n\}$ does not have accumulation points in X. If we denote by $\bar{A}$ the closure of the set A in βR, then $\bar{A} \cap X = A$; in particular it follows that A is closed in R. By Corollary 3 to Theorem 5.1, $\bar{A} \cap \bar{N} = \bar{A} \cap \beta N = 0$, i.e. $\bar{A} \subset \beta R \setminus \beta N \subset X$ and $A = \bar{A}$. Hence it follows that A is an infinite compact set with the empty derived set. This contradiction proves that the function f is bounded, i.e. that the space X is pseudo-compact.

Since N is a closed subset of X, a closed subset of a pseudo-compact space is not necessarily pseudo-compact.

Example 4 also shows that the Cartesian product of pseudo-compact spaces is not necessarily pseudo-compact. In fact, by Corollary 4 to Theorem 5.1 for every $n \in N$ the set $\overline{\{n\}} = \{n\}$ is open in βN; thus the set $\Delta_1 = \{(n, n)\}_{n=1}^{\infty}$ is open in $\beta N \times \beta N$ and in $X \times Y$. It follows that $\Delta_1 \subset X \times Y$ is closed and open in $X \times Y$. The function $f: X \times Y \to R$, defined by means of the formula $f(n, n) = n$ for $n \in N$ and $f(x, y) = 0$ for $(x, y) \notin \Delta_1$, is continuous and not bounded. Hence $X \times Y$ is not pseudo-compact. ∎

EXERCISES

A. Prove that a Hausdorff space X is countably compact if and only if every closed and countable subspace $A \subset X$ is compact.

B. Prove that the Cartesian product of a countably compact space by a compact space is countably compact.

Hint: Make use of Theorem 2.8.

C (P. Alexandroff and P. Urysohn [1929]). Let $X = C_0 \cup C_1 \subset R\times R$, where $C_0 = \{(x, 0): 0 < x \leqslant 1\}$ and $C_1 = \{(x, 1): 0 \leqslant x < 1\}$. Let us assume that the base at the point $(x_0, 0) \in C_0$ consists of the sets of the form

$$\{(x, i) \in X: x_0 - 1/n < x < x_0\} \cup \{(x_0, 0)\} \quad \text{for} \quad n = 1, 2, \ldots,$$

and that the base at the point $(x_0, 1) \in C_1$ consists of the sets of the form

$$\{(x, i) \in X: x_0 < x < x_0 + 1/n\} \cup \{(x_0, 1)\} \quad \text{for} \quad n = 1, 2, \ldots$$

Show that the topological space defined above is hereditarily Lindelöf and compact.

Hint: Make use of Exercise 7.A. In order to prove that the space is compact it is sufficient to note that X is countably compact.

D (J. Colmez [1951]). Prove that a Tychonoff space X is pseudo-compact if and only if for an arbitrary countable family of open sets $\{G_i\}_{i=1}^{\infty}$ which has the finite intersection property, the inequality $\bigcap_{i=1}^{\infty} \overline{G_i} \neq 0$ holds.

E (R. W. Bagley, E. H. Connell and J. D. McKnight [1958]). Prove that the Cartesian product of a pseudo-compact space with a compact space is pseudo-compact.

F. Show that a Tychonoff space X is pseudo-compact if and only if every real-valued continuous function defined on X assumes its bounds.

§ 10. Real-compact spaces. A topological space X is called *real-compact* if X is a Tychonoff space, and there does not exist a Tychonoff space $\tilde{X}$ which satisfies the following two conditions:

(RC1) *There exists a homeomorphism* $r: X \to r(X) \subset \tilde{X}$ *such that* $r(X) \neq \overline{r(X)} = \tilde{X}$.

(RC2) *For every mapping* $f: X \to R$ *there exists a mapping* $\tilde{f}: \tilde{X} \to R$ *such that* $\tilde{f}r = f$.

It follows from the definition that every compact space is real-compact.

LEMMA 1. *Let X be a topological space and let A be a subspace of X. If every function $g: A \to R$, such that $g(x) \geqslant 1$ for all $x \in A$, is extendable over X, then every function $f: A \to R$ can be extended over X.*

Proof. For an arbitrary function $f: A \to R$ let

$$g_1(x) = 1 + \max\big(f(x), 0\big) \quad \text{and} \quad g_2(x) = 1 - \min\big(f(x), 0\big).$$

It can easily be verified that $g_i: A \to R$ and $g_i(x) \geqslant 1$, for $i = 1, 2$ and $x \in X$. Since $f(x) = g_1(x) - g_2(x)$ for every $x \in A$, the function $F: X \to R$, where $F(x) = G_1(x) - G_2(x)$ and where $G_i: X \to R$ is an extension of g_i for $i = 1, 2$, is an extension of the function f. ∎

LEMMA 2. *Let X be a topological space and let $A \subset X$ be a subspace of X. If every function $f: A \to R$ is extendable over X, then every mapping $f: A \to \underset{s\in S}{\boldsymbol{P}} R_s$ into the Cartesian product of a number of real-lines is also* *extendable. Moreover, if* $\bar{A} = X$, *then every mapping* $f\colon A \to B = \bar{B} \subset \mathop{\boldsymbol{P}}_{s\in S} R_s$ *into a closed subspace of this product is also extendable.*

Proof. For an arbitrary mapping $f\colon A \to \mathop{\boldsymbol{P}}_{s\in S} R_s$ let us consider the extension $\tilde{f}_s\colon X \to R_s$ of the function $p_s f\colon A \to R_s$. It is easy to verify that the mapping $F = \mathop{\triangle}_{s\in S} \tilde{f}_s\colon X \to \mathop{\boldsymbol{P}}_{s\in S} R_s$ is an extension of f. If $\bar{A} = X$ and $f(A) \subset B = \bar{B} \subset \mathop{\boldsymbol{P}}_{s\in S} R_s$, then for the extension $F\colon X \to \mathop{\boldsymbol{P}}_{s\in S} R_s$ we have $F(X) = F(\bar{A}) \subset \overline{F(A)} \subset \bar{B} = B$, so that $F\colon X \to B$. ∎

THEOREM 1. *A Tychonoff space* X *is real-compact if and only if for every point* $x_0 \in \beta X \setminus \beta(X)$ *there exists a function* $h\colon \beta X \to I$ *such that* $h(x_0) = 0$ *and* $h(x) > 0$ *for* $x \in \beta(X)$.

Proof. Let us suppose that X is a real-compact space and let us consider an arbitrary point $x_0 \in \beta X \setminus \beta(X)$. Since $\tilde{X} = \beta(X) \cup \{x_0\} \subset \beta X$ is a Tychonoff space satisfying condition (RC1), there exists a function $f\colon \beta(X) \to R$ which is not extendable over $\tilde{X}$. By virtue of Lemma 1, we can assume that $f(x) \geqslant 1$ for $x \in \beta(X)$. The function $h_0\colon \beta(X) \to I$ defined by means of the formula $h_0(x) = [f(x)]^{-1}$ is extendable over βX; let $h\colon \beta X \to I$ be its extension. In order to complete the proof it is sufficient to verify that $h(x_0) = 0$. But if $h(x_0) = a \neq 0$, then the function $f\colon \beta(X) \to R$ would be extendable to the function $\tilde{f}\colon \tilde{X} \to R$ defined by means of the formula $\tilde{f}(x) = [h(x)]^{-1}$, contrary to the assumption.

Let us now assume that the space X is not real-compact. Then there exists a space $\tilde{X}$ containing X as a dense proper subset and such that every function $g\colon X \to R$ can be extended over $\tilde{X}$. We can assume without loss of generality that $\tilde{X} \setminus X = \{\tilde{x}\}$. Theorem 2.5 implies that

$$\beta X \subset I^{w(\beta X)} \subset \mathop{\boldsymbol{P}}_{s\in S} R_s,$$

where $R_s = R$ for every $s \in S$ and $\bar{\bar{S}} = w(\beta X)$. Thus, by virtue of Lemma 2, there exists an extension $\tilde{\beta}\colon \tilde{X} \to \beta X$ of the mapping $\beta\colon X \to \beta X$, and by the lemma to Theorem 4.7, the point $x_0 = \tilde{\beta}(\tilde{x})$ belongs to $\beta X \setminus \beta(X)$.

We shall now show that $h(x_0) > 0$ for every function $h\colon \beta X \to I$ such that $h(x) > 0$ for $x \in \beta(X)$.

For every function $h\colon \beta X \to I$ which satisfies the inequality $h(x) > 0$ for $x \in \beta(X)$ the formula $g(x) = [h\beta(x)]^{-1}$ defines a function $g\colon X \to R$. Since $g(x) \geqslant 1$ for $x \in X$, we have $\tilde{g}(\tilde{x}) \geqslant 1$ for the extension $\tilde{g}\colon \tilde{X} \to R$. But the functions $(\tilde{g})^{-1}$ and $h\beta$ are identical on the space X, whence $h(x_0) = \tilde{h}(\beta(\tilde{x})) = [\tilde{g}(\tilde{x})]^{-1} > 0$. ∎

THEOREM 2. *Every Lindelöf space is real-compact.*

Proof. Let us suppose that X is a Lindelöf space and let $x_0 \in \beta X \setminus \beta(X)$. For every point $x \in X$ let us consider a function $f_x \colon \beta X \to I$ such that $f_x(x_0) = 0$ and $f_x(\beta(x)) = 1$. Assuming $U_x = f_x^{-1}((\frac{1}{2}, 1])$ for $x \in X$, we infer from Theorem 7.5 that there exists a sequence $\{x_i\}$ of points of the space X such that $\beta(X) \subset \bigcup_{i=1}^{\infty} U_{x_i}$. The function $h \colon \beta X \to I$, where $h(x) = \sum_{i=1}^{\infty} \frac{1}{2^i} f_{x_i}(x)$, is continuous according to Theorem 1.4.2. It can easily be verified that $h(x_0) = 0$ and $h(x) > 0$ for $x \in \beta(X)$. ■

THEOREM 3. *In order that a space X be compact it is necessary and sufficient that X be pseudo-compact and real-compact.*

Proof. Every compact space is pseudo-compact and real-compact. If a non-compact space X is real-compact, then, since $\tilde{X} = \beta X \neq \beta(X)$ satisfies condition (RC1), there exists a function $f \colon X \to R$ which is not extendable over βX. The function f cannot be bounded; thus the space X is not pseudo-compact. ■

EXAMPLE 1. From the last theorem it follows that all the spaces considered in the examples of Paragraph 9 are not real-compact. ■

EXAMPLE 2. We shall give here an example of a real-compact space which is not a Lindelöf space. The discrete space of power $\mathfrak{c}$ proves to be a good example (cf. Exercise 1.F and Theorem 4).

Let g be an arbitrary one-to-one function of the discrete space X of power $\mathfrak{c}$ onto I. There exists an extension $G \colon \beta X \to I$ of the mapping g over βX. If we consider a point $x_0 \in \beta X \setminus \beta(X)$, then there exists exactly one point $x_1 \in \beta(X)$ such that $G(x_1) = G(x_0)$. Let $a \in I$ denote a number different from $G(x_1)$. Since x_1 is an isolated point of the space $\beta(X)$ and $\beta(X)$ is locally compact, x_1 is also an isolated point of the space βX. The function $G_1 \colon \beta X \to I$ defined by means of the formula

$$G_1(x) = \begin{cases} G(x) & \text{for} \quad x \neq x_1, \\ a & \text{for} \quad x = x_1 \end{cases}$$

is therefore continuous by Theorem 2.1.6. The function $f \colon \beta X \to I$ defined by the formula $f(x) = |G_1(x) - G(x_0)|$ is positive on $\beta(X)$ and vanishes at the point x_0. We infer from Theorem 1 that X is real-compact. ■

In connection with Example 2 the following question can be raised: is every discrete space real-compact? This problem is equivalent to the famous problem of set theory concerning the measurability of cardinal numbers.

Let $\mathfrak{A}$ be a family of sets with the property that for every sequence $A_1, A_2, \ldots$ of elements of $\mathfrak{A}$ the union $\bigcup_{i=1}^{\infty} A_i$ belongs to $\mathfrak{A}$. By a *countably additive two-valued measure* defined on $\mathfrak{A}$ we understand any function μ defined on $\mathfrak{A}$ which assumes the values 0 and 1 and is such that

$$\mu(\bigcup_{i=1}^{\infty} A_i) = \sum_{i=1}^{\infty} \mu(A_i),$$

where $A_i \in \mathfrak{A}$ for $i = 1, 2, \ldots$ and $A_i \cap A_j = 0$ for $i \neq j$.

A cardinal number $\mathfrak{m}$ is called *non-measurable* provided that the only countably additive two-valued measure defined on the family of all subsets of a set X of power $\mathfrak{m}$ which vanishes on single-point sets is identically equal to zero.

The class $\mathfrak{C}$ of non-measurable cardinal numbers obviously contains the number $\aleph_0$. It can be proved that if $\mathfrak{m} \in \mathfrak{C}$, then every cardinal number less than $\mathfrak{m}$, the sum of $\mathfrak{m}$ cardinal numbers belonging to $\mathfrak{C}$, and the number $2^{\mathfrak{m}}$, also belong to $\mathfrak{C}$. It has been proved lately that the least cardinal number which cannot be obtained from the number $\aleph_0$ by means of the operations described above (called the *first strongly inaccessible aleph*) also belongs to $\mathfrak{C}$.

The question whether every cardinal number is non-measurable is known as the *problem of measurability of cardinal numbers.*

It can be proved that the discrete space of power $\mathfrak{m}$ is real-compact if and only if $\mathfrak{m}$ is a non-measurable number (see Exercise E). By the above remarks, all discrete spaces are real-compact from the practical point of view. Indeed, measurable cardinal numbers, even if they exist, are so large that the definition of a set of such a power is practically impossible.

The proof of the following theorem, which gives an important characterization of real-compact spaces, is preceded by the following lemma.

LEMMA. *Let $\mathfrak{f}$ denote the family of all real-valued continuous functions defined on a Tychonoff space X. The mapping $F = \underset{f\in\mathfrak{f}}{\triangle} f\colon X \to \underset{f\in\mathfrak{f}}{\boldsymbol{P}} R_f$, where $R_f = R$ for every $f \in \mathfrak{f}$, is a homeomorphic embedding and is such that for every real-valued continuous function $f\colon X \to R$ there exists a function $\tilde{f}\colon \underset{f\in\mathfrak{f}}{\boldsymbol{P}} R_f \to R$ such that $\tilde{f}F = f$.*

Proof. It follows from the Diagonal Lemma that F is a homeomorphic embedding. It can easily be verified that $\tilde{f}$ can be defined as the projection $p_f\colon \underset{f\in\mathfrak{f}}{\boldsymbol{P}} R_f \to R_f = R$ onto the f-th axis of the product $\underset{f\in\mathfrak{f}}{\boldsymbol{P}} R_f$. ■

THEOREM 4. *A topological space is real-compact if and only if it is homeomorphic to a closed subset of the Cartesian product of a number of real-lines.*

Proof. Let us suppose that X is real compact. Let F be the mapping defined in the lemma. From the definition of a real-compact space and from the lemma it follows that $\overline{F(X)} = F(X)$. The space X is therefore homeomorphic to a closed subset of the product of real-lines.

Let us now assume that X is a closed subset of the Cartesian product of real-lines $\underset{s\in S}{\boldsymbol{P}} R_s$ and let $r: X \to \tilde{X}$ denote a homeomorphic embedding of X into a Tychonoff space $\tilde{X}$ which satisfies condition (RC2). We can evidently assume that $\overline{r(X)} = \tilde{X}$. For every $s \in S$ there exists a function $\tilde{p}_s: \tilde{X} \to R$ such that $\tilde{p}_s r = p_s$. It is an extension of the projection onto the s-th axis. Let $F = \underset{s\in S}{\triangle} \tilde{p}_s: \tilde{X} \to \underset{s\in S}{\boldsymbol{P}} R_s$. Now since $Fr(x) = x$, $F(\tilde{X}) = F\big(\overline{r(X)}\big) \subset \overline{Fr(X)} = \overline{X} = X$ holds and $F: \tilde{X} \to X$. The function $rF: \tilde{X} \to \tilde{X}$ is equal to the identity on $r(X)$, indeed, $rF\big(r(x)\big) = r(x)$ for every $x \in X$. By virtue of Theorem 1.5.2, $rF(y) = y$ for every $y \in \tilde{X}$, but since $rF(\tilde{X}) \subset r(X)$, $r(X) = \tilde{X}$ holds. Thus no Tychonoff space $\tilde{X}$ satisfying condition (RC2) satisfies condition (RC1), so that X is a real-compact space. ■

Theorem 4 implies

THEOREM 5. *Every closed subspace of a real-compact space is real-compact.* ■

Theorem 4 and Theorems 2.3.2 and 2.3.4 imply

THEOREM 6. *The Cartesian product of an arbitrary number of real-compact spaces is real-compact.* ■

COROLLARY. *The limit of an inverse system of real-compact spaces is real-compact.* ■

The characterizations of real-compact spaces given above and the definition of that class of spaces are extrinsic. We shall now state an intrinsic necessary and sufficient condition that a space be real-compact. For any Tychonoff space X we shall denote by $\mathfrak{D}_0(X)$ the family of all sets of the form $f^{-1}(0)$, where $f: X \to I$. Sets of the family $\mathfrak{D}_0(X)$ are closed. By the evident equality $f_0^{-1}(0) = \bigcap_{i=1}^{\infty} f_i^{-1}(0)$, where $f_0(x) = \sum_{i=1}^{\infty} \frac{1}{2^i} f_i(x)$ and $f_i: X \to I$ for $i = 0, 1, \ldots$, we infer that the family $\mathfrak{D}_0(X)$ is closed with respect to countable intersections. Let us note that the family of subsets of X described above is of great importance in some problems of topology (for example in dimension theory) and will be studied in detail in further on in this book (the subsets in question are the so called *functionally closed sets*).

THEOREM 7. *A Tychonoff space X is real-compact if and only if every maximal subfamily of $\mathfrak{D}_0(X)$ which has the countable intersection property has the non-empty intersection.*

Proof. The space X will be considered as a subspace of βX.

Let us assume that the space X has the property described in the theorem and let us consider a point $x_0 \in \beta X \setminus X$. Let $\mathfrak{F} = \{f \in I^{\beta X}: f(x_0) = 0\}$ and for every $f \in \mathfrak{F}$ let $Z_f = X \cap f^{-1}(0)$. The family $\mathfrak{Z} = \{Z_f\}_{f \in \mathfrak{F}} \subset \mathfrak{D}_0(X)$ is closed with respect to countable intersections. Let us suppose that $0 \notin \mathfrak{Z}$, i.e. that the family $\mathfrak{Z}$ has the countable intersection property. We shall show that the family $\mathfrak{Z}$ is a maximal subfamily of $\mathfrak{D}_0(X)$ with this property. Let us assume that a family $\mathfrak{Z} \cup \{Z\}$, where $Z \in \mathfrak{D}_0(X)$, still has the countable intersection property. There exists a function $g: X \to I$ such that $Z = g^{-1}(0)$. Let G denote an extension of g onto βX. If $x_0 \notin G^{-1}(0)$, then there exists a function $f \in \mathfrak{F}$ such that $f^{-1}(0) \cap G^{-1}(0) = 0$. Hence

$$Z_f \cap Z = X \cap f^{-1}(0) \cap G^{-1}(0) = 0,$$

contrary to the assumption. Thus we have $x_0 \in G^{-1}(0)$ and $G \in \mathfrak{F}$, i.e. $Z \in \mathfrak{Z}$. Hence the family $\mathfrak{Z}$ is maximal. Since $\bigcap_{f \in \mathfrak{F}} Z_f = 0$, we have $0 \in \mathfrak{Z}$, i.e. there exists a function $f: \beta X \to I$ such that $f(x) > 0$ for $x \in X$ and $f(x_0) = 0$. Hence X is a real-compact space.

Let us now suppose that X is a real-compact space. Let us consider a maximal family $\mathfrak{Z} = \{Z_s\}_{s \in S} \subset \mathfrak{D}_0(X)$ with the countable intersection property. The family of closures $\{\bar{Z}_s\}_{s \in S}$ in βX has a non-empty intersection. Let $x_0 \in \bigcap_{s \in S} \bar{Z}_s$. We shall show that $x_0 \in X$. Assume the contrary. Thus there exists a function $f: \beta X \to I$ such that $f(x_0) = 0$ and $f(x) > 0$ for $x \in X$. Let $Z_i = X \cap f^{-1}([0, 1/i])$. It can easily be verified that $Z_i \in \mathfrak{D}_0(X)$ for $i = 1, 2, \ldots$ For every Z_i and $s \in S$ we have $Z_i \cap Z_s \neq 0$, for $f^{-1}([0, 1/i])$ is a neighbourhood of the point x_0. Since the maximality of the family $\mathfrak{Z}$ implies that the family is closed with respect to countable intersections, the family with the element Z_i adjoined still has the countable intersection property. We infer that $Z_i \in \mathfrak{Z}$ for $i = 1, 2, \ldots$ Since $\bigcap_{i=1}^{\infty} Z_i = 0$, we get a contradiction, which implies that $x_0 \in X$, i.e. that $\bigcap_{s \in S} Z_s \neq 0$. ■

THEOREM 8. *For every Tychonoff space X there exists, up to a homeomorphism, exactly one real-compact space vX which is subject to the following conditions:*

(1) *$v: X \to vX$ is a homeomorphic embedding and $\overline{v(X)} = vX$.*

(2) *For each function $f: X \to R$ there exists a function $\tilde{f}: vX \to R$ such that $\tilde{f}v = f$.*

The space vX, called Hewitt's real-compactification of the space X, also satisfies the following condition:

(3) *For every mapping $f: X \to Y$, where Y is a real-compact space, there exists an extension $\tilde{f}: vX \to Y$, i.e. such an $\tilde{f}$, that $\tilde{f}v = f$.*

Proof. From the lemma to Theorem 4 it follows that the space $vX = \overline{F(X)} \subset \mathop{\boldsymbol{P}}_{f \in \mathfrak{f}} R_f$ and the mapping $v = F$ satisfy conditions (1) and (2). From Theorem 4 it follows that vX is real-compact.

Property (3) follows from Theorem 4, from properties (1), (2), and from Lemma 2 to Theorem 1.

If $v_1 X$ is a real-compact space which possesses properties (1) and (2), then $v_1 X$ also has property (3) and, as in the proof of Theorem 4.4, it can be shown that $v_1 X$ and vX are homeomorphic. ■

EXERCISES

A (L. Gillman and M. Jerison [1960]). Let X be a topological space and let $A, B \subset X$ be a real-compact and a compact subspace, respectively. Prove that $A \cup B$ is real-compact.

B (T. Shirota [1952], L. Gillman and M. Jerison [1960]). Show that for every Tychonoff space X the following conditions are equivalent:

(i) Every subspace $A \subset X$ is real-compact.

(ii) $X \setminus \{x\}$ is real-compact for every $x \in X$.

(iii) Every Tychonoff space, for which there exists a one-to-one mapping onto X, is real-compact.

C. Show that there exist real-compact spaces which are not normal.

Hint: Consider the space of Example 1.2.2. Make use of the preceding exercise (cf. Exercise 1.F).

D. Prove that a Tychonoff space X is pseudo-compact if and only if $vX = \beta X$.

E (G. W. Mackey [1944]). Show that a discrete space is real-compact if and only if its power is a non-measurable cardinal number.

Hint: Make use of Theorem 7.

HISTORICAL REMARKS AND BIBLIOGRAPHIC NOTES

The concept of a (regular) compact space was introduced by L. Vietoris in [1921]. He assumed the condition of Theorem 1.12 (slightly modified) as the definition; the paper also contains proofs of Theorems 1.1, 1.6, and 1.7. Earlier, this notion (similarly defined) occured to Z. Janiszewski [1912]; Janiszewski's paper, however, does not contain any theorems about compact spaces. A proof of the equivalence of some properties which characterize compact spaces is given in papers of K. Kuratowski and W. Sierpiński [1921] and of S. Saks [1921]. The definition of a compact space adopted in this book originates in the paper of P. Alexandroff and P. Urysohn [1929] (the basic definitions and results were announced in papers of P. Alexandroff and P. Urysohn [1923a] and [1924]). They defined this class of spaces quite independently of L. Vietoris and gave a profound analysis of the notion of compactness. In particular, their paper contains Theorems 1, 2, 6 and 7 of Paragraph 1. Theorems 1.8-1.10 and 2.9 are to be found in P. Alexandroff [1927]. The concept of grid was introduced by A. V. Arhangel'skiĭ in [1959]; he also proved Theorem 1.11 and 6.9. The proof of Theorem 1.11 given in this book was communicated to the author by W. Holsztyński. The corollaries to Theorem 1.11 were known earlier. Corollary 1 is a consequence of a theorem proved by P. Alexandroff and P. Urysohn in [1929] (cf. Problem F), and Corollary 2 is to be found in P. Alexandroff [1939]. Example 1.2 is a modification of Example A_2 considered in the paper of P. Alexandroff and P. Urysohn [1929] mentioned above. The first example of a (normal) countable space without a countable base (at one point) was given by P. Urysohn in [1925]. Then J. Novák gave in [1937] an example of a (normal) countable space without a countable base at any point. Exercise 1.D was communicated to the author by Z. Słodkowski.

Theorem 2.1 was proved in a paper of A. D. Taĭmanov [1952]. Its dual statement (cf. Exercise 2.A) can be found in S. Eilenberg and N. Steenrod [1952]. Theorem 2.2 was proved by P. Alexandroff [1936]. A. Tychonoff proved Theorems 4, 5 and 6 of Paragraph 2 in [1930]; the proof of Theorem 4 given here is taken from a paper by C. Chevalley and O. Frink jr. [1941]. N. Steenrod proved Theorem 2.10 in [1936]; Theorem 2.11 can be found in S. Eilenberg and N. Steenrod [1952]. The Stone-Weierstrass theorem was proved by M. H. Stone in [1947] (see also his paper [1937]).

The compact-open topology in mapping spaces was introduced by R. H. Fox in [1945]. The notion of a k-space and Theorems 3.6 and 6.11 come from a paper by R. Arens [1946].

The notion of a compactification was considered for the first time by A. Tychonoff in [1930], where Theorem 4.2 was also proved. A systematic study was made by E. Čech [1937] and M. H. Stone [1937], who independently defined the maximal compactification βX and stated its fundamental properties (Theorem 5.1 and the corollaries) (cf. also P. Alexandroff [1939] along with M. H. Stone [1948]). Theorem 4.5 was proved by Yu. M. Smirnov in [1952]. The simple proof of Theorem 5.2 given here was found by S. Mrówka but the theorem was first proved by B. Pospíšil in [1937]. It also follows directly from a well-known theorem of set theory (see Problem L). Theorem 5.4 was proved by J. Novák in [1953]. Example 5.1 was constructed by E. Čech in [1937]. The fact that in the remainder $\beta N \setminus N$ there exists a family of power $\mathfrak{c}$ of mutually disjoint non-empty open subsets was noted by M. Nakamura and S. Kakutani in [1943]. The construction of that family given in Example 5.2 and Example 5.3 are taken from a paper of M. Katětov [1950]. The space homeomorphic to βN which is considered in Example 5.4 was constructed by A. Tychonoff in [1935]. The necessary and sufficient condition for the equality $\beta \mathop{\boldsymbol{P}}_{s\in S} X_s = \mathop{\boldsymbol{P}}_{s\in S} \beta X_s$ stated in Exercise 5.E was given by I. Glicksberg in [1959].

The notions of a locally compact space and a Lindelöf space were introduced by P. Alexandroff and P. Urysohn in [1929]. E. Lindelöf was the first to observe that the real-line had the property which we adopted as the definition of Lindelöf spaces. The one-point compactification of a locally compact space was defined by P. Alexandroff in [1924]. Theorem 6.8 was proved by S. Fomin in [1943]. Examples 7.2 and 7.3 were given by R. H. Sorgenfrey in [1947].

Spaces complete in the sense of Čech were defined in [1937] by E. Čech. The Baire Theorem, which was earlier known for a narrower class of metric complete spaces, was proved in Čech's paper. The characterization of spaces complete in the sense of Čech given in Theorem 8.2 was found by Z. Frolík in [1960] and A. Arhangel'skiĭ in [1961]. A similar characterization was found by N. A. Šanin in [1943].

The notion of a countably compact spaces was introduced by M. Fréchet in [1906]. The class of pseudo-compact spaces was defined by E. Hewitt in [1948]. The space considered in Example 9.2 was constructed by L. S. Pontriagin in [1954], and the space considered in Example 9.5 — by M. Katětov in [1951a]. An example of two countably compact spaces whose Cartesian product is not countably compact was found by H. Terasaka in [1952] and J. Novák in [1953]. We quote here Novák's example simplified by Z. Frolík [1959].

Real-compact spaces (known as *Q-spaces*) were defined by E. Hewitt in [1948]. The definition given by him is closer to functional analysis (cf. Problem W); the definition adopted in this book was given by M. Katětov [1951]. Theorem 10.1 was proved by S. Mrówka in [1959]. T. Shirota proved Theorems 10.4, 10.5, and 10.6 in [1952]; Theorem 10.5 was also proved by M. Katětov in [1951]. Theorem 10.7 was found by E. Hewitt [1948]. Theorems which showed that the class of non-measurable cardinal numbers is closed with respect to the operations enumerated in Paragraph 10 were proved by S. Ulam in [1930]. Non-measurability of the first strongly inaccessible aleph (and many greater cardinal numbers) was proved by H. J. Keisler and A. Tarski in [1964]. Hewitt's real-compactification was described by E. Hewitt in [1948]. In describing the theory of real-compact spaces we followed the papers of R. Engelking and S. Mrówka [1958] and S. Mrówka [1959a]. In particular, Example 10.2 was constructed by S. Mrówka in [1959a]. Many problems considered in the last two paragraphs of this chapter can be found in a book by L. Gillman and M. Jerison [1960].

PROBLEMS

A (K. Kuratowski and W. Sierpiński [1921], L. Vietoris [1921], P. Alexandroff and P. Urysohn [1929]). Let X be a topological space and let $M \subset X$ be a subspace. A point $x \in X$ is called a *complete accumulation* *point* of M if for every neighbourhood U of the point x, $\overline{\overline{M \cap U}} = \overline{\overline{M}}$ holds. Show that for a Hausdorff space X the following conditions are equivalent:

(i) X is compact.
(ii) Each infinite subset $M \subset X$ has a complete accumulation point.
(iii) Every transfinite decreasing sequence of closed and non-empty sets $F_1 \supset F_2 \supset \ldots \supset F_\xi \supset \ldots$, $\xi < \alpha$ has a non-empty intersection.

Hint: Note that every limit ordinal number is cofinal with an initial number (see F. Hausdorff [1914], p. 132).

B (J. W. Alexander [1939]). (a) Let X be a Hausdorff space and let $\mathfrak{S}$ denote a subbase of X. Show that X is compact if and only if every covering of X with elements of $\mathfrak{S}$ has a finite subcovering.

Hint: In the class of all families of open subsets of the space X, the property of not containing any finite family covering X is of finite character. If X is not compact, then there exists a maximal family $\mathfrak{R}$ which possesses the above property and forms a covering of X. Show that if $G_1, G_2, \ldots, G_k$ are open sets which do not belong to $\mathfrak{R}$, then the intersection $G_1 \cap G_2 \cap \ldots \cap G_k$ does not belong to $\mathfrak{R}$, and that if $G_1 \notin \mathfrak{R}$ and $G_1 \subset G_2$, then $G_2 \notin \mathfrak{R}$. Deduce that $\mathfrak{R} \cap \mathfrak{S}$ is a covering of the space X.

(b) Prove the Tychonoff Theorem making use of the above characterization of compactness.

C. Let X be an arbitrary ordered set containing more than a single point.

(a) Show that the space X with the order topology is compact if and only if any $A \subset X$ has a least upper bound.

(b) Show that every space X with the order topology induced by the ordering $<$ has a compactification cX whose topology is induced by an ordering $<'$ in cX such that for $x, y \in X$ the conditions $x < y$ and $x <' y$ are equivalent. Notice that the topology of the subspace A of the space X whose topology is induced by the ordering $<$ is, in general, different from the topology induced by this ordering in A.

(c) Prove that each space X with the topology defined by an ordering is hereditarily normal.

Hint: Assume that the space X is compact. Show that each open subset of the space X is the union of disjoint elements of the base described in Problem 1.D. Consider sets $A, B \subset X$ sucht hat $\bar{A} \cap B = 0 = A \cap \bar{B}$. Represent $X \setminus \bar{A} \cap \bar{B}$ as the union of a family $\{U_s\}_{s \in S}$ of disjoint elements of the base. Consider an analogous decomposition of the sets $U_s \setminus \bar{B}$ for such $s \in S$ that $U_s \cap A \neq 0 \neq U_s \cap B$. Show that every point $x \in B$ belongs to the closure of at most two elements of this decomposition. Make use of (b) in considering the case of a non-compact X.

(d) Verify that the topology in the set of ordinal numbers not greater than ω_1, considered in Example 5.1, is identical with the order topology induced in this set by the relation "less than" for ordinal numbers.

(e) Consider the topology in the square $0 \leqslant x \leqslant 1, 0 \leqslant y \leqslant 1$, defined by the *lexicographic order*, i.e. such an order that $(x_1, y_1) < (x_2, y_2)$ if and only if $x_1 < x_2$ or $x_1 = x_2$ but $y_1 < y_2$. Show that the space obtained in this manner is compact and satisfies the first axiom of countability, but show that it is neither separable nor perfectly normal. Show that the space from Exercise 9.C is a subspace of that space.

D (P. Alexandroff and P. Urysohn [1929]). A Hausdorff space X is said to be *absolutely closed* provided it is a closed subset of every Hausdorff space containing it. Prove that a space X is absolutely closed if and only if from each open covering $\{U_s\}_{s\in S}$ of that space we can choose a finite family $\{U_{s_1}, U_{s_2}, \ldots, U_{s_k}\}$ such that $\overline{U}_{s_1} \cup \overline{U}_{s_2} \cup \ldots \cup \overline{U}_{s_k} = X$.

Deduce that a regular space is absolutely closed if and only if it is compact.

E (M. Katětov [1940]). Prove that a topology $\mathfrak{O}$ in a space X is minimal with respect to Hausdorff topologies in that space if and only if the space $(X, \mathfrak{O})$ is absolutely closed and semi-regular.

Hint: Consider the topology $\mathfrak{O}_1$ consisting of open domains of the topology $\mathfrak{O}$.

F (P. Alexandroff and P. Urysohn [1929]). The *pseudo-weight* of a topological space X *at the point* x is the least power of a family of open sets whose intersection is equal to $\{x\}$.

Show that the weight and the pseudo-weight at every point of a compact space X are equal. Deduce Corollary 1 to Theorem 1.11.

G (E. Čech and B. Pospíšil [1938]). Show that if the weight at every point x of a compact space X is not less than an infinite cardinal number $\mathfrak{m}$, then $\overline{\overline{X}} \geqslant 2^{\mathfrak{m}}$.

Hint: Let τ denote an initial number of power $\mathfrak{m}$. For every $\alpha < \tau$ let $D(\alpha)$ denote the set of all transfinite sequences which are of type α and assume values 0 and 1. For every $f \in D(\alpha)$ and $\beta < \alpha$ let f_β denote an element of $D(\beta)$ such that $f_\beta(\gamma) = f(\gamma)$ for $\gamma < \beta$. For every $f \in D(\alpha)$ let f^i denote element of $D(\alpha+1)$ such that $(f^i)_\alpha = f$ and $f^i(\alpha) = i$ for $i = 0, 1$.

Define, by means of transfinite induction, an operation V_α, for $\alpha < \tau$, which assigns an open subset $V_\alpha(f)$ of the space X to every $f \in D(\alpha)$ in such a manner that

(1) $\overline{V_{\alpha+1}(f^i)} \subset V_\alpha(f)$ for $i = 0, 1$ and $f \in D(\alpha)$.

(2) $\overline{V_{\alpha+1}(f^0)} \cap \overline{V_{\alpha+1}(f^1)} = 0$ for $f \in D(\alpha)$.

(3) $\bigcap\limits_{\beta \leqslant \alpha} V_\beta(f_\beta) \neq 0$ for $f \in D(\alpha)$.

(for a limit number α we put $V_\alpha(f) = X$ for every $f \in D(\alpha)$).

Assign an arbitrary element of the set $\bigcap_{\alpha<\tau} V_\alpha(f_\alpha)$ to every sequence $f \in D(\tau)$. Show that if $f, f' \in D(\tau)$ differs at a non-limit number, then the assigned points are different.

Generalize the above result by proving that it is sufficient to assume that the space X is the intersection of a family consisting of $\mathfrak{m}$ open subsets of a compact space.

H (P. Alexandroff [1936], E. Marczewski [1941], N. A. Šanin [1948], R Engelking and A. Pełczyński [1963]). A compact space X is called *dyadic* if X is the continuous image of the Cantor cube $D^{\mathfrak{m}}$ for some $\mathfrak{m} \geqslant \aleph_0$.

(a) Making use of Theorem 2.3.10 show that the compact space considered in Example 1.1.2 is not dyadic if its power is greater than $\aleph_0$.

(b) Making use of Exercise 2.F show that every dyadic space of weight $\mathfrak{m} \geqslant \aleph_0$ is the image of the Cantor cube $D^{\mathfrak{m}}$.

(c) Prove that for each function $f: X \to R$ defined on a dyadic space X there exists a compact subspace $X_0 \subset X$ of weight $\aleph_0$ such that $f(X_0) = f(X)$. Show that in the above proposition R can be replaced by an arbitrary Tychonoff space of weight $\aleph_0$.

(d) Deduce from (c) that the space considered in Exercise 9.C is not dyadic and that if the Čech-Stone compactification of a Tychonoff space X is dyadic, then X is pseudo-compact.

Hint: Prove that βR is not dyadic and show that if a space X is not pseudo-compact, then it can be mapped onto a dense subset of the space R.

I (A. S. Esenin-Vol'pin [1949], B. Efimov [1963]). (a) Show that if a dyadic space X is of a weight not greater than $\mathfrak{m} \geqslant \aleph_0$ at every point of a dense subset A, then A contains a subset A_0 dense in X and of power $\leqslant \mathfrak{m}$.

Hint: Let ω_α be an initial number of power $\mathfrak{m}$. The number $\omega_{\alpha+1}$ (the first initial number greater than ω_α) is regular, i.e. a set of power $\omega_{\alpha+1}$ cannot be represented as the union of less than $\omega_{\alpha+1}$ sets of power less than $\omega_{\alpha+1}$. The assumption that A does not contain any dense subset of power $\leqslant \mathfrak{m}$ allows us to define a sequence $x_1, x_2, \ldots, x_\gamma, \ldots, \gamma < \omega_{\alpha+1}$ of points of the set A such that $x_\gamma \notin \overline{\bigcup_{\sigma<\gamma} \{x_\sigma\}}$. Let $f: D^{\mathfrak{n}} \to X$ be a mapping of the Cantor cube $D^{\mathfrak{n}} = \boldsymbol{P}_{s\in S} D_s$ onto the space X and let $\mathfrak{B}$ denote the base of the space $D^{\mathfrak{n}}$ consisting of sets of the form $\boldsymbol{P}_{s\in S} W_s$, where $W_s \neq D_s$ for a finite number of elements of the set S called the *distinguished indices* of the set $\boldsymbol{P}_{s\in S} W_s$. Note that every two disjoint elements of the base $\mathfrak{B}$ have a common distinguished index such that their projections onto the axis corresponding to it are disjoint. For every $\gamma < \omega_{a+1}$ define a family $\mathfrak{B}_\gamma \subset \mathfrak{B}$ such that $0 \neq B_\gamma = \bigcap_{B \in \mathfrak{B}_\gamma} B \subset X_\gamma = f^{-1}(x_\gamma)$ and $\overline{\overline{\mathfrak{B}_\gamma}} \leqslant \mathfrak{m}$. Now choose a point $b_\gamma \in B_\gamma$. Notice that if $U \cap X_\gamma = 0$ for some $U \in \mathfrak{B}$ and $\gamma < \omega_{a+1}$, then there exists a $B \in \mathfrak{B}_\gamma$ such that $U \cap B = 0$. For every $\gamma < \omega_{a+1}$ define a neighbourhood $U_\gamma \in \mathfrak{B}$ of the point b_γ such that $U_\gamma \cap X_\sigma = 0$ for $\sigma < \gamma$. By choosing a subsequence (also of type ω_{a+1}) one can assume that all the sets U_γ have exactly k distinguished indices. By choosing a subsequence (of the type ω_{a+1}) l times ($l = 1, 2, \ldots, k$), obtain the sets U_γ with l common distinguished indices and disjoint projections onto the corresponding axis. Deduce a contradiction.

(b) If the weight of a dyadic space X at the points of a dense subset is not greater than a cardinal number $\mathfrak{m} \geqslant \aleph_0$, show that $w(X) \leqslant \mathfrak{m}$.

J (L. Vietoris [1922]). Let X be a topological space. Let us denote by 2^X the family of all non-empty closed subsets of the space X. Verify that in the set 2^X one can define a topology (called the *Vietoris topology*) assuming that neighbourhoods of a point $A \in 2^X$ are sets of the form

$$\mathfrak{B}(U_1, U_2, \ldots, U_k) = \Big\{B \in 2^X \colon B \subset \bigcup_{i=1}^{k} U_i \text{ and } B \cap U_i \neq 0 \text{ for } i = 1, 2, \ldots, k\Big\},$$

where $U_1, U_2, \ldots, U_k$ denotes an arbitrary sequence of open subsets of the space X satisfying the conditions: $A \subset \bigcup_{i=1}^{k} U_i$ and $A \cap U_i \neq 0$ for $i = 1, 2, \ldots, k$. The topological space obtained in this manner is called the *space of subsets* of the space X. Show that the space 2^X contains a closed subset homeomorphic to the space X.

Prove that for every compact space X the space 2^X is compact.

Hint (E. Michael [1951]): Verify that the family consisting of all sets $\mathfrak{B}_1(U) = \{B \in 2^X \colon B \subset U\}$ and $\mathfrak{B}_2(U) = \{B \in 2^X \colon B \cap U \neq 0\}$, where U is an open subset of the space X, is a subbase of the space 2^X; make use of Problem B.

K (R. Arens [1946]). Let X be a regular space and let Y denote an arbitrary T_1-space. Let us suppose that the function φ, where $\varphi(f, x) = f(x)$, of the Cartesian product $Y^X \times X$ into the space Y is a mapping with respect to the compact-open topology in Y^X. Show that if the space Y contains a subset homeomorphic to the segment, then X is locally compact.

L. We say that a family $\{A_s\}_{s \in S}$ consists of *independent sets* provided that for every finite sequence $s_1, s_2, \ldots, s_k$ of elements of the set S and an arbitrary sequence $i_1, i_2, \ldots, i_k$ consisting of 0 and 1 we have the inequality

$$A_{s_1}^{i_1} \cap A_{s_2}^{i_2} \cap \ldots \cap A_{s_k}^{i_k} \neq 0,$$

where $A^0 = A$ and $A^1 = X \setminus A$.

(a) (G. Fichtenholz and L. Kantorovitch [1934] for $\mathfrak{m} = \aleph_0$, F. Hausdorff [1936] for arbitrary $\mathfrak{m} \geqslant \aleph_0$) Show that the family of all subsets of the set X of power $\mathfrak{m} \geqslant \aleph_0$ contains a subfamily of power $2^{\mathfrak{m}}$ consisting of independent subsets.

Hint: Use Problem 2.L and consider X as a dense subset of the Cantor cube of weight $2^{\mathfrak{m}}$.

(b) Deduce from (a) that the Cantor cube of weight $2^{\mathfrak{m}}$ contains a dense subset of power $\mathfrak{m}$.

Hint: Enumerate the axis of the cube $D^{2^{\mathfrak{m}}}$ by means of independent subsets of a set of power $\mathfrak{m}$.

(c) Deduce from (a) that for each $\mathfrak{m} \geqslant \aleph_0$ the power of the Čech-Stone compactification of a discrete space of power $\mathfrak{m}$, is equal to $2^{2^{\mathfrak{m}}}$ and its weight is equal to $2^{\mathfrak{m}}$.

M (E. Čech [1959], L. Gillman and M. Jerison [1960]). Show that every closed G_δ-set in the remainder $\beta X \setminus \beta(X)$ of the Čech-Stone compactification of a Tychonoff space X is at least of power $2^{\mathfrak{c}}$.

Hint: Let $f: \beta X \to I$ be a continuous function vanishing only on the set. Define a sequence of points $a_1, a_2, \ldots$ of the space $\beta(X)$ such that $f(a_1) > f(a_2) > \ldots$ and $f(a_i) \leqslant 1/i$ for $i = 1, 2, \ldots$ Notice that the closure of the set $A = \bigcup_{i=1}^{\infty} \{a_i\}$ in the space βX is equivalent to its Čech-Stone compactification and make use of Theorem 5.2.

N. Let X_0 be the set of all ordinal numbers less than ω_1. Order the product $L_0 = X_0 \times [0, 1)$, assuming that $(a_1, r_1) < (a_2, r_2)$ for $a_1 < a_2$ or $a_1 = a_2$ and $r_1 < r_2$. Consider the order topology induced in L_0 by this ordering. Show that L_0 is countably compact. Adding the point Ω to the set L_0 and assuming it to be greater than all elements of L_0 we obtain an ordered set L. Show that the set L with the induced topology is the Čech-Stone compactification of the space L_0. Prove that each subspace M of the space L_0 consisting of all points not greater than a fixed point $x \in L_0$, is homeomorphic to the segment $[0, 1]$.

Hint: Let Q denote the set of all rational numbers of the segment $(0, 1)$. Show that elements of the set Q and $M \cap (X_0 \times Q)$ can be set in sequences $r_1, r_2, \ldots$ and $s_1, s_2, \ldots$ such that $r_i < r_j$ if and only if $s_i < s_j$. Verify that the formula $f(r_i) = s_i$ defines a mapping $f: Q \to L_0$ and use Theorem 2.1.

O. (a) (A. Tychonoff [1930], E. Hewitt [1948], H. Tong [1949]) Let X and X_0 denote the spaces considered in Example 5.1. Let us denote by Y the set of all ordinal numbers not greater than the first infinite ordinal number ω_0. The space $T = X \times Y \setminus (\omega_1, \omega_0)$ is called the *Tychonoff plank*. Show that $\beta T = X \times Y$ and deduce that T is not normal.

(b) (J. Dieudonné [1939b]) Show that the space $X_0 \times X$ is countably compact and not normal. Give an example of a space which is countably compact but not regular.

(c) (P. Alexandroff and P. Urysohn [1929]) Show that a countably compact space which satisfies the first axiom of countability is regular.

P (H. H. Corson [1959]). Suppose we are given a family of non-empty Tychonoff spaces $\{X_s\}_{s \in S}$ which satisfy the second axiom of countability. For every $s \in S$ let us choose an arbitrary point $a_s \in X_s$ and let $X \subset \mathop{\boldsymbol{P}}\limits_{s \in S} X_s$ denote the set consisting of those points $\{x_s\}$ for which $x_s \neq a_s$ only for an at most countable number of $s \in S$.

Prove that $\mathop{\boldsymbol{P}}\limits_{s \in S} X_s$ is Hewitt's real-compactification of the space X.

Hint: Make use of Problem 2.S.

Moreover, if each of the spaces X_s is compact, then $\mathop{\boldsymbol{P}}\limits_{s \in S} X_s$ is the Čech-Stone compactification of the space X.

Q. (a) (E. Hewitt [1947]) Prove that for a Tychonoff space X the following conditions are equivalent:

(i) The space X has only one compactification (up to equivalence).
(ii) $\overline{\overline{\beta X \setminus \beta(X)}} \leqslant 1$.
(iii) If two sets A and B, closed in X, are completely separated, then at least one of them is compact.

(b) Show that every Tychonoff space satisfying the conditions of (a) is pseudo-compact and locally compact.

(c) Give an example of a pseudo-compact and locally-compact space which has infinitely many non-equivalent compactifications.

Hint: Make use of Example 9.5.

(d) Give an example of a Tychonoff space which is not countably compact and has only one compactification, and an example of a locally compact and countably compact space which has infinitely many non-equivalent compactifications.

R (Yu. M. Smirnov [1951c]). Show that if a subset of a Lindelöf space is normally placed in it, then it is a Lindelöf space. Prove that for a Tychonoff space X the following conditions are equivalent:

(i) The space X has the Lindelöf property.
(ii) The space X is normally placed in every compactification of it.
(iii) The space X is normally placed in its Čech-Stone compactification.
(iv) The space X is normally placed in a certain compactification of it.

Deduce that no point $x \in \beta N \setminus N$ is a G_δ-set in βN (comp. Problem M).

S (E. Hewitt [1948]). Show that a Tychonoff space X is pseudo-compact if and only if the remainder $\beta X\setminus\beta(X)$ does not contain any non-empty closed subsets, of the space βX, which are G_δ-sets.

T (A. V. Arhangel'skiĭ [1960]). Prove that if in a space X, which is complete in the sense of Čech, there exists a grid of power $\mathfrak{m}$, then $w(X)\leqslant\mathfrak{m}$. What corollaries follow?

Hint: Let $\beta X\setminus\beta(X)=\bigcup_{i=1}^{\infty}F_i$, where F_i is compact for $i=1,2,\dots$ and let $\mathfrak{N}$ denote a grid in $\beta(X)$. Apply the construction used in the proof of Theorem 1.11 to the family $\mathfrak{N}\cup\{F_i\}_{i=1}^{\infty}$ and verify directly that the intersections of elements of $\mathfrak{B}_0$ with $\beta(X)$ form a base of the space.

U (S. Mrówka [1957]). We say that a set $M\subset X$ is *regularly placed* in the space X if for every $x\in X\setminus M$ there exists a G_δ-set H such that $x\in H\subset X\setminus M$. Show that each set normally placed in a T_1-space X is regularly placed in it. Prove that every regularly placed subset of a real-compact space is real-compact. Theorem 10.1 states that X is real-compact if and only if $\beta(X)$ is regularly placed in βX. Can we replace βX by an arbitrary compactification of the space X?

V. For each Tychonoff space X let us denote by $C^*(X)$ the set of all real-valued continuous and bounded functions defined on X. Verify that $C^*(X)$ is a ring with respect to addition and multiplication.

An *ideal* in $C^*(X)$ is every proper subset $\varDelta\subset C^*(X)$ such that if $f,g\in\varDelta$, then $f+g\in\varDelta$ and if $f\in\varDelta$ and $g\in C^*(X)$, then $f\cdot g\in\varDelta$.

An ideal which is not contained in any ideal different from it is called *maximal*.

(a) Prove that each ideal is contained in a maximal ideal. Show that a Tychonoff space X is compact if and only if for each maximal ideal $\varDelta$ of the ring $C^*(X)$, there exists a point $x\in X$ such that $f\in\varDelta$ is equivalent to $f(x)=0$.

Hint: Assume that there exists a maximal ideal $\varDelta\subset C^*(X)$ such that for every point $x\in X$ there exists a function $f_x\in\varDelta$ which takes on the value 1 at the point x. Consider the covering $\{f_x^{-1}((\frac{1}{2},1])\}_{x\in X}$.

(b) (M. H. Stone [1937], I. M. Gelfand and A. N. Kolmogoroff [1939]) Assuming that the sets of the shape $U_f=\{\varDelta : f\notin\varDelta\}$ form a base, we can define a topology in the set $\mathfrak{M}$ of maximal ideals of the ring $C^*(X)$. Show that $\mathfrak{M}$ is a compact space. Assigning to each element $x\in X$ the maximal ideal $\varDelta(x)$ consisting of all functions vanishing at x, we obtain a homeomorphic embedding of the space X in $\mathfrak{M}$. Show that $\mathfrak{M}$ is the Čech-Stone compactification of the space X.

Deduce that compact spaces X and Y are homeomorphic if and only if the rings $C^*(X)$ and $C^*(Y)$ are isomorphic, i.e. if there exists a one-to-one function φ of the ring $C^*(X)$ onto the ring $C^*(Y)$

such that $\varphi(f+g) = \varphi(f)+\varphi(g)$ and $\varphi(f\cdot g) = \varphi(f)\cdot\varphi(g)$ for every $f, g \in C^*(X)$.

W. A *multiplicative linear functional* in the ring $C^*(X)$ is a function φ which assigns a real number $\varphi(f)$ to every function $f \in C^*(X)$ in such a manner that $\varphi(r_1f_1+r_2f_2) = r_1\cdot\varphi(f_1)+r_2\cdot\varphi(f_2)$ (where r_1 and r_2 denote real numbers) and $\varphi(f_1\cdot f_2) = \varphi(f_1)\cdot\varphi(f_2)$. A functional is said to be *non-trivial* whenever it is not identically equal to zero. We say that the functional φ is *determined by the point* $x \in X$ provided that $\varphi(f) = f(x)$ for every $f \in C^*(X)$.

(a) Show that X is compact if and only if every non-trivial multiplicative linear functional φ in the ring $C^*(X)$ is determined by a point.

Hint: For every functional φ the set $\Delta = \{f: \varphi(f) = 0\}$ is an ideal.

(b) (E. Hewitt [1948]) Show that a necessary and sufficient condition for a Tychonoff space X to be real-compact is that each non-trivial multiplicative linear functional in the ring $C(X)$ of all real-valued continuous functions defined on X can be determined by a point (definitions analogous to those for $C^*(X)$).

Hint: In order to prove the necessity, consider the restriction of the functional φ to $C^*(X) \subset C(X)$. Make use of the equality $C^*(X) = C^*(\beta X)$ and of the preceding problem.

X. A mapping $f: X \to Y$ is called *perfect* if f is closed and the set $f^{-1}(y)$ is compact for each $y \in Y$.

(a) (I. A. Vaĭnšteĭn [1947]) Show that if $f: X \to Y$ is a perfect mapping onto Y, then $f^{-1}(Z)$ is compact for each compact $Z \subset Y$.

(b) (M. Henriksen and J. R. Isbell [1958]) Show that for Tychonoff spaces X, Y and a mapping f of the space X onto Y the following conditions are equivalent:

(i) The mapping f is perfect.

(ii) $F(\beta X\setminus\beta(X)) = \beta Y\setminus\beta(Y)$, where $F: \beta X \to \beta Y$ is the extension of f.

(iii) For a compactification cY of the space Y we have $F(\beta X\setminus\beta(X)) = cY\setminus c(Y)$, where $F: \beta X \to cY$ is the extension of f.

(iv) For every compactification cY of the space Y we have $F(\beta X\setminus\beta(X)) = cY\setminus c(Y)$, where $F: \beta X \to cY$ is the extension of f.

Y (M. Henriksen and J. R. Isbell [1958]). We say that a class $\mathfrak{K}$ of Tychonoff spaces is *perfect* if for every two Tychonoff spaces X and Y for which there exists a perfect mapping $f: X \to Y$ onto Y, the conditions $X \in \mathfrak{K}$ and $Y \in \mathfrak{K}$ are equivalent.

Show that the classes of compact spaces, locally compact spaces, Lindelöf spaces, countably compact Tychonoff spaces, and spaces complete in the sense of Čech are perfect.

Show by means of an example that the class of pseudo-compact spaces is not perfect.

CHAPTER 4

METRIC AND METRIZABLE SPACES

The axioms of a topological space may be considered as an abstract description of the notion of proximity: a point is close to a set if it belongs to its closure. In metric spaces, the study of which is the subject of this chapter, we associate with a pair of points a real number, called their distance. The fundamental properties of distance are described by axioms. Using the distance between points one can define the distance from a point to a set. If we assume that all points for which the distance to a set A is equal to zero are close to A, and define the closure of A as the set of all points which are close to A, then we obtain a topological space. Topological spaces which can be obtained in this manner are called metrizable.

In Chapter 8 we shall consider two more systems of axioms which describe similar notions, namely uniform spaces and proximity spaces. In a uniform space we also consider the distance between two points but we measure it by an entirely different method from that used in a metric space. Proximity spaces are an abstract description of the notion of proximity of two sets.

The three notions: metric space, uniform space, and proximity space, are thus really different from the notion of a topological space. We consider them in this book because owing to numerous and interesting connections with topological spaces, they belong to general topology.

If we were governed by logical considerations alone, we should postpone the study of metric spaces until Chapter 8, i.e. we should first conclude that part of the book dealing with topological spaces only. In view of the importance of metric and metrizable spaces, however, we devote a separate chapter to them, which precedes three strictly topological chapters of a more special character.

Paragraph 1 contains the definition of a metric space and of a metrizable space. In it we show how a metric in a set X induces a topology, and introduce the notion of equivalent metrics, i.e. metrics which induce the same topology in X. In this paragraph we also prove that metrizable spaces are normal and we consider axioms of countability.

In Paragraph 2 operations on metrizable spaces are considered; we prove that subspaces, sums, and the countable Cartesian products of metrizable spaces are metrizable.

Paragraph 3 is devoted to two important classes of metric spaces, namely totally bounded spaces and complete spaces. A topological characterization of those classes is given. In this chapter we also consider the notion of compactness and prove that for metrizable spaces compactness and countable compactness are equivalent.

The last paragraph contains recent results. Following A. H. Stone, we prove a certain property of coverings of metric spaces, and the metrization theorems of R. H. Bing and of J. Nagata and Yu. M. Smirnov. The notion of local finiteness of a family of sets, which is now fundamental for general topology, occurs in this paragraph for the first time.

§ 1. Metric spaces. Metrizable spaces. *A metric space* is a pair (X, ϱ) consisting of a set X and a function ϱ with real non-negative values, defined on the Cartesian product $X \times X$, and which satisfies the following conditions:

(M1) $\varrho(x, y) = 0$ *if and only if* $x = y$.

(M2) $\varrho(x, y) = \varrho(y, x)$ *for every* $x, y \in X$.

(M3) $\varrho(x, y) + \varrho(y, z) \geqslant \varrho(x, z)$ *for every* $x, y, z \in X$.

The set X is called a *space*, its elements *points*, the function ϱ the *metric* in the set X, and the number $\varrho(x, y)$ the *distance* between the points x, y. Condition (M1) states that the distance between two different points is positive and that the distance from every point to itself is equal to zero. Condition (M2) states that the distance is a symmetric function, i.e. that it does not depend on the order of points x and y. Condition (M3), called the *triangle inequality*, states, figuratively speaking, that the sum of the lengths of two sides of a triangle is not less than the length of the third side.

A function ϱ defined on the Cartesian product $X \times X$, where X is an arbitrary set, which assumes real non-negative values and is subject to conditions (M2) and (M3) and

(M1′) $\varrho(x, x) = 0$ *for every* $x \in X$,

is called a *pseudo-metric* in the set X.

Let us suppose that a metric space (X, ϱ) is given. The set $B(x_0, r) = \{x: \varrho(x_0, x) < r\}$ is called the (*open*) *ball* of *radius* r about its *centre* $x_0 \in X$. Let us note that if $r > 0$, then $x_0 \in B(x_0, r)$ and that if $x_1 \in B(x_0, r)$ for some $x_0 \in X$ and $r > 0$, then for $r_1 = r - \varrho(x_0, x_1) > 0$, the inclusion $B(x_1, r_1) \subset B(x_0, r)$ holds. In fact, if $x \in B(x_1, r_1)$, then by property (M3),

$$\varrho(x_0, x) \leqslant \varrho(x_0, x_1) + \varrho(x_1, x) < \varrho(x_0, x_1) + r - \varrho(x_0, x_1) = r.$$

From Theorem 1.2.2 it follows that the family of open balls of positive radius is the neighbourhood system for a topology in X. Thus, every metric space (X, ϱ) induces a topological space $(X, \mathfrak{O})$. The family $\mathfrak{O}$ consists of the unions of open balls and the family of all open balls is a base for the space $(X, \mathfrak{O})$. The family of all balls $B(x, r)$ of a rational radius r about the point x is a base at this point. The space $(X, \mathfrak{O})$ satisfies, therefore, the first axiom of countability. The topology in the space X, described above, is said to be *induced by the metric* ϱ.

Since for each pair of different points $x_1, x_2 \in X$ we have $\varrho(x_1, x_2) = r > 0$, the points have disjoint neighbourhoods, namely, as folows from (M3), the balls $B(x_1, r/2)$ and $B(x_2, r/2)$. A space with the topollogy induced by a metric is, therefore, a Hausdorff space.

As in the case of topological spaces, we shall denote a metric space by the symbol X only, and it will always follow from the context which metric in X is considered.

The same construction can be made starting with the assumption that ϱ is a pseudo-metric. The spaces obtained in this manner form a very broad class, which will not be considered here. We note only that the spaces of this class are not generally T_0-spaces. In fact, the function ϱ which assigns the number zero to each pair of points of a set X is obviously a pseudo-metric; it is easy to verify that the set X with the topology induced by this metric is the space considered in Example 1.2.5. That space, in which the only open sets are the empty set and the whole space, is not a T_0-space. Pseudo-metrics will only be used as a tool in this paragraph.

The notion of a metric space allows us to distinguish an important class of topological spaces — namely, metrizable spaces. A topological space X is said to be *metrizable* whenever one can define a metric ϱ in the set X in such a manner that the topology induced by ϱ is identical with the initial topology in X. Metrics with this property will be called *metrics in the space* X. From a topological point of view, metrics are only tools which we use to describe and study metrizable spaces; their significance can be compared with that of a system of coordinates in the study of Euclidean spaces.

We lay great stress on metric spaces because many important topological spaces which are used in mathematics can be metrized; moreover, their topologies are often defined by means of metrics, usually obtained in a very natural way.

Let us note that although metrizability is a topological property, the definition of the class of metrizable spaces which we have adopted is, in contradistinction to the definitions of all classes considered so far, not strictly topological. In other words, it depends not only on the notion of an open set and notions of the set theory, but also on the operation of addition and the order relation in the set of real numbers. The reader can ask whether a topological definition of metrizable spaces can be found. Indeed, there do exist such definitions; theorems which state (in topological terms) necessary and sufficient conditions for the metrizability of a space are called *metrization theorems*. Two of them will be given in Paragraph 4 (cf. Problems 5.H and 5.I).

Two metrics ϱ_1 and ϱ_2 in the set X are called *equivalent*, provided that the topologies induced by means of those metrics are identical. It is easy to verify that this relation is an equivalence relation. We consider metrics inducing the same topology as being equivalent, since the topology in the set X is our subject and a metric is only an auxiliary tool.

Later we shall give a convenient criteria of the equivalence of metrics; but now we show how one can describe the closure of a set by means of a metric.

A sequence $x_1, x_2, \ldots$ of points of the metric space X is called *convergent* to the point $x \in X$ if the sequence of numbers $\varrho(x, x_n)$ is convergent to zero. The point x will be called the *limit* of the sequence $x_1, x_2, \ldots$ and we shall write $x = \lim x_n$. It follows from condition (M1) and (M3) that every sequence in a metric space has at most one limit.

THEOREM 1. *Let (X, ϱ) be a metric space. A point x belongs to the closure of a set $A \subset X$, with the topology induced by the metric ϱ, if and only if it is the limit of a sequence of points belonging to A.*

Proof. Let us suppose that $x \in \bar{A}$. For every natural number n there exists a point $x_n \in A \cap B(x, 1/n)$, whence $\varrho(x, x_n) < 1/n$ and $x = \lim x_n$. Now, if $x \notin \bar{A}$, then there exists an $\varepsilon > 0$ such that $A \cap B(x, \varepsilon) = 0$, from which $\varrho(x, x') \geqslant \varepsilon$ for every $x' \in A$, and no sequence in A can be convergent to the point x. ■

Theorem 1 immediately implies

THEOREM 2. *The metrics ϱ_1 and ϱ_2 defined in a set X are equivalent if and only if they induce the same convergence, i.e. if for every $x \in X$ and every sequence of points $x_1, x_2, \ldots$ from the set X the conditions $\lim \varrho_1(x, x_n) = 0$ and $\lim \varrho_2(x, x_n) = 0$ are equivalent.* ■

The least upper bound (which is a real number or the "infinite number" ∞) of the distances between points of a non-empty set A is called the *diameter* of the set A. The diameter of the non-empty set A is denoted by $\delta(A)$. Thus

$$\delta(A) = \sup_{x_1, x_2 \in A} \varrho(x_1, x_2). \tag{1}$$

Let us also define $\delta(0) = 0$.

A set A is said to be *bounded* if $\delta(A) < \infty$. A metric ϱ in a set X is said to be *bounded by a real number* r if $\delta(X) < r$, where $\delta(X)$ denotes the diameter of the space X. The notion of a *pseudo-metric bounded by a real number* r is defined anologously.

THEOREM 3. *In every metric space* (X, ϱ) *there exists a metric* ϱ_1 *equivalent to* ϱ *and bounded by number* 1.

Proof. Let us define for $x, y \in X$

$$\varrho_1(x, y) = \min(\varrho(x, y), 1). \tag{2}$$

We shall verify that ϱ_1 is a metric. It has properties (M1) and (M2), since the metric ϱ has those properties. Let us now suppose that x, y and z denote arbitrary points of the set X and let $a = \varrho(x, y)$, $b = \varrho(y, z)$, and $c = \varrho(x, z)$.

Since each of the numbers $2, 1+a, 1+b$, and $a+b$ is not less than either 1 or c, we have

$$\min(2, 1+a, 1+b, a+b) \geqslant \min(1, c)$$

and

$$\begin{aligned}\varrho_1(x, y)+\varrho_1(y, z) &= \min(1, a)+\min(1, b)\\ &= \min(2, 1+a, 1+b, a+b) \geqslant \min(1, c) = \varrho_1(x, z).\end{aligned}$$

Hence ϱ_1 has also property (M3). The metric ϱ_1 is evidently bounded by 1. The equivalence of the metrics ϱ and ϱ_1 follows from Theorem 2 and formula (2). ∎

EXAMPLE 1. Let X be an arbitrary set. Let us assume that for $x, y \in X$

$$\varrho(x, y) = \begin{cases} 1, & \text{if} \quad x \neq y, \\ 0, & \text{if} \quad x = y. \end{cases}$$

A simple calculation shows that ϱ is a metric. Since $B(x, 1) = \{x\}$, the metric ϱ induces the discrete topology in X. Every discrete space is thus metrizable. Any space that does not satisfy the first axiom of countability is an example of a non-metrizable space. Such is, for instance, the space considered in Example 1.1.2, where $\overline{\overline{X}} > \aleph_0$. ∎

EXAMPLE 2. The real-line R and the segment I are also metrizable; we can define the distance between two points as the absolute value of their difference. It can easily be observed that we have defined the family of open subsets of R and I as the unions of balls defined by means of the above metric. ∎

EXAMPLE 3. Let us consider a set S of power $\mathfrak{m} \geqslant \aleph_0$. For every $s \in S$ let $I_s = I \times \{s\}$. We define an equivalence relation R in the set $\bigcup_{s \in S} I_s$ by means of the condition

$$(x, s_1) R (y, s_2) \text{ if and only if either } x = y \text{ and } s_1 = s_2 \text{ or } x = 0 = y.$$

It is easy to see that the formula

$$\varrho([(x, s_1)], [(y, s_2)]) = \begin{cases} |x-y|, & \text{if} \quad s_1 = s_2, \\ x+y, & \text{if} \quad s_1 \neq s_2 \end{cases}$$

defines a metric in the set of equivalence classes under the relation R. For each $\mathfrak{m}$ the metric space obtained in this manner does not depend on the choice of the set S (up to a homeomorphism). The space will be called a *hedgehog with* $\mathfrak{m}$ *prickles* and denoted by $J(\mathfrak{m})$. A base of the space $J(\mathfrak{m})$ consists of balls with rational radii and centres of the form (w, s), where w is a rational number and $s \in S$. Hence it follows that $w(J(\mathfrak{m})) \leqslant \mathfrak{m}$. Since the subspace of $J(\mathfrak{m})$ consisting of the points of the form $(1, s)$, where $s \in S$, is a discrete space of power $\mathfrak{m}$, we have $w(J(\mathfrak{m})) = \mathfrak{m}$. ■

EXAMPLE 4. Let $X = R \times R$ be the Euclidean plane. For the points $z_1 = (x_1, y_1)$ and $z_2 = (x_2, y_2)$ let us define

$$\varrho(z_1, z_2) = \begin{cases} |y_1 - y_2|, & \text{if} \quad x_1 = x_2, \\ |y_1| + |y_2| + |x_1 - x_2|, & \text{if} \quad x_1 \neq x_2. \end{cases}$$

The reader can verify that ϱ is in fact a metric. One can say that this metric characterizes the situation in a wooded country with a river $y = 0$. The inhabitants of that country, in order to get to the water, have cut out paths perpendicular to the river. If someone wishes to go from a place (x_1, y_1) to a place (x_2, y_2), he would find out that the best solution is to go straight to the river, swim to get nearest to (x_2, y_2), and then walk again through the wood. The metric "river" on the plane not equivalent to the metric considered in Example 1. ■

EXAMPLE 5. Let us consider the set H consisting of all infinite sequences $\{x_i\}$ composed of real numbers satisfying the condition $\sum_{i=1}^{\infty} x_i^2 < \infty$. We can define a metric in the set H assuming that for $x = \{x_i\}$ and $y = \{y_i\}$

$$\varrho(x, y) = \sqrt{\sum_{i=1}^{\infty} (x_i - y_i)^2}.$$

To begin with, we shall verify that ϱ is correctly defined, i.e. that the series in the definition is convergent.

We shall use the Cauchy inequality

$$\Big|\sum_{i=1}^{n} a_i b_i\Big| \leqslant \sqrt{\sum_{i=1}^{n} a_i^2} \cdot \sqrt{\sum_{i=1}^{n} b_i^2},$$

which holds for systems $a_1, a_2, \ldots, a_n$ and $b_1, b_2, \ldots, b_n$ of real numbers (1).

(1) Let $a = \sum_{i=1}^{n} a_i^2$, $b = \sum_{i=1}^{n} b_i^2$, and $c = \sum_{i=1}^{n} a_i b_i$. In order to prove the Cauchy inequality, i.e. the inequality $c^2 \leqslant ab$, it is sufficient to note that the equation $ax^2 + 2cx + b = \sum_{i=1}^{n} (a_i x + b_i)^2 = 0$ has no distinct real solutions.

Let us note that for each two points $x = \{x_i\}$ and $y = \{y_i\}$ belonging to H, the inequality

$$\sum_{i=1}^{n}(x_i-y_i)^2 = \sum_{i=1}^{n}x_i^2-2\sum_{i=1}^{n}x_iy_i+\sum_{i=1}^{n}y_i^2$$

$$\leqslant \sum_{i=1}^{n}x_i^2+2\sqrt{\sum_{i=1}^{n}x_i^2}\cdot\sqrt{\sum_{i=1}^{n}y_i^2}+\sum_{i=1}^{n}y_i^2$$

$$=\Bigl(\sqrt{\sum_{i=1}^{n}x_i^2}+\sqrt{\sum_{i=1}^{n}y_i^2}\Bigr)^2 \leqslant \Bigl(\sqrt{\sum_{i=1}^{\infty}x_i^2}+\sqrt{\sum_{i=1}^{\infty}y_i^2}\Bigr)^2$$

holds for every n. Hence the series which appears in the definition of ϱ is convergent and $\varrho(x, y)$ is well defined.

It is clear that the function ϱ satisfies conditions (M1) and (M2). We shall prove the triangle inequality.

Let $x = \{x_i\}$, $y = \{y_i\}$, and $z = \{z_i\}$ be arbitrary points of the space H. Let us write

$$x^n = \{x_1, x_2, \ldots, x_n, 0, \ldots\}, \qquad y^n = \{y_1, y_2, \ldots, y_n, 0, \ldots\},$$

$$z^n = \{z_1, z_2, \ldots, z_n, 0, \ldots\}$$

and let $a_i = x_i-y_i$, $b_i = y_i-z_i$, $c_i = x_i-z_i$.

By the Cauchy inequality,

$$\varrho^2(x^n, z^n) = \sum_{i=1}^{n}c_i^2 = \sum_{i=1}^{n}(a_i+b_i)^2 = \sum_{i=1}^{n}a_i^2+2\sum_{i=1}^{n}a_ib_i+\sum_{i=1}^{n}b_i^2$$

$$\leqslant \sum_{i=1}^{n}a_i^2+2\sqrt{\sum_{i=1}^{n}a_i^2}\cdot\sqrt{\sum_{i=1}^{n}b_i^2}+\sum_{i=1}^{n}b_i^2$$

$$=\Bigl(\sqrt{\sum_{i=1}^{n}a_i^2}+\sqrt{\sum_{i=1}^{n}b_i^2}\Bigr)^2 = [\varrho(x^n, y^n)+\varrho(y^n, z^n)]^2.$$

The inequality

$$\varrho(x^n, z^n) \leqslant \varrho(x^n, y^n)+\varrho(y^n, z^n) \leqslant \varrho(x, y)+\varrho(y, z),$$

which holds true for $n = 1, 2, \ldots$, evidently implies the inequality $\varrho(x, z) \leqslant \varrho(x, y)+\varrho(y, z)$.

It is easy to verify that the subset $H_0 \subset H$ consisting of all sequences $\{x_i\}$, where all numbers x_i are rational and only a finite number are different from zero, is countable and dense in H with respect to the topology induced by ϱ. The space H is therefore separable. We call it the *Hilbert space.* ■

A simple characterization of mappings of metric spaces can be given by means of a metric, namely, condition (iii) of Theorem 1.4.1 implies

THEOREM 4. *Let X and Y be metrizable spaces and let ϱ_1 and ϱ_2 denote metrics in the spaces X and Y respectively. A function f of the set X into Y is a mapping if and only if for each point $x \in X$ and every $\varepsilon > 0$ there exists a number $\delta > 0$ such that for every $x' \in X$ satisfying the condition $\varrho_1(x, x') < \delta$ we have the inequality $\varrho_2(f(x), f(x')) < \varepsilon$.* ∎

Let (X, ϱ) be a metric space, let x be a point, and $A \neq 0$ a subset of X. We define

$$d(x, A) = \inf_{a \in A} \varrho(x, a).$$

Let us also define $d(x, 0) = 1$ for every $x \in X$. The number $d(x, A)$ is called the *distance* from the point x to the set A.

LEMMA. *For a fixed subset A and an arbitrary pair of points x, y of the metric space X we have the inequality*

$$|d(x, A) - d(y, A)| \leqslant \varrho(x, y).$$

Proof. We can of course assume that $A \neq 0$. For every $\varepsilon > 0$ there exists a $z \in A$ such that $\varrho(y, z) < d(y, A) + \varepsilon$. Hence

$$d(x, A) \leqslant \varrho(x, z) \leqslant \varrho(x, y) + \varrho(y, z) < \varrho(x, y) + d(y, A) + \varepsilon$$

and

$$d(x, A) - d(y, A) < \varrho(x, y) + \varepsilon.$$

Since ε is arbitrary, we have

$$d(x, A) - d(y, A) \leqslant \varrho(x, y).$$

By the symmetry of the assumptions, we also have

$$d(y, A) - d(x, A) \leqslant \varrho(x, y). \ ∎$$

The lemma and Theorem 4 imply

THEOREM 5. *For each $A \subset X$ the distance $d(x, A)$ is a continuous function.* ∎

Theorems 1 and 5 imply

COROLLARY 1. *Let X be a metrizable space and let ϱ be a metric in the space X. For every set $A \subset X$,*

$$\bar{A} = \{x : d(x, A) = 0\}. \ ∎$$

Let us mention two more corollaries to Theorem 5.

COROLLARY 2. *Every closed subset of metrizable space is a G_δ-set.*

Indeed, if $\bar{A} = A$, then writing $d(x, A)$ by $d(x)$ we have

$$A = d^{-1}(0) = d^{-1}\Big(\bigcap_{n=1}^{\infty} [0, 1/n)\Big) = \bigcap_{n=1}^{\infty} d^{-1}([0, 1/n)). \blacksquare$$

COROLLARY 3. *Every metrizable space is normal.*

Indeed, every metrizable space X is a Hausdorff space; moreover, for each pair of closed and disjoint sets $A, B \subset X$, the function $f: X \to I$ defined by means of the formula

$$f(x) = \frac{d(x, A)}{d(x, A) + d(x, B)}$$

assumes the value 0 on the set A and the value 1 on the set B. $\blacksquare$

We have already noted that every metrizable space satisfies the first axiom of countability. Example 1 shows that there exist metrizable spaces which do not satisfy the second axiom of countability. The corollary to the following theorem gives necessary and sufficient conditions for a metrizable space to satisfy the second axiom of countability.

THEOREM 6. *For every cardinal number $\mathfrak{m} \geqslant \aleph_0$ and a metrizable space X the following conditions are equivalent:*

(i) $w(X) \leqslant \mathfrak{m}$.

(ii) *Every open covering of the space X contains a subcovering of power $\leqslant \mathfrak{m}$.*

(iii) *X contains a dense subset of power $\leqslant \mathfrak{m}$.*

Proof. By virtue of Theorem 1.1.6, the implication (i) $\Rightarrow$ (ii) holds.

We shall now prove that (ii) $\Rightarrow$ (iii). Let X be a metrizable space with property (ii) and let ϱ denote a metric in X. For every natural number n let us choose a subcovering $\mathfrak{B}_n = \{U_s\}_{s \in S_n}$ from the covering $\{B(x, 1/n)\}_{x \in X}$ of the space X such that $\overline{\overline{S_n}} \leqslant \mathfrak{m}$ and $U_s \neq 0$ for $s \in S_n$. Let $x_s \in U_s$ for $s \in S_n$ and $n = 1, 2, \ldots$ We shall show that the set $D = \{x_s\}_{s \in \bigcup_{n=1}^{\infty} S_n}$, whose power is obviously not greater than $\mathfrak{m}$, is dense in the space X. For this purpose it is sufficient to prove that for each non-empty open set $U \subset X$ there exist an n and $s \in S_n$ such that

$$U_s \subset U. \tag{3}$$

We may evidently assume that $U = B(x, r)$, where $r > 0$. Let n denote a natural number such that $2/n < r$. Since $\mathfrak{B}_n$ is a covering, there exists an $s \in S_n$ such that $x \in U_s$. Furthermore, since $\delta(U_s) \leqslant 2/n$, (3) is satisfied.

We shall now prove the implication (iii) $\Rightarrow$ (i). Let ϱ be a metric in X and let A denote a dense subset of X such that $\overline{\overline{A}} \leqslant \mathfrak{m}$. Let us denote by $\mathfrak{B}$ the family of all balls with rational radii and centres belonging to A. It is obvious that $\overline{\overline{\mathfrak{B}}} \leqslant \mathfrak{m}$. We shall show that $\mathfrak{B}$ is a base of the space X.

Let us consider a point $x \in X$ and its neighbourhood U. We can assume that $U = B(x, r)$, where $r > 0$. Since the set A is dense in X, we infer that there exists a point $x_0 \in A \cap B(x, r/3)$. Denoting by r_0 an arbitrary rational number which satisfies the inequality $r/3 < r_0 < r/2$, we have

$$x \in B(x_0, r_0) \subset B(x, r) = U \quad \text{and} \quad B(x_0, r_0) \in \mathfrak{B}. \ \blacksquare$$

COROLLARY. *For a metrizable space X the following conditions are equivalent*:

(i) *X satisfies the second axiom of countability.*
(ii) *X is a Lindelöf space.*
(iii) *X is separable.* ■

EXERCISES

A. Prove that a metric space is an $\mathscr{L}^*$ space (see Problem 1.S) if we define the limit as in this paragraph. Is condition (L*4) of Problem 1.T also satisfied?

B. Show that for an arbitrary metric space (X, ϱ) the formula

$$\varrho_1(x, y) = \frac{\varrho(x, y)}{1 + \varrho(x, y)}$$

defines a metric equivalent to ϱ and bounded by number 1.

C. Prove that a function f of a metrizable space X into a metrizable space Y is a mapping if and only if for each $x, x_1, x_2, \ldots$ belonging to X the equality $x = \lim x_n$ implies the equality $f(x) = \lim f(x_n)$. Verify that f is a homeomorphism if and only if the above equalities are equivalent.

§ 2. Operations on metrizable spaces. First of all, let us note that a subspace M of a metrizable space X is metrizable. In fact, assuming that the distance between two points in M is equal to the distance in X, we define a metric in M. The reader can verify without any difficulty that the topology induced in M by this metric is identical with the topology of the subspace.

THEOREM 1. *The sum of an arbitrary family of disjoint metrizable spaces is metrizable.*

Proof. Let $\{X_s\}_{s \in S}$ denote a family of disjoint metrizable spaces. According to Theorem 1.3, we can assume that the metric ϱ_s in the space X_s is bounded by number 1, i.e. that for each pair of points $x, y \in X_s$ the inequality $\varrho_s(x, y) \leqslant 1$ holds.

Let $X = \bigoplus_{s \in S} X_s$. Let us assume for $x, y \in X$ that

$$\varrho(x, y) = \begin{cases} \varrho_s(x, y), & \text{if } x, y \in X_s \text{ for some } s \in S, \\ 1, & \text{otherwise.} \end{cases}$$

We shall show that the above formula defines a metric in X. Conditions (M1) and (M2) are obviously satisfied. Thus it remains to verify condition (M3). Let x, y and z denote three arbitrary points of the space X. We shall prove that

$$\varrho(x, z) \leqslant \varrho(x, y)+\varrho(y, z). \tag{1}$$

If $x, z \in X_s$ for some $s \in S$, then the left side of (1) is equal to $\varrho_s(x, z)$. The right side is equal to $\varrho_s(x, y)+\varrho_s(y, z)$ if $y \in X_s$, and to 2 if $y \notin X_s$. In both cases, (1) holds, but if $x \in X_{s_1}$ and $z \in X_{s_2}$, where $s_1 \neq s_2$, then $\varrho(x, z) = 1$ and for the point y we have either $y \notin X_{s_1}$ or $y \notin X_{s_2}$. Thus at least one of the terms on the right side of (1) is equal to 1, from which we see that (1) holds.

It can easily be verified that for each $s \in S$ the subset X_s is open in X with respect to the topology induced by ϱ. Since ϱ induces the initial topology in X_s, the theorem follows from Theorem 2.2.2. ∎

Let a countable family of metrizable spaces $\{X_i\}_{i=1}^{\infty}$ be given. Let us suppose that ϱ_i denotes a metric bounded by number 1 in the space X_i for $i = 1, 2, \ldots$ Let us consider the product $\mathop{\boldsymbol{P}}\limits_{i=1}^{\infty} X_i$ and let us define the distance from a point $x = \{x_i\}$ to a point $y = \{y_i\}$ by means of the formula

$$\varrho(x, y) = \sum_{i=1}^{\infty} \frac{1}{2^i} \varrho_i(x_i, y_i). \tag{2}$$

The reader can verify without any difficulty that ϱ satisfies all conditions of a metric. The question may be raised as to whether the topology induced by the metric (2) in the set $\mathop{\boldsymbol{P}}\limits_{i=1}^{\infty} X_i$ is identical with the Tychonoff topology. A positive answer is given by the following

THEOREM 2. *Let $\{X_i\}_{i=1}^{\infty}$ be a sequence of metrizable spaces and let ϱ_i denote a metric bounded by number 1 in the space X_i. The topology induced by the metric ϱ given by formula (2) in the set $X = \mathop{\boldsymbol{P}}\limits_{i=1}^{\infty} X_i$ is the same as the topology of the Cartesian product of the family of spaces.*

Proof. If for $x, y \in X$ we have $\varrho(x, y) < \varepsilon/2^i$, then $\varrho_i(x_i, y_i) < \varepsilon$; hence by Theorem 1.4, the projection p_i onto the i-th axis is a mapping provided that we consider X with the topology induced by the metric ϱ. From the definition of the Tychonoff topology we infer that the topology induced by ϱ is stronger than the topology of the Cartesian product.

We shall show that every set, open with respect to the topology induced by ϱ, is open with respect to the Tychonoff topology. This will imply that both topologies are identical.

Let U denote an open set in the topology induced by ϱ and let $x = \{x_i\} \in U$. There exists $r > 0$ such that $B(x, r) \subset U$. We shall prove that there exist: a natural number n and open sets $B_i \subset X_i$, where $i = 1, 2, \ldots, n$, such that

$$x \in \bigcap_{i=1}^{n} p_i^{-1}(B_i) \subset B(x, r) \subset U. \tag{3}$$

Let n denote a natural number such that

$$\sum_{i=n+1}^{\infty} \frac{1}{2^i} = \frac{1}{2^n} < r/2. \tag{4}$$

For every $i \leqslant n$ let us define

$$B_i = B(x_i, r/2) = \{x \in X_i \colon \varrho_i(x_i, x) < r/2\}.$$

For every $y = \{y_i\} \in \bigcap_{i=1}^{n} p_i^{-1}(B_i)$ we have $\varrho_i(x_i, y_i) < r/2$ for $i \leqslant n$, so that, according to (2) and (4)

$$\varrho(x, y) = \sum_{i=1}^{n} \frac{1}{2^i} \varrho_i(x_i, y_i) + \sum_{i=n+1}^{\infty} \frac{1}{2^i} \varrho_i(x_i, y_i) < r/2 + r/2 = r;$$

thus (3) holds and the theorem has been proved. ∎

COROLLARY 1. *The Hilbert cube $I^{\aleph_0}$ is metrizable.* ∎

A similar argument as to the proof of Theorem 2.3.8 shows that the Cartesian product of uncountably many spaces, containing more than a single point, does not satisfy the first axiom of countability. By Theorem 2, this yields

COROLLARY 2. *The Cartesian product of a family $\{X_s\}_{s \in S}$ of non-empty metrizable spaces is metrizable if and only if all spaces of the family, with the exception perhaps of a countable number, contain exactly one point.* ∎

The definition of an inverse system immediately implies

COROLLARY 3. *The limit of an inverse system $\{X_\sigma, \pi_\varrho^\sigma, \Sigma\}$, consisting of metrizable spaces with $\overline{\overline{\Sigma}} \leqslant \aleph_0$, is metrizable.* ∎

THEOREM 3. *A compact space is metrizable if and only if it satisfies the second axiom of countability.*

Proof. Each compact space is a Lindelöf space; thus the necessity of the condition follows from Theorem 1.6.

Since every compact space is a Tychonoff space, the condition is sufficient by virtue of Theorem 2.3.8 and Corollary 1 to Theorem 2. ∎

THEOREM 4. *A space which satisfies the second axiom of countability is metrizable if and only if it is regular.*

Proof. By Corollary 3 to Theorem 1.5, every metrizable space is regular.

Let us now suppose that a space X satisfies the second axiom of countability and is regular. By virtue of Theorem 1.5.6, X is normal, and it is a Tychonoff space. We infer from Theorem 2.3.8 that X is embeddable in the Hilbert cube $I^{\aleph_0}$, whence X is metrizable. ∎

COROLLARY. *The Hilbert cube $I^{\aleph_0}$ is a universal space for separable metrizable spaces and for compact metrizable spaces.* ∎

Theorems 3 and 4 are metrization theorems. They give a topological necessary and sufficient condition for a space to be metrizable but they apply only to certain classes of spaces, namely to compact spaces and spaces satisfying the second axiom of countability.

EXAMPLE 1. Let X_i denote a metrizable space for $i = 1, 2, \ldots, n$ and let ϱ_i be a metric in X_i. Let us assume that

(5) $$\varrho(x, y) = \sqrt{\sum_{i=1}^{n} \varrho_i(x_i, y_i)^2}$$

for a pair of points $x = \{x_i\}$ and $y = \{y_i\}$ belonging to $X_1 \times X_2 \times \ldots \times X_n$. One can show, as in Example 1.5, that ϱ satisfies the triangle inequality. Since conditions (M1) and (M2) are obviously satisfied, ϱ is a metric. The reader can verify that it induces the topology of the Cartesian product in $X_1 \times X_2 \times \ldots \times X_n$. Hence it will follow that the topology of the Cartesian product in the space R^n is the same as the topology defined by the usual metric in this space. The reader can also verify that the notion of a bounded set in the space R^n, which was introduced in Paragraph 3.2, is the same as the notion of a bounded set in the metric space R^n. ∎

The quotient spaces of metrizable spaces are not necessarily metrizable. Example 3.2.2 shows that the quotient space of a separable metrizable space by a closed equivalence relation does not always satisfy the first axiom of countability. It can be shown, however, (see Problem U) that if R is a closed equivalence relation in a metric space X and the quotient space X/R satisfies the first axiom of countability, then X/R is metrizable. Compactness of the equivalence classes under the closed equivalence relation R is another assumption under which the quotient space X/R of a metrizable space X is metrizable (see Problem S).

The last part of this paragraph is devoted to mapping spaces.

Let us suppose that a topological space X and a metric space (Y, ϱ) are given. We say that a mapping $f: X \to Y$ is *bounded* whenever the set $f(X) \subset Y$ is bounded. In the set of all bounded mappings of the space X into the space Y a metric $\hat{\varrho}$ can be defined by the following formula:

(6) $$\hat{\varrho}(f, g) = \sup_{x \in X} \varrho\big(f(x), g(x)\big).$$

Since the sets $f(X)$ and $g(X)$ are bounded, we have $\varrho(f, g) < \infty$; the verification that $\hat{\varrho}$ has properties (M1)-(M3) is left to the reader.

The notion of a bounded mapping is not a topological notion; it depends on the choice of a metric in the space Y. It follows from Theorem 1.3 that one can define, in Y, a metric with respect to which all mappings of X into Y are bounded. We are thus able to define a metric in Y^X, whence also to introduce a topology in this set, but unfortunately that topology depends on the choice of the metric in the space Y.

EXAMPLE 2. Let Y be the subset of the real-line consisting of the points $1/n$ and $-1/n$ for $n = 1, 2, \ldots$ Evidently Y is a discrete space of power $\aleph_0$. Let us construct two equivalent metrics in Y. Let ϱ_1 denote the usual metric of the real-line, and let ϱ_2 be the metric which assigns the distance 1 to each pair of distinct points. Let us denote by X the subspace of R consisting of natural numbers. The set Y^X is the same as the set of all functions of X into Y.

The two metrics ϱ_1 and ϱ_2 described above define two metrics $\hat{\varrho}_1$ and $\hat{\varrho}_2$ in the set Y^X. We shall show that the metrics $\hat{\varrho}_1$ and $\hat{\varrho}_2$ are not equivalent.

Let $f_i\colon X \to Y$ be defined by means of the formula $f_i(i) = -1/i$ and $f_i(n) = 1/n$ for $n \neq i$, and let $f\colon X \to Y$ be defined by means of the formula $f(n) = 1/n$ for $n = 1, 2, \ldots$ It is easy to verify that $\hat{\varrho}_1(f, f_i) = 2/i$ but $\hat{\varrho}_2(f, f_i) = 1$. According to Theorem 1.2, this implies that the metrics $\hat{\varrho}_1$ and $\hat{\varrho}_2$ are not equivalent. ∎

From the topological point of view there is, therefore, no reason to consider the topology in Y^X induced by the metric (6). On the other hand, the space Y^X with the topology induced by the metric $\hat{\varrho}$ has many interesting properties and is useful in mathematics mainly because the Baire Theorem is valid in it under some assumptions concerning the space Y, as we shall see in the following paragraph. Moreover, as is shown by Theorem 6 for the important case of a compact X, the topology described in Y^X above is identical with the compact-open topology.

We shall now prove

THEOREM 5. *Let X be an arbitrary topological space and let (Y, ϱ) denote a metric space with the bounded metric. Let us consider the space Y^X with the topology induced by the metric $\hat{\varrho}$. The function φ of the Cartesian product $Y^X \times X$ into Y, defined by the formula $\varphi(f, x) = f(x)$, is a mapping. Thus, by Theorem* 3.3.6, *the topology in Y^X is stronger than the compact--open topology.*

Proof. Let $(f_0, x_0) \in Y^X \times X$ and $f_0(x_0) = y_0$. Let us consider an arbitrary ball $B(y_0, \varepsilon)$, where $\varepsilon > 0$. Since f_0 is a mapping, there exists a neighbourhood $V \subset X$ of the point x_0 such that $f_0(V) \subset B(y_0, \varepsilon/2)$. It can easily be verified that $\varphi\big(B(f_0, \varepsilon/2) \times V\big) \subset B(y_0, \varepsilon)$, so that φ is in fact a mapping. ∎

Let us note that if X is a compact space, then, according to Theorem 1.5 and corollary to Theorem 3.2.7, each mapping $f: X \to Y$ into a metrizable space Y is bounded with respect to every metric ϱ in the space Y. Hence, for a compact X, $\hat{\varrho}$ is a metric in the whole space Y^X.

THEOREM 6. *If X is a compact space and Y is a metrizable space, then he topology in the space Y^X induced by the metric $\hat{\varrho}$ (see formula (6)), where ϱ is an arbitrary metric in the space Y, is the same as the compact-open topology. Hence it does not depend on the choice of the metric ϱ.*

Proof. According to Theorem 5 it is sufficient to show that each ball $B(f', \varepsilon') = \{f \in Y^X : \hat{\varrho}(f', f) < \varepsilon'\}$ is open with respect to the compact-open topology in the space Y^X. If $f \in B(f', \varepsilon')$, then there exists an $\varepsilon > 0$ such that $B(f, \varepsilon) \subset B(f', \varepsilon')$. Hence it is sufficient to show that for every $f \in Y^X$ and $\varepsilon > 0$ there exists a set $V \subset Y^X$ open with respect to the compact-open topology and such that

$$f \in V \subset B(f, \varepsilon). \tag{7}$$

For every $x \in X$ let us consider the set $U_x = f^{-1}\big(B(f(x), \varepsilon/4)\big)$. The family $\{U_x\}_{x \in X}$ is a covering of the space X, whence, this space being compact, there exists a finite sequence of points $x_1, x_2, \ldots, x_k \in X$ such that

$$X = \bigcup_{i=1}^{k} U_{x_i}. \tag{8}$$

Let us assume that for $i = 1, 2, \ldots$

$$Z_i = \overline{U}_{x_i} = \overline{f^{-1}\big(B(f(x_i), \varepsilon/4)\big)} \quad \text{and} \quad V_i = B\big(f(x_i), \varepsilon/3\big). \tag{9}$$

The sets $Z_1, Z_2, \ldots, Z_k$ are compact subsets of the space X, and the sets $V_1, V_2, \ldots, V_k$ are open in the space Y. Hence the set

$$V = \bigcap_{i=1}^{k} M(Z_i, V_i)$$

is open with respect to the compact-open topology in the space Y^X. We shall show that for this V formula (7) holds.

It follows from (9) that $f(Z_i) \subset V_i$ for $i = 1, 2, \ldots, k$, whence $f \in V$. Let us now consider an arbitrary $g \in V$. For every $x \in X$ there exists, by (8) and (9), an index $i \leqslant k$ such that $x \in Z_i$. We thus have $g(x) \in V_i$ and $f(x) \in V_i$. Since $\delta(V_i) < 2\varepsilon/3$, and since the point x is arbitrary, $\hat{\varrho}(g, f) < \varepsilon$ holds. ∎

In order to complete this paragraph we shall illustrate the role of the topology of uniform convergence in the mapping space R^X.

Let X be a topological space and let (Y, ϱ) denote a metric space. A sequence $\{f_n\}$, where $f_n: X \to Y$, will be said to be *uniformly convergent* to a function f of the space X into Y if for every $\varepsilon > 0$ there exists a number N such that if $n \geqslant N$, then $\varrho\big(f(x), f_n(x)\big) < \varepsilon$ for every $x \in X$.

The proof of the following theorem is a repetition of the proof of Theorem 1.4.2.

THEOREM 7. *Let X be a topological space, (Y, ϱ) a metric space, and $\{f_n\}$ a sequence of mappings of X into Y. If the sequence $\{f_n\}$ is uniformly convergent to a function f of the space X into Y, then f is a mapping.* ■

It is easy to verify that a sequence of mappings $\{f_n\}$, where $f_n: X \to Y$, is uniformly convergent to a mapping $f: X \to Y$ if and only if $\lim \hat{\varrho}_1(f, f_n) = 0$ (i.e. if $f = \lim f_n$ in the metric space $(Y^X, \hat{\varrho}_1)$), where $\varrho_1(x, y) = \min(1, \varrho(x, y))$. Formula (1) of Paragraph 2.6 and Theorem 1.1 thus imply

THEOREM 8. *For an arbitrary topological space X the space R^X with the topology of uniform convergence is metrizable. The topology of uniform convergence in R^X is induced by the metric $\hat{\varrho}$ (see formula (6)), where ϱ is a metric in R and $\varrho(x, y) = \min(1, |x-y|)$.* ■

EXERCISES

A. Show that for every metric space (X, ϱ) the function of the Cartesian product $X \times X$ into R which assigns to each pair $(x, y) \in X \times X$ the distance $\varrho(x, y)$ is continuous.

B. Let $\{X_i\}_{i=1}^{\infty}$ be a countable family of metric spaces and let ϱ_i denote a metric bounded by number 1 in X_i. Show that the sequence of points $x_1, x_2, \ldots$, where $x_j = \{x_i^j\} \in \mathop{\boldsymbol{P}}\limits_{i=1}^{\infty} X_i$, is convergent (with respect to the metric defined by formula (2) in the space $\mathop{\boldsymbol{P}}\limits_{i=1}^{\infty} X_i$) to the point $x = \{x_i\} \in \mathop{\boldsymbol{P}}\limits_{i=1}^{\infty} X_i$ if and only if the sequence $x_i^1, x_i^2, \ldots$ is convergent to the point x_i for $i = 1, 2, \ldots$

C (V. E. Šneĭder [1945]). Show that a compact space X is metrizable if and only if $\Delta = \{(x, x) \in X \times X : x \in X\}$ is a G_δ-set in the Cartesian product $X \times X$.

Hint: Let $\Delta = \bigcap_{i=1}^{\infty} G_i$, where G_i is open in $X \times X$ for $i = 1, 2, \ldots$ Define for $i = 1, 2, \ldots$ a finite open covering $\mathfrak{A}_i$ of the space X such that $U \times U \subset G_i$ for each $U \in \mathfrak{A}_i$.

D. Prove that the Hilbert cube $I^{\aleph_0}$ is homeomorphic to the subset of the Hilbert space consisting of the points $\{x_i\}$ for which $0 \leqslant x_i \leqslant 1/i$ for $i = 1, 2, \ldots$

E (K. Kuratowski [1935]). A mapping f of the metric space (X_1, ϱ_1) into the space (X_2, ϱ_2) is called an *isometry* provided that $\varrho_1(x, y) = \varrho_2(f(x), f(y))$ for each pair of points $x, y \in X_1$.

Let (X, ϱ) be a metric space and let $x_0 \in X$ denote an arbitrary point. Let us assume that for each $a \in X$, $f_a(x) = \varrho(x, a) - \varrho(x, x_0)$.

Show that f_a is a continuous and bounded real-valued function and that in assigning the function $f_a \in R^X$ to a point $a \in X$, we get an isometry of the space (X, ϱ) into the space of all bounded mappings of the space X into R.

F. Making use of Theorem 3.3.5, Exercise 3.7.C, and Corollary 3 to Theorem 2 prove that if X is a locally compact Lindelöf space, then for each metrizable Y the space Y^X with the compact-open topology is metrizable. Is the assumption that X is a Lindelöf space essential?

§ 3. Totally bounded spaces and complete spaces. Compactness in metrizable spaces. A subset D of a metric space X with the metric ϱ will be called an *ε-net* in X if for every point $x \in X$ there exists an $x' \in D$ such that $\varrho(x, x') < \varepsilon$.

A metric space (X, ϱ) is said to be *totally bounded* if for each $\varepsilon > 0$ there exists a finite ε-net $\{x_1, x_2, \ldots, x_k\}$ in X. A metrizable space X will be called *metrizable in a totally bounded manner* provided that there exists a metric ϱ in X such that (X, ϱ) is totally bounded.

The first definition describes a class of metric spaces; the second one a class of topological spaces which contains, together with a space X, all spaces homeomorphic to X. The definition of this class, however, is not topological because we make use of the notion of a metric.

We shall now consider the class of totally bounded metric spaces and prove that the class of spaces metrizable in a totally bounded manner is the same as the class of separable metrizable spaces. This fact, together with the corollary to Theorem 1.6 and Theorem 2.4 give a topological characterisation of spaces metrizable in a totally bounded manner. Namely, they are the spaces which are regular and satisfy the second axiom of countability.

However, we shall first give

EXAMPLE 1. The space (X, ϱ) considered in Example 1.1 is not totally bounded if the set X is infinite. In fact, the space X does not contain any finite ε-net, even for $\varepsilon = 1$.

The reader can verify without any difficulty that the real-line R with the usual metric, the hedgehog $J(\mathfrak{m})$ described in Example 1.3, and the plane with the metric "river", are not totally bounded.

On the other hand, an arbitrary segment $J = [a, b]$ is totally bounded. Indeed, for every $\varepsilon > 0$ the set $J \cap \{i/n: i = 0, \pm 1, \pm 2, \ldots\}$, where n is a natural number such that $1/n < \varepsilon$, is a finite ε-net in J. In the same manner it can be verified that an open segment (a, b) is totally bounded. Since the space R is homeomorphic to the segment $(-1, 1)$, it is clear that a space homeomorphic to a totally bounded space is not necessarily totally bounded. ■

THEOREM 1. *Let (X, ϱ) be a totally bounded space and let M denote an arbitrary subset of X. The metric space (M, ϱ) is also totally bounded.*

Proof. Let $\varepsilon > 0$ be given. Let $\{x_1, x_2, \ldots, x_k\}$ be an $\varepsilon/2$-net in X and let $x_{m_1}, x_{m_2}, \ldots, x_{m_l}$ denote those points of the $\varepsilon/2$-net whose distance from M is less than $\varepsilon/2$.

Let $x_1', x_2', \ldots, x_l'$ be arbitrary points of the set M such that

$$(1) \qquad \varrho(x_j', x_{m_j}) < \varepsilon/2 \quad \text{for} \quad j = 1, 2, \ldots, l.$$

We shall show that the set $\{x_1', x_2', \ldots, x_l'\}$ is an ε-net in M. Let x be an arbitrary point in M. By the definition of the points $x_1, x_2, \ldots, x_k$, there exists an $i \leqslant k$ such that

$$(2) \qquad \varrho(x_i, x) < \varepsilon/2.$$

Thus $x_i = x_{m_j}$ for some $j \leqslant l$ and, according to (1) and (2), the inequality $\varrho(x'_j, x) < \varepsilon$ holds. ■

THEOREM 2. *Let $\{(X_i, \varrho_i)\}_{i=1}^{\infty}$ denote a sequence of totally bounded metric spaces such that the metric ϱ_i is bounded by number 1 for $i = 1, 2, \ldots$ The Cartesian product $\mathop{\boldsymbol{P}}_{i=1}^{\infty} X_i$, with the metric defined by means of (2) in the preceding paragraph, is totally bounded.*

Proof. Let $\varepsilon > 0$. Let us consider a natural number n such that $1/2^n < \varepsilon/2$ and for each $i \leqslant n$ let us choose an $\varepsilon/2$-net $\{x_1^{(i)}, x_2^{(i)}, \ldots, x_{k(i)}^{(i)}\}$ in the space X_i. Let $x_0^{(i)}$ be an arbitrary point of the space X_i for $i = n+1, n+2, \ldots$

Let us consider, in $\mathop{\boldsymbol{P}}_{i=1}^{\infty} X_i$, the set D consisting of points of the form:

$$(3) \quad y = \{x_{j_1}^{(1)}, x_{j_2}^{(2)}, \ldots x_{j_n}^{(n)}, x_0^{(n+1)}, x_0^{(n+2)}, \ldots\}, \text{ where } 1 \leqslant j_i \leqslant k(i) \text{ for } i \leqslant n.$$

The set D is finite and we shall show that it is an ε-net in the space $\mathop{\boldsymbol{P}}_{i=1}^{\infty} X_i$. Let $x = \{x_i\}$ denote an arbitrary point of the Cartesian product. For each $i \leqslant n$ there exists a number $1 \leqslant j_i \leqslant k(i)$ such that $\varrho_i(x_i, x_{j_i}^{(i)}) < \varepsilon/2$. Hence for $y \in D$, defined by (3), we have

$$\varrho(x, y) = \sum_{i=1}^{n} \frac{1}{2^i} \varrho_i(x_i, x_{j_i}^{(i)}) + \sum_{i=n+1}^{\infty} \frac{1}{2^i} \varrho_i(x_i, x_0^{(i)}) < \varepsilon/2 + \varepsilon/2 = \varepsilon. \;\blacksquare$$

COROLLARY. *The Hilbert cube $I^{\aleph_0}$ with the metric defined by the formula*

$$\varrho(x, y) = \sum_{i=1}^{\infty} \frac{1}{2^i} |x_i - y_i|, \text{ where } x = \{x_i\} \text{ and } y = \{y_i\},$$

is totally bounded. ■

THEOREM 3. *In order that a metrizable space X be metrizable in a totally bounded manner it is necessary and sufficient that X be separable.*

Proof. Sufficiency of the condition follows from the corollaries to Theorems 2.4 and 2, and from Theorem 1.

In order to prove that separability is a necessary condition let us note that if D_n is a finite $1/n$-net in X, then $D = \bigcup_{n=1}^{\infty} D_n$ is a dense countable subset of X. ■

Theorems 3, 2.4, and the corollary to Theorem 1.6 imply

COROLLARY. *A topological space is metrizable in a totally bounded manner if and only if it is regular and satisfies the second axiom of countability.* ■

We shall now consider another important class of metric spaces, namely complete spaces.

We say that a sequence $\{x_n\}$ consisting of points of a metric space (X, ϱ) satisfies *Cauchy's condition* if for each $\varepsilon > 0$ there exists a natural number N such that for every $n, m \geqslant N$, the inequality $\varrho(x_n, x_m) < \varepsilon$ holds.

A metric space (X, ϱ) is said to be *complete* if for each sequence of points $\{x_n\}$ which satisfies Cauchy's condition there exists a point $x \in X$ such that $x = \lim x_n$, i.e. if in the space X, every sequence satisfying Cauchy's condition is convergent.

A metrizable space X will be called *metrizable in a complete manner* if there exists a metric ϱ in X such that (X, ϱ) is a complete space.

The remarks, which were made at the beginning of the paragraph in connection with the total boundedness of a space, are valid for the class of complete spaces and spaces metrizable in a complete manner. As in that case, we shall first prove some theorems on the class of spaces which are metrizable in a complete manner and then give a topological characterization of that class. Let us start, however, with an example.

EXAMPLE 2. The discrete space of Example 1.1 is complete because every sequence satisfying Cauchy's condition is constant for sufficiently large indices.

We shall prove that the real-line R with the usual metric is complete. Let us consider a sequence $\{x_n\}$ of real numbers which satisfies Cauchy's condition. There exists an N such that for every $n \geqslant N$ the inequality $|x_n - x_N| \leqslant 1$ holds, i.e. all terms of the sequence with indices not smaller than N lie in the segment $J = [x_N - 1, x_N + 1]$. Since J is compact, it follows from Theorem 3.9.6 that there exist a point $x \in J$ and an increasing sequence $n_1, n_2, \ldots$ of natural numbers such that $|x - x_{n_i}| < 1/i$ for $i = 1, 2, \ldots$ A simple calculation shows that the sequence $\{x_n\}$ is convergent to the point x.

The segment $(-1, 1)$ with the usual metric is not complete, because the sequence $\{1 - 1/n\}$ satisfies Cauchy's condition but is not convergent to any point of the segment $(-1, 1)$. Since the segment $(-1, 1)$ is homeomorphic to the real-line, it is metrizable in a complete manner. This example shows that a space homeomorphic to a complete space is not necessarily complete and that completeness of a space is not hereditary even with respect to open subsets. ■

Let us note that if (X, ϱ) is a complete metric space, then there exists in X a metric ϱ_1, bounded by number 1, such that (X, ϱ_1) is also complete. It is the metric described in Theorem 1.3. In fact, a sequence $\{x_n\}$ of points of the set X satisfies Cauchy's condition in (X, ϱ) if and only if it satisfies this condition in (X, ϱ_1).

We leave to the reader the verification that each convergent sequence in a metric space satisfies Cauchy's condition.

The following two theorems give some characterizations of complete spaces; the second one is analogous to the characterization of compact spaces by means of families of closed sets which have the finite intersection property.

THEOREM 4 (Cantor). *A metric space (X, ϱ) is complete if and only if, for every decreasing sequence of non-empty and closed subsets $F_1 \supset F_2 \supset \ldots$ such that $\lim \delta(F_i) = 0$, the intersection $\bigcap_{i=1}^{\infty} F_i$ is non-empty.*

Proof. Let (X, ϱ) be a complete space and let $\{F_i\}$ denote a sequence of non-empty closed sets which satisfy the conditions

$$\lim \delta(F_i) = 0 \text{ and } F_{i+1} \subset F_i \text{ for } i = 1, 2, \ldots \tag{4}$$

Let us choose a point $x_n \in F_n$ for every $n = 1, 2, \ldots$ It is easy to verify that all terms of the sequence $\{x_n\}$ which have indices larger than i belong to the set F_i. Therefore, by virtue of (4) this sequence satisfies Cauchy's condition and is convergent. Let $x = \lim x_n$. Since the sets F_i are closed, $x \in F_i$ for $i = 1, 2, \ldots$, so that $\bigcap_{i=1}^{\infty} F_i \neq 0$.

Let (X, ϱ) be a metric space which has the property described in the theorem and let $\{x_i\}$ denote a sequence of points of X which satisfies Cauchy's condition. Let us define $F_i = \overline{\{x_i, x_{i+1}, \ldots\}}$. The sets F_i are closed and satisfy conditions (4), whence there exists a point $x \in \bigcap_{i=1}^{\infty} F_i$. It is easy to verify that $x = \lim x_i$. Thus every sequence which satisfies Cauchy's condition is convergent, i.e. the space (X, ϱ) is complete. ■

Theorems 4 and 3.9.2 imply

COROLLARY 1. *If a countably compact space X is metrizable, then for every metric ϱ in the space X, the space (X, ϱ) is complete.* ■

COROLLARY 2. *If (X, ϱ) is a metric space and A denotes a subset of X such that the space (A, ϱ) is complete, then A is closed in X.*

Proof. For every point $x \in \bar{A}$ the sequence of sets $F_1, F_2, \ldots$, where $F_i = A \cap \overline{B(x, 1/i)}$ satisfies the conditions of the theorem. Since the intersection $\bigcap_{i=1}^{\infty} F_i$, which is non-empty by the completeness of (A, ϱ), can contain only the point x, we have $x \in A$. ■

Evidently, the above corollary is not valid if we assume that A is only metrizable in a complete manner.

THEOREM 5. *A metric space (X, ϱ) is complete if and only if for each family $\{F_s\}_{s\in S}$, which consists of closed subsets of X, which has the finite intersection property and which, for every $\varepsilon > 0$, contains a set of diameter less than ε, the intersection $\bigcap_{s\in S} F_s$ is not empty.*

Proof. The sufficiency of the condition follows immediately from Theorem 4.

We shall prove that this condition is satisfied for every complete space. Let us suppose that there is given a family $\{F_s\}_{s\in S}$ which consists of closed subsets of X, which has the finite intersection property, and which for each $\varepsilon > 0$ contains a set of diameter less than ε. For each $n = 1, 2, \ldots$ let $s_n \in S$ denote an index such that $\delta(F_{s_n}) \leqslant 1/n$. It is easy to note that the sets $F_i = \bigcap_{j\leqslant i} F_{s_j}$ satisfy the assumptions of the preceding theorem. There exists, therefore, a point $x \in X$ such that $x \in \bigcap_{i=1}^{\infty} F_i$. Moreover, $\bigcap_{i=1}^{\infty} F_i = \{x\}$ holds. We shall show that $x \in F_{s_0}$ for every $s_0 \in S$. Indeed, defining $F'_i = F_{s_0} \cap F_i$ for $i = 1, 2, \ldots$ we again obtain a sequence which satisfies the assumptions of the preceding theorem. Since

$$0 \neq \bigcap_{i=1}^{\infty} F'_i = F_{s_0} \cap \bigcap_{i=1}^{\infty} F_i = F_{s_0} \cap \{x\},$$

the point x belongs to F_{s_0}. ■

We now proceed the consideration of the properties of operations on complete spaces.

THEOREM 6. *Let (X, ϱ) be a complete metric space and let $A \subset X$ denote a closed subspace. The space (A, ϱ) is also complete.*

Proof. Each sequence of points in A which satisfies Cauchy's condition is convergent to a point $x \in X$. Then, since A is closed, x belongs to A. ■

THEOREM 7. *Let $\{(X_i, \varrho_i)\}_{i=1}^{\infty}$ denote a sequence of complete metric spaces such that for $i = 1, 2, \ldots$ the metric ϱ_i is bounded by number 1. The Cartesian product $\mathop{\boldsymbol{P}}_{i=1}^{\infty} X_i$, with the metric defined by formula (2) of the preceding pargaraph, is complete.*

Proof. If a sequence $\{x_n\}$, where $x_n = \{x_n^{(i)}\}$ and $x_n^{(i)} \in X_i$, satisfies Cauchy's condition, then for each $i = 1, 2, \ldots$ the sequence $\{x_n^{(i)}\}$ lying in X_i also satisfies this condition. Since the space X_i is complete, there exists a point $x^{(i)} \in X_i$ such that $x^{(i)} = \lim x_n^{(i)}$. It is easy to verify that the sequence $\{x_n\}$ is convergent to the point $x = \{x^{(i)}\}$. ■

THEOREM 8. *Let X be a topological space, (Y, ϱ) a complete metric space, and ϱ a metric bounded by number 1. The space Y^X with the metric $\hat{\varrho}$ defined by formula (6) of the preceding paragraph is complete.*

Proof. Let $\{f_n\}$ be a sequence of elements of the space $(Y^X, \hat{\varrho})$ which satisfies Cauchy's condition. For every $x \in X$ the sequence $\{f_n(x)\}$ satisfies Cauchy's condition in the space (Y, ϱ). Assigning the limit of the sequence $\{f_n(x)\}$ to the point $x \in X$, we define a function f of the space X into the space Y. It is easy to verify that the sequence $\{f_n\}$ is uniformly convergent to f. By virtue of Theorem 2.7, $f \in Y^X$ and $\lim \hat{\varrho}(f, f_n) = 0$, from which follows that the sequence $\{f_n\}$ is convergent. ■

As we have already noted, the completeness of a metric space is hereditary only with respect to closed subsets. Theorem 9 below shows that the situation is quite different for spaces metrizable in a complete manner; this property is hereditary with respect to subsets which are G_δ-sets. From Theorem 11 and from the existence of metrizable spaces which are not complete in the sense of Čech (see Exercise 3.8.A) it follows, however, that metrizability in a complete manner is not a hereditary property.

THEOREM 9. *Let (X_0, ϱ_0), where ϱ_0 is a metric bounded by number 1, be a complete metric space, and let $X \subset X_0$ denote a G_δ-set. The space X is metrizable in a complete manner.*

Proof. By our assumption $X = \bigcap_{i=1}^{\infty} G_i$, where $G_i \subset X_0$ is open for $i = 1, 2, \ldots$ Let

$$F_i = X_0 \setminus G_i \quad \text{and} \quad f_i(x) = \big(d(x, F_i)\big)^{-1} \quad \text{for} \quad x \in X.$$

By virtue of Theorem 1.5, f_i is a continuous function, $f_i: X \to R$. Let (X_i, ϱ_i) denote the real-line with the metric $\varrho_i(x, y) = \min(1, |x-y|)$ for $i = 1, 2, \ldots$ In view of the Diagonal Lemma, $\varphi = \mathop{\triangle}_{i=0}^{\infty} f_i : X \to \mathop{\boldsymbol{P}}_{i=0}^{\infty} X_i$, where $f_0(x) = x$ for $x \in X$, is a homeomorphic embedding.

Space $\mathop{\boldsymbol{P}}_{i=0}^{\infty} X_i$ with the metric defined by formula (2) of the preceding paragraph is, according to Theorem 7, complete. It is sufficient, by Theorem 6, to show that $\varphi(X)$ is a closed subset of the Cartesian product $\mathop{\boldsymbol{P}}_{i=0}^{\infty} X_i$, i.e. that an arbitrary point $x = \{x_i\} \in \mathop{\boldsymbol{P}}_{i=0}^{\infty} X_i \setminus \varphi(X)$ is contained together with a neighbourhood V in the complement of the set $\varphi(X)$.

To begin with, let us suppose that $x_0 \in X$. Since $x \notin \varphi(X)$, for some i we have the inequality $x_i \neq f_i(x_0)$. Let U_1 and U_2 be disjoint neighbourhoods of the points x_i and $f_i(x_0)$ respectively. Since the function f_i is continuous, there exists a neighbourhood U_0 of the point x_0 in the space X_0 such that $f_i(U_0 \cap X) \subset U_2$. It is easy to verify that

$$x = \{x_i\} \in V = p_0^{-1}(U_0) \cap p_i^{-1}(U_1) \subset \mathop{\boldsymbol{P}}_{i=0}^{\infty} X_i \setminus \varphi(X). \tag{5}$$

Let us now suppose that $x_0 \notin X$, whence $x_0 \in F_i$ for some $i \geqslant 1$. Let $r > 0$ be such a number that $1/r > x_i + 1$ and let $U_0 = B(x_0, r)$, $U_1 = \{x \in R : x < x_i + 1\}$. It is easy to verify that (5) is still valid. ■

THEOREM 10. *Every metrizable space is embeddable in a complete metric space.*

Proof. Let X be a metrizable space and let ϱ_1 denote a metric in X bounded by number 1. By virtue of Theorem 8, the space I^X with the metric $\varrho(f, g) = \sup_{x \in X} |f(x) - g(x)|$ is complete. Let us assign to every point $x_0 \in X$ the function $F(x_0) \in I^X$ defined by means of the formula $[F(x_0)](x) = \varrho_1(x_0, x) = d(x, \{x_0\})$. We shall now prove the formula:

$$\varrho\big(F(x_1), F(x_2)\big) = \varrho_1(x_1, x_2), \tag{6}$$

from which, according to Theorem 1.4, it follows that F is a homeomorphism onto the set $F(X) \subset I^X$.

First of all let us note that for every $x \in X$,

$$[F(x_1)](x) - [F(x_2)](x) = \varrho_1(x_1, x) - \varrho_1(x_2, x) \leqslant \varrho_1(x_1, x_2).$$

By the symmetry of assumptions, $[F(x_2)](x) - [F(x_1)](x) \leqslant \varrho_1(x_1, x_2)$, so that

$$\varrho\big(F(x_1), F(x_2)\big) \leqslant \varrho_1(x_1, x_2).$$

Since $[F(x_1)](x_2) - [F(x_2)](x_2) = \varrho_1(x_1, x_2)$, we also have the inequality

$$\varrho\big(F(x_1), F(x_2)\big) \geqslant \varrho_1(x_1, x_2),$$

which completes the proof of formula (6) and of the theorem. ■

THEOREM 11. *A topological space is metrizable in a complete manner if and only if it is metrizable and complete in the sense of Čech.*

Proof. Let X be a space metrizable in a complete manner, and let ϱ denote such a metric in X that the space (X, ϱ) is complete. From Theorem 5 it follows that each family of closed subsets of the space X, which has the finite intersection property and contains sets of diameter less than the covering $\mathfrak{A}_i = \{B(x, 1/i)\}_{x \in X}$ for $i = 1, 2, \ldots$, has a non-empty intersection. The space X is therefore complete in the sense of Čech by virtue of Theorem 3.8.2.

Let us now consider a metrizable space X which is complete in the sense of Čech.

By virtue of Theorem 10, X can be embedded in a metric and complete space Y. We might consider the closure of X in Y, and assume that X is dense in Y. Let cY be an arbitrary compactification of the space Y. Evidently cY is also a compactification of the space X, from which by Theorem 3.8.1, $c(X)$ is a G_δ-set in cY, and thus also in $c(Y)$. By virtue of Theorem 9, the space X is metrizable in a complete manner. ■

The last part of this paragraph is devoted to the compactness of metrizable spaces.

THEOREM 12. *Let X be a countably compact metrizable space and let ϱ denote a metric in X. The metric space (X, ϱ) is totally bounded.*

Proof. Let us suppose that (X, ϱ) is not totally bounded. Thus for some $\varepsilon > 0$ there is no finite ε-net in X. In other words, for every finite sequence $x_1, x_2, \ldots, x_k \in X$ there exists a point $x_{k+1} \in X$ such that $\varrho(x_i, x_{k+1}) \geqslant \varepsilon$ for all $i \leqslant k$. Starting from an arbitrary point $x_1 \in X$ one can define inductively an infinite sequence $x_1, x_2, \ldots$ in the space X such that $\varrho(x_i, x_j) \geqslant \varepsilon$ for $i \neq j$. It is easy to verify that the set $F = \{x_1, x_2, \ldots\}$ has no accumulation point, whence, according to Theorem 3.9.6, the space X is not countably compact. ■

Theorems 3 and 12 imply the following

COROLLARY. *Each countably compact metrizable space is separable.* ■

THEOREM 13. *For metrizable spaces the notions of compactness and countable compactness are equivalent.*

Proof. Compactness always implies countable compactness. An arbitrary countably compact and metrizable space is, by virtue of the corollary to Theorem 12, separable. Hence by the corollary to Theorem 1.6, it is a Lindelöf space. But every countably compact Lindelöf space is, by Theorem 3.9.1, compact. ■

We shall give here a criterion for compactness of metrizable spaces which employs only the properties of a metric.

THEOREM 14. *A metrizable space X is compact if and only if for some (or, equivalently, for every) metric ϱ in X the metric space (X, ϱ) is totally bounded and complete.*

Proof. The necessity of the condition follows from Corollary 1 to Theorem 4, and from Theorems 12 and 13.

Let us now suppose that the space (X, ϱ) is simultaneously totally bounded and complete.

Let us consider a $1/2n$-net $\{x_1^{(n)}, x_2^{(n)}, \ldots, x_{k(n)}^{(n)}\}$ in X for $n = 1, 2, \ldots$ Defining $B_i^{(n)} = B(x_i^{(n)}, 1/2n)$ for $i = 1, 2, \ldots, k(n)$ we have for every n:

$$X = \bigcup_{i=1}^{k(n)} B_i^{(n)}, \qquad \delta(B_i^{(n)}) \leqslant 1/n \quad \text{for} \quad i \leqslant k(n). \tag{7}$$

We shall show that every infinite set $A \subset X$ has an accumulation point. By virtue of Theorems 3.9.6 and 13, this will complete our proof.

Since the set A is infinite, one of the sets $A \cap B_i^{(1)}$, where $i \leqslant k(1)$, must also be infinite by virtue of (7). Let us denote it by A_1; we thus have

$$A \supset A_1, \quad \delta(A_1) \leqslant 1, \quad \overline{\overline{A_1}} \geqslant \aleph_0.$$

Similarly, we define a set A_2 which is equal to one of the sets $A_1 \cap B_i^{(2)}$ for $i \leqslant k(2)$ and has the following properties:

$$A \supset A_1 \supset A_2, \quad \delta(A_2) \leqslant 1/2, \quad \overline{\overline{A_2}} \geqslant \aleph_0.$$

By means of induction one can define a sequence of sets $A_1, A_2, \ldots$ such that

(8) $A \supset A_1 \supset A_2 \supset \ldots, \quad \delta(A_i) \leqslant 1/i, \quad$ and $\quad \overline{\overline{A_i}} \geqslant \aleph_0$ for $i = 1, 2, \ldots$

By virtue of Theorem 4, there exists a point $x \in \bigcap_{i=1}^{\infty} \overline{A}_i$. It follows from (8) that every neighbourhood of the point x contains infinitely many elements of the set A; x is therefore an accumulation point of the set A. ■

THEOREM 15. *For every open covering $\mathfrak{U}$ of a compact metric space X there exists an $\varepsilon > 0$ such that the covering $\{B(x, \varepsilon)\}_{x \in X}$ is a refinement of $\mathfrak{U}$.*

Proof. For every $x \in X$ let us choose an $\varepsilon_x > 0$ such that the ball $B(x, 2\varepsilon_x)$ is contained in an element of the covering $\mathfrak{U}$. From the covering $\{B(x, \varepsilon_x)\}_{x \in X}$ of the space X, a finite covering can be chosen. There exists, therefore, a finite number of points $x_1, x_2, \ldots, x_k \in X$ such that

$$X \subset B(x_1, \varepsilon_{x_1}) \cup B(x_2, \varepsilon_{x_2}) \cup \ldots \cup B(x_k, \varepsilon_{x_k}).$$

It can easily be verified that $\varepsilon = \min(\varepsilon_{x_1}, \varepsilon_{x_2}, \ldots, \varepsilon_{x_k})$ satisfies the conclusion of the theorem. ■

EXERCISES

A. Prove that a metric space (X, ϱ) is totally bounded if and only if for every $\varepsilon > 0$ there exist sets $A_1, A_2, \ldots, A_k$ such that

$$X = \bigcup_{i=1}^{k} A_i \quad \text{and} \quad \delta(A_i) < \varepsilon \quad \text{for} \quad i = 1, 2, \ldots, k.$$

B. What are the assumptions under which the sum of totally bounded (complete) metric spaces is totally bounded (complete)?

C. Prove that the plane with the metric "river", the hedgehog $J(\mathfrak{m})$, and the Hilbert space is complete.

D. Prove directly that for a space metrizable in a complete manner, Baire's Theorem 3.8.6 is valid. Deduce that metrizability in a complete manner is not a hereditary property.

Hint: For an arbitrary non-empty open set $G \subset X$ construct, as in the proof of Theorem 3.8.6, a sequence of sets $G_0 = G, G_1, G_2, \ldots$ such that

$$0 \neq \overline{G}_i \subset G_{i-1} \setminus \overline{N}_i \quad \text{and} \quad \delta(\overline{G}_i) < 1/i \quad \text{for} \quad i = 1, 2, \ldots$$

E. Show that a metrizable space X is compact if and only if each sequence $\{x_i\}$ in X contains a convergent subsequence (cf. Exercise 1.6.C).

F (A. Lindenbaum [1926]). Show that each isometry f (see Exercise 2.E) of a compact metric space X into itself is a mapping onto X.

Hint: Assume that there exists a point $x \in X \setminus f(X)$ and consider the sequence $x, f(x), ff(x), \ldots$

§ 4. Metrization theorems. We shall begin with the definition of some basic concepts of this paragraph. A family of subsets of a space X is called *locally finite* if every point $x \in X$ has a neighbourhood which intersects only a finite number of its elements. A family of subsets of a space X is called *discrete* if every point $x \in X$ has a neighbourhood which intersects at most one element of that family. Evidently, every discrete family is locally finite.

Let us note two simple properties of locally finite families.

THEOREM 1. *For an arbitrary locally finite family* $\{A_s\}_{s \in S}$ *of subsets of a space* X *we have the equality* $\overline{\bigcup_{s \in S} A_s} = \bigcup_{s \in S} \bar{A}_s$.

Proof. Since the inclusion $\bigcup_{s \in S} \bar{A}_s \subset \overline{\bigcup_{s \in S} A_s}$ is obvious, it is sufficient to show that the converse inclusion holds.

Let us suppose that $x \in \overline{\bigcup_{s \in S} A_s}$. Since the family in question is locally finite, x has a neighbourhood U such that the set $S_0 = \{s \in S\colon U \cap A_s \neq 0\}$ is finite. Hence it follows that $x \notin \overline{\bigcup_{s \in S_1} A_s}$, where $S_1 = S \setminus S_0$. Moreover, since

$$x \in \overline{\bigcup_{s \in S} A_s} = \overline{\bigcup_{s \in S_1} A_s} \cup \overline{\bigcup_{s \in S_0} A_s},$$

we have

$$x \in \overline{\bigcup_{s \in S_0} A_s} = \bigcup_{s \in S_0} \bar{A}_s \subset \bigcup_{s \in S} \bar{A}_s. \ \blacksquare$$

COROLLARY. *Let* $\mathfrak{F} = \{F_s\}_{s \in S}$ *be a locally finite family of subsets of a space* X *and let* $F = \bigcup_{s \in S} F_s$. *If all sets of the family* $\mathfrak{F}$ *are closed, then the set* F *is closed; if the family* $\mathfrak{F}$ *consists of open-and-closed sets, then the set* F *is open-and-closed.* $\blacksquare$

THEOREM 2. *If* $\{A_s\}_{s \in S}$ *is a locally finite (discrete) family of subsets of a space* X, *then the family* $\{\bar{A}_s\}_{s \in S}$ *is also locally finite (discrete).*

The proof of this simple theorem is left to the reader. $\blacksquare$

A family of sets is said to be *σ-locally finite* (*σ-discrete*) if it can be represented as the union of countably many locally finite (discrete) families.

One of the most important properties of metrizable spaces is given by the following

THEOREM 3 (A. H. Stone). *Each open covering of a metrizable space has an σ-discrete open refinement.*

Proof. Let $\{U_s\}_{s\in S}$ be an open covering of a metrizable space X. Let us consider a metric ϱ in the space X and let us define

$$U_{s,n} = \{x: d(x, X\setminus U_s) > 1/2^n\} \quad \text{for } s\in S \text{ and } n = 1, 2, \ldots$$

The sets $U_{s,n}$ are open according to Theorem 1.5; moreover, we have

$$(1) \qquad U_s = \bigcup_{n=1}^{\infty} U_{s,n}.$$

From the lemma to Theorem 1.5 it follows that

$$(2) \qquad \text{if } x\in U_{s,n} \text{ and } y\notin U_{s,n+1}, \text{ then } \varrho(x, y) > 1/2^{n+1},$$

for in this case $d(x, X\setminus U_s)-d(y, X\setminus X_s) > 1/2^n-1/2^{n+1} = 1/2^{n+1}$.

Let $<$ be a relation which well-orders the set S and let

$$(3) \qquad V_{s_0,n} = U_{s_0,n}\setminus \overline{\bigcup_{s<s_0} U_{s,n+1}}.$$

For each pair of distinct elements $s_1, s_2\in S$ we have either $s_1 < s_2$ or $s_2 < s_1$. Depending on which of these relations holds, we have by virtue of (3):

$$V_{s_2,n} \subset X\setminus U_{s_1,n+1} \quad \text{or} \quad V_{s_1,n} \subset X\setminus U_{s_2,n+1}.$$

Thus it follows from (2) that if $x\in V_{s_1,n}$ and $y\in V_{s_2,n}$, where $s_1, s_2\in S$ and $s_1 \neq s_2$, then $\varrho(x, y) > 1/2^{n+1}$. Hence since no ball of radius $1/2^{n+2}$ meets two distinct elements of the family we infer that the family of open sets $\{V_{s,n}\}_{s\in S}$ is discrete for $n = 1, 2, \ldots$

In order to complete the proof it suffices to verify that the family $\{V_{s,n}\}_{n=1,s\in S}^{\infty}$ is a covering of the space X. Let us consider a point $y\in X$ and let $s(y)$ be the first element of the set S such that $y\in U_{s(y)}$. In view of (1), $y\in U_{s(y),n}$ for some n. Since $y\notin U_{s,n+2}$ for $s < s(y)$, and because of (2) we have

$$B(y, 1/2^{n+2}) \cap \bigcup_{s<s(y)} U_{s,n+1} = 0;$$

hence we deduce that $y\in V_{s(y),n}$. ∎

THEOREM 4. *Every metrizable space X has a σ-discrete base.*

Proof. Let us denote by ϱ a metric in X and let $\mathfrak{B}_n$ be a σ-discrete open covering which is a refinement of the covering consisting of all balls with radius $1/n$ in X. The σ-discrete family $\mathfrak{B} = \bigcup_{n=1}^{\infty} \mathfrak{B}_n$ is, as can easily be verified, a base of the space X. ∎

COROLLARY. *Every metrizable space has a σ-locally finite base.* ■

We find that the existence of a σ-locally finite base is also a sufficient condition for the metrizability of a regular space.

We shall first prove a lemma which is a generalization of Theorem 1.5.6.

LEMMA 1. *A regular space which has a σ-locally finite base is normal.*

Proof. Let $\mathfrak{B} = \bigcup_{n=1}^{\infty} \mathfrak{B}_n$, where $\mathfrak{B}_n$ is a locally finite family, be a base of a regular space X. Let A and B be disjoint closed subsets of X.

For every $x \in A$ there exists a $V_x \in \mathfrak{B}$ such that

$$x \in V_x \subset \overline{V}_x \subset X \setminus B.$$

We have, therefore,

$$A \subset \bigcup_{x \in A} V_x \quad \text{and} \quad \overline{V}_x \cap B = 0. \tag{4}$$

Similarly, for every $y \in B$ there exists a $U_y \in \mathfrak{B}$ such that

$$B \subset \bigcup_{y \in B} U_y \quad \text{and} \quad \overline{U}_y \cap A = 0. \tag{5}$$

Let

$$V_n = \bigcup_{V_x \in \mathfrak{B}_n} V_x \quad \text{and} \quad U_n = \bigcup_{U_y \in \mathfrak{B}_n} U_y.$$

By virtue of Theorem 1, $\overline{V}_n = \bigcup_{V_x \in \mathfrak{B}_n} \overline{V}_x$ and $\overline{U}_n = \bigcup_{U_y \in \mathfrak{B}_n} \overline{U}_y$, whence, according to (4) and (5),

$$B \cap \overline{V}_n = 0 = A \cap \overline{U}_n \quad \text{for} \quad n = 1, 2, \ldots$$

Let

$$G_n = V_n \setminus \bigcup_{i \leqslant n} \overline{U}_i, \quad H_n = U_n \setminus \bigcup_{i \leqslant n} \overline{V}_i.$$

It is easy to verify that

$$A \subset U = \bigcup_{n=1}^{\infty} G_n, \quad B \subset V = \bigcup_{n=1}^{\infty} H_n, \quad \text{and} \quad U \cap V = 0. \ ■$$

LEMMA 2. *Let a T_1-space X be given and let $\{\varrho_n\}_{n=1}^{\infty}$ denote a family of pseudo-metrics in X bounded by number 1. Let us assume that the following conditions are satisfied:*

(a) *$\varrho_n\colon X \times X \to R$ is a continuous function for $n = 1, 2, \ldots$*

(b) *For every $x \in X$ and a non-empty closed subset $A \subset X$ such that $x \notin A$, there exists an n such that $d_n(x, A) = \inf_{a \in A} \varrho_n(x, a) > 0$.*

Then the space X is metrizable and the function ϱ defined by means of the formula

$$\varrho(x, y) = \sum_{n=1}^{\infty} \frac{1}{2^n} \varrho_n(x, y)$$

is a metric in X.

Proof. It is clear that $\varrho(x, x) = 0$ and that ϱ satisfies conditions (M2) and (M3). Since X is a T_1-space, for each pair of distinct points $x, y \in X$ the condition $x \notin \overline{\{y\}} = y$ holds and $\varrho(x, y) > 0$; thus ϱ is a metric. Let $d(x, A)$ denote the distance from a point to a set defined by means of the metric ϱ. In order to prove that ϱ is a metric in the space X it is sufficient, by virtue of Corollary 1 to Theorem 1.5, to show that

$$d(x, A) = 0 \text{ if and only if } x \in \bar{A}.$$

If $x \notin \bar{A}$, then by virtue of (b), there exists an n such that $d_n(x, \bar{A}) = r > 0$. In this case, therefore, we have $d(x, A) \geqslant d(x, \bar{A}) \geqslant r/2^n > 0$. On the other hand, according to Theorem 1.4.2, it follows from (a) that $\varrho: X \times X \to R$ is a continuous function. The function $f: X \to R$, where $f(x) = d(x, A)$, is also continuous by the lemma to Theorem 1.5. It follows that if $x \in \bar{A}$ then $f(x) \in f(\bar{A}) \subset \overline{f(A)} = \{0\}$, i.e. $d(x, A) = 0$. ∎

THEOREM 5 (Nagata-Smirnov). *A necessary and sufficient condition for a topological space to be metrizable is that the space be regular and have a σ-locally finite base.*

Proof. The necessity of the condition follows from Corollary 3 to Theorem 1.5 and from the corollary to Theorem 4.

We shall now prove that the condition is sufficient. Let us consider a regular space X which has a base $\mathfrak{B}$ such that $\mathfrak{B} = \bigcup_{n=1}^{\infty} \mathfrak{B}_n$, where $\mathfrak{B}_n = \{U_s\}_{s \in S_n}$ is a locally finite family. For a fixed pair of natural numbers (m, n) and for every $s \in S_n$ let V_s be the union of all elements of $\mathfrak{B}_m$ whose closure is contained in U_s. It follows from Theorem 1 that $\bar{V}_s \subset U_s$, whence by Lemma 1, there exists a function $f_s: X \to I$ which vanishes on $X \setminus U_s$ and assumes the value 1 on V_s.

For every point $x \in X$ there exists a neighbourhood $U(x)$ and a finite subfamily $S(x) \subset S_n$ such that for $s \in S_n \setminus S(x)$ we have the equality $U_s \cap U(x) = 0$. Let us consider the covering $\{U(x) \times U(y)\}_{x,y \in X}$ of the space $X \times X$ and on every set of this covering let us define a real-valued continuous function $g_{x,y}: U(x) \times U(y) \to R$ by means of the formula

$$g_{x,y}(a, b) = \sum_{s \in S(x) \cup S(y)} |f_s(a) - f_s(b)|.$$

Since the remaining functions f_s vanish on the set $U(x) \cup U(y)$, this formula can also be written in the form

$$g_{x,y}(a, b) = \sum_{s \in S_n} |f_s(a) - f_s(b)|.$$

Hence the family $\{g_{x,y}\}_{x,y \in X}$ is compatible and, by Theorem 2.1.5, it defines a function $g_m^n: X \times X \to R$. The function $\varrho_m^n: X \times X \to R$ defined by the formula $\varrho_m^n(x, y) = \min(1, g_m^n(x, y))$ is a pseudo-metric.

If m and n run over all natural numbers, we obtain a countable family of pseudo-metrics in X which satisfy condition (a) of Lemma 2. Condition (b) is also satisfied, for, suppose we are given a point $x \in X$ and a non-empty closed subset $A \subset X$ such that $x \notin A$. Then there exist sets $W, U \in \mathfrak{B}$ such that $x \in W \subset \overline{W} \subset U$ and $A \subset X \setminus U$. For some m and n we thus have $W = U_{s'}$, where $s' \in S_m$, and $U = U_s$, where $s \in S_n$. The function f_s corresponding to the pair (m, n) satisfies the conditions $f_s(x) = 1$ and $f_s(a) = 0$ for $a \in A$. Thus $\inf_{a \in A} \varrho_m^n(x, a) = 1$ and the conclusion of the theorem follows from Lemma 2. ∎

Let us note that Theorem 5 implies that the conditions given in Theorems 2.3 and 2.4 are sufficient for the metrizability. Moreover, Theorems 4 and 5 imply

THEOREM 6 (Bing). *A necessary and sufficient condition for a topological space X to be metrizable is that X be regular and have a σ-discrete base.* ∎

To complete this paragraph we shall prove a theorem on the existence of a universal space for metrizable spaces of weight $\mathfrak{m} \geqslant \aleph_0$.

THEOREM 7. *For every $\mathfrak{m} \geqslant \aleph_0$ the Cartesian product of $\aleph_0$ copies of the hedgehog $J(\mathfrak{m})$ is a universal space for metrizable spaces of weight $\mathfrak{m}$.*

Proof. The Cartesian product in question is a metric space of weight $\mathfrak{m}$ by Example 1.3 and Theorem 2.2.

Let us now consider a metrizable space X of weight $\mathfrak{m}$. By virtue of Theorem 4, there exists a base $\mathfrak{B} = \{U_s\}_{s \in S}$ in X such that $S = \bigcup_{n=1}^{\infty} S_n$, where $\mathfrak{B}_n = \{U_s\}_{s \in S_n}$ is a discrete family. According to Theorem 1.1.7 we can assume that $\overline{\overline{S}} = \mathfrak{m}$. Without loss of generality we can assume that the set S is identical with the set S used in Example 1.3 for the construction of the hedgehog $J(\mathfrak{m})$.

For a fixed pair of natural numbers (m, n) and every $s \in S_n$ let V_s be the union of all elements of $\mathfrak{B}_m$ whose closure is contained in U_s. It follows from Theorem 1 that $\overline{V}_s \subset U_s$, whence there exists a function $f_s: X \to I_s$ vanishing outside U_s and assuming the value 1 on V_s.

By virtue of Theorem 2, the family $\{\overline{U}_s\}_{s\in S_n}$ is discrete. Thus each pair of distinct sets of this family are disjoint and the set $A_n = \bigcup_{s\in S_n} \overline{U}_s$ is closed. From Theorem 1 it also follows that the set $\bigcup_{\substack{s\in S_n\\ s\neq s_0}} \overline{U}_s = A_n \setminus \overline{U}_{s_0}$ is closed for every $s_0 \in S_n$; hence, by virtue of Theorem 2.2.2., $A_n = \bigoplus_{s\in S_n} \overline{U}_s$. According to Theorem 2.1.5, the formula

$$g_{n,m}(x) = \big[\big(f_s(x), s\big)\big], \qquad \text{where} \qquad x \in \overline{U}_s,$$

defines a mapping $g_{n,m}: A_n \to J(\mathfrak{m})$. Let $B_n = X \setminus \bigcup_{s\in S_n} U_s$. B_n is, therefore, a closed set and $A_n \cup B_n = X$. Let s_0 be an element of S. The mapping $f_{n,m}: B_n \to J(\mathfrak{m})$ defined by means of the formula $f_{n,m}(x) = [(0, s_0)]$ for $x \in B_n$ is compatible with $g_{n,m}$. Hence, according to Theorem 2.1.6, they define a mapping $h_{n,m}: X \to J(\mathfrak{m})$. It is easy to verify that the family of mappings $\{h_{n,m}\}_{n,m=1}^{\infty}$ distinguishes points from closed sets. By the Diagonal Lemma, the space is imbeddable in the countable Cartesian product of the space $J(\mathfrak{m})$. ■

The reader has surely noted that in order to prove the embeddability of X into a Cartesian product of $\aleph_0$ copies of the space $J(\mathfrak{m})$, we have only used the fact that there exists a σ-discrete base in X and that X is normal. Since, by virtue of Lemma 1 to Theorem 5, the normality of a regular space follows from the existence of a σ-discrete base, we have incidentally given another proof of Theorem 6.

EXERCISES

A. Let $\{A_s\}_{s\in S}$ be a localy finite family of subsets of topological space X.

(a) Show that $\mathrm{Fr}(\bigcup_{s\in S} A_s) \subset \bigcup_{s\in S} \mathrm{Fr}\, A_s$.

(b) Prove that if each member of the family under consideration is nowhere dense, then the union $\bigcup_{s\in S} A_s$ is nowhere dense.

B. Show that Theorem 2.1.6 remains valid after replacing the assumption that the given family is finite by the assumption that it is locally finite.

C. Verify that the space considered in Example 1.5.1 satisfies the second axiom of countability (thus it has a σ-discrete base).

D. Show that a T_1-space has a base which is the union of a finite number of locally finite families if and only if it is discrete.

HISTORICAL REMARKS AND BIBLIOGRAPHIC NOTES

The concept of a metric space was introduced by M. Fréchet in his thesis [1906]. For many years these spaces were of central consideration to topologists. Without any doubt the class of metrizable spaces is the best known class of topological spaces. The monograph of K. Kuratowski [1958] and [1961] is a veritable encyclopaedia on this subject.

Theorems 2.3 and 2.4 were proved by P. Urysohn in [1924] and [1925a], respectively. In the original formulation of the second theorem the regularity of the space was replaced by its normality. A. Tychonoff proved in [1925] that the theorem is valid in the formulation given here (see Theorem 1.5.6). The mapping space with the distance defined by formula (6), Paragraph 2, was considered for the first time in the thesis of M. Fréchet. He noted, however, that the idea of the distance belonged to K. Weierstrass. Totally bounded spaces were defined by F. Hausdorff in [1927]. Complete spaces and spaces metrizable in a complete manner were defined by M. Fréchet in [1906]. G. Cantor proved a particular case of Theorem 3.4; the formulation given here was found by F. Hausdorff in [1914]. Theorem 3.5 was proved by K. Kuratowski (in the 1st edition of [1958], p. 203). Theorem 3.9 was proved by P. Alexandroff in [1924] and Theorem 3.10 by F. Hausdorff in [1914]. Hausdorff's proof was a generalization of the construction of real numbers made by Cantor. The simple proof given here was found by K. Kuratowski in [1935]; a similar idea occurred to Fréchet [1910]. The topological characterization of complete metrizable spaces was given by E. Čech in [1937].

The first general theorem on the metrization of topological spaces was proved by P. Alexandroff and P. Urysohn in [1923], but the necessary and sufficient condition was artificial and not very useful. In particular, the metrization theorems of Urysohn (2.3 and 2.4) did not follow from it. Theorem 4.4 was proved by J. Nagata and Yu. M. Smirnov in [1950] and [1951a], respectively. R. H. Bing proved his Theorem 4.6 in [1951]. In the proofs of those two theorems, Theorem 4.3, proved by A. H. Stone in [1948], was of great importance. Theorem 4.7 was proved by H. J. Kowalsky in [1957].

PROBLEMS

A. Let (X, ϱ) be a non-separable metric space. Show that there exists a non-countable set $A \subset X$ such that for some $\varepsilon > 0$ we have $\varrho(x, y) \geqslant \varepsilon$ for every two distinct elements x, y of the set A. Deduce that the properties (B)-(S) of Problem 1.Q are equivalent for metrizable spaces. Making use of Theorem 2.3.10 prove that, in Problem 2.R and 2.S, instead of mappings into a T_2-space with a countable base we can consider mappings into an arbitrary metrizable space.

Hint: The property "$\varrho(x, y) \geqslant \varepsilon$ for every two distinct elements x, y of the set A" is of finite character.

B (P. Urysohn [1927]). We say that a topological space X satisfies the *second axiom of countability at the point* $x \in X$, whenever the point x has a neighbourhood $V \subset X$ which (considered as a subspace of X) satisfies the second axiom of countability. If a topological space X satisfies the second axiom of countability at each point $x \in X$, then we say that X satisfies this axiom *locally*.

Verify that the space $J(\mathfrak{c})$ does not satisfy the second axiom of countability at the point 0. Construct a metric space which does not satisfy this axiom at any point.

C (P. Alexandroff [1924b], W. Sierpiński [1933]). Show that every metrizable space satisfying the second axiom of countability locally can be represented as the union of a number of open-and-closed subspaces which satisfy the second axiom of countability.

Hint: Consider an arbitrary point $x \in X$ and a neighbourhood V_1 of x which satisfies the second axiom of countability. For all points of a countable dense set D_1 in V_1 consider those spheres with centres in D_1 and rational radii which are separable. Let V_2 be the union of V_1 and of all those spheres. The space V_2 satisfies the second axiom of countability. Repeat this procedure and show that after a countable number of steps we obtain an open-and-closed set.

D (K. Kuratowski [1948]). Let X be an arbitrary metrizable space and let $M \subset X$ be a subspace. For every family $\{U_s\}_{s \in S}$ of open sets in M there exists a family $\{V_s\}_{s \in S}$ of sets open in X such that $U_s = M \cap V_s$ for every $s \in S$ and the condition $\bigcap_{s \in S_1} U_s = 0$ implies $\bigcap_{s \in S_1} V_s = 0$ for each finite subset $S_1 \subset S$. Formulate a dual theorem for closed sets.

Hint: $V_s = \{x: \varrho(x, U_s) < \varrho(x, M \setminus U_s)\}$.

E (M. Fréchet [1910]). Show that for every two countable and dense subsets of a Euclidean space R^n there exists a homeomorphism of R^n onto itself which maps one of those sets onto the other.

Hint: We say that a set $A \subset R^n$ is in a *general position* if for each pair of points $x, y \in A$, where $x = (x_1, x_2, \ldots, x_n)$, $y = (y_1, y_2, \ldots, y_n)$, the difference $x_i - y_i$ is different from zero for $i = 1, 2, \ldots, n$. Show that for each countable set $A \subset R^n$ there exists a homeomorphism of R^n onto itself which maps the set A onto a set in general position. Two sequences $x_1, x_2, \ldots$ and $y_1, y_2, \ldots$, where $x_j = (x_1^j, x_2^j, \ldots, x_n^i)$ and $y_j = (y_1^j, y_2^j, \ldots$ $\ldots, y_n^j)$ which are in general position, are called *similar* provided for every choice of indices j, k the numbers $x_i^j - x_i^k$ and $y_i^j - y_i^k$ are either both positive or both negative for $i = 1, 2, \ldots, n$. Show that elements of two countable and dense subsets of R^n which are in general position can be set in similar sequences.

F (M. Katětov [1948]). Show that a compact space X is metrizable if and only if the Cartesian product $X \times X \times X$ is perfectly normal.

Hint: Make use of Problem 2.E and Exercise 2.C.

G (M. K. Fort, jr. [1951]). Show that the space R^I with the pointwise topology is not metrizable.

Hint: An elementary subdivision of a segment $[a, b]$ is a family consisting of intervals $[x_0, x_1], [x_1, x_2], \ldots,$ where $x_i = \frac{x_{i-1}+b}{2}$ for $i = 1, 2, \ldots$ and $x_0 = 0$. A function whose graph is a broken line joining the points $(a, 0), (x_n, 0), (x_{n+1}, r), (x_{n+2}, r), (x_{n+3}, 0)$, and $(b, 0)$ is called a *function of type* (n, r). Let S_1 be an elementary subdivision of the segment $[0, 1]$ and let S_{k+1} be the union of elementary subdivisions of all segments belonging to S_k for $k = 1, 2, \ldots$ Let us define $S = \bigcup_{i=1}^{\infty} S_i$ and let g be a one-to-one function of S onto the set N of natural numbers. For every $m, n \in N$ and $J \in S_n$ let $f_{n,m}^J \in R^J$ be a function of type $(m, 1)$ when $g(J) \leqslant m$ and a function of type $\big(m, (g(J))^{1-}\big)$ when $g(J) > m$. The family $\{f_{n,m}^J\}_{J \in S_n}$ defines a function $f_{n,m} \in R^I$.

Assume that a metric ϱ in R^I induces the pointwise topology and verify that for every $n \in N$ we have $\lim f_{n,m} = f_0$, where $f_0(x) = 0$ for $x \in I$. Deduce that there exists a sequence $\{N_n\}$ such that if $m_n \geqslant N_n$, then $\varrho(f_{n,m_n}, f_0) < 1/n$ for $n = 1, 2, \ldots$ Deduce a contradiction by means of a sequence $\{f_{n,m_n}\}$ and a decreasing sequence of intervals $\{J_n\}$ such that $f_{n,m_n}(x) = 1$ for $x \in J_n$ where $m_n \geqslant N_n$ for $n = 1, 2, \ldots$

H (F. Hausdorff [1914], E. Michael [1951]). Let A and B denote non-empty subsets of a bounded metric space (X, ϱ). The number

$$\operatorname{dist}(A, B) = \max\{\sup_{a \in A} d(a, B), \sup_{b \in B} d(b, A)\}$$

is called the *Hausdorff distance* of the sets A and B.

Show that $\operatorname{dist}(A, B)$ is a metric in the set 2^X of all non-empty and closed subsets of the space X. Verify that the topology defined by that distance depends on the choice of a metric in the space X. Show that for a compact space X the Hausdorff distance induces the Vietoris topology in 2^X (see Problem 3.J).

Prove that if a space (X, ϱ) is totally bounded (complete), then the space 2^X with the Hausdorff distance is also totally bounded (complete).

I. Let (X, ϱ) be a metric space. Two sequences $\{x_i\}$ and $\{y_i\}$ of points of this space which satisfy Cauchy's condition are called *equivalent* if $\lim \varrho(x_i, y_i) = 0$. Let us denote the set of equivalence classes of this relation by $\tilde{X}$. Show that $\tilde{X}$ with the metric $\tilde{\varrho}([\{x_i\}], [\{y_i\}]) = \lim \varrho(x_i, y_i)$ is a complete metric space. Assigning the point $[\{x_i\}]$, where $x_i = x$ for $i = 1, 2, \ldots,$ to the point $x \in X$ we define an isometry of X into $\tilde{X}$ under which the image of the space X is dense in $\tilde{X}$. Verify that the space $\tilde{X}$ is the unique (up to an isometry) metric space which has the above property; it is called the *completion* of the space X (cf. Exercise 2.E).

Show that if X is separable (totally bounded), then $\tilde{X}$ is also separable (totally bounded).

J. Let X be a topological space and let Y denote a metric space. Let M be a subset of X and let $f: M \to Y$ be a mapping. We say that the *oscillation* of the mapping f at the point x *is less* than ε if there exists a neighbourhood V of the point x such that $\delta(f(V) \cap M) < \varepsilon$.

Show that the set of points at which the oscillation of f is less than ε is open and contains M.

Prove that if Y is metrizable in a complete manner, then each mapping $f: M \to Y$ defined on an arbitrary subset M of a topological space X can be extended over a G_δ-set H such that $M \subset H \subset \overline{M}$.

Deduce that if a subspace M of a metrizable space X is metrizable in a complete manner, then M is a G_δ-set in X.

K (M. Lavrentieff [1924]). Let X and Y be metrizable in a complete manner and let $M \subset X$, $N \subset Y$ be two subspaces. Each homeomorphism $f: M \to N$ can be extended to a homeomorphism $F: H \to G$, where $M \subset H \subset X$ and $N \subset G \subset Y$ and H, G are G_δ-sets.

Hint: Consider extensions of f and f^{-1} over G_δ-sets in X and Y respectively. The required sets H and G are projections of the intersection of graphs of those extensions onto X and Y.

L (P. Alexandroff [1927], F. Hausdorff [1927], W. Sierpiński [1928]). Show that for every closed subset A of the Cantor set $D^{\aleph_0}$ there exists a mapping $f: D^{\aleph_0} \to A$ such that $f|A = id_A$.

Making use of Theorems 3.2.2 and 2.3, deduce that every compact metrizable space is the continuous image of the Cantor set (cf. Theorem 3.2.2 and Problem 3.H (a)).

Hint (P. R. Halmos [1963]): The metric defined by the formula

$$\sigma(x, y) = \sum_{i=1}^{\infty} \frac{1}{10^i} |x_i - y_i|,$$

where $x = \{x_i\}, y = \{y_i\}$, induces the usual topology in the set $D^{\aleph_0}$. Note that if $\sigma(x, y) = \sigma(x, z)$, then $y = z$, and deduce that for each point $x \in D^{\aleph_0}$ there exists exactly one point $a \in A$ such that $\sigma(x, a) = d(x, A)$.

M (B. Efimov [1963]). Show that for an arbitrary closed subset F of the Cantor cube $D^{\mathfrak{m}}$ which is a G_δ-set, there exists a mapping $g: D^{\mathfrak{m}} \to F$ such that $g|F = id_F$. Deduce that the property "X is a dyadic space" is a hereditary property with respect to closed G_δ-sets.

Hint (R. Engelking and A. Pełczyński [1963]): Define a function $f: D^{\mathfrak{m}} \to R$ which vanishes only on the set F and make use of Exercise 3.2.F and of the preceding problem.

N (B. Efimov [1963a]). Show that every dyadic compactification cX of a metrizable space X is of weight $\aleph_0$, i.e. is a metrizable space.

Hint (R. Engelking and A. Pełczyński [1963]): To begin with, note that it follows from Problem A that the space X must be separable. Then prove that there exists a compactification $c'X$ of the space X which satisfies the condition $c'X \leqslant cX$ and is of weight $\aleph_0$. Make use of Problem 3.H (c).

O. Show that every metrizable compact space is either countable or contains a subspace homeomorphic to the Cantor set, and is thus of power $\mathfrak{c}$.

Hint: Use Problem 3.G and 1.P. For the direct proof make use of Problem 1.P, reduce the problem to the case of a perfect X, and define inductively non-empty open sets $V_{i_1,i_2,\ldots i_k}$, where $i_1, i_2, \ldots, i_k$ is a finite sequence consisting of zeros and ones, in such a manner that

(a) $$\overline{V}_{i_1,i_2,\ldots,i_k,0} \cap \overline{V}_{i_1,i_2,\ldots,i_k,1} = 0$$

and

(b) $$\overline{V}_{i_1,i_2,\ldots,i_k,j} \subset V_{i_1,i_2,\ldots,i_k} \quad \text{for} \quad j = 0, 1.$$

To every infinite sequence $i_1, i_2, \ldots$ consisting of zeros and ones assign a point belonging to $\bigcap_{k=1}^{\infty} \overline{V}_{i_1,i_2,\ldots,i_k}$ and show that points assigned to different sequences are different.

P (E. Čech [1937]). Let X and Y be metrizable spaces. Show that X is homeomorphic to Y if and only if βX is homeomorphic to βY.

Q (Yu. M. Smirnov [1956a]). Let X be a locally compact space. Show that if $X = \bigcup_{i=1}^{\infty} M_i$, where M_i are spaces satisfying the second axiom of countability, then X is metrizable.

Hint: Make use of the notion of a grid.

R. Show that a metrizable space X is compact if and only if for each metric ϱ in the space X the space (X, ϱ) is totally bounded.

S (K. Morita and S. Hanai [1956], A. H. Stone [1956]). Let X be a metrizable space and let R denote a closed equivalence relation in X. Prove that if the equivalence classes of the relation R are compact, then the space X/R is metrizable. In other words, show that the image of a metrizable space under a perfect mapping is metrizable.

Hint (N. Bourbaki [1958]): Prove that there exists a σ-discrete base in X/R. For this purpose show, by means of a modification of the proof of Theorem 4.3, that every covering of the space X by inverse images of open subsets of X/R has a σ-discrete refinement formed of the inverse images of open subsets of X/R.

T (I. A. Vaĭnsteĭn [1947]). Let X be a metrizable space and let R be a closed equivalence relation in X. Prove that if the space X/R satisfies the first axiom of countability, then for every equivalence class K of the relation R the set $\mathrm{Fr}\,K$ is compact.

Hint: Let $\{U_i\}_{i=1}^{\infty}$ be the family of inverse images of a countable base of neighbourhoods of the class $K \in X/R$. The assumption that $\mathrm{Fr}\,K$ is not countably compact implies the existence of a discrete family $\{G_i\}_{i=1}^{\infty}$ of open subsets of X and of a sequence of points $x_1, x_2, \ldots$ such that $x_i \in X \setminus K$ and $x_i \in G_i \cap U_i$ for $i = 1, 2, \ldots$ Deduce a contradiction.

U (K. Morita and S. Hanai [1956], A. H. Stone [1956]). Let X be a metrizable space and let R denote a closed equivalence relation in X. Prove that if the space X/R satisfies the first axiom of countability, then it is metrizable.

Hint: For every equivalence class K of the relation R let $L(K) = \mathrm{Fr}\,K$ when $\mathrm{Fr}\,K \neq 0$, and let $L(K)$ be an arbitrary point of K when $\mathrm{Fr}\,K = 0$. Let X' be the union of all sets $L(K)$ and let R' denote the equivalence relation in X' defined by the decomposition of X' into the sets $L(K)$. Show that the relation R' is closed and that the space X'/R' is homeomorphic to X/R and then make use of Problem S.

V (J. Nagata [1950]). Show that if a topological space X has a locally finite closed covering $\{F_s\}_{s\in S}$ consisting of metrizable spaces, then X is metrizable.

Hint (A. H. Stone [1956]): Let $\{F'_s\}_{s\in S}$ be a family of disjoint topological spaces such that the spaces F_s and F'_s are homeomorphic for every $s \in S$. Define a closed relation R in the space $X' = \bigoplus_{s\in S} F'_s$ in such a manner that the space X'/R is homeomorphic to X.

W (E. Michael [1953]). Making use of the metrization theorem of Nagata-Smirnov, show that the Cartesian product of a perfectly normal space by a metrizable space is perfectly normal.

CHAPTER 5

PARACOMPACT SPACES

The concept of paracompactness is quite recent, it was introduced in 1944. Since that time it has been fully recognized not only in topology but also in many branches of analysis. The importance of the class of paracompact spaces lies in the fact that it contains two important classes of topological spaces; namely Lindelöf spaces (thus also compact spaces) and metrizable spaces. When this class of spaces was distinguished, it was found that many theorems of topology and analysis which had been proved under the assumption of compactness remained valid for paracompact spaces. In order to obtain the proofs of those more general theorems it has frequently been sufficient to replace the term "finite" by the term "locally finite" in the proofs of the known theorems. It has also been found that the notion of local finiteness is very natural and useful for the examination and description of topological spaces.

The study of the class of paracompact spaces is the subject of Paragraph 1. We begin by showing that paracompact spaces are normal and we proceed by giving three theorems which contain some characterizations of paracompact spaces. The characterization by means of the partition of unity is of great importance for analysis. Paracompactness of metrizable spaces is a consequence of characterization by σ-locally finite coverings and of Theorem 4.4.3. In view of the importance of this fact we give another, more direct proof. At the end of the paragraph we consider a new axiom of separation — collectionwise normality, and operations on paracompact spaces.

Paragraph 2 is devoted to countably paracompact spaces. Theorems 1 and 2 of that paragraph contain some conditions equivalent to countable paracompactness in the class of normal spaces. Some of those conditions, like condition (iv) of Theorem 2.1, are very close to normality.

The notion of countable paracompactness sometimes seems a little artificial. In fact, that class is insignificant in comparison with the class of paracompact spaces. It is interesting mainly because of Theorem 2.2, which is of some importance in homotopy theory (see Problem V), and because of the famous question of whether every normal space is countably paracompact. Countable paracompactness also enters into the examination of semi-continuous functions on topological spaces (see Problem R).

In Paragraph 3 we consider strongly paracompact and weakly paracompact spaces. The class of weakly paracompact spaces is interesting because of Theorem 3.2, which states that every collectionwise normal and weakly paracompact space is paracompact. Strong paracompactness is an interesting strengthening of paracompactness. It is of some importance in dimension theory and in algebraic topology. We prove only one theorem which contains three conditions equivalent to strong paracompactness concerning this class. It follows that Lindelöf spaces are strongly paracompact.

§ 1. Paracompact spaces. We shall use the notion of a locally finite family of sets, which was introduced in Chapter 4, to define an important class of topological spaces, namely paracompact spaces. A topological space X is said to be *paracompact* if X is a Hausdorff space and every open covering of X has a locally finite open refinement.

It is worth noting that in the definition of paracompactness the term "refinement" cannot be replaced by the term "subcovering". In fact, it is easy to notice that each discrete space is paracompact: the covering, consisting of one-point sets, is open and locally finite, and is a refinement of every covering of that space, while on the other hand, it is impossible to choose a locally finite subcovering from the covering $\{Z \cap (-n, n)\}_{n=1}^{\infty}$ of the set Z of integers.

The definition of a paracompact space immediately implies

THEOREM 1. *Every compact space is paracompact.* ∎

We have already stated that metrizable spaces and Lindelöf spaces are paracompact, but this fact is not at all obvious; it follows from the characterizations of paracompact spaces which are given further on.

LEMMA. *Let X be a paracompact space and let A and B be a pair of disjoint and closed subsets. If for every $x \in B$ there exist open sets U_x, V_x such that $A \subset U_x$, $x \in V_x$ and $U_x \cap V_x = 0$, then there also exist open sets U, V which satisfy the conditions $A \subset U$, $B \subset V$, and $U \cap V = 0$.*

Proof. The family $\{X \setminus B\} \cup \{V_x\}_{x \in B}$ is a covering of the space X. It follows from the definition of paracompactness that this covering has an open locally finite refinement $\{W_s\}_{s \in S}$. Let $S_1 = \{s \in S: W_s \subset V_x$ for some $x \in B\}$. Then

$$A \cap \overline{W}_s = 0 \quad \text{for } s \in S_1 \quad \text{and} \quad B \subset \bigcup_{s \in S_1} W_s.$$

By virtue of Theorem 4.4.1, we have $\bigcup_{s \in S_1} \overline{W}_s = \overline{\bigcup_{s \in S_1} W_s}$, whence the set $U = X \setminus \bigcup_{s \in S_1} \overline{W}_s$ is open. It is easy to see that the sets U and $V = \bigcup_{s \in S_1} W_s$ satisfy the conclusion of the lemma. ∎

THEOREM 2. *Every paracompact space is normal.*

Proof. Assuming that in the above lemma the set A consists of a single point, we infer that every paracompact space is regular. Hence using the lemma again we obtain the theorem. ■

Let us notice that since each Lindelöf space is paracompact, the last theorem is a common generalization of Theorems 1.5.6, 3.1.7, and 3.7.2. Moreover, from Theorem 4 proved below it immediately follows that each regular space which has a σ-locally finite base is paracompact. Therefore Theorem 2 implies Lemma 1 to Theorem 4.4.5. In all these cases the proof can be obtained by a modification of the proof of Theorem 1.5.6. Thus we have the situation which we announced in the introduction to this chapter.

The family $\{f_s\}_{s\in S}$ of continuous functions defined on a space X with values in the segment $[0,1]$ is called a *partition of unity* provided that $\sum_{s\in S} f_s(x) = 1$ for every $x \in X$. This equality denotes that for a fixed $x_0 \in X$ only countably many functions $\{f_s\}_{s\in S}$ assume values different from zero at the point x_0 and that the series $\sum_{i=1}^{\infty} f_{s_i}(x_0)$, where $\{s_1, s_2, \ldots\} = \{s: f_s(x_0) \neq 0\}$, is convergent and its sum equal to 1. Since the series under consideration is absolutely convergent, the arrangement of terms is of no importance. The fact that the sum of the series is 1 means that the least upper bound of the set of numbers of the form $f_{s_{i_1}}(x_0)+f_{s_{i_2}}(x_0)+\ldots+f_{s_{i_n}}(x_0)$ is equal to 1.

A partition of unity $\{f_s\}_{s\in S}$ is called *locally finite* provided that the covering $\{f_s^{-1}((0,1])\}_{s\in S}$ is locally finite. In this case, for every point x_0 there exist a neighbourhood U_0 and a finite set $S_0 = \{s_1, s_2, \ldots, s_n\} \subset S$ such that $f_s(x) = 0$ for $x \in U_0$, $s \in S \setminus S_0$ and $\sum_{i=1}^{n} f_{s_i}(x) = 1$ for $x \in U_0$.

We say that the partition of unity $\{f_s\}_{s\in S}$ is *subordinate* to the covering $\{A_t\}_{t\in T}$ if the covering $\{f_s^{-1}((0,1])\}_{s\in S}$ is a refinement of $\{A_t\}_{t\in T}$.

By means of a partition of unity we can give an important characterization of paracompact spaces, which is useful not only in topology but also in analysis and differential geometry.

A covering of a topological space X is called *point finite* if every point $x \in X$ belongs only to a finite number of elements of that covering. Clearly every locally finite covering is point finite, but not conversely. In fact, the covering of the segment I, consisting of the segment I and the intervals $(1/n+1, 1/n)$ for $n = 1, 2, \ldots$, is point finite but not locally finite.

LEMMA 1. *For each point finite open covering $\{U_s\}_{s\in S}$ of a normal space X there exists an open covering $\{V_s\}_{s\in S}$ of that space such that $\overline{V}_s \subset U_s$ for every $s \in S$.*

Proof. Let us consider the family $\mathfrak{G}$ of functions G which are defined on the set S and satisfy the following conditions:
(a) $G(s) = U_s$, or $G(s)$ is an open set in X such that $\overline{G(s)} \subset U_s$.
(b) $\bigcup_{s \in S} G(s) = X$.
Let us define a partial ordering in the family $\mathfrak{G}$, assuming that $G_1 \leqslant G_2$ if for every $s \in S$ the condition $G_1(s) \neq U_s$ implies $G_2(s) = G_1(s)$.

Let $\mathfrak{G}_0 \subset \mathfrak{G}$ be a linearly ordered subset of the family $\mathfrak{G}$. We shall show that the function G_0 defined by the formula $G_0(s) = \bigcap_{G \in \mathfrak{G}_0} G(s)$ belongs to $\mathfrak{G}$. Condition (a) is evidently satisfied, thus we have to show that the sets $\{G_0(s)\}_{s \in S}$ form a covering of the space X. Let x be an arbitrary point of the space X. We shall show that $x \in G_0(s)$ for some $s \in S$.

Since the covering $\{U_s\}_{s \in S}$ is point finite, there exists a finite subset $S_0 = \{s_1, s_2, \ldots, s_k\} \subset S$ such that $x \in U_{s_i}$ for $i = 1, 2, \ldots, k$, but $x \notin U_s$ for $s \in S \setminus S_0$. If $G_0(s_i) = U_{s_i}$ for some $s_i \in S_0$, then $x \in G_0(s_i)$. We can therefore assume that for each $i = 1, 2, \ldots, k$ there exists a function $G_i \in \mathfrak{G}_0$ such that $G_i(s_i) \neq U_{s_i}$. Since the family $\mathfrak{G}_0$ is linearly ordered, there exists a $j \leqslant k$ such that $G_i \leqslant G_j$ for $i = 1, 2, \ldots, k$. The family $\{G_j(s)\}_{s \in S}$ is a covering, so that $x \in G_j(s_i) = G_0(s_i)$ for some $s_i \in S_0$.

Since $G \leqslant G_0$ for every $G \in \mathfrak{G}_0$, it follows from the Kuratowski-Zorn Lemma that there exists in $\mathfrak{G}$ a maximal element G. To complete the proof it is sufficient to show that the inclusion

$$\overline{G(s)} \subset U_s$$

holds for every $s \in S$.

Let us suppose that $\overline{G(s_0)} \cap (X \setminus U_{s_0}) \neq 0$ for some $s_0 \in S$. The set $A = X \setminus \bigcup_{s_0 \neq s \in S} G(s)$ is closed and is contained in $G(s_0)$. By the normality of X there exists an open set V such that $A \subset V \subset \overline{V} \subset G(s_0)$. Since it follows from (a) that $G(s_0) = U_{s_0}$, the formula

$$G_0(s_0) = V \subset \overline{V} \subset U_{s_0} \quad \text{and} \quad G_0(s) = G(s) \quad \text{for} \quad s \neq s_0$$

defines an element $G_0 \in \mathfrak{G}$ such that $G_0 \geqslant G$ and $G_0 \neq G$. This contradicts the maximality of G, and thus shows that $\overline{G(s)} \subset U_s$ for every $s \in S$. ∎

LEMMA 2. *If an open covering $\mathfrak{U}$ of a topological space X has a partition of unity $\{f_s\}_{s \in S}$ subordinated to it, then $\mathfrak{U}$ has a locally finite open refinement.*

Proof. To begin with, let us remark that for any function $\varphi \colon X \to I$, where $\varphi(x_0) > 0$, there exists a neighbourhood U_0 of the point x_0 and a finite set $S_0 = \{s_1, s_2, \ldots, s_k\} \subset S$ such that

(1) $$f_s(x) < \varphi(x) \quad \text{for} \quad x \in U_0 \text{ and } s \in S \setminus S_0.$$

Indeed, there exists a set $S_0 = \{s_1, s_2, \ldots, s_k\} \subset S$ such that $1-\sum_{i=1}^{n} f_{s_i}(x_0) < \varphi(x_0)$. It is easily seen that S_0 and the neighbourhood $U_0 = \{x \in X: 1-\sum_{i=1}^{n} f_{s_i}(x) < \varphi(x)\}$ of point x_0 satisfy (1).

For every $x \in X$ there exists $s(x) \in S$ such that $f_{s(x)}(x) > 0$. The corollary to Theorem 2.1.5 and the above remark for $\varphi = f_{s(x)}$ imply that the formula

$$f(x) = \sup_{s \in S} f_s(x)$$

defines a continuous function $f: X \to (0, 1]$. For every $s \in S$ the set

$$V_s = \{x: f_s(x) > \tfrac{1}{2} f(x)\}$$

is open. It is easy to see that $\{V_s\}_{s \in S}$ is an open covering of the space X, which is a refinement of $\mathfrak{U}$. The local finiteness of this covering follows from (1), where $\varphi = \frac{1}{2} f$. ■

THEOREM 3. *For a T_1-space X the following conditions are equivalent:*

(i) *The space X is paracompact.*

(ii) *Every open covering of X has a locally finite partition of unity subordinated to it.*

(iii) *Every open covering of X has a partition of unity subordinated to it.*

Proof. Let us suppose that X is a paracompact space. Let $\mathfrak{A}$ be an open covering of X. Let us denote by $\mathfrak{U} = \{U_s\}_{s \in S}$ an open and locally finite covering which is a refinement of $\mathfrak{A}$. By virtue of Lemma 1, there exists a covering $\{V_s\}_{s \in S}$ of the space X such that $\overline{V}_s \subset U_s$ for every $s \in S$. It follows from the Urysohn Lemma that there exists a function $g_s: X \to I$ such that $g_s(x) = 1$ for $x \in \overline{V}_s$ and $g_s(x) = 0$ for $x \in X \setminus U_s$. Since the covering $\mathfrak{U}$ is locally finite, the function $g = \sum_{s \in S} g_s$ is correctly defined. It is easy to verify that $\{f_s\}_{s \in S}$, where $f_s = g_s/g$, is a locally finite partition of unity subordinated to $\mathfrak{A}$. Thus the implication (i) ⇒ (ii) has been proved.

Since the implication (ii) ⇒ (iii) is obvious, it is sufficient to show that (iii) ⇒ (i). By Lemma 2, it remains to show that any T_1-space X satisfying (iii) is a Hausdorff space. We shall show that X is a Tychonoff space. Let $x \in X$, $\overline{F} = F \subset X$ and $x \notin F$. Let us consider the covering $\mathfrak{U} = \{X \setminus F, X \setminus \{x\}\}$ of the space X and a partition of unity $\{f_s\}_{s \in S}$ subordinated to it. Thus there exists an $s_0 \in S$ such that $f_{s_0}(x) = a > 0$ and the set $f_{s_0}^{-1}((0, 1])$ is not contained in $X \setminus \{x\}$ i.e. it is contained in $X \setminus F$ and $f_{s_0}(F) \subset \{0\}$. The function $f: X \to I$ defined by the formula $f(x) = \min\left(\frac{1}{a} f_{s_0}(x), 1\right)$ satisfies the conditions $f(x) = 1$ and $f(F) \subset \{0\}$. ■

We shall now state a theorem containing three further conditions equivalent to paracompactness. The paracompactness of metrizable spaces and Lindelöf spaces is a consequence of this theorem. The proof of the theorem follows from lemmas which are stated and proved below.

THEOREM 4. *For a regular space X the following conditions are equivalent:*

(i) *The space X is paracompact.*

(ii) *Every open covering of X has an open σ-locally finite refinement.*

(iii) *Every open covering of X has a locally finite refinement (consisting of arbitrary sets).*

(iv) *Every open covering of X has a closed locally finite refinement.*

LEMMA 1. *Every open and σ-locally finite covering $\mathfrak{V}$ of a topological space X has a locally finite refinement.*

Proof. Let $\mathfrak{V} = \bigcup_{n=1}^{\infty} \mathfrak{V}_n$, where $\mathfrak{V}_n = \{V_s\}_{s \in S_n}$ is locally finite. For every $s_0 \in S_n$ let

$$V_{s_0}^* = V_{s_0} \setminus \bigcup_{k<n} \bigcup_{s \in S_k} V_s.$$

The family $\mathfrak{V}^* = \{V_s^*\}_{s \in S}$, where $S = \bigcup_{n=1}^{\infty} S_n$, is a refinement of $\mathfrak{V}$. We shall show that the covering $\mathfrak{V}^*$ is locally finite. For every $x \in X$ let k be the least natural number such that $x \in \bigcup_{s \in S_k} V_s$ and let $x \in V_{s_0} \in \mathfrak{V}_k$. It is easy to verify that V_{s_0} is a neighbourhood of x disjoint with all V_s^* for $s \in \bigcup_{n>k} S_n$. Since the family $\mathfrak{V}_n$ is locally finite, there exists a neighbourhood U_n of the point x which meets only a finite number of elements of this family. The neighbourhood $U_1 \cap U_2 \cap \ldots \cap U_k \cap V_{s_0}$ of the point x meets only a finite number of elements of the covering $\mathfrak{V}^*$. ■

LEMMA 2. *If every open covering of a regular space X has a locally finite refinement, then every open covering of that space also has a closed locally finite refinement.*

Proof. Let $\{U_s\}_{s \in S}$ be an open covering of the space X. Since X is regular, there exists a covering $\{V_t\}_{t \in T}$ of it such that for every $t \in T$ we have $\overline{V}_t \subset U_s$ for some $s \in S$. It follows from Theorem 4.4.2 that if $\{A_w\}_{w \in W}$ is a locally finite refinement of $\{V_t\}_{t \in T}$, then $\{\overline{A}_w\}_{w \in W}$ is a closed locally finite refinement of $\{U_s\}_{s \in S}$. ■

LEMMA 3. *If every open covering of a regular space X has a closed locally finite refinement, then X is paracompact.*

Proof. Let $\mathfrak{U}$ be an open covering of the space X and let $\mathfrak{A}$ be a locally finite (arbitrary) refinement of $\mathfrak{U}$. For every $x \in X$ let $V(x)$ be a neighbourhood of the point x meeting only a finite number of elements of $\mathfrak{A}$ and let $\mathfrak{B}$ be a locally finite closed refinement of $\{V(x)\}_{x \in X}$. For every

$A \in \mathfrak{A}$ let $U_A \in \mathfrak{U}$ satisfy the condition $A \subset U_A$ and let B_A be the union of those $B \in \mathfrak{B}$ for which $B \cap A = 0$. The sets $W_A = U_A \cap (X \setminus B_A)$ form an open refinement of $\mathfrak{U}$. We shall show that it is locally finite.

For every $x \in X$ there exists a neighbourhood W which meets only a finite number of elements of the covering $\mathfrak{B}$. Let us assume that they are $B_1, B_2, \ldots, B_n$. Since $B_i \subset V(x_i)$ for $i = 1, 2, \ldots, n$, B_i meets only a finite number of elements of $\mathfrak{A}$. Let us assume that they are $A_{i,1}, A_{i,2}, \ldots \ldots, A_{i,n_i}$. The definition of the set W_A implies that if it meets the neighbourhood W, then there exists a $B \in \mathfrak{B}$ such that $W \cap B \neq 0$ and $B \cap A \neq 0$. Hence A is one of the sets $A_{i,j}$, where $1 \leqslant i \leqslant n$ and $1 \leqslant j \leqslant n_i$. ■

The proof of Theorem 4 has therefore been completed. ■

Two important corollaries follow from Theorem 4, Theorem 4.4.3 and the obvious fact that every countable covering is σ-locally finite.

COROLLARY 1. *Every metrizable space is paracompact.* ■

COROLLARY 2. *Every Lindelöf space is paracompact.* ■

Since these corollaries are very important, we shall give proofs which are more direct and make use only of Lemma 2 to Theorem 3.

Proof of Corollary 1. It is sufficient to prove that for every open covering $\mathfrak{U}$ of a metric space (X, ϱ) there exists a family of functions $\{f_s\}_{s \in S} \subset I^X$ such that

(2) For every $s \in S$ there exists a $U \in \mathfrak{U}$ such that $f_s^{-1}\big((0, 1]\big) \subset U$.

(3) $\sum_{s \in S} f_s(x) = F(x) \leqslant 1$ for $x \in X$.

(4) $|F(x) - F(y)| \leqslant \varrho(x, y)$ for $x, y \in X$.

(5) For every $x_0 \in X$ there exists an $s_0 \in S$ such that $f_{s_0}(x_0) > 0$.

Indeed, conditions (4) and (5) imply that $F: X \to (0, 1]$. Hence by virtue of (2) and (3), $\{f_s/F\}_{s \in S}$ is a partition of unity subordinated to the covering $\mathfrak{U}$.

Properties (2)-(4) are of finite character. Hence, by the Tuckey Lemma, there exists a maximal family $\mathfrak{f} = \{f_s\}_{s \in S} \subset I^X$ which satisfies conditions (2)-(4). We shall show that condition (5) is also satisfied. Let us suppose that for $x_0 \in U_0 \in \mathfrak{U}$ we have $f_s(x_0) = 0$ for every $s \in S$. We can evidently assume that $U_0 \neq X$ and $\delta(X) \leqslant 1$. Let $d(x) = d(x, X \setminus U_0)$ and let

$$\bar{F}(x) = \max\big(F(x), d(x)\big) \quad \text{and} \quad \bar{f}(x) = \bar{F}(x) - F(x).$$

The lemma to Theorem 4.1.5 and (4) imply that $|\bar{F}(x) - \bar{F}(y)| \leqslant \varrho(x, y)$ for $x, y \in X$. If we add the function $\bar{f} \in I^X$ to the family $\mathfrak{f}$, conditions (2)-(4) are still satisfied. The maximality of the family $\mathfrak{f}$ implies that $\bar{f} = f_{s_0}$ for some $s_0 \in S$, which is impossible because $\bar{f}(x_0) \neq 0 = f_{s_0}(x_0)$. This contradiction proves that the family $\{f_s\}_{s \in S}$ satisfies condition (5). ■

Proof of Corollary 2. Let $\mathfrak{U}$ be an open covering of a Lindelöf space X. By Theorem 3.7.2, for every $x \in X$ there exists a function $f_x: X \to I$ such that $f_x(x) = 1$ and $f_x^{-1}((0,1]) = V_x \subset U_x \in \mathfrak{U}$. Let us choose a countable covering $\{V_{x_i}\}_{i=1}^{\infty}$ from the covering $\{V_x\}_{x \in X}$. The functions $f_i = \frac{1}{2^i} f_{x_i}$ are continuous. By Theorem 1.4.2, their sum $F = \sum_{i=1}^{\infty} f_i$ is continuous and assumes only positive values. Thus the family $\{f_i/F\}_{i=1}^{\infty}$ is a partition of unity subordinated to the covering $\mathfrak{U}$. ■

To state the next theorem we need certain ideas connected with the concept of a covering. Let a covering $\mathfrak{A} = \{A_s\}_{s \in S}$ of a set X be given. The set $\mathrm{St}(M, \mathfrak{A}) = \bigcup_{A_s \cap M \neq 0} A_s$ is called the *star of the set* $M \subset X$ *relative to the covering* $\mathfrak{A}$. The star of a one-point set $\{x\}$ is called the *star of the point* x *relative to the covering* $\mathfrak{A}$ and is denoted by the symbol $\mathrm{St}(x, \mathfrak{A})$. We shall say that the covering $\mathfrak{A} = \{A_s\}_{s \in S}$ is a *star-refinement* of the covering $\mathfrak{B} = \{B_t\}_{t \in T}$ if for every $s \in S$ there exists a $t_s \in T$ such that $\mathrm{St}(A_s, \mathfrak{A}) \subset B_{t_s}$. If for every $x \in X$ there exists a $t_x \in T$ such that $\mathrm{St}(x, \mathfrak{A}) \subset B_{t_x}$, then we say that the covering $\mathfrak{A}$ is a *pointwise star-refinement* of the covering $\mathfrak{B}$.

The following theorem contains three conditions equivalent to paracompactness. Like Theorem 4, it follows from some lemmas which are stated and proved below.

THEOREM 5. *For a regular space X the following conditions are equivalent:*

(i) *The space X is paracompact.*
(ii) *Every open covering of X has an open pointwise star-refinement.*
(iii) *Every open covering of X has an open star-refinement.*
(iv) *Every open covering of X has an open σ-discrete refinement.*

LEMMA 1. *If an open covering $\{U_s\}_{s \in S}$ of a topological space X has a closed locally finite refinement, then it also has an open pointwise star-refinement.*

Proof. Let $\{F_t\}_{t \in T}$ be a closed locally finite refinement of $\{U_s\}_{s \in S}$. For every $t \in T$ let us denote by $s(t)$ a fixed element of the set S such that $F_t \subset U_{s(t)}$. It follows from the local finiteness of the covering $\{F_t\}_{t \in T}$ that the set $T(x) = \{t \in T: x \in F_t\}$ is finite for every $x \in X$. According to Theorem 4.4.1 this implies that the set

$$V_x = \bigcap_{t \in T(x)} U_{s(t)} \cap (X \setminus \bigcup_{t \notin T(x)} F_t). \tag{6}$$

is open for every $x \in X$. Since $x \in V_x$, we infer that $\mathfrak{B} = \{V_x\}_{x \in X}$ is an open covering of the space X. Let us consider a point $x_0 \in X$ and an index $t_0 \in T(x_0)$. From (6) it follows that if $x_0 \in V_x$, then $t_0 \in T(x)$ and $V_x \subset U_{s(t_0)}$.

We thus have that $\mathrm{St}(x_0, \mathfrak{B}) \subset U_{s(t_0)}$, which proves that the covering $\mathfrak{B}$ is a pointwise star-refinement of $\{U_s\}_{s \in S}$. ■

LEMMA 2. *If a covering $\mathfrak{A} = \{A_s\}_{s \in S}$ of an arbitrary set is a pointwise star-refinement of a covering $\mathfrak{B} = \{B_t\}_{t \in T}$ which is a pointwise star-refinement of a covering $\mathfrak{C} = \{C_w\}_{w \in W}$, then $\mathfrak{A}$ is a star-refinement of $\mathfrak{C}$.*

Proof. Let us consider a fixed $s_0 \in S$ and for every $x \in A_{s_0}$ let us choose $t(x) \in T$ such that

$$A_{s_0} \subset \mathrm{St}(x, \mathfrak{A}) \subset B_{t(x)}. \tag{7}$$

We thus have

$$\mathrm{St}(A_{s_0}, \mathfrak{A}) = \bigcup_{x \in A_{s_0}} \mathrm{St}(x, \mathfrak{A}) \subset \bigcup_{x \in A_{s_0}} B_{t(x)}. \tag{8}$$

According to (7), we have that $x_0 \in B_{t(x)}$ for a fixed $x_0 \in A_{s_0}$ and every $x \in A_{s_0}$. This yields

$$\bigcup_{x \in A_{s_0}} B_{t(x)} \subset \mathrm{St}(x_0, \mathfrak{B}).$$

This inclusion and (8) yield

$$\mathrm{St}(A_{s_0}, \mathfrak{A}) \subset \mathrm{St}(x_0, \mathfrak{B}) \subset C_w$$

for some $w \in W$. ■

The proof of the following lemma is analogous to the proof of Theorem 4.4.3.

LEMMA 3. *If every open covering of a topological space X has an open star-refinement, then every open covering of the space X has an open σ-discrete refinement.*

Proof. Let $\mathfrak{U} = \{U_s\}_{s \in S}$ be an open covering of the space X. Let us assume that $\mathfrak{U}_0 = \mathfrak{U}$ and let us denote by $\mathfrak{U}_1, \mathfrak{U}_2, \ldots$ a sequence of open coverings of the space X which satisfy the following condition:

(9) $\mathfrak{U}_{n+1}$ is a star-refinement of the covering $\mathfrak{U}_n$ for $n = 1, 2, \ldots$

Suppose that

$$U_{s,n} = \{x\colon x \text{ has a neighbourhood } V \text{ such that } \mathrm{St}(V, \mathfrak{U}_n) \subset U_s\}$$

for $s \in S$ and $n = 1, 2, \ldots$ For every $n = 1, 2, \ldots$ the family $\{U_{s,n}\}_{s \in S}$ is evidently an open covering of X which is a refinement of the covering $\mathfrak{U}$. We note that

(10) if $x \in U_{s,n}$ and $y \notin U_{s,n+1}$,

then there is no set $U \in \mathfrak{U}_{n+1}$ such that $x, y \in U$.

Indeed, by (9), for every $U \in \mathfrak{U}_{n+1}$ there exists a $W \in \mathfrak{U}_n$ such that $\mathrm{St}(U, \mathfrak{U}_{n+1}) \subset W$. Thus if $x \in U \cap U_{s,n}$, then $W \subset \mathrm{St}(x, \mathfrak{U}_n) \subset U_s$, whence $\mathrm{St}(U, \mathfrak{U}_{n+1}) \subset U_s$ and $U \subset U_{s,n+1}$.

Let us suppose that the set S is well ordered by the relation $<$ and let

$$(11) \qquad V_{s_0,n} = U_{s_0,n} \setminus \overline{\bigcup_{s<s_0} U_{s,n+1}}.$$

For every pair of distinct elements $s_1, s_2 \in S$ we have either that $s_1 < s_2$ or $s_2 < s_1$. Depending on which of these relations holds, we have by virtue of (11)

$$V_{s_2,n} \subset X \setminus U_{s_1,n+1} \quad \text{or} \quad V_{s_1,n} \subset X \setminus U_{s_2,n+1}.$$

Thus it follows from (10) that if $x \in V_{s_1,n}$ and $y \in V_{s_2,n}$, where $s_1 \neq s_2$, then there is no set $U \in \mathfrak{U}_{n+1}$ which would contain x and y. We infer that the family of open sets $\{V_{s,n}\}_{s \in S}$ is discrete for $n = 1, 2, \ldots$

In order to complete the proof it is sufficient to verify that the family $\{V_{s,n}\}_{n=1,s\in S}^{\infty}$ is a covering of the space X. Let us consider a point $y \in X$ and let $s(y)$ be the first element of the set S such that $y \in U_{s(y),n}$ for a certain natural number n. Such an element $s(y)$ exists because the sets $\{U_{s,n}\}_{s\in S}$ form a covering of the space X for every n. Since $y \notin U_{s,n+2}$ for $s < s(y)$, we infer by virtue of (10) that

$$\mathrm{St}(y, \mathfrak{U}_{n+2}) \cap \bigcup_{s<s(y)} U_{s,n+1} = 0$$

and this yields $y \in V_{s(y),n}$. ■

Proof of Theorem 5. The implication (i) ⇒ (ii) follows from Lemma 1 and Theorem 4. The implications (ii) ⇒ (iii) and (iii) ⇒ (iv) are consequences of Lemma 2 and 3, respectively. The implication (iv) ⇒ (i) follows from Theorem 4. ■

The definition of paracompactness, adopted in this book, and the name of this property emphasize the analogies between compactness and paracompactness. On the other hand, one can consider paracompactness as a strengthening of normality (see condition (iii) of Theorem 5 and Exercise A). Another strengthening of normality, weaker than paracompactness, is the property called collectionwise normality.

We say that a topological space X is *collectionwise normal* if X is a T_1-space and if for every discrete family $\{F_s\}_{s\in S}$ of closed subsets of X there exists a discrete family $\{V_s\}_{s\in S}$ of open sets such that $F_s \subset V_s$ for every $s \in S$. Evidently every collectionwise normal space is normal.

THEOREM 6. *Every paracompact space is collectionwise normal.*

Proof. Let $\mathfrak{F} = \{F_s\}_{s\in S}$ be a discrete family of closed subsets of a paracompact space X. For every $x \in X$ let us consider a neighbourhood H_x which meets at most one element of $\mathfrak{F}$. Let $\mathfrak{W} = \{W_t\}_{t\in T}$ be an open star-refinement of $\mathfrak{H} = \{H_x\}_{x\in X}$. This refinement exists by Theorem 5. It suffices to verify that each element of $\mathfrak{W}$ meets at most one element of the family $\{V_s\}_{s\in S}$, where $V_s = \mathrm{St}(F_s, \mathfrak{W})$. This follows, however, from the fact that for every $t \in T$ there exists an $x \in X$ such that $\mathrm{St}(W_t, \mathfrak{W}) \subset H_x$. Thus if $W_t \cap V_s \neq 0$, then $H_x \cap F_s \neq 0$. ■

The reader has certainly noticed that the construction used in the proof of Theorem 6 leads also from the locally finite family $\{F_s\}_{s \in S}$ to the locally finite family $\{V_s\}_{s \in S}$ (cf Problem U).

In Chapter 4 we have shown that the notions of compactness and countable compactness are equivalent for metrizable spaces. We find that this equivalence holds for a wider class of spaces, namely for paracompact spaces.

LEMMA. *Every locally finite family of non-empty subsets of a countably compact space is finite.*

Proof. Let $\mathfrak{A}$ be an infinite family of non-empty subsets of the space X. For every $A \in \mathfrak{A}$ one can choose a point $a_A \in A$ in such a manner that the set $B = \bigcup_{A \in \mathfrak{A}} \{a_A\}$ is infinite. If X is countably compact, then by virtue of Theorem 3.9.6, the set B has an accumulation point x in X. Each neighbourhood of the point x meets infinitely many elements of the family $\mathfrak{A}$ which, consequently, is not locally finite. ■

Let us observe that the above lemma and corollary to Theorem 2.1.6 imply:

COROLLARY. *Every normal and countably compact space is collectionwise normal.* ■

THEOREM 7. *Every paracompact and countably compact space is compact.*

Proof. Let X be paracompact and countably compact. Let $\mathfrak{A}$ be an open covering of the space X. By virtue of the paracompactness of X, there exists a locally finite open covering $\mathfrak{B}$ which is a refinement of $\mathfrak{A}$. It follows from the lemma that $\mathfrak{B}$ is a finite covering, so that X is a compact space. ■

Let us now give some examples.

EXAMPLE 1. From Theorem 7 it follows that a space X which is countably compact but not compact is not paracompact. Therefore, by virtue of Example 3.9.1, the space X of all ordinal numbers less than ω_1 is not paracompact. In view of the corollary to the lemma to Theorem 7, the space X is collectionwise normal. ■

In Example 2 we shall describe a general method of the modification of topological spaces, which will be used in Examples 3 and 4.

EXAMPLE 2. Let M be an arbitrary subspace of a topological space X. It can easily be verified that if the sets of the form $U \cup K$, where U is open in X and $K \subset X \setminus M$, are defined to be open, we obtain a topology in X. Let us denote the space obtained by X_M. The spaces X and X_M consist of the same points but have distinct families of open sets: the topology in X_M is stronger than the topology in X. The set $X \setminus M$ and each of its subsets is open in X_M, i.e. the subspace $X \setminus M$ of the space X_M is discrete. The subspace $M \subset X_M$ is closed and has the same topology as the subspace $M \subset X$.

Some properties of the space X also belong to the space X_M. For instance, it is clear that if X is a T_i-space, where $i = 0, 1, 2$, then X_M is also a T_i-space. We shall show that this also remains valid for $i = 3$ and $3\frac{1}{2}$.

Let X be a T_i-space, where $i = 3$ or $3\frac{1}{2}$, and let x denote a point of the space X_M. Let F be a closed subset of the space X_M which does not contain x. Choose an open subset U of X and a set $K \subset X \setminus M$ such that

$$x \in U \cup K \quad \text{and} \quad F \cap (U \cup K) = 0.$$

If $x \in K$, then the set $\{x\}$ is open-and-closed and the point x is completely separated from the set F; we can therefore assume that $x \in U$.

If $i = 3$, then there exists a set V open in X such that $x \in V \subset \overline{V} \subset U$, where $\overline{V}$ denotes the closure of the set V in the space X. Thus V and $X \setminus \overline{V}$ contain x and F, respectively, and are disjoint open subsets of the space X_M.

But if $i = 3\frac{1}{2}$, then there exists a continuous function $f: X \to I$ such that $f(x) = 0$ and $f(X \setminus U) \subset \{1\}$. Since f is continuous on X_M, the sets $\{x\}$ and F are completely separated in X_M.

The space X_M is not necessarily normal even under the assumption that X is compact (see Exercise E). We shall show that X_M is a normal space provided that X is a T_1-space, and that for every two sets A_1, B_1 which are closed in M and disjoint there exist sets U, V open in X such that

$$A_1 \subset U, \quad B_1 \subset V, \quad \text{and} \quad U \cap V = 0; \tag{12}$$

this is the case if, for example, X is normal and M is a closed subspace of X.

By the above remarks X_M is a T_1-space. Let us consider two closed and disjoint subsets A, B of the space X_M. According to the definition of the topology in X_M we have

$$A = E \cap C, \quad B = F \cap D, \quad \text{where} \quad M \subset C,\ M \subset D,$$

and the sets E, F are closed in X. The sets $A_1 = A \cap M = E \cap M$ and $B_1 = B \cap M = F \cap M$ are closed and disjoint in M. Let U and V be open subsets of the space X which satisfy (12). It is easy to verify that the sets $(U \setminus B) \cup (A \setminus M)$ and $(V \setminus A) \cup (B \setminus M)$, open in X_M, are disjoint and contain the sets A and B, respectively.

Let us now suppose that the space X is hereditarily paracompact, i.e. that every subspace of X is paracompact (this condition is satisfied if, for instance, X is metrizable). We shall show that the space X_M is also hereditarily paracompact. Since every subspace of the space X_M is of the form $X'_{M'}$, where $X' \subset X$ and $M' = M \cap X'$, it is sufficient to verify that X_M is paracompact. Every open covering of the space X_M is of the form $\{U_s \cup K_s\}_{s\in S}$, where U_s is an open subset of X and $K_s \subset X \setminus M$ for every $s \in S$. The covering $\{U_s\}_{s\in S}$ of the space $U = \bigcup_{s\in S} U_s$ has an open locally finite refinement $\{V_t\}_{t\in T}$. It can be verified without any difficulty that by adding individual points of the set $X \setminus U$ to this covering we obtain a locally finite open covering of the space X_M which is a refinement of the covering $\{U_s \cup K_s\}_{s\in S}$. ∎

EXAMPLE 3. We shall now give an example of a normal space which is not collectionwise normal. Let R be the set of real numbers and let $\mathfrak{S}$ denote the family of all subsets of R.

For every $S \in \mathfrak{S}$ let $D_S = \{0, 1\}$ with the discrete topology and let $Y = \boldsymbol{P}_{S\in\mathfrak{S}} D_S$. Elements of the space Y are, therefore, functions defined on the family $\mathfrak{S}$ and assume values 0 and 1. For every $r \in R$ let the function $f_r \in Y$ be defined by means of the formula

$$f_r(S) = \begin{cases} 0 & \text{for} \quad r \notin S, \\ 1 & \text{for} \quad r \in S, \end{cases}$$

and let $M = \{f_r\}_{r\in R}$. The intersection of the neighbourhood $U = p_{\{r\}}^{-1}(1)$ of the point f_r in the space Y with the set M consists of the point f_r only; thus M is a discrete subspace of Y. Let us consider two disjoint and non-empty subsets A, B of the subspace $M \subset Y$, and the disjoint subsets of R:

$$S_A = \{r \in R: f_r \in A\}, \qquad S_B = \{r \in R: f_r \in B\}.$$

The sets

$$U = p_{S_A}^{-1}(1) \cap p_{S_B}^{-1}(0) \quad \text{and} \quad V = p_{S_A}^{-1}(0) \cap p_{S_B}^{-1}(1)$$

are disjoint, open in Y and contain A and B respectively. By virtue of the preceding example, the space $X = Y_M$ is normal.

It suffices to show that X is not collectionwise normal. Since the space M is discrete and since the set $X \setminus M$ is open, the family $\{f_r\}_{r\in R}$ is discrete. Let us suppose that the space X is collectionwise normal. There exists, therefore, a family $\{V_r\}_{r\in R}$ of mutually disjoint open subsets of X such that $f_r \in V_r$ for every $r \in R$. Since $V_r = U_r \cup K_r$, where U_r is open in Y and $K_r \subset Y \setminus M$, we have $f_r \in U_r$ and $\{U_r\}_{r\in R}$ is a family of power $\mathfrak{c}$ consisting of mutually disjoint, non-empty, open subsets of the space $Y = \boldsymbol{P}_{S\in\mathfrak{S}} D_S$, contrary to Theorem 2.3.10. ∎

We will now examine operations on paracompact spaces. Let us begin with two theorems of a positive character.

THEOREM 8. *Let X be a paracompact space and let $M \subset X$ denote a subset which is an F_σ-set. The subspace M is paracompact.*

Proof. Let $M = \bigcup_{i=1}^{\infty} F_i$, where F_i is a closed subset of X for $i = 1, 2, \ldots$ Let us consider an open covering $\{U_s\}_{s\in S}$ of the space M and let us denote by $\{V_s\}_{s\in S}$ a family of open subsets of the space X such that $U_s = V_s \cap M$ for every $s \in S$. The family $\{V_s\}_{s\in S} \cup \{X \setminus F_i\}$ is an open covering of the space X for $i = 1, 2, \ldots$; thus it has a locally finite open refinement $\mathfrak{A}_i$. Let us define $\mathfrak{B}_i = \{U \cap M \colon U \in \mathfrak{A}_i \text{ and } U \cap F_i \neq 0\}$. It is easy to verify that $\mathfrak{B} = \bigcup_{i=1}^{\infty} \mathfrak{B}_i$ is a σ-locally finite open covering of M which is a refinement of $\{U_s\}_{s\in S}$. By virtue of Theorem 4, the space M is paracompact. ∎

The following corollary (which can also be proved directly) results from Theorem 8.

COROLLARY. *A closed subspace of a paracompact space is paracompact.* ∎

THEOREM 9. *The sum $\bigoplus_{s\in S} X_s$ of a family $\{X_s\}_{s\in S}$ of disjoint topological spaces is paracompact if and only if X_s is paracompact for every $s \in S$.*

Proof. If $\bigoplus_{s\in S} X_s$ is paracompact, then by the corollary of the preceding theorem, X is paracompact for every $s \in S$.

Now let X_s be paracompact for every $s \in S$ and let us consider an open covering $\mathfrak{V} = \{V_t\}_{t\in T}$ of the space $\bigoplus_{s\in S} X_s$. For every $s \in S$ the family $\mathfrak{V}_s = \{X_s \cap V_t\}_{t\in T}$ is an open covering of the space X_s. Let $\mathfrak{A}_s$ be a locally finite open covering of X_s which is a refinement of $\mathfrak{V}_s$. It is easy to verify that $\bigcup_{s\in S} \mathfrak{A}_s$ is a locally finite open covering of the space $\bigoplus_{s\in S} X_s$ which is a refinement of $\mathfrak{V}$. ∎

We shall now show that the Cartesian product $X \times Y$ of a paracompact space X and a metrizable space Y is not necessarily paracompact or even normal.

EXAMPLE 4. Let us consider the segment I with the natural topology and its subspaces W and V consisting of all rational and irrational numbers, respectively. By virtue of Example 2, the space $X = I_W$ is hereditarily paracompact. Let us define $Y = V$ and consider the closed and disjoint subsets $A = W \times Y$, $B = \{(x, x) \colon x \in V\}$ of the product $X \times Y$. Let U be an open subset of $X \times Y$ which contains B. To prove that $X \times Y$ is not normal it is sufficient to show that $A \cap \overline{U} \neq 0$.

Let

$$V_i = \{x \in V \colon \{x\} \times B(x, 1/i) \subset U\} \quad \text{for} \quad i = 1, 2, \ldots, \tag{13}$$

where $B(x, 1/i) = \{y \in V: \varrho(x, y) < 1/i\}$ and ϱ denotes the usual metric of the real-line. Since W is the union of a sequence of nowhere dense (one-point) sets, the Baire Theorem implies that V is not an F_σ-set in I and since, as can easily be verified, $V = \bigcup_{i=1}^{\infty} V_i$, $W \cap \overline{V}_i \neq 0$ for a certain i, where $\overline{V}_i$ denotes the closure of V_i in the segment I. Let us choose a point $x \in W \cap \overline{V}_i$ and a point $y \in V = Y$ such that $\varrho(x, y) < 1/2i$. Since $(x, y) \in A$, it suffices to show that for every neighbourhood Q of the point x in the space X and every neighbourhood S of the point y in the space Y we have $(Q \times S) \cap U \neq 0$.

From the definition of the topology in the space $X = I_W$ it follows that $Q = G \cup K$, where G is open in I and $K \subset V$. Since the point x belongs to W, we infer that $x \in G$; but x belongs also to $\overline{V}_i$, so that there exists an $x' \in G \cap V_i$ such that $\varrho(x', x) < 1/2i$. Therefore $(x', y) \in Q \times S$ and

$$\varrho(x', y) \leqslant \varrho(x', x) + \varrho(x, y) < 1/2i + 1/2i = 1/i.$$

In view of (13) this yields $(x', y) \in U$, i.e. $(Q \times S) \cap U \neq 0$. ■

If we are only intersted in the normality of the Cartesian product of two paracompact spaces, the following simpler example can be given.

EXAMPLE 5. From Corollary 2 to Theorem 4 and from Example 3.7.2 it follows that the space X considered in Example 1.2.1 is paracompact. On the other hand, the Cartesian product $X \times X$ is not normal (see Example 2.3.2). ■

A discrete space of an arbitrary power is, as we already know, paracompact. Since every topological space X is a continuous image of a discrete space, we infer that the continuous image of a paracompact space is not necessarily paracompact.

To complete this paragraph we shall prove

THEOREM 10. *The Cartesian product $X \times Y$ of a paracompact space X by a compact space Y is paracompact.*

Proof. Let us consider an open covering $\{U_s\}_{s \in S}$ of the space $X \times Y$. For every $(x, y) \in X \times Y$ there exist a neighbourhood $V_{x,y}$ of the point x in X and a neighbourhood $W_{x,y}$ of y in Y such that $V_{x,y} \times W_{x,y} \subset U_s$ for some $s \in S$. For a fixed $x_0 \in X$ the family $\{(V_{x_0,y} \times W_{x_0,y}) \cap (\{x_0\} \times Y)\}_{y \in Y}$ is an open covering of the compact space $\{x_0\} \times Y$. There exists, therefore, a finite number of points $y_1, y_2, \ldots, y_{k(x_0)}$ such that

$$(14) \qquad \{x_0\} \times Y \subset \bigcup_{i=1}^{k(x_0)} (V_{x_0,y_i} \times W_{x_0,y_i}).$$

Let $V(x_0) = \bigcap_{i=1}^{k(x_0)} V_{x_0,y_i}$. The family $\{V(x)\}_{x \in X}$ is an open covering of the space X. There exists, therefore, an open covering $\{V_t\}_{t \in T}$ which is locally finite and is a refinement of $\{V(x)\}_{x \in X}$. For every $t \in T$ let $x_t \in X$ denote a point such that $V_t \subset V(x_t)$ and let $W_{t,i} = W_{x_t,y_i}$ for $i \leqslant k(x_t) = k(t)$, where the points $y_1, y_2, \ldots, y_{k(x_t)}$ satisfy (14), x_0 being replaced by x_t. It is easy to verify that the covering $\{V_t \times W_{t,i}\}_{i=1,t\in T}^{k(t)}$ is locally finite and that it is a refinement of the covering $\{U_s\}_{s\in S}$. ■

EXERCISES

A. Prove that a T_1-space X is normal if and only if each finite open covering of X has an open star-refinement.

Hint: First consider coverings consisting of two elements.

B. Show that for every open covering $\{U_s\}_{s\in S}$ of a paracompact space X there exists a locally finite and open covering $\{V_s\}_{s\in S}$ of that space such that $V_s \subset U_s$ for every $s \in S$.

C. (a) (C. H. Dowker [1952]) Show that if, for every discrete family $\{F_s\}_{s\in S}$ of closed subsets of a T_1-space X, there exists a family $\{V_s\}_{s\in S}$ consisting of mutually disjoint open subsets of that space such that $F_s \subset V_s$ for $s \in S$, then X is collectionwise normal.

Hint: Consider closed sets $A = \bigcup_{s\in S} F_s$ and $B = X \setminus \bigcup_{s\in S} V_s$.

(b) Show that a closed subspace of a collectionwise normal space is collectionwise normal.

D. Show that for every countable discrete family $\{F_i\}_{i=1}^{\infty}$ of closed subsets of a normal space X there exists a discrete family $\{U_i\}_{i=1}^{\infty}$ of open subsets of X such that $F_i \subset U_i$ for $i = 1, 2, \ldots$

Hint: Make use of Exercise 4.4.B and of the method developed in the proof of the corollary to Theorem 2.1.6.

E. Give an example of a compact space X and a subspace M such that the space X_M defined in Example 2 is not normal.

Hint: Consider the space of Example 2.3.3 or any other compact space containing a non-normal subspace.

F (L. F. McAuley [1956]). Give an example of a normal and separable space which is not paracompact.

Hint: Let Y be a subspace of the Tychonoff cube $T = I^{c}$ homeomorphic to the space X_0 of Example 3.5.1 and let D be a countable dense subset of T. Consider the space $A(T)$ of Exercise 3.1.E and its subspace $Y_1 \cup D_2$. Make use of the fact that from every two disjoint and closed subsets of the space X_0 at least one is compact.

§ 2. Countably paracompact spaces. A topological space X is called *countably paracompact* if it is a Hausdorff space and every countable open covering of X has a locally finite open refinement. Paracompact spaces and countably compact spaces are obviously countably paracompact.

Before proceeding to the theorem which gives some equivalent conditions to countable paracompactness for normal spaces, let us prove a lemma, in the formulation of which we shall use the notion of a star-finite covering. A covering $\mathfrak{A}$ of a topological space X is said to be *star-*

-finite if for every $A_0 \in \mathfrak{A}$ the intersection $A_0 \cap A$ is non-empty for only a finite number of elements A of the covering $\mathfrak{A}$. Of course, every star-finite covering is locally finite.

LEMMA. *Every countable covering of a normal space consisting of open F_σ-sets has a star-finite countable open refinement.*

Proof. Let us consider an open covering $\{U_i\}_{i=1}^{\infty}$ of a normal space X such that $U_i = \bigcup_{j=1}^{\infty} F_{i,j}$, where $F_{i,j}$ is closed for $i, j = 1, 2, \ldots$ By the normality of X, there exists a function $f_{i,j}: X \to I$ for every $i, j = 1, 2, \ldots$ such that $f_{i,j}(x) = 0$ for $x \in X \setminus U_i$ and $f_{i,j}(x) = 1$ for $x \in F_{i,j}$. Let us consider the function defined by means of the formula $f(x) = \sum_{i=1}^{\infty} \frac{1}{2^i} f_i(x)$, where $f_i(x) = \sum_{j=1}^{\infty} \frac{1}{2^j} f_{i,j}(x)$. Since $f_i^{-1}(0) = X \setminus U_i$ and $\{U_i\}_{i=1}^{\infty}$ is a covering of the space X, the inequality $0 < f(x) \leqslant 1$ holds for every $x \in X$.

Let us consider the sets

$$V_k = f^{-1}\big((1/k, 1]\big) \quad \text{and} \quad F_k = f^{-1}([1/k, 1]) \quad \text{for} \quad k = 1, 2, \ldots$$

The families $\{V_k\}_{k=1}^{\infty}$ and $\{F_k\}_{k=1}^{\infty}$ are coverings of the space X. The first is open and the second is closed.

We shall prove that the sets

$$U_{k,j} = U_j \cap (V_{k+1} \setminus F_{k-1}), \quad \text{where} \quad j \leqslant k = 1, 2, \ldots \text{ and } F_0 = 0,$$

form a star-finite covering of the space X. Let $x \in X$ and let us suppose that k is the least natural number such that $x \in F_k$. Since, as can easily be verified, $F_k \subset \bigcup_{j \leqslant k} U_j$, there exists a $j \leqslant k$ such that $x \in U_j$. Thus we have $x \in U_j \cap (F_k \setminus F_{k-1}) \subset U_{k,j}$. For every k, j and n where $j \leqslant k$ and $n \geqslant k+2$ we have that $U_{k,j} \subset V_{k+1} \subset F_{n-1}$. Hence $U_{k,j} \cap U_{n,i} = 0$ for $n \geqslant k+2$ and $i \leqslant n$. The covering $\{U_{k,j}\}_{k=1, j \leqslant k}^{\infty}$ is therefore star-finite. ∎

THEOREM 1. *For a normal space X the following conditions are equivalent:*

(i) *The space X is countably paracompact.*

(ii) *For each open countable covering $\{U_i\}_{i=1}^{\infty}$ of the space X there exists an open and locally finite covering $\{V_i\}_{i=1}^{\infty}$ of this space such that $\overline{V}_i \subset U_i$ for $i = 1, 2, \ldots$*

(iii) *Every countable open covering of the space X has a point-finite open refinement.*

(iv) *For each open countable covering $\{U_i\}_{i=1}^{\infty}$ of the space X there exists a closed covering $\{F_i\}_{i=1}^{\infty}$ of this space such that $F_i \subset U_i$ for $i = 1, 2, \ldots$*

(v) *For each decreasing sequence* $F_1 \supset F_2 \supset \ldots$ *of closed subsets of the space* X, *where* $\bigcap_{i=1}^{\infty} F_i = 0$, *there exists a sequence* $W_1, W_2, \ldots$ *of open subsets of* X *such that* $\bigcap_{i=1}^{\infty} W_i = 0$ *and* $F_i \subset W_i$ *for* $i = 1, 2, \ldots$

(vi) *Every countable open covering of the space* X *has a star-finite open refinement.*

Proof. The implications (ii) $\Rightarrow$ (iii) and (vi) $\Rightarrow$ (i) are obvious. The implication (iv) $\Rightarrow$ (v) follows immediately from the de Morgan formulas. To prove the theorem it is therefore sufficient to show that (i) $\Rightarrow$ (ii), (iii) $\Rightarrow$ (iv), and (v) $\Rightarrow$ (vi).

First, we shall show that (i) $\Rightarrow$ (ii). Let $\{U_i\}_{i=1}^{\infty}$ be an open countable covering of a normal space X and let $\{W_s\}_{s\in S}$ be an open, locally finite refinement. For every $s \in S$ let $i(s)$ denote the least natural number such that $W_s \subset U_{i(s)}$ and let us define

$$W_i = \bigcup_{i(s)=i} W_s.$$

The sets W_i form a locally finite covering of the space X, and $W_i \subset U_i$ for every natural number i. By virtue of Lemma 1 to Theorem 1.3, there exists an open covering $\{V_i\}_{i=1}^{\infty}$ of the space X such that $\overline{V}_i \subset W_i$ for $i = 1, 2, \ldots$ It is easy to see that this covering is locally finite.

In order to prove the implication (iii) $\Rightarrow$ (iv), it is sufficient to replace the term "locally finite" by the term "point finite" in the preceding proof, and to put $F_i = \overline{V}_i$.

We shall now prove that (v) $\Rightarrow$ (vi). Let $\{U_i\}_{i=1}^{\infty}$ be an arbitrary countable open covering of the normal space X which satisfies (v). The sets $F_1, F_2, \ldots$, where $F_i = X \setminus \bigcup_{j\leqslant i} U_j$, are closed and form a decreasing sequence such that $\bigcap_{i=1}^{\infty} F_i = 0$. There exists, therefore, a sequence $W_1, W_2, \ldots$ consisting of open subsets of X such that $\bigcap_{i=1}^{\infty} W_i = 0$ and $F_i \subset W_i$ for $i = 1, 2, \ldots$ Let us suppose that the function $f_i\colon X \to I$ satisfies the conditions:

$$f_i(F_i) \subset \{0\} \quad \text{and} \quad f_i(X \setminus W_i) \subset \{1\}.$$

The F_σ-set $V_i = f_i^{-1}\big((0,1]\big) = \bigcup_{n=1}^{\infty} f_i^{-1}\big([1/n, 1]\big)$ is an open F_σ-set and

$$X \setminus W_i \subset V_i \subset X \setminus F_i = \bigcup_{j\leqslant i} U_j. \tag{1}$$

Since $\bigcup_{i=1}^{\infty} (X \setminus W_i) = X \setminus \bigcap_{i=1}^{\infty} W_i = X$, the family $\{V_i\}_{i=1}^{\infty}$ is a covering of the space X. By the lemma it has an open star-finite countable refinement $\{G_k\}_{k=1}^{\infty}$. For every k let us choose an $i(k)$ such that $G_k \subset V_{i(k)}$. It follows from (1) that $\bigcup_{k=1}^{\infty} \{G_k \cap U_1, G_k \cap U_2, \ldots, G_k \cap U_{i(k)}\}$ is a star-finite refinement of $\{U_i\}_{i=1}^{\infty}$. ■

We shall now give another interesting characterization of normal countably paracompact spaces. Let us begin with a lemma.

LEMMA. *The Cartesian product $X \times Y$ of a normal countably paracompact space X by a compact space Y, which satisfies the second axiom of countability, is a normal space.*

Proof. Let us denote a countable base of the space Y by $\{G_i\}_{i=1}^{\infty}$ and let $\mathfrak{S}$ denote the family of all finite subsets of the set of natural numbers. For every $S \in \mathfrak{S}$ let $G_S = \bigcup_{i \in S} G_i$. Let us denote the projection onto X by $p: X \times Y \to X$. By virtue of Theorem 3.2.8, p is a closed mapping. For every $M \subset X \times Y$ let M_x denote the projection of the set $(\{x\} \times Y) \cap M$ onto Y.

Let A and B be disjoint and closed subsets of $X \times Y$. For every $S \in \mathfrak{S}$ let us define

$$U_S = \{x: A_x \subset G_S \subset \overline{G}_S \subset Y \setminus B_x\}. \tag{2}$$

It can easily be seen that

$$X \setminus U_S = \{x: A_x \cap (Y \setminus G_S) \neq 0\} \cup \{x: B_x \cap \overline{G}_S \neq 0\}$$
$$= p[A \cap (X \times (Y \setminus G_S))] \cup p[B \cap (X \times \overline{G}_S)],$$

whence U_S is open. Making use of the compactness of Y, it is not difficult to verify that $\{U_S\}_{S \in \mathfrak{S}}$ is a covering of the space X; obviously it is a countable covering. Therefore, by condition (ii) of Theorem 1, there exists an open locally finite covering $\{W_S\}_{S \in \mathfrak{S}}$ such that $W_S \subset \overline{W}_S \subset U_S$ for every $S \in \mathfrak{S}$.

The set $U = \bigcup_{S \in \mathfrak{S}} (W_S \times G_S)$ is open and we shall show that

$$A \subset U \quad \text{and} \quad B \subset V = X \times Y \setminus \overline{U}. \tag{3}$$

For every $(x, y) \in A$ we have $x \in W_S \subset U_S$ for some $S \in \mathfrak{S}$. It follows from (2) that in this case we have $(x, y) \in W_S \times G_S \subset U$. The first part of (3) is therefore valid.

Let us assume that there exists a point $(x, y) \in B \cap \overline{U}$. Since the covering $\{W_S\}_{S \in \mathfrak{S}}$ is locally finite, there exists a neighbourhood H of the point $x \in X$ which meets only a finite number of elements of this covering. Thus the neighbourhood $H \times Y$ of the point $(x, y) \in B$ meets only a finite number, $W_{S_1} \times G_{S_1}, W_{S_2} \times G_{S_2}, \ldots, W_{S_k} \times G_{S_k}$, of elements of the family $\{W_S \times G_S\}_{S \in \mathfrak{S}}$. But since $(x, y) \in \overline{U}$, we have $(x, y) \in \bigcup_{i=1}^{k} \overline{W_{S_i} \times G_{S_i}}$ and

$$(x, y) \in B \cap \overline{W_{S_i} \times G_{S_i}} = B \cap (\overline{W}_{S_i} \times \overline{G}_{S_i}) \subset B \cap (U_{S_i} \times \overline{G}_{S_i}) \tag{4}$$

for some $i \leqslant k$. From (4) it follows that $x \in U_{S_i}$ and $y \in B_x \cap \bar{G}_{S_i}$, contrary to (2). This contradiction completes the proof of (3) and of the lemma. ∎

THEOREM 2. *A topological space X is normal and countably paracompact if and only if the Cartesian product $X \times I$, where I denotes the segment $[0, 1]$ with the natural topology, is normal.*

Proof. The lemma implies that the product $X \times I$ is normal for a normal and countably paracompact space X.

Let X be a topological space such that $X \times I$ is normal. Since X is homeomorphic to a closed subspace $X \times \{0\}$ of the normal space $X \times I$, we infer that X is normal. We shall show that X satisfies condition (v) of Theorem 1.

Let $F_1, F_2, \ldots$ denote a decreasing sequence of closed subsets of the space X such that $\bigcap_{i=1}^{\infty} F_i = 0$. The sets $U_j = (X \setminus F_j) \times [0, 1/j) \subset X \times I$ are open for $j = 1, 2, \ldots$ On the other hand, the sets

$$A = X \times I \setminus \bigcup_{j=1}^{\infty} U_j \quad \text{and} \quad B = X \times \{0\}$$

are closed and disjoint. Therefore, there exist disjoint sets U and V, open in $X \times Y$, which contain A and B respectively. The sets $W_i = \{x : (x, 1/i) \in U\}$ are open for $i = 1, 2, \ldots$ and since $\bar{U} \cap B = 0$, we have $\bigcap_{i=1}^{\infty} W_i = 0$. In order to complete the proof it suffices to show that $F_i \subset W_i$ for $i = 1, 2, \ldots$

Let us consider $x \in F_i$. Since $x \notin X \setminus F_j$ for $j \leqslant i$ and since $1/i \notin [0, 1/j)$ for $j > i$, we have $(x, 1/i) \notin \bigcup_{j=1}^{\infty} U_j$. We infer that

$$(x, 1/i) \in X \times I \setminus \bigcup_{j=1}^{\infty} U_j = A \subset U \quad \text{for} \quad x \in F_i,$$

and this yields $F_i \subset W_i$. ∎

It is not yet known whether normal spaces, which are not countably paracompact, exist. An example of such a space was constructed under the assumption that there exists a *Suslin set*, i.e. a set X which is ordered by the relation $<$ such that each family of disjoint non-empty sets of the form $(a, b) = \{x \in X : a < x < b\}$, where $a, b \in X$ and $a < b$, is countable, and which does not contain any countable subset which intersects every non-empty set (a, b). In other words, the set X ordered by the relation $<$ is a Suslin set if considered as a topological space (with the order topology induced by the ordering $<$; see Problem 1.D) it satisfies condition (S) but does not satisfy condition (D) (see Problem 1.Q). The problem of the existence of Suslin sets, raised by Suslin in Fundamenta Mathematicae, vol. I (1921), is still unsolved.

Finally let us observe that it follows from Example 1.1 and from the countable paracompactness of a countably compact space that there exist collectionwise normal and countably paracompact spaces which are not paracompact. Since there exist non-regular countably compact spaces (see Exercise 3.O), a countably paracompact space is not necessarily regular.

EXERCISES

A. Show that a normal space X is countably paracompact if and only if every countable open covering of X has a partition of unity (or, equivalently, a locally finite partition of unity) subordinate to it.

B. Prove that the sum of an arbitrary family of disjoint countably paracompact spaces, and a closed subspace of a countably paracompact space, are countably paracompact.

C (C. H. Dowker [1951]). Prove that the Cartesian product $X \times Y$ of a countably paracompact space X by a compact space Y is countably paracompact. Note that under the additional assumptions of normality of X this follows from condition (v) of Theorem 1 and Theorem 3.2.8.

§ 3. Weakly paracompact spaces and strongly paracompact spaces. A topological space X is called *weakly paracompact* if X is a Hausdorff space and every open covering of the space X has an open point-finite refinement. Every paracompact space is weakly paracompact, and it follows from Theorem 2.1 that every normal weakly paracompact space is countably paracompact.

Before examining weakly paracompact spaces let us prove a lemma concerning point-finite coverings. A covering $\mathfrak{A}$ of the space X is called *irreducible*, provided that no family $\mathfrak{A}_0 \subset \mathfrak{A}$ which is different from $\mathfrak{A}$ is a covering of the space X.

LEMMA. *Every point-finite covering $\{A_s\}_{s \in S}$ of a topological space X contains an irreducible subcovering.*

Proof. Let us consider the family $\mathfrak{G}$ of functions G defined on the set S and satisfying the following two conditions:

(a) $G(s) = A_s$ or $G(s) = 0$.

(b) $\bigcup_{s \in S} G(s) = X$.

Let us introduce a partial ordering in the family $\mathfrak{G}$ assuming that if the condition $G_1(s) = 0$ implies $G_2(s) = 0$ then $G_1 \leqslant G_2$. Let $\mathfrak{G}_0 \subset \mathfrak{G}$ denote a linearly ordered subset of the family $\mathfrak{G}$. In the same manner as in the proof of Lemma 1 to Theorem 1.3 one can verify that the function G_0, defined by means of the formula $G_0(s) = \bigcap_{G \in \mathfrak{G}_0} G(s)$, belongs to the family $\mathfrak{G}$ and that $G \leqslant G_0$ for every $G \in \mathfrak{G}_0$. Therefore, a maximal element G exists in the family $\mathfrak{G}$. The covering $\{A_s\}_{s \in S_1}$, where $S_1 = \{s \in S: G(s) \neq 0\}$, is evidently irreducible. ■

THEOREM 1. *For weakly paracompact spaces the notions of compactness and countable compactness are equivalent.*

Proof. It is sufficient to show that each weakly paracompact and countably compact space X is compact.

Let $\mathfrak{U}$ be an open covering of the space X. By virtue of the lemma there exists an irreducible point-finite open covering $\mathfrak{V} = \{V_t\}_{t \in T}$ which is a refinement of $\mathfrak{U}$. We shall show that $\mathfrak{V}$ is finite. From the irreducibility of $\mathfrak{V}$ it follows that for every $t \in T$ there exists a point $x_t \in V_t \setminus \bigcup_{t' \neq t} V_{t'}$. Since the sets $\{V_t\}_{t \in T}$ form a covering of the space X, each point $x \in X$ has a neighbourhood containing exactly one point of the set $A = \{x_t\}_{t \in T}$. Thus we have $A^{\mathrm{d}} = 0$, and since the space X is countably compact, we infer that the set A, and consequently the set T, is finite. ■

THEOREM 2. *Every collectionwise normal and weakly paracompact space X is paracompact.*

Proof. By virtue of Theorem 1.5 it is sufficient to prove that every point-finite open covering $\mathfrak{U} = \{U_s\}_{s \in S}$ of the space X has a σ-discrete open refinement.

First, for every $i = 0, 1, 2, \ldots$ we shall define a discrete family $\mathfrak{V}_i = \{V_T\}_{T \in \mathfrak{T}_i}$, which consists of open subsets of X and is a refinement of $\mathfrak{U}$ in such a manner, that the sets $W_i = \bigcup_{T \in \mathfrak{T}_i} V_T$ are subject to the following condition:

(1) If $x \in X$ belongs to at most i elements of the covering $\mathfrak{U}$, then $x \in \bigcup_{j=0}^{i} W_j$.

Let us define $\mathfrak{V}_0 = 0$ and assume that the families $\mathfrak{V}_i$ satisfying condition (1) have already been defined for $i \leqslant n$. Let us denote by $\mathfrak{T}_{n+1}$ the family of all subsets of the set S which consists of $n+1$ elements and let us define

$$A_T = \Big(X \setminus \bigcup_{j=0}^{n} W_j\Big) \cap \Big(X \setminus \bigcup_{s \notin T} U_s\Big) \quad \text{for } T \in \mathfrak{T}_{n+1}. \tag{2}$$

To begin with, let us note that

$$A_T \subset \bigcap_{s \in T} U_s \quad \text{for every } T \in \mathfrak{T}_{n+1}. \tag{3}$$

Indeed, if for a point $x \in A_T$ and for a certain $s_0 \in T$ we had $x \notin U_{s_0}$, then the point x would belong, by (2), to at most n elements of the covering $\mathfrak{U}$, contrary to (1).

We shall show that every point $x \in X$ has a neighbourhood $V(x)$ which intersects at most one set A_T for $T \in \mathfrak{T}_{n+1}$. If x belongs to $n+2$ elements $U_{s_1}, U_{s_2}, \ldots, U_{s_{n+2}}$ of the covering $\mathfrak{U}$, then assuming $V(x) = \bigcap_{i=1}^{n+2} U_{s_i}$, we have by virtue of (2), that $V(x) \cap A_T = 0$ for every

$T \in \mathfrak{T}_{n+1}$. If x belongs only to $m \leqslant n$ elements of the covering $\mathfrak{U}$, then by (1), $\bigcup_{j=0}^{n} W_j$ is a neighbourhood of the point x disjoint with all sets A_T; but if x belongs to exactly $n+1$ elements $U_{s_1}, U_{s_2}, \ldots, U_{s_{n+1}}$ of the covering $\mathfrak{U}$, then A_{T_0}, where $T_0 = \{s_1, s_2, \ldots, s_{n+1}\}$, is the only element of the family $\{A_T\}_{T \in \mathfrak{T}_{n+1}}$ which may meet the neighbourhood $\bigcap_{i=1}^{n+1} U_{s_i}$ of the point x.

Thus the family $\{A_T\}_{T \in \mathfrak{T}_{n+1}}$ is a discrete family of closed subsets of the space X. Let $\{P_T\}_{T \in \mathfrak{T}_{n+1}}$ denote a discrete family of open sets such that $A_T \subset P_T$ for every $T \in \mathfrak{T}_{n+1}$. We shall show that the family $\mathfrak{V}_{n+1} = \{V_T\}_{T \in \mathfrak{T}_{n+1}}$ of open sets, where

$$V_T = P_T \cap \bigcap_{s \in T} U_s, \tag{4}$$

has the required properties. The family $\mathfrak{V}_{n+1}$ is obviously discrete and it is a refinement of $\mathfrak{U}$. Let us now suppose that $x \in X$ is an element of at most $n+1$ elements of $\mathfrak{U}$. Then there exists a $T \in \mathfrak{T}_{n+1}$ such that $x \in X \setminus \bigcup_{s \notin T} U_s$. We thus have

$$x \in X \setminus \bigcup_{s \notin T} U_s = \Big[\Big(X \setminus \bigcup_{j=0}^{n} W_j\Big) \cup \bigcup_{j=0}^{n} W_j\Big] \cap \Big(X \setminus \bigcup_{s \notin T} U_s\Big) \subset A_T \cup \bigcup_{j=0}^{n} W_j.$$

Hence, by virtue of (3), (4), and of the inclusion $A_T \subset P_T$, it follows that $x \in \bigcup_{j=0}^{n+1} W_j$.

Since $\mathfrak{U}$ is a point-finite covering, (1) implies that $\bigcup_{i=1}^{\infty} \mathfrak{V}_i$ is an open σ-discrete covering of the space X, which is a refinement of $\mathfrak{U}$. ∎

EXAMPLE 1. The Hausdorff non-regular space X described in Example 1.5.1, is weakly paracompact.

Let $\mathfrak{U} = \{U_s\}_{s \in S}$ be an arbitrary open covering of the space X. The subspace $X_1 = X \setminus [-1/2, 1/2]$ of the space X has the same topology as the set X_1 considered as the subspace of the real-line; it is therefore paracompact. The covering $\{X_1 \cap U_s\}_{s \in S}$ of the space X_1 has an open locally finite refinement $\{V_s\}_{s \in S_1}$ consisting of sets open in X_1, and thus also open in X. We have therefore

$$X \setminus [-1/2, 1/2] \subset \bigcup_{s \in S_1} V_s. \tag{5}$$

The topology of the space $X_i = [1/i+1, 1/i] \cup [-1/i, -1/i+1]$ is, for $i = 2, 3, \ldots$, the same as the topology in the set X_i considered as the subspace of the real-line; it is therefore a compact space. Thus for every $i = 2, 3, \ldots$ there exists a finite set $S_i \subset S$ such that $X_i \subset \bigcup_{s \in S_i} U_s$.

The family $\{V_s\}_{s\in S_i}$, where $V_s = U_s \cap [(1/i+2, 1/i-1) \cup (-1/i-1, -1/i+2)]$ for $s \in S_i$, consists of open subsets of X and

$$(6)\quad [1/i+1, 1/i] \cup [-1/i, -1/i+1] \subset \bigcup_{s\in S_i} V_s \quad \text{for} \quad i = 2, 3, \ldots$$

Let s_0 denote an element of the set S such that $0 \in U_{s_0}$ and let $S_0 = \{s_0\}$, $V_{s_0} = U_{s_0}$, $S' = \bigcup_{i=0}^{\infty} S_i$. By virtue of (5), (6) and the condition $0 \in V_{s_0}$, the family $\{V_s\}_{s\in S'}$ is an open covering of the space X. It is easy to verify that this covering is point finite. ∎

There exist collectionwise normal spaces which are not weakly paracompact. For instance, by virtue of Theorem 1 and Example 1.1, the space of all ordinal numbers less than ω_1 has this property.

Let us now proceed to the consideration of strongly paracompact spaces.

Generalizing the notion of a star-finite covering, we say that the family $\{A_s\}_{s\in S}$ of subsets of a space X is *star-finite* (*countable*) if for every $s_0 \in S$ the set $\{s \in S: A_s \cap A_{s_0} \neq 0\}$ is finite (countable).

Let us note that a star-finite family is not necessarily locally finite.

A topological space X is called *strongly paracompact* if X is a Hausdorff space and every open covering of it has an open star-finite refinement. Thus, every strongly paracompact space is paracompact and, consequently, normal.

Let $\mathfrak{A} = \{A_s\}_{s\in S}$ be a family of subsets of a set X. A finite sequence $A_s = A_{s_1}, A_{s_2}, \ldots, A_{s_k} = A_{s'}$ of elements of $\mathfrak{A}$ such that $A_{s_i} \cap A_{s_{i+1}} \neq 0$ for $i = 1, 2, \ldots, k-1$, will be called a *chain* in $\mathfrak{A}$, which joins the elements A_s and $A_{s'}$. The family $\mathfrak{A}$ is said to be *connected* if every two elements of the family can be joined by a chain in $\mathfrak{A}$. The *components* of the family $\mathfrak{A}$ are its maximal connected subfamilies, i.e. connected subfamilies which are not proper subsets of any connected subfamilies of $\mathfrak{A}$.

We note the following obvious

LEMMA 1. *Every family $\mathfrak{A}$ of subsets of a set X is the union of its components. If $\mathfrak{A}_1 = \{A_s\}_{s\in S_1}$ and $\mathfrak{A}_2 = \{A_s\}_{s\in S_2}$ are different components of the family $\mathfrak{A}$, then $\bigcup_{s\in S_1} A_s \cap \bigcup_{s\in S_2} A_s = 0$.* ∎

LEMMA 2. *Every star-countable and connected family $\mathfrak{A} = \{A_s\}_{s\in S}$ of subsets of a set X is countable.*

Proof. Let us consider an arbitrary $s_0 \in S$ and assume that $S_0 = \{s_0\}$. We define a sequence of sets $S_1, S_2, \ldots$ by means of the formula

$$S_{i+1} = \{s \in S: A_s \cap A_{s'} \neq 0 \text{ for some } s' \in S_i\}.$$

Since $\mathfrak{A}$ is a connected family, we infer that $S = \bigcup_{i=0}^{\infty} S_i$. Without any difficulty it can be proved inductively that $\overline{\overline{S_i}} \leqslant \aleph_0$ for $i = 1, 2, \ldots$ Hence S is countable. ■

THEOREM 3. *For a regular space X the following conditions are equivalent:*

(i) *The space X is strongly paracompact.*
(ii) *Every open covering of the space X has a closed locally finite and star-finite refinement.*
(iii) *Every open covering of the space X has a closed locally finite and star-countable refinement.*
(iv) *Every open covering of the space X has an open star-countable refinement.*

Proof. We shall prove the implication (i) $\Rightarrow$ (ii). Let $\mathfrak{U}$ be an open covering of the space X and let $\mathfrak{V} = \{V_t\}_{t\in T}$ denote its open star-finite refinement. Since X is normal and $\mathfrak{V}$ is locally finite, we infer from Lemma 1 to Theorem 1.3 that there exists a closed locally finite covering $\mathfrak{F} = \{F_t\}_{t\in T}$ such that $F_t \subset V_t$ for every $t \in T$. Evidently $\mathfrak{F}$ is the locally finite and star-finite refinement of $\mathfrak{U}$.

The implication (ii) $\Rightarrow$ (iii) is obvious and we proceed to the proof of the implication (iii) $\Rightarrow$ (iv). Let $\mathfrak{U} = \{U_s\}_{s\in S}$ be an open covering of the space X and let $\mathfrak{F}$ denote its closed locally finite and star-countable refinement. The covering $\mathfrak{F}$ is the union of its components $\{\mathfrak{F}_t\}_{t\in T}$; by Lemma 2 each component is countable, $\mathfrak{F}_t = \{F_{t,i}\}_{i=1}^{\infty}$. The sets $D_t = \bigcup_{i=1}^{\infty} F_{t,i}$ are disjoint, so that by the local finiteness of $\mathfrak{F}$ and by virtue of Theorem 4.4.1, they are open-and-closed. For every $t \in T$ and a natural number i let $s(t, i)$ denote such an element of S that $F_{t,i} \subset U_{s(t,i)}$. The family $\{D_t \cap U_{s(t,i)}\}_{i=1,t\in T}^{\infty}$ is an open star-countable covering of the space X, which is a refinement of $\mathfrak{U}$.

We shall now prove the implication (iv) $\Rightarrow$ (i). To begin with, we shall prove that every regular space satisfying (iv) is paracompact. Let us consider an open covering $\mathfrak{U}$ of the space X and let $\mathfrak{V}$ be its open star-countable refinement. Let $\{\mathfrak{V}_t\}_{t\in T}$, where $\mathfrak{V}_t = \{V_{t,i}\}_{i=1}^{\infty}$, be the family of components of this covering, which, by Lemma 2, are countable. The family $\{V_{i,t}\}_{t\in T}$ is discrete for a fixed i, whence $\mathfrak{V}$ is an open σ-discrete covering. By virtue of Theorem 1.5, X is a paracompact space.

Let us now assume that $\mathfrak{U}$ denotes an open covering of the space X and let $\mathfrak{V}$ be an open star-countable refinement. Let us consider the decomposition $\mathfrak{V} = \bigcup_{t\in T} \mathfrak{V}_t$ of the covering $\mathfrak{V}$ into the union of components $\mathfrak{V}_t = \{V_{t,i}\}_{i=1}^{\infty}$ and let $D_t = \bigcup_{i=1}^{\infty} V_{t,i}$ for $t \in T$. The sets D_t are open and disjoint, whence they are also closed. By virtue of the corollary to Theorem 1.8, each of the subspaces D_t, for $t \in T$, is paracompact and, consequently, countably paracompact. For every $t \in T$, let $\mathfrak{F}_t = \{F_{t,i}\}_{i=1}^{\infty}$ denote a closed covering of the space D_t which satisfies the condition $F_{t,i} \subset V_{t,i}$. The existence of such a covering follows from condition (iv) of Theorem 2.1. Let us denote a continuous function of X into I by $f_{t,i}$ such that $f_{t,i}(x) = 1$ for $x \in F_{t,i}$ and $f_{t,i}(x) = 0$ for $x \in X \setminus V_{t,i}$. The family $\{U_{t,i}\}_{i=1}^{\infty}$, where $U_{t,i} = f_{t,i}^{-1}((1/2, 1])$, is a refinement for every $t \in T$ of the covering $\{V_{t,i}\}_{i=1}^{\infty}$ of D_t consisting of open F_σ-sets. Making use of lemma to Theorem 2.1, let us consider for every $t \in T$ an open star-finite countable covering $\{G_{t,j}\}_{j=1}^{\infty}$ of the space D_t, which is a refinement of $\{U_{t,i}\}_{i=1}^{\infty}$. The covering $\{G_{t,j}\}_{j=1, t \in T}^{\infty}$ is an open star-finite refinement of $\mathfrak{U}$. ■

Let us notice that the assumption of the local finiteness of coverings in conditions (ii) and (iii) is essential. Indeed, for every T_1-space the covering consisting of single points is a closed star-finite refinement of every open covering.

Theorem 3 yields immediately

COROLLARY. *Every Lindelöf space is strongly paracompact.* ■

EXAMPLE 2. The Cartesian product of strongly paracompact spaces is not necessarily strongly paracompact, as shown in Example 3.7.3. ■

EXERCISES

A. Show that a closed subspace of a weakly (strongly) paracompact space is weakly (strongly) paracompact.

B. Prove that the sum of an arbitrary family of disjoint weakly (strongly) paracompact spaces is weakly (strongly) paracompact.

C. Prove that the notions of paracompactness and strong paracompactness are equivalent for locally compact spaces.

D. Prove that a locally compact space X is paracompact if and only if there exists in X a family $\{X_s\}_{s \in S}$ of disjoint subspaces which have the Lindelöf property and are such that $X = \bigoplus_{s \in S} X_s$.

HISTORICAL REMARKS AND BIBLIOGRAPHIC NOTES

The notion of a paracompact space was introduced by J. Dieudonné in [1944]; this paper also contains Theorems 2 and 10 of Paragraph 1. The notion of a locally finite covering was used earlier by P. Alexandroff, namely in [1924]. In [1940] J. W. Tukey distinguished the class of spaces satisfying condition (iii) of Theorem 1.5 and called them *fully normal.* He proved, among other things, that every metrizable space is fully normal. A. H. Stone showed in [1948] that the class of fully normal spaces coincided with the class of paracompact spaces and concluded that metrizable spaces were paracompact. Theorems 1.3 and 1.4 were proved by E. Michael in [1953]. His paper also contains the characterization of paracompact spaces by σ-discrete coverings (condition (iv) of Theorem 5). Lemma 1 to Theorem 1.3 can be found in a book of S. Lefschetz [1942]. The simple proof of Lemma 2 was given by M. R. Mather in [1964]. A proof of the paracompactness of metrizable spaces in which that lemma is used can be found in papers of M. R. Mather [1964] and G. Mokobodzki [1964]. An analogous proof of the paracompactness of Lindelöf spaces comes from the paper of M. R. Mather. The theorem is a consequence of the corollary to Theorem 3.3. The corollary was given by K. Morita in [1948]. Collectionwise normal spaces were defined by R. H. Bing in [1951], who adopted a slightly different definition (see Exercise 1.C); Theorem 1.6 and Example 1.3 are also given in his paper. The idea of the modification of topological spaces which was described in Example 1.2 comes from the papers of R. H. Bing [1951] and O. Hanner [1951]; it was developed by E. Michael in [1963], where Example 1.4 can be found. The class of countably paracompact spaces was defined simultaneously by M. Katětov in [1951a] and C. H. Dowker in [1951]. They both proved Theorem 2.1. Theorem 2.2 comes from the paper of C. H. Dowker [1951]. The lemma to Theorem 2.1 was given by K. Morita in [1948]. The example of a normal space which is not countably compact, constructed under the assumption that there exist Suslin spaces, can be found in the paper of M. Rudin [1955]. Weakly paracompact spaces and strongly paracompact spaces were defined simultaneously by a few mathematicians. Theorem 3.1 and the preceding lemma are proved by R. Arens and J. Dugundji in [1950]; Theorem 3.2 was proved independently by E. Michael in [1955] and K. Nagami in [1955]. Theorem 3.3 was proved by Yu. M. Smirnov in [1956a].

PROBLEMS

A (E. Michael [1957]). A family $\{A_s\}_{s\in S}$ of subsets of a topological space X is called *closure-preserving* if $\bigcup_{s\in S_1} \overline{A}_s = \overline{\bigcup_{s\in S_1} A_s}$ for every $S_1 \subset S$.

(a) Show that for a topological space X the following conditions are equivalent:

(i) Every open covering of the space X has a closed, closure-preserving refinement:

(ii) For every open covering $\{U_s\}_{s\in S}$ of the space X there exists a closed, closure-preserving covering $\{F_s\}_{s\in S}$ such that $F_s \subset U_s$ for every $s \in S$.

(b) Prove that a T_1-space X satisfying condition (i) is collectionwise normal.

B (E. Michael [1957]). (a) Prove that for a regular space X property (i) of Problem A is equivalent to paracompactness.

Hint: Let $\{U_s\}_{s\in S}$ be an open covering of the space X. Assuming that the set S is well ordered by the relation $<$, construct a sequence of closure-preserving, closed coverings $\mathfrak{F}_1, \mathfrak{F}_2, \ldots$ of the space X, where $\mathfrak{F}_i = \{F_{s,i}\}_{s\in S}$, such that $F_{s,i} \subset U_s$ for $s \in S$ and $F_{s,i+1} \cap F_{s',i} = 0$ for $s > s'$. Then consider the open covering $\mathfrak{V} = \{V_{s,i}\}_{i=1,s\in S}^{\infty}$ of the space X, where $V_{s,i} = X \setminus \bigcup_{s' \neq s} F_{s',i}$. Show that $V_{s,i} \subset U_s$ for $s \in S$ and $V_{s,i} \cap V_{s',i} = 0$ for $s \neq s'$. Making use of the results of Problem A, find a σ-discrete open refinement of the covering $\mathfrak{V}$.

(b) Making use of the criterion of paracompactness which is given in (a), show that if $f: X \to Y$ is a closed mapping of a paracompact space X onto a T_1-space Y, then Y is paracompact.

C (M. Henriksen and J. R. Isbell [1958]). Prove that the class of paracompact spaces and the class of countably paracompact Tychonoff spaces are perfect (see Problem 3.Y).

D. Prove the following properties of hereditary paracompactness:

(a) (J. Dieudonné [1944]) A space X is hereditarily paracompact if and only if every open subspace of it is paracompact.

(b) (C. H. Dowker [1947a]) Every paracompact, perfectly normal space is hereditarily paracompact.

(c) (E. Michael [1963]) Every separable, hereditarily paracompact space is perfectly normal.

E. (a) Show that a T_1-space X is collectionwise normal if and only if for every cardinal number $\mathfrak{m} \geqslant \aleph_0$, a closed subset $A \subset X$, and for a mapping $f: A \to J(\mathfrak{m})$, there exists an extension $F: X \to J(\mathfrak{m})$ of the mapping f over X.

Hint: When constructing F, define a sequence $F_1, F_2, \ldots$ of mappings of X into $J(\mathfrak{m})$ in such a manner that $\varrho(F_i(x), F_{i+1}(x)) \leqslant 1/2^i$ for every $x \in X$, and $\varrho(f(x), F_i(x)) \leqslant 1/2^i$ for every $x \in A$.

(b) (V. Šediva [1959]) Show that every subspace of a collectionwise normal space which is an F_σ-set is collectionwise normal.

Hint: Cf. Problem 2.C.

F (E. Michael [1953]). Show that the Cartesian product $X \times Y$ of a paracompact and perfectly normal space X by a metrizable space Y is paracompact.

Hint: Show that condition (ii) of Theorem 1.4 is satisfied for $X \times Y$. Make use of Problem 4.W and of the fact that the family $\mathfrak{B}$ constructed in the proof of Theorem 1.8 is σ-locally finite in the space X.

G (A. H. Stone [1948]). Prove that for the Cartesian product $X = \boldsymbol{P}_{s\in S} X_s$ of metrizable spaces the following conditions are equivalent:

(i) The product X is normal.

(ii) The product X is collectionwise normal.
(iii) The product X is paracompact.
(iv) The family $\{X_s\}_{s\in S}$ contains at most countably many non-compact spaces.

Hint: Make use of Problem 2.T.

H (A. V. Arhangel'skiĭ [1960a]). We say that a base $\mathfrak{B}$ of a topological space X is *regular*, if for every point $x \in X$ and every neighbourhood U of x there exists a neighbourhood V of x such that the set of elements of $\mathfrak{B}$ which meet V and $X \setminus U$ simultaneously is finite. Show that a topological space is metrizable if and only if it is a T_1-space and has a regular base.

Hint (J. Nagata [1963]): Show that maximal elements of a regular base (i.e. elements which are not proper subsets of any element of that base) form a locally finite covering and that by taking this covering away from the given base, we obtain a regular base of the derived set. Iterate this procedure and note that the regular base is σ-locally finite. Prove that a T_1-space which has a regular base is regular.

I (P. Alexandroff [1960]). We say that a base $\mathfrak{B}$ of a topological space X is *point-regular* if for every point $x \in X$ and every neighbourhood U of x the set of elements of $\mathfrak{B}$, which contain x and meet $X \setminus U$, is finite. Show that a topological space is metrizable if and only if it is collectionwise normal and has a point-regular base.

Hint: Show that maximal elements of a point-regular base form a point-finite covering. Deduce that a Hausdorff space which has a point--regular base is weakly paracompact. As in the preceding problem, decompose the point-regular base into a countable family of point-finite coverings and make use of Theorem 3.2.

J (Yu. M. Smirnov [1951a]). Show that if a normal space X has an open, locally finite covering $\{V_s\}_{s\in S}$, where V_s is metrizable for every $s \in S$, then X is metrizable. Deduce that a paracompact and locally metrizable space X (i.e. a space such that every point $x \in X$ has a metrizable neighbourhood) is metrizable.

K (E. Michael [1963]). By means of a modification of Example 1.4 define spaces X and Y such that the product $X \times Y$ is not normal but that:

(a) X is a hereditarily paracompact Lindelöf space, and Y is a metrizable space.

Hint (K. Kuratowski and W. Sierpiński [1926]): Show by means of transfinite induction that for every set X of power $\mathfrak{c}$ and a family $\mathfrak{C}$ of its subsets which is of power $\mathfrak{c}$ and consists of sets of power $\mathfrak{c}$, there exists a set $A \subset X$ such that $\overline{\overline{A}} = \mathfrak{c}$ and $C \cap A \neq 0 \neq C \setminus A$ for every $C \in \mathfrak{C}$. Making use of Problem 4.O, deduce that the real-line contains a subset of power $\mathfrak{c}$ such that its every compact subset, as well as every compact subset of its complement, is countable.

(b) X is a separable Lindelöf space, and Y is a metrizable space.

Hint: Construct a separable Lindelöf space which contains the space X of (a) as a closed subset.

L. (a) Show that if M is a subspace of a hereditarily normal space X, then the space X_M defined in Example 1.2 is hereditarily normal.

(b) Let X be a T_1-space and let M denote its subspace such that for every family $\{F_s\}_{s\in S}$ of closed subsets of M which is discrete in M there exists a family $\{U_s\}_{s\in S}$ which is discrete in X and consists of open subsets of X such that $F_s \subset U_s$ for every $s \in S$. Show that the space X_M is collectionwise normal.

(c) (L. F. McAuley [1958]) Show that for a T_1-space X the following conditions are equivalent:

(i) X is hereditarily collectionwise normal.

(ii) Every open subspace of X is collectionwise normal.

(iii) For every family $\{F_s\}_{s\in S}$ of subsets of X which is discrete in the union $\bigcup_{s\in S} F_s$ and consists of sets closed in this union there exists a family $\{U_s\}_{s\in S}$ discrete in X and consisting of open subsets of X such that $F_s \subset U_s$ for every $s \in S$.

Deduce that if M is a subspace of a hereditarily collectionwise normal space X, then the space X_M is hereditarily collectionwise normal.

Hint: Cf. Problem 2.B.

M (K. Borsuk [1933], J. Dugundji [1951]). Let X be a metrizable space and let $A \subset X$ denote a closed subset. Show that to every continuous real-valued function $f\colon A \to R$ we can assign an extension $E(f) = F\colon X \to R$ in such a manner that

$$\sup_{x\in X} |[E(f)](x)| = \sup_{x\in A} |f(x)|$$

and

$$E(f_1+f_2) = E(f_1)+E(f_2)$$

for every $f, f_1, f_2\colon A \to R$.

Hint (R. Arens [1952]): Find an open, locally finite refinement $\{V_s\}_{s\in S}$ of the covering $\{B(x, 1/4\, d(x, A))\}_{x\in X\setminus A}$ of the space $X\setminus A$. For every $s \in S$ choose a point $x_s \in X\setminus A$ such that $V_s \subset B(x_s, 1/4\, d(x_s, A))$ and a point $a_s \in A$ such that $d(a_s, x_s) < 5/4\, d(x_s, A)$. Define a partition of unity $\{g_s\}_{s\in S}$ on $X\setminus A$ which satisfies the condition $g_s(X\setminus V_s) \subset \{0\}$ for every $s \in S$ and define:

$$E(f)(x) = \begin{cases} f(x) & \text{for} \quad x \in A, \\ \sum_{s\in S} f(a_s)\cdot g_s(x) & \text{for} \quad x \in X\setminus A. \end{cases}$$

Making use of the inequality $\varrho(a, a_s) < 3\varrho(a, x)$ which holds for every $a \in A$ and $x \in V_s$, prove continuity of the extension.

N (K. Gęba and Z. Semadeni [1960]). Show that an operation E which would assign to every function $f: \beta N \setminus N \to R$ its extension $E(f): \beta N \to R$ in such a manner that

$$\sup_{x \in \beta N} |[E(f)](x)| = \sup_{x \in \beta N \setminus N} |f(x)|$$

and

$$E(f_1+f_2) = E(f_1)+E(f_2)$$

for every $f, f_1, f_2: \beta N \setminus N \to R$, cannot exist.

Hint: Consider the family $\{U_t\}_{t \in I}$ of subsets of the space $\beta N \setminus N$ constructed in Example 3.5.2 and the family of functions $\{f_t\}_{t \in I}$, where $f_t: \beta N \setminus N \to R$ is defined by means of the formula

$$f_t(x) = \begin{cases} 1 & \text{for} \quad x \in U_t, \\ 0 & \text{for} \quad x \in (\beta N \setminus N) \setminus U_t. \end{cases}$$

O. (a) (F. Hausdorff [1938]) Let A be a closed subspace of a metric space X and let $f: A \to B$ denote a mapping of A onto a metric space B. Show that the space B can be isometrically embedded in a metric space Y in such a manner that B is closed in Y and f can be extended to a mapping $F: X \to Y$ such that $F|X \setminus A$ is a homeomorphism of $X \setminus A$ onto $Y \setminus B$.

Hint (R. Arens [1952]): Let $C^*(S)$ be the set of all bounded and continuous real-valued functions defined on a topological space S with the metric defined by means of formula (6), Paragraph 4.2.

Consider the composition $f^*: A \to C^*(B)$ of the mapping f and the isometric embedding of B in $C^*(B)$ defined in Exercise 4.2.E. Show that the method of extension described in the hint to Problem M allows us to extend f^* to a mapping $F^*: X \to C^*(B)$. Consider the space $Z = C^*(B) \times R \times C^*(X)$ and the mapping $F: X \to Z$ defined by means of the formula $F(x) = \big(f^*(x), d(x, A), d(x, A) \cdot d_x\big)$, where ϱ is a bounded metric in the space X and $d_x(y) = \varrho(x, y)$.

Show that we can assume Y to be equal to $F(X) \subset Z$.

(b) Verify that if a mapping f of (a) is a homeomorphism, then the mapping F constructed in the hint to (a) is also a homeomorphism.

Hint: Show that if $\{V_s\}_{s \in S}$ is a covering of the space $X \setminus A$ described in the hint to Problem M, and $\{a_s\}_{s \in S}$ denotes the subset of A which was defined there, then for every $a \in A$ and $x \in V_s$ we have the inequality $\varrho(a, x) < \varrho(a, a_s) + 2d(x, A)$.

(c) (F. Hausdorff [1930]) Let A be a closed subspace of a metrizable space X. Prove that each metric in the space A can be extended to a metric in the space X.

(d) (V. Niemytzki and A. Tychonoff [1928]) Show that a metrizable space is compact if and only if for each metric ϱ in the space X the space (X, ϱ) is complete.

P (A. V. Arhangel'skiĭ [1961]). A Tychonoff space X is called *locally complete* in the sense of Čech if every point $x \in X$ has a neighbourhood complete in the sense of Čech.

(a) Show that a paracompact space locally complete in the sense of Čech is complete in the sense of Čech.

Hint: Make use of the criterion given in Theorem 3.8.2; notice that it is valid if we assume that the family $\{F_s\}_{s \in S}$ contains sets of diameter less than $\mathfrak{A}_i$ for infinitely many i.

(b) Show that the assumption of paracompactness in (a) is essential.

Hint: Consider the space obtained by removing points of the form $(\alpha, 0)$, where α is a non-limit ordinal number, from the space L_0 described in Problem 3.N.

Q (C. H. Dowker [1951], M. Katětov [1951a]). Note that every perfectly normal space is countably paracompact.

R (C. H. Dowker 1951, M. Katětov [1951a]). A real-valued function f defined on a topological space X is called *upper* (*lower*) semi-continuous if for every $x \in X$ and $r \in R$, where $f(x) < r$ $(f(x) > r)$, there exists a neighbourhood U of the point x such that $f(x') < r$ $(f(x') > r)$ for every $x' \in U$.

Show that a normal space X is countably paracompact if and only if for every pair of real-valued functions g, h, where g is upper semi-continuous and h is lower semi-continuous, and where they satisfy the inequality $g(x) < h(x)$ for every $x \in X$, there exists a continuous function $f: X \to R$ such that $g(x) < f(x) < h(x)$ for every $x \in X$.

S (H. Tong [1948] and [1952], M. Katětov [1951]). Show that in a normal space X for every pair of real-valued functions g, h such that g is upper semi-continuous and h is lower semi-continuous which satisfy the inequality $g(x) \leqslant h(x)$ for every $x \in X$, there exists a continuous function $f: X \to R$ such that $g(x) \leqslant f(x) \leqslant h(x)$ for every $x \in X$.

Hint: Modify the proof of the Urysohn Lemma.

T (M. J. Mansfield [1957]). A normal space X is countably paracompact if and only if for each countable, locally finite family $\{F_i\}_{i=1}^{\infty}$ of closed subsets of X there exists a locally finite family $\{V_i\}_{i=1}^{\infty}$ of open sets such that $F_i \subset V_i$ for $i = 1, 2, \ldots$

Hint for the "only if" part: Let $\mathfrak{S}$ be the family of finite sets of natural numbers. For every $x \in X$ choose a neighbourhood U_x which meets only sets F_i with indices belonging to $S = S(x) \in \mathfrak{S}$. Assume that $U_S = \bigcup_{S(x)=S} U_x$; consider an open locally finite covering $\{W_S\}_{S \in \mathfrak{S}}$, where $W_S \subset U_S$ for $S \in \mathfrak{S}$, and define $V_i = \bigcup_{i \in S} W_S$.

U (M. Katětov [1958], V. Šediva [1959]). Show that a T_1-space is collectionwise normal and countably paracompact if and only if for each locally finite family $\{F_s\}_{s\in S}$ of closed subsets of X there exists a locally finite family $\{V_s\}_{s\in S}$ of open subsets such that $F_s \subset V_s$ for every $s \in S$.

Hint for the "only if" part: To begin with, notice that under the additional assumption that no point belongs to more than i sets of the family $\{F_s\}_{s\in S}$, the existence of the family $\{V_s\}_{s\in S}$ follows from collectionwise normality (use induction with respect to the number i). In the general case, let $F = \bigcup_{s\in S} F_s$ and let S_k be the subset of F consisting of points which belong to at most k sets of the family $\{F_s\}_{s\in S}$. Consider a locally finite closed covering $\{E_i\}_{i=1}^{\infty}$ which is a refinement of the open covering $\{S_k\}_{k=1}^{\infty}$ of the space F and, making use of the preceding problem, consider a locally finite family $\{V_i\}_{i=1}^{\infty}$ of open subsets of X such that $E_i \subset V_i$ for $i = 1, 2, \ldots$ Let $\{V_{s,i}\}_{s\in S}$ denote a locally finite family of open subsets of X (for $i = 1, 2, \ldots$), such that $F_s \cap E_i \subset V_{s,i}$; define $V_s = \bigcup_{i=1}^{\infty} (V_{s,i} \cap V_i)$.

V (K. Borsuk [1937], C. H. Dowker [1951]). Let X and Y be topological spaces and let f_0, f_1 denote mappings of X into Y. If there exists a mapping $F: X \times I \to Y$ such that $F(x, i) = f_i(x)$ for $i = 0, 1$, then we say that the mappings f_0 and f_1 are *homotopic* and we call F the *homotopy* between f_0 and f_1.

Show that for every countably paracompact space X, a closed subspace M, and two homotopic mappings of M into the sphere S^n, the extendability of f_0 over X implies the extendability of f_1. Moreover, for every extension of f_0 a homotopic extension of f_1 can be found.

Hint (C. H. Dowker [1947]): Let $F: M \times I \to S^n$ be the homotopy between f_0 and f_1 and let $f_0^*: X \to S^n$ denote the extension of f_0. The combination of the mappings F and f_0 (considered as a mapping of $X \times \{0\}$ into S^n) can be extended, by virtue of Theorem 2.1.3 and Exercise 3.2.C, to a mapping $G: U \to S^n$, where $U \subset X \times I$ is an open set containing $X \times \{0\} \cup M \times I$. From Theorem 3.2.8 it follows that there exists an open set $V \subset X$ such that $M \times I \subset V \times I \subset U$. Consider the mapping $F^*: X \times I \to S^n$ defined by the formula: $F^*(x, t) = G(x, tg(x))$, where $g: X \to I$ is an arbitrary function satisfying the conditions $g(X \setminus V) \subset \{0\}$ and $g(M) \subset \{1\}$.

W (K. Iseki and S. Kasahara [1957], B. T. Levšenko [1957]). Prove that a regular space is countably compact if and only if every open point-finite covering of that space has a finite open refinement.

X (J. Kerstan [1957]). Prove that for a Tychonoff space X the following conditions are equivalent:

(i) The space X is pseudo-compact.

(ii) Every locally finite open covering of the space X has a finite open refinement.

(iii) Every locally finite open covering of the space X is finite.

Y (E. Michael [1955]). Verify that the space X considered in Example 1.3 is not weakly paracompact.

Hint: Prove that every point-finite open covering of the space X has a locally finite open refinement.

Z (E. Michael [1955]). Let X_0 be the subspace of the space X, considered in Example 1.3, consisting of all functions which assume values different from zero only on a finite number of elements from the family $\mathfrak{S}$, and of all functions belonging to the subspace M. Verify that the space X_0 is normal and weakly paracompact but, not collectionwise normal.

CHAPTER 6

CONNECTED SPACES

The property of connectedness examined in this chapter is quite different from the properties considered in the preceding chapters. In particular, the fact that a space is connected does not imply that it belongs to any class of topological spaces defined before, nor does connectedness result from being a member of any of those classes. Figuratively speaking, a connected space consists of a single piece in contrast with spaces consisting of many pieces separated from one another, as for example is the case of a discrete space.

In Paragraph 1 we define connected spaces and study their behaviour under operations. We find that the class of connected spaces is closed under the Cartesian product, and — with the additional assumption of compactness — under the inverse limit operation. At the end of the paragraph the concepts of a component and quasi-component are examined. The component of a point $x \in X$ is the maximal connected set containing x; the quasi-component is the intersection of all open-and-closed sets containing x. In a compact space components and quasi-components coincide.

In paragraph 2, four classes of topological spaces, which have the property of being highly disconnected, are considered. They are totally disconnected spaces, 0-dimensional spaces, strongly 0-dimensional spaces, and extremally disconnected spaces. A totally disconnected space is defined as a space which contains no connected subspace except single points and the empty set. The classes of 0-dimensional and strongly 0-dimensional spaces are connected with the notion of the dimension of a space. Dimension theory allows us to assign a non-negative integer number (or "the infinite number" ∞), called the dimension, to every non-empty topological space. This can be done in several ways. The dimension of a space is in a sense the measure of its connectedness. The names of "0-dimensional" and "strongly 0-dimensional" are derived from the fact that such spaces have dimension zero by two different definitions of dimension. The two classes will be considered quite independently of dimension theory. The study of these spaces, however, is an introduction to the theory of dimension presented in Chapter 7. Extremally disconnected spaces constitute a more specialized class which, on first sight, might be considered artificial. This class, however, is very important in the theory of Boolean algebras and in some problems of functional analysis.

The paragraph begins with the definitions of totally disconnected spaces and 0-dimensional spaces. Next, we introduce and examine the notion of a functionally closed and open set, which is necessary for the definition of a strongly 0-dimensional space. The two theorems which are proved in the paragraph state that strong 0-dimensionality is equivalent to 0-dimensionality for Lindelöf spaces and that for compact spaces, the two properties are equivalent to total disconnectedness. Further, we prove some theorems concerning operations on those classes of spaces. The end of the paragraph is devoted to extremally disconnected spaces.

§ 1. Connected spaces. Operations on connected spaces. A topological space X is called *connected* if it cannot be represented as the sum $X_1 \oplus X_2$ of two non-empty subspaces $X_1, X_2 \subset X$. We start with the formulation of some conditions equivalent to the connectedness of a space.

THEOREM 1. *For a topological space X the following conditions are equivalent*:

(i) *X is connected.*

(ii) *The empty set and the whole space are the only open-and-closed subsets of X.*

(iii) *If $X = X_1 \cup X_2$, where $X_1 \cap \overline{X}_2 = 0 = \overline{X}_1 \cap X_2$, then one of the sets X_1, X_2 is empty.*

(iv) *Every mapping $f: X \to D$ of the space X into the discrete two-point space $D = \{0, 1\}$ is constant, i.e. either $f(x) = 0$ for every $x \in X$ or $f(x) = 1$ for every $x \in X$.*

Proof. To prove the implication (i) ⇒ (ii) it is sufficient to observe that if $X_1 \subset X$ were an open-and-closed subset different from the empty set and from the whole space then, by Theorem 2.2.2, we should have that $X = X_1 \oplus X_2$, where $X_2 = X \setminus X_1$ and $X_1 \neq 0 \neq X_2$.

We proceed to the proof of the implication (ii) ⇒ (iii). Let us suppose that $X = X_1 \cup X_2$, where $X_1 \cap \overline{X}_2 = 0 = \overline{X}_1 \cap X_2$. We have $\overline{X}_1 \subset X \setminus X_2 \subset X_1$, whence $X_1 = \overline{X}_1$ and similarly $X_2 = \overline{X}_2$. Since the sets X_1 and X_2 are disjoint and closed in X, they are open-and-closed, and it follows from (ii) that one of them is empty.

To prove the implication (iii) ⇒ (iv) it is sufficient to notice that if for $f: X \to D$ we have that $X_1 = f^{-1}(0) \neq 0$ and $X_2 = f^{-1}(1) \neq 0$, then, by the obvious equalities $X = X_1 \cup X_2$ and $X_1 \cap \overline{X}_2 = 0 = \overline{X}_1 \cap X_2$, the space X does not satisfy condition (iii).

The implication (iv) ⇒ (i) follows from the fact that if (i) is not satisfied, i.e. if $X = X_1 \oplus X_2$ and $X_1 \neq 0 \neq X_2$, then, by Theorem 2.2.3, the formulas $f(x) = 0$ for $x \in X_1$ and $f(x) = 1$ for $x \in X_2$ define a mapping $f: X \to D$ for which $f(X) = D$ holds. ∎

COROLLARY 1. *A space X is connected if and only if it cannot be represented as the union $X_1 \cup X_2$ of two closed, non-empty, and disjoint subsets.* ∎

It is evident that Corollary 1 remains valid if we replace the term "closed" by the term "open".

COROLLARY 2. *Every connected Tychonoff space containing at least two points is of a power not less than $\mathfrak{c}$.*

Indeed, if X is a connected Tychonoff space and $x_1, x_2 \in X$ are two distinct points, then, by the definition of a Tychonoff space, there exists a function $h: X \to I$ such that $h(x_1) = 0$ and $h(x_2) = 1$. If we had $r \notin h(X)$ for some $r \in I$, then the mapping $f = gh: X \to D$, where $g: I \setminus \{r\} \to D$ and $g(x) = 0$ for $x < r$ and $g(x) = 1$ for $x > r$, would be a mapping onto D, contrary to the connectedness of X. Therefore we have $f(X) = I$ and hence $\overline{\overline{X}} \geqslant \mathfrak{c}$. ∎

Condition (iv) is naturally followed by

COROLLARY 3. *If X is a connected space and $f: X \to Y$ is a mapping onto the space Y, then Y is connected.* ∎

EXAMPLE 1. It follows from Example 2.2.1 that a discrete space containing more than a single point and the space of Example 1.2.1 are not connected. From the same example it is obvious that the set R of all real numbers is connected. By Corollary 3 to Theorem 1, it follows that every segment (closed, open, or with one end included) is connected. The empty set and the space consisting of a single point are obviously connected spaces. The two-point space $F = \{0, 1\}$, for which the empty set, $\{0\}$, and $\{0, 1\} = F$ are the only open sets, is connected. ∎

EXAMPLE 2. We shall now give an example of a countable connected space. It follows from Corollary 2 to Theorem 1 that such a space cannot be a Tychonoff space. Since every regular countable space is a Lindelöf space, we infer from Theorem 3.7.2 that every countable regular space is normal. Therefore a connected and countable space can be at most a Hausdorff space.

Let us denote by X the set of points $(r_1, r_2) \in R^2$, where r_1, r_2 are rational numbers and $r_2 \geqslant 0$. The set X is therefore countable. For each point $x = (r_1, r_2) \in X$ let $U_i(x) = \{x\} \cup \{(r, 0): |r-(r_1 - r_2/\sqrt{3})| < 1/i$ or $|r-(r_1 + r_2/\sqrt{3})| < 1/i\}$, for $i = 1, 2, \ldots$ If $r_2 > 0$, then the set $U_i(x)$ consists of the point x and those rational points of the axis $y = 0$ whose distance from a vertex of the equilateral triangle with one vertex x and the other two vertices belonging to the axis $y = 0$ is less than $1/i$. If the point x belongs to the axis $y = 0$, then $U_i(x)$ is the set of rational points of that axis whose distance from the point x is less than $1/i$. It can easily be verified that the family $\{\mathfrak{B}(x)\}_{x\in X}$, where $\mathfrak{B}(x) = \{U_i(x)\}_{i=1}^{\infty}$, is subject to conditions (BP1)-(BP4) of Chapter 1, i.e. that it generates a Hausdorff topology in the set X. All points whose distance from the straight line passing through the point x and inclined to the positive direction of the axis $y = 0$ at an angle of 60^0 is not greater than $1/i$, and all points whose distance from the straight line passing through the point x and inclined to the positive direction of the axis $y = 0$ at an angle of 120^0 is not greater than $1/i$, belong to the closure of the set $U_i(x)$. Therefore, for two arbitrary points $x_1, x_2 \in X$ and natural numbers i_1, i_2 we have $\overline{U_{i_1}(x_1)} \cap \overline{U_{i_2}(x_2)} \neq 0$. Consequently, the space X cannot be represented as the union of two non-empty open-and-closed subsets and it is therefore connected. ■

We shall now examine operations on connected spaces. It is clear that a subspace of a connected space is not necessarily connected. However, the class of connected subspaces of a given topological space has many interesting properties. In the sequel we shall say that a subset A of a topological space X is connected provided that the subspace A of the space X is connected.

Subsets A, B of a topological space X are called *separated* if $\overline{A} \cap B = 0 = A \cap \overline{B}$. Two disjoint subsets are separated if and only if neither of them contains an accumulation point of the other. In particular, closed and disjoint sets $A, B \subset X$ are separated. Also, open and disjoint sets $A, B \subset X$ are separated. If the sets $A, B \subset X$ are separated, and $A_1 \subset A$, $B_1 \subset B$, then the sets A_1 and B_1 are also separated. The proof of the following theorem is left to the reader.

THEOREM 2. *A subspace C of a topological space X is connected if and only if for each pair of sets X_1, X_2, which are separated in X and satisfy the condition $C = X_1 \cup X_2$, we have either $X_1 = 0$ or $X_2 = 0$.* ■

COROLLARY. *If C is a connected subspace of a topological space X, then for each pair of sets X_1, X_2 which are separated in X and such that $C \subset X_1 \cup X_2$ we have either $C \subset X_1$ or $C \subset X_2$.*

Indeed, the sets $X_1 \cap C$ and $X_2 \cap C$ are separated in X and their union is equal to C; thus, by virtue of the theorem, one of them is empty and C is contained in the other. ■

THEOREM 3. *Let $\{C_s\}_{s\in S}$ be a family of connected subspaces of a topological space X. If, for a certain $s_0 \in S$, the set C_{s_0} is not separated from any of the sets of the family $\{C_s\}_{s\in S}$, then the union $\bigcup_{s\in S} C_s$ is connected.*

Proof. Let $C = \bigcup_{s\in S} C_s = X_1 \cup X_2$, where X_1 and X_2 are separated in X. By the corollary to the preceding theorem, the set C_{s_0} is contained in one of the sets X_1, X_2, say in X_1. Since each set C_s is also contained in one of those sets and is not separated from C_{s_0}, we have $C_s \subset X_1$ for each $s \in S$. Thus we have $C \subset X_1$ and $X_2 = 0$. ■

COROLLARY 1. *If a family $\{C_s\}_{s\in S}$ of subsets of a topological space X consists of connected sets and $\bigcap_{s\in S} C_s \neq 0$, then $\bigcup_{s\in S} C_s$ is connected.* ■

COROLLARY 2. *If a subspace $C \subset X$ is connected, then every subspace $A \subset X$ such that $C \subset A \subset \overline{C}$ is also connected.*

Indeed, the family $\{C\} \cup \big\{\{x\}\big\}_{x\in A}$ satisfies the assumptions of Theorem 3, C_{s_0} being replaced with C. ■

COROLLARY 3. *If a topological space X contains a dense connected subspace, then X is connected.* ■

COROLLARY 4. *If every pair of points of a topological space X can be joined in X by a connected set, then X is connected.*

Proof. Let us suppose that p is a fixed point of the space X and for every $x \in X$ let C_x denote a connected subset of X containing the points p and x. The family $\{C_x\}_{x\in X}$ satisfies the assumptions of Corollary 1 and the union of all sets belonging to it fills up the whole space X. ■

From the definition of connectedness it immediately follows that the sum of an arbitrary family containing more than one element and consisting of disjoint non-empty topological spaces is not connected.

THEOREM 4. *The Cartesian product $\boldsymbol{P}_{s\in S} X_s$ is non-empty and connected if and only if for each $s \in S$ the space X_s is non-empty and connected.*

Proof. If $\boldsymbol{P}_{s\in S} X_s$ is non-empty, then the projection $p_s\colon \boldsymbol{P}_{s\in S} X_s \to X_s$ is a mapping onto the space X_s. Therefore, by Corollary 3 to Theorem 1, the connectedness of the product $\boldsymbol{P}_{s\in S} X_s$ implies the connectedness of all the spaces from the family $\{X_s\}_{s\in S}$.

We begin the proof of the second part of our theorem by pointing out that the Cartesian product of two connected spaces X_1 and X_2 is connected. This follows from Corollary 4 to the preceding theorem, since for two arbitrary points (x_1, y_1) and (x_2, y_2) of the product $X_1 \times X_2$ the set $X_1 \times \{y_1\} \cup \{x_2\} \times X_2$ is connected (it is the union of two connected sets which have one common point) and it contains the two points. By induction, we immediately infer that the Cartesian product of any finite number of connected spaces is connected.

Now let us consider the family $\{X_s\}_{s\in S}$ consisting of non-empty connected spaces and let us choose a point $a_s \in X_s$ for every $s \in S$. Let us denote by $\mathfrak{S}$ the family of all finite subsets of the set S and for $T \in \mathfrak{S}$ let

$$C_T = \boldsymbol{P}_{s\in S} A_s, \text{ where } A_s = \{a_s\} \text{ for } s \notin T \text{ and } A_s = X_s \text{ for } s \in T.$$

From that part of our theorem which has already been proved, it follows that the family $\{C_T\}_{T\in\mathfrak{S}}$ consists of connected sets. According to Corollary 1 to Theorem 3, the set $\bigcup_{T\in\mathfrak{S}} C_T$ is connected, for $a = \{a_s\} \in \bigcap_{T\in\mathfrak{S}} C_T \neq 0$. Since the union $\bigcup_{T\in\mathfrak{S}} C_T$ is a dense subset of the product $\boldsymbol{P}_{s\in S} X_s$, it is sufficient to apply Corollary 3 to Theorem 3 in order to complete the proof. ∎

COROLLARY. *The Euclidean space R^n, the Tychonoff cube $I^{\mathfrak{m}}$, and the Alexandroff cube $F^{\mathfrak{m}}$ are connected.* ∎

It follows from Corollary 3 to Theorem 1 that quotient spaces of connected spaces are connected.

Now we shall give an example which shows that the inverse limit of a system of connected spaces is not necessarily connected.

EXAMPLE 3. Let us suppose that X is the plane R^2 without the open segment which joins the point $x_1 = (-1, 0)$ with the point $x_2 = (1, 0)$. Let us denote by $\mathfrak{E}$ the family of all plane domains bounded by ellipses with foci at the points x_1 and x_2, and let $X_S = S \cap X$ for every $S \in \mathfrak{E}$. Obviously, X_S is connected. The set $\mathfrak{E}$ can be directed by inclusion. Let $\pi_{S_2}^{S_1}: X_{S_1} \to X_{S_2}$ denote the embedding for $S_2 \leqslant S_1$, i.e. for $S_1 \subset S_2$. It can easily be verified that $\{X_S, \pi_{S_2}^{S_1}, \mathfrak{E}\}$ is an inverse system of connected spaces and that the limit of this system consists of only two points, x_1 and x_2 (see Example 2.5.2), and is not connected. ∎

A connected and compact space is called a *continuum*.

The following theorem describes an important property of continua.

THEOREM 5. *If all the spaces X_σ of an inverse system $\boldsymbol{S} = \{X_\sigma, \pi_\varrho^\sigma, \Sigma\}$ are continua, then the limit $X = \varprojlim \boldsymbol{S}$ is also a continuum.*

Proof. By Theorem 3.2.10, the space X is compact; thus it is sufficient to show that X is a connected space. Let us suppose that there exist sets X_1 and X_2, closed in X, and such that

$$X = X_1 \cup X_2 \quad \text{and} \quad X_1 \cap X_2 = 0. \tag{1}$$

Let

$$X_{1,\sigma} = \pi_\sigma(X_1), \qquad X_{2,\sigma} = \pi_\sigma(X_2), \qquad \text{and} \qquad Y_\sigma = X_{1,\sigma} \cap X_{2,\sigma}$$

for each $\sigma \in \Sigma$. It follows from Theorem 3.1.8 that the sets $X_{1,\sigma}$ and $X_{2,\sigma}$ (and hence also the sets Y_σ) are compact. Since for $\varrho \leqslant \sigma$

$$\begin{aligned}\pi_\varrho^\sigma(Y_\sigma) &= \pi_\varrho^\sigma(X_{1,\sigma} \cap X_{2,\sigma}) \subset \pi_\varrho^\sigma(X_{1,\sigma}) \cap \pi_\varrho^\sigma(X_{2,\sigma}) \\ &= \pi_\varrho^\sigma\pi_\sigma(X_1) \cap \pi_\varrho^\sigma\pi_\sigma(X_2) = \pi_\varrho(X_1) \cap \pi_\varrho(X_2) = X_{1,\varrho} \cap X_{2,\varrho} = Y_\varrho,\end{aligned}$$

we infer that $\boldsymbol{S}' = \{Y_\sigma, \pi_\varrho^\sigma | Y_\sigma, \Sigma\}$ is an inverse system of compact spaces. Since the sets X_1 and X_2 are closed, it can easily be verified that the limit of the system S' is contained in $X_1 \cap X_2$. Because of (1), this limit is empty; thus it follows from Theorem 3.2.10 that

$$(2) \qquad Y_{\sigma_0} = X_{1,\sigma_0} \cap X_{2,\sigma_0} = 0 \quad \text{for some } \sigma_0 \in \Sigma.$$

It follows from the normality of the space X_{σ_0} that there exist two open sets U_{1,σ_0} and U_{2,σ_0} such that

$$(3) \qquad X_{1,\sigma_0} \subset U_{1,\sigma_0}, \quad X_{2,\sigma_0} \subset U_{2,\sigma_0}, \quad \text{and} \quad U_{1,\sigma_0} \cap U_{2,\sigma_0} = 0.$$

For every $\sigma \in \Sigma$ such that $\sigma_0 \leqslant \sigma$ let

$$U_{i,\sigma} = (\pi^{\sigma}_{\sigma_0})^{-1}(U_{i,\sigma_0}) \quad \text{for} \quad i = 1, 2, \quad \text{and} \quad Z_\sigma = X_\sigma \setminus (U_{1,\sigma} \cup U_{2,\sigma}).$$

Assuming $Z_\sigma = X_\sigma$ for those $\sigma \in \Sigma$ which do not satisfy the condition $\sigma_0 \leqslant \sigma$, we obtain, as can easily be verified, the inverse system of compact spaces $S'' = \{Z_\sigma, \pi^{\sigma}_{\varrho} | Z_\sigma, \Sigma\}$. Since $\underleftarrow{\lim} S'' \subset X$ and since by (1) and (3) we have $\pi_{\sigma_0}(X) \cap Z_{\sigma_0} = 0$, the equality $\underleftarrow{\lim} S'' = 0$ holds. By virtue of Theorem 3.2.10, $Z_\sigma = 0$ for some $\sigma \in \Sigma$. If $\sigma \geqslant \sigma_0$, then $X_\sigma = U_{1,\sigma} \cup U_{2,\sigma}$; hence by the connectedness of X_σ and by the equality $U_{1,\sigma} \cap U_{2,\sigma} = 0$ which follows from (3), we infer that $U_{i,\sigma} = 0$ for i equal to 1 or 2. Since

$$X_{i,\sigma} = \pi_\sigma(X_i) \subset (\pi^{\sigma}_{\sigma_0})^{-1} \pi^{\sigma}_{\sigma_0} \pi_\sigma(X_i) = (\pi^{\sigma}_{\sigma_0})^{-1}(X_{i,\sigma_0}) \subset U_{i,\sigma},$$

we have that $X_{i,\sigma} = 0$ and $X_i = 0$ for this case. If σ does not satisfy the condition $\sigma \geqslant \sigma_0$, then $X_\sigma = 0$ and $X = \underleftarrow{\lim} S = 0$. Hence in both cases one of the closed sets X_1, X_2 satisfying (1) is empty; thus the space X is connected. ■

COROLLARY. *The intersection* $\bigcap_{i=1}^{\infty} C_i$ *of a decreasing sequence of continua* $C_1 \supset C_2 \supset \ldots$ *is a continuum.* ■

The mapping space Y^X is not necessarily connected for connected X and Y. The examination of the connectedness of this space leads to interesting results, which lie outside the scope of this book. For instance, it can be proved that the space $(S^{n-1})^X$ with the compact-open topology is connected for $X \subset R^n$ if and only if the space $R^n \setminus X$ is connected; however, the proof is rather difficult and is based on quite different methods from those considered in this book. Since for two homeomorphic subsets X_1, X_2 of the space R^n, the spaces $(S^{n-1})^{X_1}$ and $(S^{n-1})^{X_2}$ are obviously homeomorphic, this implies, in particular, the important and profound theorem stating that $R^n \setminus X_1$ is connected if and only if $R^n \setminus X_2$ is connected. This theorem is a strong generalization of the classical Jordan Theorem on disconnecting the plane by a curve homeomorphic to the circle S^1.

The *component* of a point x in a topological space X is the union of all connected subsets of the space which contain the point x. From

Corollary 1 to Theorem 3 it follows immediately that the component of a point $x \in X$ is always connected. Moreover, from Corollary 2 to Theorem 3 it follows that components are closed subsets of the space X. The components of two points $x_1, x_2 \in X$ are either identical or disjoint.

In Paragraph 2 we shall use the following simple

THEOREM 6. *The component of the point $x = \{x_s\}$ in the Cartesian product $\underset{s \in S}{\boldsymbol{P}} X_s$ is the set $\underset{s \in S}{\boldsymbol{P}} C_s$, where C_s is the component of the point x_s in the space X_s.*

Proof. Let C be the component of the point $x = \{x_s\}$ in the product $\underset{s \in S}{\boldsymbol{P}} X_s$. Since, by Corollary 3 to Theorem 1, the set $p_s(C)$ is connected, we infer that $p_s(C) \subset C_s$ for every $s \in S$. Hence $C \subset \underset{s \in S}{\boldsymbol{P}} C_s$ and by virtue of Theorem 4 we have $C = \underset{s \in S}{\boldsymbol{P}} C_s$. ∎

The *quasi-component* of a point x in a topological space X is the intersection of all open-and-closed subsets of the space X which contain the point x. Quasi-components are closed in the space X. Quasi-components of two points $x_1, x_2 \in X$ are either identical or disjoint.

THEOREM 7. *The component S of a point x in a topological space X is contained in the quasi-component Q of that point.*

Proof. Let F be an open-and-closed subset of the space X which contains the point x. Since the sets F and $X \setminus F$ are separated, the sets $S \cap F$ and $S \setminus F$ are also separated and, since $x \in S \cap F \neq 0$, it follows from Theorem 2 that $S \setminus F = 0$, i.e. $S \subset F$. But the set F is arbitrary, so that $S \subset Q$. ∎

THEOREM 8. *In a compact space X the component of a point $x \in X$ is identical with its quasi-component.*

Proof. In view of Theorem 7 it is sufficient to prove that the quasi-component Q of x is connected.

Let us suppose that for some pair of disjoint sets $X_1, X_2 \subset Q$ which are closed in Q (and thus also in X) the equality $Q = X_1 \cup X_2$ holds and $x \in X_1$. By the normality of the compact space X, there exist sets U and V open in X such that

$$X_1 \subset U, \quad X_2 \subset V, \quad \text{and} \quad U \cap V = 0. \tag{4}$$

Thus we have $Q \subset U \cup V$ and by virtue of Corollary 2 to Theorem 3.1.3 there exist a finite number of open-and-closed sets $F_1, F_2, \ldots, F_k$ such that $Q \subset F = F_1 \cap F_2 \cap \ldots \cap F_k \subset U \cup V$. The set F is open-and-closed. Since

$$\overline{U \cap F} \subset \overline{U} \cap F = \overline{U} \cap (U \cup V) \cap F = U \cap F,$$

$U \cap F$ is an open-and-closed set containing x, so that $Q \subset U \cap F$ and

(5) $$X_2 \subset Q \subset U \cap F \subset U.$$

From (4) and (5) it follows that $X_2 = 0$, which proves that the set Q is connected. ■

EXAMPLE 4. We shall give an example of a space in which components are different from quasi-components.

Let X be the subset of the plane R^2 consisting of the segments $I_n = \{(x, y): 0 \leqslant x \leqslant 1, y = 1/n\}$ for $n = 1, 2, \ldots$ and of the points $p_0 = (0, 0)$ and $p_1 = (1, 0)$. The segments I_n and the points p_0, p_1 are the components of the space X. We shall show that the quasi-component Q of the point p_0 is the set $\{p_0, p_1\}$. Every open-and-closed set F which contains the point p_0 contains all terms of the sequence $\{(0, 1/n)\}$, with the exception perhaps of a finite number. Since they are connected, it contains the corresponding segments I_n. The set F must therefore contain all terms of the sequence $\{(1, 1/n)\}$, with the exception perhaps of a finite number, and its limit p_1. Hence we infer that $\{p_0, p_1\} \subset Q$. It is easy to see that no point different from p_0 and p_1 belongs to Q. ■

EXERCISES

A. Describe all the connected subsets of the real-line.

Hint: Prove that any connected subset of the real-line is convex.

B. Let us suppose that in a topological space X we are given a sequence $C_1, C_2, \ldots$ of connected sets which satisfy the condition $C_i \cap C_{i+1} \neq 0$ for $i = 1, 2, \ldots$ Show that $C = \bigcup_{i=1}^{\infty} C_i$ is connected.

C. Prove that a compact metric space (X, ϱ) is connected if and only if for every two points $a, b \in X$ and every $\varepsilon > 0$ there exists a sequence $x_1, x_2, \ldots, x_k \in X$ such that

$$x_1 = a,\ x_k = b, \quad \text{and} \quad \varrho(x_i, x_{i+1}) < \varepsilon \quad \text{for} \quad i = 1, 2, \ldots, k-1.$$

D. Prove that for connected spaces, strong paracompactness and the Lindelöf property are equivalent. Give an example of a metric space which is not strongly paracompact.

§ 2. Various kinds of disconnectedness. A topological space X is called *totally disconnected* if X is a T_1-space and does not contain connected subspaces consisting of more than a single point. A space X is therefore totally disconnected if it is a T_1-space and if the component of every point $x \in X$ is the set consisting of the point x.

A topological space X is said to be 0-*dimensional* if X is a non-empty T_1-space and has a base consisting of open-and-closed sets. Every 0-dimensional space is evidently a Tychonoff space.

THEOREM 1. *Every 0-dimensional space is totally disconnected.*

Proof. If a subset A of a 0-dimensional space X contains two different points x_1 and x_2, then there exists an open-and-closed subset $F \subset X$ such that $x_1 \in F \subset X \setminus \{x_2\}$. Since the sets $A \setminus F$ and $A \cap F$ are separated and non-empty, A is not connected. ∎

We precede the definition of strongly 0-dimensional spaces with some auxiliary notions. A subset A of a topological space X is called *functionally closed* in X whenever there exists a continuous real-valued function $f : X \to R$ such that $A = f^{-1}(0)$. Of course, every functionally closed set is closed. Let us consider two continuous real-valued functions $f, g: X \to R$ defined on a topological space X. Since for the functions $h_1, h_2 : X \to R$ defined by the formulas

$$h_1(x) = f(x)\cdot g(x), \quad \text{and} \quad h_2(x) = |f(x)| + |g(x)|$$

we have

$$h_1^{-1}(0) = f^{-1}(0) \cup g^{-1}(0) \quad \text{and} \quad h_2^{-1}(0) = f^{-1}(0) \cap g^{-1}(0),$$

the union and the intersection of two (and of a finite number) of functionally closed sets is a functionally closed set. Every set of the form $f^{-1}(F)$, where $f: X \to R$ and F is a closed subset of the real-line R, is functionally closed in X. This follows from the fact that, according to Theorem 4.1.5, the formula

$$g(x) = d\big(f(x), F\big)$$

defines a continuous real-valued function $g : X \to R$ and $f^{-1}(F) = g^{-1}(0)$ by Corollary 1 to this theorem.

The complement of a functionally closed set is called *functionally open* in the space considered (1). Evidently every functionally open set is open. The union and the intersection of two (and of a finite number) of functionally open sets is a functionally open set. Every set of the form $f^{-1}(U)$, where $f : X \to R$ and U is an open subset of the real-line R, is functionally open in X. Every open-and-closed subset of a space X is functionaly open and closed in the space X.

A family $\{A_s\}_{s \in S}$ consisting of subsets of a topological space X is called *functionally closed* (*open*) if all the sets A_s are functionally closed (open).

THEOREM 2. *Functionally closed and disjoint subsets A, B of a topological space X are completely separated.*

---

(1) The terms "functionally closed set" and "functionally open set" adopted in this book seem to be more convenient than the generally used terms "zero-set" and "cozero-set".

Proof. Let $f, g: X \to R$ denote such functions that

$$A = f^{-1}(0) \quad \text{and} \quad B = g^{-1}(0).$$

Since $A \cap B = 0$, the formula $h(x) = |f(x)|\cdot(|f(x)|+|g(x)|)^{-1}$ defines a continuous function $h: X \to I$. It is easy to verify that $A = h^{-1}(0)$ and $B = h^{-1}(1)$. ■

A topological space X is called *strongly* 0-*dimensional* provided that X is a non-empty Tychonoff space and every finite functionally open covering $\{U_i\}_{i=1}^{n}$ of the space X has a finite open subcovering $\{V_i\}_{i=1}^{m}$ such that $V_i \cap V_j = 0$ for $i \neq j$. The covering $\{V_i\}_{i=1}^{m}$ consists therefore of open-and-closed sets and is functionally open.

Lemma 1. *For each two completely separated sets A, B of a strongly 0-dimensional space X there exists an open-and-closed subset $U \subset X$ such that*

$$A \subset U \quad \textit{and} \quad U \subset X \setminus B.$$

Proof. Let $f: X \to I$ denote such a continuous function that

$$f(A) \subset \{0\} \quad \text{and} \quad f(B) \subset \{1\}.$$

The sets $f^{-1}\big((0,1]\big)$ and $f^{-1}\big([0,1)\big)$ form a functionally open covering of the space X. Let $\mathfrak{A}$ be a refinement of it consisting of disjoint open sets. The set U which is the union of all elements of the covering $\mathfrak{A}$ which intersect A, is open-and-closed and

$$A \subset U \subset f^{-1}\big([0,1)\big) \subset X \setminus B. \ ■$$

Corollary. *Every strongly 0-dimensional space is 0-dimensional.* ■

Lemma 2. *If for each pair A, B of completely separated subsets of a topological space X (of a normal space X) there exists an open-and-closed subset $U \subset X$ such that*

$$A \subset U \quad \textit{and} \quad U \subset X \setminus B,$$

then for every functionally open (open) finite covering $\{U_i\}_{i=1}^{n}$ of the space X there exists an open covering $\{V_i\}_{i=1}^{n}$ such that $V_i \subset U_i$ for $i = 1, 2, \ldots$ and $V_i \cap V_j = 0$ for $i \neq j$.

Proof. We use induction.

For $n = 1$ the lemma is valid. Let us assume that it is valid for $n < m$ and let us consider a functionally open (open) covering $\{U_i\}_{i=1}^{m}$ of the space X. By the assumption there exists a covering $W_1, W_2, \ldots, W_{m-1}$ of the space X consisting of disjoint open-and-closed sets such that

$$W_i \subset U_i \quad \text{for} \quad i < m-1 \quad \text{and} \quad W_{m-1} \subset U_{m-1} \cup U_m.$$

The sets $W_{m-1} \setminus U_{m-1}$ and $W_{m-1} \setminus U_m$ are disjoint and functionally closed (closed), so that they are completely separated. Therefore, there exists an open-and-closed set $U \subset X$ such that

$$W_{m-1} \setminus U_{m-1} \subset U \quad \text{and} \quad U \subset X \setminus (W_{m-1} \setminus U_m) = (X \setminus W_{m-1}) \cup U_m.$$

We infer that

$$W_{m-1} \setminus U \subset U_{m-1} \quad \text{and} \quad W_{m-1} \cap U \subset U_m.$$

It is not difficult to verify that the covering $\{V_i\}_{i=1}^m$, where

$$V_i = W_i \quad \text{for} \quad i < m-1,$$

$$V_{m-1} = W_{m-1} \setminus U, \quad \text{and} \quad V_m = W_{m-1} \cap U,$$

is an open covering of the space X such that $V_i \subset U_i$ for $i = 1, 2, \ldots, m$ and $V_i \cap V_j = 0$ for $i \neq j$. ∎

Lemmas 1 and 2 imply

THEOREM 3. *A non-empty Tychonoff space X is strongly 0-dimensional if and only if for each pair of completely separated subsets A, B of the space X, there exists an open-and-closed set $U \subset X$ such that $A \subset U \subset X \setminus B$.* ∎

Theorem 3 and Lemma 2 imply

THEOREM 4. *A non-empty normal space X is strongly 0-dimensional if and only if every finite open covering $\{U_i\}_{i=1}^n$ of X has a finite open refinement $\{V_i\}_{i=1}^m$ such that $V_i \cap V_j = 0$ for $i \neq j$.* ∎

THEOREM 5. *0-dimensionality and strong 0-dimensionality are equivalent with respect to Lindelöf spaces.*

Proof. It is sufficient to show that for every two disjoint and closed subsets A, B of a 0-dimensional Lindelöf space X there exists an open-and-closed set $U \subset X$ such that

$$A \subset U \quad \text{and} \quad U \subset X \setminus B.$$

For every $x \in X$ there exists an open-and-closed set $U_x \subset X$ containing x and such that

$$A \cap U_x = 0 \quad \text{or} \quad B \cap U_x = 0.$$

From the covering $\{U_x\}_{x \in X}$ let us choose a countable subcovering $\{U_{x_i}\}_{i=1}^{\infty}$. The sets

$$V_i = U_{x_i} \setminus \bigcup_{j<i} U_{x_j}, \quad i = 1, 2, \ldots$$

are open-and-closed, disjoint, and form a covering of the space X. It can easily be verified that we can define U to be the union of all elements of the covering $\{V_i\}_{i=1}^{\infty}$ which meet A. ∎

THEOREM 6. *Total disconnectedness, 0-dimensionality, and strong 0-dimensionality are equivalent with respect to non-empty compact spaces.*

Proof. By virtue of the preceding theorem and Theorem 1, it is sufficient to prove that if a compact space X is totally disconnected, then the family $\mathfrak{B}$ of all open-and-closed subsets of X is a base of this space. Let x be a point of X and let $U \subset X$ denote an arbitrary neighbourhood of it. By virtue of Theorem 1.8, the set $\{x\} \subset U$ is the intersection of all open-and-closed sets which contain x. According to Corollary 2 to Theorem 3.1.3, there exists a finite number of open-and-closed sets $F_1, F_2, \ldots, F_k$ such that $x \in F = F_1 \cap F_2 \cap \ldots \cap F_k \subset U$. Since $F \in \mathfrak{B}$, we infer that $\mathfrak{B}$ is a base of the space X. ■

THEOREM 7. *Total disconnectedness* (0-*dimensionality*) *is a hereditary property* (*with respect to non-empty subsets*).

If X is a strongly 0-*dimensional space and $M \subset X$ is a non-empty subset such that every continuous function $f\colon M \to I$ is extendable over X, then M is also strongly* 0-*dimensional.*

In particular, for normal spaces strong 0-*dimensionality is hereditary with respect to non-empty closed subsets.*

Proof. The first part of the theorem is obvious. The second follows from Theorem 3, because under the assumption concerning M, each pair of completely separated subsets of M is completely separated in X. ■

THEOREM 8. *A Tychonoff space X is strongly* 0-*dimensional if and only if its Čech-Stone compactification βX is strongly* 0-*dimensional.*

Proof. By the preceding theorem it suffices to show that if X is strongly 0-dimensional, then βX has the same property. Let A, B be an arbitrary pair of completely separated subsets of βX. There exists a function $f\colon \beta X \to I$ such that $f(A) \subset \{0\}$ and $f(B) \subset \{1\}$. The sets $A_1 = X \cap f^{-1}([0, 1/3))$ and $B_1 = X \cap f^{-1}((2/3, 1])$ are completely separated in X. By theorem 3 there exists an open-and-closed set $U \subset X$ such that $A_1 \subset U$ and $B_1 \subset X \setminus U$. From Corollary 4 to Theorem 3.5.1 it follows that $\overline{U}$ is open-and-closed in βX. We have $A \subset \overline{A}_1 \subset \overline{U}, B \subset \overline{B}_1$ and $\overline{B}_1 \cap \overline{U} = 0$. Hence $A \subset \overline{U} \subset \beta X \setminus B$ and βX is strongly 0-dimensional by virtue of Theorem 3. ■

Theorem 7 and the theorems on the form of closed and open sets in the sum of spaces immediately imply

THEOREM 9. *The sum $\bigoplus_{s \in S} X_s$ of the family $\{X_s\}_{s \in S}$ of* (*non-empty*) *disjoint topological spaces is totally disconnected* (0-*dimensional, strongly* 0-*dimensional*) *if and only if the space X_s is totally disconnected* (0-*dimensional, strongly* 0-*dimensional*) *for every $s \in S$.* ■

THEOREM 10. *The Cartesian product $\mathbf{P}_{s \in S} X_s$ is totally disconnected* (0-*dimensional*) *if and only if the space X_s is totally disconnected* (0-*dimensional*) *for every $s \in S$.*

Proof. Since each of the spaces X_s is homeomorphic to a subset of the Cartesian product $\underset{s\in S}{\boldsymbol{P}} X_s$ by virtue of Theorem 7, it is sufficient to prove that the Cartesian product $\underset{s\in S}{\boldsymbol{P}} X_s$ of totally disconnected (0-dimensional) spaces is totally disconnected (0-dimensional). For totally disconnected spaces this follows from Theorem 1.6, and for 0-dimensional spaces this follows from the fact that the sets of the form $\underset{s\in S}{\boldsymbol{P}} W_s$, where W_s is an open-and-closed set in the space X_s and the set $\{s\in S\colon W_s \neq X_s\}$ is finite, form a base of the space $\underset{s\in S}{\boldsymbol{P}} X_s$ and are open-and-closed in this space. ■

COROLLARY. *The inverse limit of a system of totally disconnected (0-dimensional) spaces is totally disconnected (0-dimensional or empty).* ■

THEOREM 11. *The Cantor cube $D^{\mathfrak{m}}$ of weight $\mathfrak{m}$ is a universal space for 0-dimensional spaces of weight $\mathfrak{m}$ for every $\mathfrak{m} \geqslant \aleph_0$.*

Proof. Since the two-point discrete space $D = \{0, 1\}$ is 0-dimensional, it follows from the preceding theorem that $D^{\mathfrak{m}}$ is 0-dimensional.

Let us consider an arbitrary 0-dimensional space X of weight $\mathfrak{m}$. By virtue of Theorem 1.1.7, there exists a base $\mathfrak{B} = \{U_s\}_{s\in S}$ in the space X consisting of open-and-closed sets and such that $\overline{\overline{S}} = \mathfrak{m}$. For every $s\in S$ let the mapping $f_s\colon X \to D$ be defined by the formula

$$f_s(x) = \begin{cases} 1 & \text{for} \quad x\in U_s, \\ 0 & \text{for} \quad x\in X\setminus U_s. \end{cases}$$

From the Diagonal Lemma it follows that the mapping $F = \underset{s\in S}{\triangle} f_s$ is a homeomorphic embedding of the space X into the Cantor cube $D^{\mathfrak{m}} = \underset{s\in S}{\boldsymbol{P}} D_s$. ■

COROLLARY. *Every 0-dimensional space X of weight $\mathfrak{m}$ has a 0-dimensional compactification of weight $\mathfrak{m}$.*

In fact, the compactification is the closure of a space homeomorphic to X in $D^{\mathfrak{m}}$. ■

By virtue of Theorem 3.2.2, there exists a mapping f of a closed subspace $X \subset D^{\aleph_0}$ onto the segment I (cf. Exercise 3.2.B). We infer from Theorem 3.2.9 that the space $X/R(f)$ is homeomorphic to the segment; thus the quotient space of a totally disconnected (0-dimensional, strongly 0-dimensional) space is not necessarily totally disconnected (0-dimensional, strongly 0-dimensional).

EXAMPLE 1. A discrete space of an arbitrary power >0 is strongly 0-dimensional. The space of ordinal numbers not greater than ω_1, which was defined in Example 3.5.1, is 0-dimensional. Since this space is compact, it is also strongly 0-dimensional. The space considered in Example 1.2.1 is 0-dimensional (see Example 2.2.1). Since this space is a Lindelöf space (see Example 3.7.2), it is also strongly 0-dimensional. From Example 1.1 it follows that a totally disconnected (in particular a 0-dimensional) subspace of the real-line does not contain any segment. It is easy to see that every non-empty subspace of the line which does not contain any segment is 0-dimensional. Thus a non-empty subspace of the real line is 0-dimensional (or, equivalently, strongly 0-dimensional) if and only if it does not contain any segment. In particular, the space of all rational numbers and the space of all irrational numbers are 0-dimensional. It follows from Theorems 10 and 5 that the space consisting of those points of the space R^n (the cube I^n, the Hilbert cube $I^{\aleph_0}$) whose coordinates are rational is strongly 0-dimensional. Similarly, the subspace of the space R^n (the cube I^n, the Hilbert cube $I^{\aleph_0}$), consisting of those points whose coordinates are irrational, is strongly 0-dimensional. ■

We shall now give an example of a totally disconnected metric separable space which is not 0-dimensional.

EXAMPLE 2. Let X be the subset of the Hilbert space H (see Example 4.1.5) consisting of all sequences $\{r_i\}$, where r_i is rational.

The space X is totally disconnected. In order to prove this, let us consider a pair of distinct points $r = \{r_i\}$, $s = \{s_i\}$. There exists a natural number i_0 such that $r_{i_0} \neq s_{i_0}$; we can evidently assume that $r_{i_0} < s_{i_0}$. For each irrational number t, satisfying the condition $r_{i_0} < t < s_{i_0}$, the set

$$F = \{\{x_i\} \in X \colon x_{i_0} < t\}$$

is open-and-closed in X, and contains r but not s. Hence every connected subset of the space X contains at most one point.

Let us now consider the point $x_0 = \{0, 0, \ldots, 0, \ldots\}$ in the space X and its neighbourhood $U = B(x_0, 1) = \{\{x_i\} \in X \colon \sum_{i=1}^{\infty} x_i^2 < 1\}$. We shall show that for every neighbourhood V of the point x_0 which is contained in U we have $\operatorname{Fr} V \neq 0$, i.e. the set V is not open-and-closed.

Let us define by means of induction a sequence of rational numbers $a_1, a_2, \ldots$ which satisfy the condition:

$$(1) \qquad x_k = \{a_1, a_2, \ldots, a_k, 0, \ldots\} \in V, \qquad d(x_k, X \setminus V) \leqslant 1/k.$$

It is easy to notice that (1) is satisfied for $k = 1$ if we assume that $a_1 = 0$. Let us suppose that the rational numbers $a_1, a_2, \ldots, a_{n-1}$ have already been defined and condition (1) is satisfied for all $k \leqslant n-1$. The sequence

$$x_i^n = \{a_1, a_2, \ldots, a_{n-1}, i/n, 0, 0, \ldots\}$$

is an element of the space H for $i = 0, 1, 2, \ldots$ Since $x_0^n \in V$ and since the inclusion $V \subset U$ yields $x_n^n \notin V$, there exists an $i_0 < n$ such that $x_{i_0}^n \in V$

and $x_{i_0+1}^n \notin V$. It can easily be verified that condition (1) is satisfied for $k = n$ if we assume that $a_n = i_0/n$. The construction of the sequence $a_1, a_2, \ldots$ is thus completed. Since, by (1), the inequality $\sum_{i=1}^{k} a_i^2 < 1$ holds for $k = 1, 2, \ldots$, the sequence $a = \{a_i\}$ belongs to the space X. It also follows from (1) that $a \in \overline{V} \cap \overline{X \setminus V} = \operatorname{Fr} V \neq 0$. ■

In Example 3 we shall describe a 0-dimensional normal space which is not strongly 0-dimensional.

EXAMPLE 3. Let us denote the set of all rational numbers of the segment I by T. The condition:

$$xRy \text{ if and only if } (x-y) \in T,$$

defines an equivalence relation in the set I. Each equivalence class of the relation R is dense in I and countable. The family of all equivalence classes is thus of power $\mathfrak{c}$. Let us choose a subfamily of power $\overline{\omega}_1$ which does not contain the class T and let us arrange its elements in a transfinite sequence of the type ω_1, i.e.

$$Q_0, Q_1, Q_2, \ldots, Q_\alpha, \ldots, \qquad \alpha < \omega_1.$$

By Example 1, the set $S_\alpha = I \setminus \bigcup_{\gamma \geqslant \alpha} Q_\gamma$ is 0-dimensional for every $\alpha < \omega_1$. Let us denote the space of all ordinal numbers not greater than ω_1 by X^* (see Example 3.5.1) and let $X = X^* \setminus \{\omega_1\}$. For every $\alpha < \omega_1$ the set $X_\alpha = \{\gamma \in X^* : \gamma \leqslant \alpha\}$ is open-and-closed in X^*. Let us consider the product $X^* \times I$ and its subspaces

$$Y_\alpha = \bigcup_{\gamma \leqslant \alpha} (\{\gamma\} \times S_\gamma), \qquad Y = \bigcup_{\gamma < \omega_1} (\{\gamma\} \times S_\gamma), \qquad \text{and} \qquad Y^* = Y \cup (\{\omega_1\} \times I).$$

The space $Y_\alpha = Y \cap (X_\alpha \times I)$ is open-and-closed in Y. Moreover, $Y_\alpha \subset X_\alpha \times S_\alpha$ for every $\alpha < \omega_1$, whence by virtue of Theorems 10 and 7, the space Y_α is 0-dimensional. The space $Y = \bigcup_{\alpha < \omega_1} Y_\alpha$ is thus also 0-dimensional. Since $X_\alpha \times I$ is a compact space which satisfies the second axiom of countability, it is metrizable according to Theorem 4.2.3. The subspace Y_α is also metrizable and, consequently, it is normal.

We shall show that the spaces Y^* and Y are normal. Let us consider two disjoint closed subsets A and B of the space Y^*. The sets $A_1 = A \cap (Y^* \setminus Y)$ and $B_1 = B \cap (Y^* \setminus Y)$ are compact. Hence we infer from Theorem 3.1.4 that there exist in Y^* open sets U and V such that

(2) $$A_1 \subset U, \quad B_1 \subset V, \quad \text{and} \quad U \cap V = 0.$$

It is easy to verify that for a certain $\alpha < \omega_1$ we have the formulas

(3) $$A \cap (Y^* \setminus Y_\alpha) \subset U \quad \text{and} \quad B \cap (Y^* \setminus Y_\alpha) \subset V.$$

It follows from formulas (2), (3), and from the normality of the space Y_a, that the sets A and B are contained in disjoint open sets, i.e. that the space Y^* is normal.

Let us now consider a pair A, B of disjoint closed subsets of the space Y. In order to prove that Y is normal it is sufficient to show that the closures of the sets A, B in the space Y^* are disjoint. If there existed a point $(\omega_1, x) \in \bar{A} \cap \bar{B}$, then we would be able to find two sequences $\{a_i\}$, $\{\beta_i\}$ of ordinal numbers and two sequences $\{x_i\}$, $\{y_i\}$ of real numbers such that

$$a_i < \beta_i < a_{i+1}, \quad |x-x_i| < 1/i, \quad |x-y_i| < 1/i,$$
$$(a_i, x_i) \in A, \quad (\beta_i, y_i) \in B \quad \text{for} \quad i = 1, 2, \ldots,$$

and, by the same reasoning as in Example 3.5.1, this would yield $A \cap B \neq 0$.

We shall now prove that every continuous function $f: Y \to I$ can be extended over the space Y^*. To begin with, let us observe that since for every $t \in T$ the function f is constant on a set of the form $(X \setminus X_{a_0}) \times \{t\}$, where $a_0 < \omega_1$ (cf. Example 3.5.1), there exists an $a_0 < \omega_1$ such that the function f is constant on each of the sets $(X \setminus X_{a_0}) \times \{t\}$, where $t \in T$. In order to prove the extendability of f over the space Y^* it is sufficient to show that the function $f | Y \setminus Y_{a_0}$ is extendable over $Y^* \setminus Y_{a_0}$. Thus, without any loss of generality we can assume that the function f is constant on each of the sets $X \times \{t\}$, where $t \in T$. The space $X \times T \subset Y$ is dense in $X^* \times I$, so that, by virtue of Theorem 2.1.4, it is sufficient to show that the function $\varphi = f | X \times T$ is extendable over $X^* \times I$.

For every $a < \omega_1$ let us consider the function $\varphi_a: T \to I$ defined by the formula $\varphi_a(t) = \varphi(a, t)$. It follows that

$$\varphi^{-1}(A) = X \times \varphi_0^{-1}(A) \subset X^* \times \varphi_0^{-1}(A) \tag{4}$$

and

$$\varphi_a^{-1}(A) = \varphi_0^{-1}(A) \tag{5}$$

for every $A \subset I$ and $a < \omega_1$.

Let A, B denote disjoint and closed subsets of I. By virtue of (4), we have

$$\overline{\varphi^{-1}(A)} \cap \overline{\varphi^{-1}(B)} \subset X^* \times [\overline{\varphi_0^{-1}(A)} \cap \overline{\varphi_0^{-1}(B)}], \tag{6}$$

where the closure is applied in $X^* \times I$ and in I respectively.

Since for every number $r \in I$ there exists an $a < \omega_1$ such that $T \cup \{r\} \subset S_a$, and since φ_a is extendable over S_a, we infer from (5) and from Theorem 3.2.1 that

$$r \notin \overline{\varphi_a^{-1}(A)} \cap \overline{\varphi_a^{-1}(B)} = \overline{\varphi_0^{-1}(A)} \cap \overline{\varphi_0^{-1}(B)}.$$

We thus have $\overline{\varphi_0^{-1}(A)} \cap \overline{\varphi_0^{-1}(B)} = 0$ and, by (6) and Theorem 3.2.1, φ is extendable over $X^* \times I$.

If the space Y were strongly 0-dimensional, then, by virtue of Theorem 3, there would exist an open-and-closed set $U \subset Y$ such that $X \times \{0\} \subset U$ and $X \times \{1\} \subset Y \setminus U$, and the function $f\colon Y \to I$ defined by means of the formula

$$f(x) = \begin{cases} 0 & \text{for} \quad x \in U, \\ 1 & \text{for} \quad x \in Y \setminus U, \end{cases}$$

would be, by the above remarks, extendable to a function $f^*\colon Y^* \to I$. But since the set Y is dense in Y^*, we would have $f^*(Y^*) \subset \overline{f(Y)} = \{0, 1\}$, whence it would follow that $f^*(Y^* \setminus Y) = \{0, 1\}$, contrary to the connectedness of the set $Y^* \setminus Y = \{\omega_1\} \times I$. Hence Y is not strongly 0-dimensional.

Since the space Y is 0-dimensional, it follows from Theorems 11 and 6 that strong 0-dimensionality is not a hereditary property. The example of the space Y also shows that the 0-dimensionality of a space is not equivalent to the 0-dimensionality of its Čech-Stone compactification (cf. Theorem 8), for by virtue of Corollary 6 to Theorem 3.5.1, we have $\beta Y^* = \beta Y$. ■

We shall now define a class of spaces which are even more disconnected. A topological space X is said to be *extremally disconnected* if that X is a Hausdorff space and the closure $\overline{U}$ of each open set $U \subset X$ is open. Clearly, every discrete space is extremally disconnected. The set of all rational numbers is an example of a strongly 0-dimensional space which is not extremally disconnected. Every non-empty regular extremally disconnected space X is 0-dimensional. Indeed, for every point $x \in X$ and its neighbourhood $U \subset X$ there exists a neighbourhood W of the point x such that $x \in W \subset \overline{W} \subset U$. Since X is extremally disconnected, $\overline{W}$ is open-and-closed, whence open-and-closed sets form a base of the space X. It is also easy to verify that every extremally disconnected space is totally disconnected.

THEOREM 12. *A Tychonoff space X is extremally disconnected if and only if its Čech-Stone compactification βX is extremally disconnected.*

Proof. Let us assume that X is extremally disconnected and let us consider an open set $U \subset \beta X$. The closure $X \cap \overline{U \cap X}$ of the set $U \cap X$ in the space X is open-and-closed. By virtue of Theorem 1.3.6,

$$\overline{U} = \overline{X \cap U} \subset \overline{X \cap \overline{U}} = \overline{X \cap \overline{U \cap X}} \subset \overline{\overline{U \cap X}} = \overline{U};$$

hence, according to Corollary 4 to Theorem 3.5.1, the set $\overline{U}$ is open-and--closed in βX.

Let us now consider a Tychonoff space X such that βX is extremally disconnected, and an open set $U \subset X$. Let W denote an open subset of βX such that $W \cap X = U$. By virtue of Theorem 1.3.6, $\overline{U} = \overline{W \cap X} = \overline{W}$, whence the closure $\overline{U} \cap X = \overline{W} \cap X$ of the set U in the space X is open-and-closed. ∎

COROLLARY. *The space βN, i.e. the Čech-Stone compactification of the set of natural numbers with the discrete topology, is extremally disconnected.* ∎

Theorems 12, 6, and 8 yield

THEOREM 13. *Every non-empty extremally disconnected Tychonoff space is strongly 0-dimensional.* ∎

THEOREM 14. *A Hausdorff space X is extremally disconnected if and only if for every two disjoint sets U, V which are open in X we have the equality $\overline{U} \cap \overline{V} = 0$.*

Proof. Let U and V be disjoint and open subsets of an extremally disconnected space X. Since $U \cap V = 0$, we infer that $\overline{U} \cap V = 0$, but the set $\overline{U}$ is also open, whence $\overline{U} \cap \overline{V} = 0$.

Let us now suppose that each pair of disjoint and open subsets of a T_2-space X has disjoint closures. Let us consider an open set $U \subset X$. Since U and $X \setminus \overline{U}$ are disjoint open sets, we have $\overline{U} \cap \overline{X \setminus \overline{U}} = 0$, i.e. $\overline{U} \subset X \setminus \overline{X \setminus \overline{U}} = \operatorname{Int} \overline{U}$ and $\overline{U}$ is open. The space X is therefore extremally disconnected. ∎

The reader can prove without any difficulty

THEOREM 15. *The sum $\bigoplus_{s \in S} X_s$ of a family $\{X_s\}_{s \in S}$ of disjoint topological spaces is extremally disconnected if and only if the space X_s is extremally disconnected for every $s \in S$.* ∎

The Cartesian product of extremally disconnected spaces is not necessarily extremally disconnected. It is easy to verify that the Cantor set $D^{\aleph_0}$ is not extremally disconnected.

EXAMPLE 4. We shall show that the space $\beta N \setminus N$ is not extremally disconnected; this will imply that extremal disconnectedness is not a hereditary property.

Let X be the non-normal Tychonoff space defined in Example 3.5.3. There exist closed and disjoint sets $A, B \subset X$ which cannot be separated by disjoint open sets in X; evidently, we can assume (cf. Example 1.5.2) that $A, B \subset X \setminus N$. Let $\{U_t\}_{t \in I}$ be the family of open subsets of the space $\beta N \setminus N$ which is considered in Example 3.5.3. Let us define

$$W_A = \bigcup_{x_t \in A} U_t \quad \text{and} \quad W_B = \bigcup_{x_t \in B} U_t .$$

Let us assume that the space $\beta N \setminus N$ is extremally disconnected. Since W_A and W_B are disjoint open subsets, their closures in $\beta N \setminus N$ are disjoint. By virtue of Theorem 3.6.5, the set $\beta N \setminus N$ is closed in βN, whence $\overline{W}_A \cap \overline{W}_B = 0$, where the closure operator is applied in the space βN. By the normality of the space βN, there exist sets U and V open in βN, disjoint and such that

$$A \subset \overline{W}_A \subset U \quad \text{and} \quad B \subset \overline{W}_B \subset V.$$

The sets $X \cap U$ and $X \cap V$ are disjoint and open in X, and contain A and B respectively. This contradiction shows that the space $\beta N \setminus N$ is not extremally disconnected. ■

EXERCISES

A. Show that the family of functionally closed subsets of a normal space is the same as the family of closed subsets of the space which are G_δ-sets.

Show by means of an example that the assumption of normality is essential.

The product of a countable number of functionally closed sets is functionally closed (see p. 155). Show that the assumption of countability is essential.

B. Show that if, by adding a point to a strongly 0-dimensional space, we obtain a Tychonoff space, then the space obtained is also strongly 0-dimensional.

C (C. H. Dowker [1955]). Show that one point can be added to the space considered in Example 2.3 in such a manner that either the space obtained is normal but not 0-dimensional, or it is normal and strongly 0-dimensional.

Hint: Add the point $(\omega_1, 0)$; replace the subset $Y^* \setminus Y$ of the space Y^* by a point.

D. Show that an open subspace and a dense subspace of an extremally disconnected space are extremally disconnected.

E. Show that an extremally disconnected space does not contain any subspace homeomorphic to the subspace of the real line consisting of numbers $1/i$, where $i = \pm 1, \pm 2, \ldots$, and of number 0.

Deduce that among metrizable spaces discrete spaces are the only extremally disconnected ones.

HISTORICAL REMARKS AND BIBLIOGRAPHIC NOTES

The definition of a connected space was given by C. Jordan; the property of spaces equivalent to connectedness for compact metrizable spaces and described in Exercise 1.C was considered earlier by G. Cantor. A systematic study of connected spaces was initiated in F. Hausdorff's book [1914] and in B. Knaster and K. Kuratowski's paper [1921]. From these works we took all the theorems of Paragraph 1, except two: Theorem 1.5 is suggested as an exercise in S. Eilenberg and N. Steenrod's book [1952], and Theorem 1.8 was proved by M. R. Šura-Bura in [1941]. The first, rather complicated example of a countable connected space was given by P. Urysohn in [1925]; the space of Example 1.2 was constructed by R. H. Bing in [1953]. The theorem on the equivalence of the connectedness of the spaces $(S^{n-1})^X$ and $R^n \setminus X$ for $X \subset R^n$ was proved by K. Borsuk in [1932] under the additional assumption of the compactness of X (for the topology in $(S^{n-1})^X$ induced by the metric defined by formula (6), Paragraph 4.2). For an arbitrary $X \subset R^n$ this theorem has recently been proved by K. Kuratowski in Appendix I to his book [1961]. The notion of a totally disconnected space was introduced by F. Hausdorff in [1914], and the concept of a 0-dimensional space by W. Sierpiński in [1921], before the development of the dimension theory. Strongly 0-dimensional spaces were considered only in connection with dimension theory. (See the historical remarks and bibliographic notes to Chapter 7). Theorems 2.1, 2.4, 2.5, 2.6, and 2.11 were proved by N. Vedenissoff in [1939]. Example 2.2 comes from P. Erdös's paper [1940] (an analogous but more complicated example can be found in W. Sierpiński [1921]). Example 2.3 was constructed by C. H. Dowker [1955]. Extremally disconnected spaces were defined by M. H. Stone in [1937a]. The proof given in Example 2.4 that the space $\beta N \setminus N$ is not extremally disconnected is adopted from L. Gillman and M. Jerison's book [1960], but the fact was known earlier.

PROBLEMS

A. Show that a space X is connected if an only if for every open covering $\{U_s\}_{s \in S}$ and every two points $x_1, x_2 \in X$ there exists a finite sequence $s_1, s_2, \ldots, s_k$ of elements of S such that

$$x_1 \in U_{s_1},\ x_2 \in U_{s_k}, \quad \text{and} \quad U_{s_i} \cap U_{s_j} \neq 0 \text{ if and only if } |i-j| \leqslant 1.$$

B. Let X be a set ordered by the relation $<$ which contains more than one element. Show that the space X with the order topology induced by the ordering $<$ is connected if and only if the relation $<$ orders the set X in a continuous manner.

C (L. Vietoris [1923]). Let X be an arbitrary topological space. Show that the space of subsets 2^X is connected if and only if X is connected.

Hint: Show that the subset S_k of the space 2^X, consisting of all sets which contain not more than k elements, is a continuous image of the Cartesian product $X_1 \times X_2 \times \ldots \times X_k$, where $X_i = X$ for $i = 1, 2, \ldots, k$, and show that the union $\bigcup_{k=1}^{\infty} S_k$ is dense in 2^X.

D. Let X be a topological space and let R denote an equivalence relation in X. Show that if the space X/R together with all equivalence classes of the relation R is connected, then X is also a connected space.

E. We say that a space X is *locally connected* if for every point $x \in X$ and every neighbourhood U of x there exists a connected set C contained in U such that $x \in \operatorname{Int} C$. Prove that a space is locally connected if and only if the components of its open subspaces are open.

F. Give necessary and sufficient conditions for the sum and the Cartesian product of a family of spaces to be locally connected.

G. Show that a T_1-space X is simultaneously connected and locally connected if and only if for each open covering $\{U_s\}_{s\in S}$ of X and every pair of points $x_1, x_2 \in X$ there exists a finite sequence $s_1, s_2, \ldots, s_k$ of elements of S and a sequence $V_1, V_2, \ldots, V_k$ of open and connected subsets of X such that $x_1 \in V_1$, $x_2 \in V_k$, $V_i \subset U_{s_i}$ for $i = 1, 2, \ldots, k$, and $V_i \cap V_j \neq 0$ if and only if $|i-j| \leqslant 1$.

H. A space X is called *arcwise connected* if for every pair of points $x_1, x_2 \in X$ there exists a homeomorphic embedding h of the segment I into X such that $h(0) = x_1$ and $h(1) = x_2$. Prove that each arcwise connected space is connected. Give an example of a compact and connected subset of the plane which is not arcwise connected.

I. A space X is said to be *locally arcwise connected* if for every point $x \in X$ and every neighbourhood U of x there exists a neighbourhood V of the point x such that for every $y \in V$ there exists a homeomorphic embedding $h\colon I \to U$ such that $h(0) = x$ and $h(1) = y$. Verify that a locally arcwise connected space is locally connected. Give an example of a locally connected and arcwise connected space which is not locally arcwise connected (cf. Problem J).

J (S. Mazurkiewicz [1920], R. L. Moore [1916]). Show that each open connected and locally connected subset V of a compact and metrizable space X is arcwise connected.

Deduce that every metrizable and locally connected continuum X is arcwise connected and locally arcwise connected.

Hint: For arbitrary points $x_1, x_2 \in V$ consider the sequences $V_1^n, V_2^n, \ldots \ldots, V_{k(n)}^n$, where $n = 1, 2, \ldots$, consisting of open connected subsets of the space X which satisfy the conditions:

(1) $x_1 \in V_1^n$, $x_2 \in V_{k(n)}^n$, $\delta(V_i^n) \leqslant 1/n$ for $i = 1, 2, \ldots, k(n)$.
(2) $V_i^n \cap V_j^n \neq 0$ if and only if $|i-j| \leqslant 1$.
(3) $\overline{V}_i^1 \subset V$ for $i = 1, 2, \ldots, k(1)$.
(4) If $n > 1$, then for every $i \leqslant k(n)$ there exists a $j \leqslant k(n-1)$ such that $\overline{V}_i^n \subset V_j^{n-1}$.

Considering similar decompositions of the segment I prove that the set $\bigcap_{n=1}^{\infty} \bigcup_{i=1}^{k(n)} \overline{V}_i^n$ is homeomorphic to I.

K. Let (X, ϱ) be a compact locally arcwise connected metric space. Show that for every $\eta > 0$ there exists an $\varepsilon > 0$ such that for every two points $x, y \in X$ whose distance is not greater than η there exists a homeomorphic embedding $h\colon I \to X$ which is subject to the conditions:

$$h(0) = x, \quad h(1) = y, \quad \delta\big(h(I)\big) < \varepsilon.$$

L (H. Hahn [1914], S. Mazurkiewicz [1920], W. Sierpiński [1920]). Show that for a metrizable continuum X the following conditions are equivalent:

(i) There exists a mapping $f: I \to X$ onto X.

(ii) For each metric ϱ in the space X and every $\varepsilon > 0$ there exist sets $F_1, F_2, \ldots, F_k$ connected and closed in X such that $X = \bigcup_{i=1}^{k} F_i$ and $\delta(F_i) \leqslant \varepsilon$ for $i = 1, 2, \ldots, k$.

(iii) X is locally connected.

Hint: To prove the implication (iii) $\Rightarrow$ (i) make use of Problems J and 4.L.

M. Show that a continuum X is locally connected if and only if every open covering of it has a finite refinement consisting of continua. Deduce that a continuous image of a locally connected continuum is a locally connected continuum provided that it is a Hausdorff space. Is the assumption of compactness essential?

N. Prove that X is arcwise connected if and only if for every two points $x_1, x_2 \in X$ there exists a mapping $f: I \to X$ such that $f(0) = x_1$ and $f(1) = x_2$.

O (K. Kuratowski [1961]). Show that the quasi-component of the point $x = \{x_s\}$ in the Cartesian product $\underset{s\in S}{\boldsymbol{P}} X_s$ is the set $\underset{s\in S}{\boldsymbol{P}} Q_s$, where Q_s is the quasi-component of the point x_s in the space X_s.

P. Show that for every topological space X of weight $\mathfrak{m}$ there exists a mapping $f: X \to D^{\mathfrak{m}}$ into the Cantor cube of weight $\mathfrak{m}$ such that the inverse images of points of the space $f(X) \subset D^{\mathfrak{m}}$ are the quasi-components of the space X.

Deduce that for a compact space X the relation R in the set X defined by means of the condition

xRy if and only if y belongs to the quasi-component of x,

is a closed equivalence relation and that the space X/R is totally disconnected.

Q. Prove that for a Hausdorff space X the following conditions are equivalent:

(i) X is extremally disconnected.

(ii) For each closed subset $F \subset X$ the set $\operatorname{Int} F$ is closed.

(iii) For each open subset $G \subset X$ we have $\overline{G} \cap \overline{X \setminus \overline{G}} = 0$.

R (L. Gillman and M. Jerison [1960]). Let N be the set of all natural numbers with the discrete topology. Show that the space $\beta N \times \beta N$ is not extremally disconnected.

Hint: Consider the open set $\bigcup_{n=1}^{\infty} \{(n, n)\}$.

Deduce that the space $\beta N \times \beta N$ is not homeomorphic to the space $\beta(N \times N)$.

CHAPTER 7

DIMENSION OF TOPOLOGICAL SPACES

In this chapter we shall generalize the notion of the dimension of Euclidean spaces and assign to certain topological spaces an integer not less than -1 which is called the dimension of the space. Number -1 is assigned only to the empty space. To those spaces whose dimension is greater than any natural number we assign the "infinite number" ∞. We find that the dimension-function can be defined in various ways. We shall consider three kinds of dimensions of a topological space X: $\operatorname{ind} X$, $\operatorname{Ind} X$, and $\dim X$. The natural domains for these dimension--functions are the classes of regular, normal, and Tychonoff spaces respectively. The dimension-functions develop some peculiar properties when extended to broader classes of spaces. Since a subspace of a normal space is not necessarily normal, we infer that the dimension Ind is not necessarily defined on a subspace of a space on which this dimension is defined. The same situation holds in measure theory; a subset of a measurable set is not necessarily measurable.

Dimension theory is not part of a classical course of general topology. This is because dimension theory which was created for compact metric spaces and then developed for separable spaces, can only be partially generalized to topological spaces. Furthermore, the basic theorem in the dimension theory of separable spaces, which states that the dimensions ind, Ind, and dim are equal, is valid neither for the class of metrizable spaces nor for compact spaces. Thus, in general topology we have three dimension theories instead of one, and they are weaker and less harmonious than the dimension theory of separable metric spaces. However, those theories are sufficiently developed to be included in a book on general topology. The reader will see that they contain many interesting theorems and throw light on the theory of dimension of separable metric spaces.

This chapter is connected with Paragraph 6.2 in which we have developed a part of dimension theory, namely the theory of spaces of dimension zero. The connection with other chapters is rather vague. Although we use many earlier results, we do consider very different problems and develop different methods. The proofs of the theorems are generally longer and more complicated. We shall not utilize the results in the next chapter. The present chapter is chiefly meant for readers familiar with the classical dimension theory of separable metric spaces; thus it can be omitted by readers who only want to get acquainted with the basic notions and results of general topology.

We begin Paragraph 1 with the definition of the dimensions ind, Ind, and dim, and with some immediate consequences of those definitions. We find, for instance, that $\operatorname{ind} X \leqslant \operatorname{Ind} X$ for an arbitrary normal space X. We then prove two theorems on the swelling and shrinking of coverings of a topological space. Those theorems are essential for the examination of the covering dimension dim. From the second theorem it follows, in particular, that for normal spaces the definition of the dimension dim can be expressed in a much simpler way. The end of the paragraph is devoted to theorems on the connection of the dimension of a space X with the dimension of its Čech-Stone compactification βX.

Paragraph 2 is devoted to a more precise examination of the dimension dim. We begin with two theorems which state some conditions for a space, which has a closed covering consisting of sets of dimension not greater than n, to have itself dimension not greater than n. From the lemma to the second of those theorems there follows an important characterization of the dimension of paracompact spaces which will be used in the next paragraph. Further, we show that $\dim X \leqslant \operatorname{ind} X$ for every Lindelöf space X and that $\dim X \leqslant \operatorname{Ind} X$ for every normal space X. The end of the paragraph is devoted to the proof of a theorem characterizing the dimension dim by means of partitions. That theorem is of great importance because it leads, through the theorem on the extendability of mappings into the sphere S^n (see Problem M), to a homological characterization of the dimension dim.

In the last paragraph we develop dimension theory in metrizable spaces. We start with the basic theorem of Katětov and Morita which states that for a metrizable space X the equality $\operatorname{Ind} X = \dim X$ is valid. Making use of the results of the preceding paragraphs we infer that for separable metrizable spaces all three dimensions are equal. The next theorems give a characterization of the dimension Ind for metrizable spaces by means of a decomposition into the union of 0-dimensional sets and by means of the existence of a special base. Those characterizations imply theorems on the dimension of the union and Cartesian product of spaces. The proofs of these theorems are based on the theorem of Katětov-Morita. A method which allows us to omit this difficult theorem is outlined in the exercises. The paragraph ends with the theorem on the dimension of Euclidean spaces: $\operatorname{ind} R^n = \operatorname{Ind} R^n = \dim R^n = n$. We deduce this theorem, the proof of which requires deep insight into the structure of the space R^n, from the well-known fixed-point theorem. In order to make the book complete we end the chapter with an Appendix containing a proof of the fixed-point theorem.

§ 1. Definitions and basic properties of the dimensions: ind, Ind, **and** dim. Let X be an arbitrary regular space and let n denote a non-negative integer. We say that

(MU1) $\operatorname{ind} X = -1$ *if and only if* $X = 0$.

(MU2) $\operatorname{ind} X \leqslant n$ *if for every point* $x \in X$ *and every neighbourhood* $V \subset X$ *of* x *there exists an open set* $U \subset X$ *such that*

$$x \in U \subset \overline{U} \subset V \quad \textit{and} \quad \operatorname{ind} \operatorname{Fr} U \leqslant n-1.$$

(MU3) $\operatorname{ind} X = n$ *if* $\operatorname{ind} X \leqslant n$ *is true and* $\operatorname{ind} X \leqslant n-1$ *is false.*

(MU4) $\operatorname{ind} X = \infty$ *if* $\operatorname{ind} X \leqslant n$ *is false for every* n.

Conditions (MU1)-(MU4) assign to every regular space X an integer $\operatorname{ind} X$ greater than -2 or the "infinite number" ∞. The number $\operatorname{ind} X$ is called the *Menger-Urysohn dimension* or the *small inductive dimension* of the space X. It can easily be verified that if two spaces X and Y are homeomorphic, then $\operatorname{ind} X = \operatorname{ind} Y$.

It follows immediately from the definition of the Menger-Urysohn dimension of a regular space X that $\operatorname{ind} X \leqslant n$ if and only if there exists a base $\mathfrak{B}$ in X such that $\operatorname{ind} \operatorname{Fr} U \leqslant n-1$ for every $U \in \mathfrak{B}$. In particular, $\operatorname{ind} X = 0$ if and only if X is 0-dimensional in the sense of Paragraph 6.2.

In order to get uniform formulations we shall assume that for every integer n the following formulas hold: $n \leqslant \infty$, $n+\infty = \infty+n = \infty$.

Since the regularity of a space is a hereditary property, we infer that if $\operatorname{ind} X$ is defined and M is a subspace of X, then $\operatorname{ind} M$ is also defined.

THEOREM 1. *If* M *is a subspace of a regular space* X, *then* $\operatorname{ind} M \leqslant \operatorname{ind} X$.

Proof. The theorem is evidently valid if $\operatorname{ind} X = -1$. Let us suppose that we have already proved the theorem under the assumption that the dimension of the space under consideration does not exceed $n-1$. Let X be a regular space of dimension $\leqslant n$, and M a subspace. Let x be a point in M with a neighbourhood V. Let V_1 be an open set in X such that $V = M \cap V_1$. Since $\operatorname{ind} X \leqslant n$, there exists an open set $U_1 \subset X$ such that

$$x \in U_1 \subset \overline{U}_1 \subset V_1 \quad \text{and} \quad \operatorname{ind} \operatorname{Fr} U_1 \leqslant n-1. \tag{1}$$

Thus the set $U = U_1 \cap M$ is a neighbourhood of the point x in the space M. Its closure in this space is contained in V, and the boundary set (also in this space) $\operatorname{Fr} U = M \cap \overline{U_1 \cap M} \cap \overline{M \setminus U_1}$ is a subspace of the boundary of U_1. Making use of the inductive assumption and of formula (1) we infer that $\operatorname{ind} M \leqslant n$. ∎

Let X be an arbitrary normal space and let n denote a non-negative integer. We shall say that

(BČ1) $\operatorname{Ind} X = -1$ *if and only if* $X = 0$.

(BČ2) $\operatorname{Ind} X \leqslant n$ *if for every closed set* $A \subset X$ *and every open set* $V \subset X$ *containing it there exists an open set* $U \subset X$ *such that*

$$A \subset U \subset \overline{U} \subset V \quad \textit{and} \quad \operatorname{Ind} \operatorname{Fr} U \leqslant n-1.$$

(BČ3) $\operatorname{Ind} X = n$ *if* $\operatorname{Ind} X \leqslant n$ *is true and* $\operatorname{Ind} X \leqslant n-1$ *is false.*

(BČ4) $\operatorname{Ind} X = \infty$ *if* $\operatorname{Ind} X \leqslant n$ *is false for every* n.

Conditions (BČ1)-(BČ4) assign to every normal space X an integer $\operatorname{Ind} X$ greater than -2 or the "infinite number" ∞. The number $\operatorname{Ind} X$ is called the *Brouwer-Čech dimension* or the *large inductive dimension* of the space X. It can easily be verified that if two spaces X and Y are homeomorphic, then $\operatorname{Ind} X = \operatorname{Ind} Y$.

It follows from Theorem 6.2.3 that a normal space X is strongly 0-dimensional in the sense of Paragraph 6.2 if and only if $\operatorname{Ind} X = 0$.

The reader can prove inductively without any difficulty the following theorem, which justifies the terms: small, large inductive dimensions.

THEOREM 2. *For every normal space X we have* $\operatorname{ind} X \leqslant \operatorname{Ind} X$. ∎

Since normality is not a hereditary property (see Example 2.3.3), the Brouwer-Čech dimension is not defined for some subspaces of normal spaces. On the other hand, it follows from Theorem 2.1.2 that if $\operatorname{Ind} X$ is defined, then $\operatorname{Ind} M$ is also defined for each closed subspace $M \subset X$. Moreover, the following theorem can be proved analogously to Theorem 1.

THEOREM 3. *If M is a closed subspace of a normal space X, then* $\operatorname{Ind} M \leqslant \operatorname{Ind} X$. ∎

It follows from Example 6.2.3 that the above theorem is not valid if we replace the assumption that M is closed by a weaker assumption, namely that it is normal, i.e. we assume only that $\operatorname{Ind} M$ is defined.

Let X be a topological space and let $\mathfrak{A}$ denote a family of subsets of X. We say that the family $\mathfrak{A}$ is of *order* n if n is the greatest integer satisfying the condition: the family $\mathfrak{A}$ contains $n+1$ sets which have a non-empty intersection. If the order of the family $\mathfrak{A}$ is $\leqslant n$, then for every $n+2$ distinct elements $A_{s_1}, A_{s_2}, \ldots, A_{s_{n+2}}$ of the family $\mathfrak{A}$ we have

$$A_{s_1} \cap A_{s_2} \cap \ldots \cap A_{s_{n+2}} = 0.$$

In particular, a family of order -1 can contain only the empty set, and a family of order 0 consists of disjoint sets. The order of a family $\mathfrak{A}$ will be denoted by the symbol $\operatorname{ord} \mathfrak{A}$.

Let us recall (see Paragraph 6.2) that a set of the form $f^{-1}(0)$, where $f\colon X \to R$, is called functionally closed in the topological space X, and that the complement of a functionally closed set is called functionally open. A functionally open (closed) covering is a covering consisting of functionally open (closed) sets.

Let X be a Tychonoff space and let n denote an integer greater than -2. We shall say that

(ČL1) $\dim X \leqslant n$ *if every finite functionally open covering of the space* X *has a finite functionally open refinement of order* $\leqslant n$.

(ČL2) $\dim X = n$ *if* $\dim X \leqslant n$ *is true and* $\dim X \leqslant n-1$ *is false.*

(ČL3) $\dim X = \infty$ *if* $\dim X \leqslant n$ *is false for every* n.

Conditions (ČL1)-(ČL3) assign to every Tychonoff space X an integer $\dim X$ greater than -2 or the "infinite number" ∞. The number $\dim X$ is called the *Čech-Lebesgue dimension* or the *covering dimension* of the space X. Evidently, if two spaces X and Y are homeomorphic, then $\dim X = \dim Y$.

It follows from the definition of the Čech-Lebesgue dimension that $\dim X = -1$ if and only if $X = 0$ and that $\dim X = 0$ if and only if X is strongly 0-dimensional in the sense of Paragraph 6.2.

Since the property "X is a Tychonoff space" is a hereditary property, we infer that if $\dim X$ is defined, then $\dim M$ is also defined for every subspace $M \subset X$. To prove the counterparts of Theorems 1 and 3 for the Čech-Lebesgue dimension we need some properties of functionally closed and open sets. We prove two theorems about them which will be used frequently in the sequel. Analogous theorems are valid for arbitrary closed and open sets under the assumption that the space considered is normal. We shall give these formulations in brackets.

Let $\{A_s\}_{s \in S}$ be an arbitrary family of subsets of the space X. A *swelling* of this family is a family $\{B_s\}_{s \in S}$ consisting of subsets of X such that $A_s \subset B_s$ for every $s \in S$ and the conditions

$$A_{s_1} \cap A_{s_2} \cap \ldots \cap A_{s_m} = 0 \quad \text{and} \quad B_{s_1} \cap B_{s_2} \cap \ldots \cap B_{s_m} = 0$$

are equivalent for every choice of indices $s_1, s_2, \ldots, s_m \in S$.

THEOREM 4. *Every finite family* $\{F_i\}_{i=1}^k$ *of functionally closed* (*closed*) *subsets of a topological* (*normal*) *space* X *has a swelling* $\{U_i\}_{i=1}^k$ *consisting of functionally open sets.*

Furthermore, if $\{V_i\}_{i=1}^k$ *is a family of functionally open* (*open*) *subsets of the space* X *such that* $F_i \subset V_i$ *for* $i = 1, 2, \ldots, k$, *then the swelling* $\{U_i\}_{i=1}^k$ *can be chosen in such a manner that* $\overline{U}_i \subset V_i$ *for* $i = 1, 2, \ldots, k$.

Proof. Let us consider all intersections of the form $F_{i_1} \cap F_{i_2} \cap \ldots \cap F_{i_m}$, such that $F_1 \cap F_{i_1} \cap F_{i_2} \cap \ldots \cap F_{i_m} = 0$. Their union

S_1 is a functionally closed (closed) set disjoint with the set F_1. By virtue of Theorem 6.2.2 (Urysohn Lemma), there exists a function $f_1\colon X \to I$ such that

$$f_1(F_1) \subset \{0\} \quad \text{and} \quad f_1(S_1) \subset \{1\}.$$

It is easy to verify that $K_1 = f_1^{-1}([0, 1/2])$ is a functionally closed set such that the family $\{K_1, F_2, F_3, \ldots, F_k\}$ is a swelling of the family $\{F_i\}_{i=1}^k$.

Let us now assume that for every $i = 1, 2, \ldots, n$ we have found a function $f_i\colon X \to I$ such that $f_i(F_i) \subset \{0\}$ and that $\{K_1, K_2, \ldots$ $\ldots, K_n, F_{n+1}, \ldots, F_k\}$, where $K_i = f_i^{-1}([0, 1/2])$, is a swelling of the family $\{F_i\}_{i=1}^k$. The union S_{n+1} of all intersections of sets belonging to the family $\{K_1, K_2, \ldots, K_n, F_{n+1}, \ldots, F_k\}$ which are disjoint with the set F_{n+1}, is, as in the previous case, functionally closed (closed) and disjoint from F_{n+1}. There exists, therefore, a function $f_{n+1}\colon X \to I$ such that

$$f_{n+1}(F_{n+1}) \subset \{0\} \quad \text{and} \quad f_{n+1}(S_{n+1}) \subset \{1\},$$

and $\{K_1, K_2, \ldots, K_{n+1}, F_{n+2}, \ldots, F_k\}$, where $K_{n+1} = f_{n+1}^{-1}([0, 1/2])$, is a swelling of the family $\{F_i\}_{i=1}^k$. Thus we can assume that the functions $f_1, f_2, \ldots, f_k$ of X into I have been defined in such a manner that $f_i(F_i) \subset \{0\}$ and that $\{K_i\}_{i=1}^k$, where $K_i = f_i^{-1}([0, 1/2])$, is a swelling of the family $\{F_i\}_{i=1}^k$. It can easily be verified that the family $\{U_i\}_{i=1}^k$, where $U_i = f_i^{-1}([0, 1/2))$, satisfies the conclusion of our theorem.

To prove the second part of the theorem the sets U_i should be replaced by the sets $g_i^{-1}([0, 1/2))$ for $i = 1, 2, \ldots, k$, where $g_i\colon X \to I$ is chosen in such a manner that $g_i(F_i) \subset \{0\}$ and $g_i(X \setminus U_i \cap V_i) \subset \{1\}$. ∎

Let $\{A_s\}_{s \in S}$ be an arbitrary covering of a space X. A *shrinking* of this covering is a covering $\{B_s\}_{s \in S}$ of the space X such that $B_s \subset A_s$ for every $s \in S$. The order of a shrinking of a covering $\mathfrak{A}$ does not exceed the order of $\mathfrak{A}$.

THEOREM 5. *Every finite functionally open (open) covering $\{V_i\}_{i=1}^k$ of a topological (normal) space X has a shrinking $\{F_i\}_{i=1}^k$ and a shrinking $\{W_i\}_{i=1}^k$, which are functionally closed and open respectively, and such that $F_i \subset W_i \subset \overline{W}_i \subset V_i$ for $i = 1, 2, \ldots, k$.*

Proof. The family $\{X \setminus V_i\}_{i=1}^k$ is functionally closed (closed) and the intersection of all its elements is empty. The elements of a functionally open swelling $\{U_i\}_{i=1}^k$, which exists by Theorem 4, also have an empty intersection. The family $\{F_i\}_{i=1}^k$, where $F_i = X \setminus U_i$, is a functionally closed shrinking of the covering $\{V_i\}_{i=1}^k$. The existence of sets $W_1, W_2, \ldots$ $\ldots, W_k$, which together with the sets $F_1, F_2, \ldots, F_k$ satisfy the conclusion of our theorem, follows from Theorem 6.2.2 (Urysohn Lemma). ∎

That part of the theorem which concerns normal spaces also follows from Lemma 1 to Theorem 5.1.3 and the Urysohn Lemma.

For normal spaces the definition of the dimension dim can be stated in a simpler form. Namely, Theorem 5 implies

THEOREM 6. *For a normal space X the inequality* $\dim X \leqslant n$ *holds if and only if every finite open covering of the space X has a finite open refinement of order $\leqslant n$.* ■

THEOREM 7. *If M is a subspace of a Tychonoff space X such that every function $f: M \to I$ can be extended over X, then* $\dim M \leqslant \dim X$.

In particular, if M is a closed subspace of a normal space X, then $\dim M \leqslant \dim X$.

Proof. Suppose we are given a Tychonoff space X, such that $\dim X \leqslant n$, its subspace M, satisfying the assumptions of the theorem, and a functionally open covering $\{V_i\}_{i=1}^k$ of the space M. Let us denote by $\{F_i\}_{i=1}^k$ a functionally closed shrinking of the given covering, which exists by virtue of Theorem 5. According to Theorem 6.2.2, there exists for every $i = 1, 2, \ldots, k$ a function $f_i: M \to I$ such that

$$(2) \qquad f_i(F_i) \subset \{1\} \quad \text{and} \quad f_i(M \setminus V_i) \subset \{0\}.$$

Let $\bar{f}_i: X \to I$ be an extension of the function f_i. The sets $\bar{f}_1^{-1}((1/2, 1])$, $\bar{f}_2^{-1}((1/2, 1]), \ldots, \bar{f}_k^{-1}((1/2, 1])$, and $\bigcap_{i=1}^{k} \bar{f}_i^{-1}([0, 1))$ form a functionally open covering of the space X. Let us denote it by $\mathfrak{A}$. It follows from formula (2) that

$$(3) \qquad M \cap \bar{f}_i^{-1}((1/2, 1]) \subset V_i \text{ for } i = 1, 2, \ldots, k \text{ and}$$
$$M \cap \bigcap_{i=1}^{k} \bar{f}_i^{-1}([0, 1)) = 0.$$

Since $\dim X \leqslant n$, the covering $\mathfrak{A}$ has a finite functionally open refinement $\mathfrak{B}$ of order $\leqslant n$. It follows from formulas (3) that the intersections of elements of the covering $\mathfrak{B}$ with the set M form a finite functionally open refinement of the covering $\{V_i\}_{i=1}^k$. The order of this covering is evidently not greater than n. We infer, therefore, that $\dim M \leqslant n$. ■

The reader will have noticed that the theorems of this paragraph generalize the theorems which in Paragraph 6.2 were proved only for dimension 0. In fact, Theorems 1, 3, and 7 are generalizations of Theorem 6.2.7, while Theorem 2 is a generalization of the corollary to Lemma 1 to Theorem 6.2.3, and Theorem 6 is a generalization of Theorem 6.2.4. A generalization of Theorem 6.2.9 is given below. We leave the proof to the reader.

THEOREM 8. *Let $\{X_s\}_{s \in S}$ be a family of disjoint regular (normal, Tychonoff) spaces and let $X = \bigoplus_{s \in S} X_s$. A necessary and sufficient condition that* $\operatorname{ind} X \leqslant n$ $(\operatorname{Ind} X \leqslant n, \dim X \leqslant n)$ *is that the inequality* $\operatorname{ind} X_s \leqslant n$ $(\operatorname{Ind} X_s \leqslant n, \dim X_s \leqslant n)$ *should hold for every $s \in S$.* ■

Theorems 6.2.3, 6.2.5, and 6.2.6 cannot be generalized in such a simple manner. It is still not known whether small and large inductive dimensions coincide for Lindelöf spaces or, even, for compact spaces. On the other hand, there exist examples (see Problem E below) of compact spaces for which the dimensions ind and dim, or Ind and dim, are different. The following two theorems are counterparts of Theorems 6.2.3, 6.2.5, and 6.2.6 in terms of dimension theory.

THEOREM 9. *The conditions* $\operatorname{Ind} X = 0$ *and* $\dim X = 0$ *are equivalent for every normal space* X. ■

THEOREM 10. *The conditions* $\operatorname{ind} X = 0$, $\operatorname{Ind} X = 0$, *and* $\dim X = 0$ *are equivalent for every Lindelöf space* X. *If* X *is compact, then these conditions are equivalent to the total disconnectedness of the space* X. ■

We shall now describe an operator Ex which assigns to every open subset of a Tychonoff space X an open set in βX; then, we shall give two theorems which are generalizations of Theorem 6.2.8 and which establish connections between the dimension of a Tychonoff space and the dimension of its Čech-Stone compactification.

For every open subset U of a Tychonoff space X the set

$$\operatorname{Ex} U = \beta X \setminus (\overline{X \setminus U}),$$

where $\overline{X \setminus U}$ denotes the closure of the set $X \setminus U$ in the space βX, is open in βX. Let us note that

$$X \cap \operatorname{Ex} U = X \setminus (\overline{X \setminus U}) = X \setminus X \cap (\overline{X \setminus U}) = U,$$

and for every open set $V \subset \beta X$, where $X \cap V = U$, we have that

$$\overline{X \setminus U} = \overline{X \setminus (X \cap V)} = \overline{X \setminus V} \subset \overline{\beta X \setminus V} = \beta X \setminus V,$$

and

$$V \subset \beta X \setminus \overline{X \setminus U} = \operatorname{Ex} U.$$

Thus $\operatorname{Ex} U$ is the largest open subset of the space βX whose intersection with X is equal to the set U.

LEMMA 1. *For every pair of open subsets* U *and* V *of a Tychonoff space* X, *the following formulas are valid*:

$$\operatorname{Ex}(U \cap V) = \operatorname{Ex} U \cap \operatorname{Ex} V,$$

$$\operatorname{Ex}(U \cup V) \supset \operatorname{Ex} U \cup \operatorname{Ex} V.$$

If either the sets U *and* V *are functionally open or the space* X *is normal, then*

$$\operatorname{Ex}(U \cup V) = \operatorname{Ex} U \cup \operatorname{Ex} V.$$

Proof. The first two formulas follow immediately from the definition of the operator Ex. It is, therefore, sufficient to prove that if either the sets U, V are functionally open or if the space X is normal, then

$$\mathrm{Ex}(U \cup V) \subset \mathrm{Ex}\,U \cup \mathrm{Ex}\,V. \tag{4}$$

Defining $A = X\setminus U$ and $B = X\setminus V$ we can replace inclusion (4) by

$$\overline{A} \cap \overline{B} \subset \overline{A \cap B}. \tag{5}$$

Let us consider an arbitrary point $x \in \overline{A} \cap \overline{B}$ with a neighbourhood $G \subset \beta X$. Let F be a functionally closed subset of the space βX such that $x \in \mathrm{Int}\,F \subset F \subset G$. We have

$$x \in \overline{A} \cap \mathrm{Int}\,F \subset \overline{A \cap F} \quad \text{and} \quad x \in \overline{B} \cap \mathrm{Int}\,F \subset \overline{B \cap F}.$$

Hence, by virtue of Corollary 1 to Theorem 3.5.1, it follows that the sets $A \cap F$ and $B \cap F$ are not completely separated. Since these sets are either functionally closed or simply closed, and since in the second case the space X is normal, we have

$$0 \neq (A \cap F) \cap (B \cap F) = (A \cap B) \cap F \subset (A \cap B) \cap G.$$

The neighbourhood G is arbitrary, whence $x \in \overline{A \cap B}$ and inclusion (5) has been proved. ■

Lemma 2. *For every normal space X and every open set $U \subset X$ we have*

$$\overline{\mathrm{Fr}\,U} = \mathrm{Fr}\,\mathrm{Ex}\,U, \tag{6}$$

where $\mathrm{Fr}\,U$ *denotes the boundary of U in the space X and* $\mathrm{Fr}\,\mathrm{Ex}\,U$ *the boundary of the set* $\mathrm{Ex}\,U$ *in the space βX.*

Proof. It follows from Theorem 1.3.6 that $\overline{U} = \overline{\mathrm{Ex}\,U}$, so that

$$\overline{\mathrm{Fr}\,U} = \overline{X \cap \overline{U} \cap \overline{X\setminus U}} \subset \overline{X \cap \overline{U}} \cap \overline{X\setminus U} \subset \overline{\mathrm{Ex}\,U} \cap \overline{(\beta X\setminus \mathrm{Ex}\,U)} = \mathrm{Fr}\,\mathrm{Ex}\,U. \tag{7}$$

By virtue of the first formula of Lemma 1, the open set $\mathrm{Ex}(X\setminus \overline{U})$ is disjoint with the set $\mathrm{Ex}\,U$, whence

$$\mathrm{Fr}\,\mathrm{Ex}\,U \subset \beta X\setminus[\mathrm{Ex}\,U \cup \mathrm{Ex}(X\setminus \overline{U})].$$

Making use of the third formula of Lemma 1, we infer that

$$\mathrm{Fr}\,\mathrm{Ex}\,U \subset \beta X\setminus \mathrm{Ex}[U \cup (X\setminus \overline{U})] = \overline{X\setminus[U \cup (X\setminus \overline{U})]} = \overline{\mathrm{Fr}\,U},$$

which, together with (7), yields (6). ■

Theorem 11. *For every normal space X we have* $\mathrm{Ind}\,X = \mathrm{Ind}\,\beta X$.

Proof. First, we shall prove that $\operatorname{Ind} X \leqslant \operatorname{Ind} \beta X$. The inequality holds if $\operatorname{Ind} \beta X = -1$. Let us suppose that it is valid for all normal spaces whose Čech-Stone compactification has the dimension, Ind, not greater than $n-1$ and let X be a normal space such that $\operatorname{Ind} \beta X \leqslant n$.

Let A be an arbitrary closed subset of the space X and let V denote an open set containing it. By virtue of Corollary 3 to Theorem 3.5.1, the closures $\overline{A}$ and $\overline{X \setminus V}$ of the sets A and $X \setminus V$ in the space βX are disjoint. There exists, therefore, an open set $U \subset \beta X$ which satisfies the conditions

$$(8) \qquad \overline{A} \subset U \subset \overline{U} \subset \beta X \setminus \overline{X \setminus V} \quad \text{and} \quad \operatorname{Ind} \operatorname{Fr} U \leqslant n-1.$$

The set $U_1 = \operatorname{Ex}(U \cap X)$ contains U, and by virtue of Theorem 1.3.6, we have $\overline{U}_1 = \overline{U \cap X} = \overline{U}$. We infer that

$$\operatorname{Fr} U_1 = \overline{U}_1 \cap \overline{\beta X \setminus U_1} \subset \overline{U} \cap \overline{\beta X \setminus U} = \operatorname{Fr} U,$$

and according to the second part of formula (8) and Theorem 3, $\operatorname{Ind} \operatorname{Fr} U_1 \leqslant n-1$. By virtue of Lemma 2, Corollary 7 to Theorem 3.5.1, and the inductive assumption, the last inequality yields $\operatorname{Ind} \operatorname{Fr}(U \cap X) \leqslant n-1$. From the first part of formula (8) and from the equality $\overline{U \cap X} = \overline{U}$ it follows that

$$A \subset X \cap U \subset X \cap \overline{X \cap U} \subset X \setminus \overline{X \setminus V} = V.$$

Hence $\operatorname{Ind} X \leqslant n$ and the inequality $\operatorname{Ind} X \leqslant \operatorname{Ind} \beta X$ is proved.

We shall show that $\operatorname{Ind} \beta X \leqslant \operatorname{Ind} X$. This inequality is valid if $\operatorname{Ind} X = -1$. Let us assume that it is valid for all normal spaces whose large inductive dimension is not greater than $n-1$ and let X be a space such that $\operatorname{Ind} X \leqslant n$.

Let A be an arbitrary closed subset of the space βX and let V denote an open set containing it. Let G and H be open subsets of the space βX which satisfy the condition

$$(9) \qquad A \subset G \subset \overline{G} \subset H \subset \overline{H} \subset V.$$

Since $\operatorname{Ind} X \leqslant n$, there exists a set U open in X and such that

$$(10) \qquad \overline{G} \cap X \subset U \subset X \cap \overline{U} \subset X \cap H \quad \text{and} \quad \operatorname{Ind} \operatorname{Fr} U \leqslant n-1,$$

where $\operatorname{Fr} U$ denotes the boundary of the set U in the space X.

From formulas (9), (10), and Lemma 1 we infer that

$$A \subset G \subset \operatorname{Ex}(G \cap X) \subset \operatorname{Ex} U;$$

moreover, making use of Theorem 1.3.6, we infer that

$$\overline{\operatorname{Ex} U} = \overline{U} \subset \overline{X \cap \overline{U}} \subset \overline{X \cap H} \subset \overline{H} \subset V.$$

Thus, making use of the second part of formula (10), of Lemma 2, of Corollary 7 to Theorem 3.5.1 and of the inductive assumption, we infer that

$$A \subset \operatorname{Ex} U \subset \overline{\operatorname{Ex} U} \subset V \quad \text{and} \quad \operatorname{Ind} \operatorname{Fr} \operatorname{Ex} U \leqslant n-1,$$

i.e. $\operatorname{Ind} \beta X \leqslant n$. We have thus proved that $\operatorname{Ind} \beta X \leqslant \operatorname{Ind} X$, which together with the already proved inverse inequality completes the proof of our theorem. ∎

The theorem proved above and Corollary 6 to Theorem 3.5.1 imply

COROLLARY. *For every normal space X and each dense subspace M which is normal and such that every function $f\colon M \to I$ is extendable over the space X, we have* $\operatorname{Ind} X = \operatorname{Ind} M$.

In particular, for every normal space X and a normal subspace T of the space βX such that $X \subset T$ we have $\operatorname{Ind} X = \operatorname{Ind} T$. ∎

THEOREM 12. *For every Tychonoff space X we have* $\dim X = \dim \beta X$.

Proof. It follows from Theorems 3.5.1 and 7 that $\dim X \leqslant \dim \beta X$. It is therefore sufficient to show that if $\dim X \leqslant n$, then $\dim \beta X \leqslant n$.

Let X be a Tychonoff space such that $\dim X \leqslant n$ and let $\{V_i\}_{i=1}^k$ denote an arbitrary finite open covering of the space βX. By virtue of Theorem 5, there exists a functionally open shrinking $\{W_i\}_{i=1}^k$ of the covering $\{V_i\}_{i=1}^k$ such that

$$\overline{W}_i \subset V_i \quad \text{for} \quad i = 1, 2, \ldots, k. \tag{11}$$

Let us denote by $\{U_i\}_{i=1}^m$ a finite functionally open covering of the space X which is a refinement, of order $\leqslant n$, of the covering $\{W_i \cap X\}_{i=1}^k$. From formula (11) and Theorem 1.3.6 it follows that if $U_i \subset W_j \cap X$, then

$$\operatorname{Ex} U_i \subset \overline{\operatorname{Ex} U_i} = \overline{X \cap \operatorname{Ex} U_i} = \overline{U}_i \subset \overline{W}_j \subset V_j.$$

Hence, by Lemma 1 to the preceding theorem we infer that $\{\operatorname{Ex} U_i\}_{i=1}^m$ is an open covering of the space βX which is a refinement of the covering $\{V_i\}_{i=1}^k$ and has order $\leqslant n$. This yields the inequality $\dim \beta X \leqslant n$. ∎

The theorem proved above and Corollary 6 to Theorem 3.5.1 imply

COROLLARY. *For every Tychonoff space X and its dense subspace M such that every function $f\colon M \to I$ is extendable over the space X we have* $\dim X = \dim M$.

In particular, for every Tychonoff space X and a subspace T of the space βX such that $X \subset T$ we have $\dim X = \dim T$. ∎

EXAMPLE 1. Since for every point x of the real-line R, (or of the circle S^1 (see Example 2.3.1)), and for every neighbourhood V of x there exists a neighbourhood U of the point x which is contained together with its closure in V and such that $\operatorname{Fr} U$ contains exactly two points, we infer that $\operatorname{ind} R \leqslant 1$ and $\operatorname{ind} S^1 \leqslant 1$. It follows from Example 6.2.1 that $\operatorname{ind} I > 0$, whence, by virtue of Theorem 1, $\operatorname{ind} R = \operatorname{ind} S^1 = \operatorname{ind} I = 1$.

For every point x of the n-dimensional Euclidean space R^n, or of the n-dimensional sphere S^n, and for every neighbourhood V of x there exists a neighbourhood U contained, together with its closure, in V and such that $\operatorname{Fr} U$ is homeomorphic to S^{n-1}. Hence, we see by induction that $\operatorname{ind} R^n \leqslant n$, $\operatorname{ind} S^n \leqslant n$ and $\operatorname{ind} I^n \leqslant n$ for every natural number n.

The Menger-Urysohn dimension of the n-dimensional Euclidean space R^n, the sphere S^n, and the cube I^n (and also the dimension Ind and dim of these spaces) is exactly equal to n. The proof of this fact is considerably more difficult than the proof of the above inequalities and will be given in Paragraph 3. ∎

EXAMPLE 2. Let Y and Y^* be the spaces considered in Example 6.2.3. We have shown there that $\operatorname{ind} Y = 0$, $\operatorname{Ind} Y > 0$, and $\dim Y > 0$. It follows from the corollaries to Theorems 11 and 12 and from the properties of the space Y and Y^* proved in Example 6.2.3 that $\operatorname{Ind} Y = \operatorname{Ind} Y^*$ and $\dim Y = \dim Y^*$.

We shall show that $\operatorname{Ind} Y^* \leqslant 1$. Let us suppose that there is given a closed set $A \subset Y^*$ and an open set $V \subset Y^*$ containing it. Let us denote by G an open subset of the segment I such that

$$A \cap (\{\omega_1\} \times I) \subset \{\omega_1\} \times G \subset \{\omega_1\} \times \overline{G} \subset V \cap (\{\omega_1\} \times I).$$

We can evidently assume that the set G is the union of a finite number of open intervals.

Making use of the compactness of the product $X^* \times I$, we can easily verify that there exists an ordinal number $\alpha < \omega_1$ such that

$$A \setminus Y_\alpha \subset Y^* \cap [(X^* \setminus X_\alpha) \times G] \subset Y^* \cap [(X^* \setminus X_\alpha) \times \overline{G}] \subset V. \tag{12}$$

Since the space Y_α is metrizable and separable and since $\operatorname{ind} Y_\alpha = 0$, we infer from Theorems 4.1.6 and 10, that there exists a set H open-and-closed in Y_α (and thus also in Y^*) and such that

$$A \cap Y_\alpha \subset H \subset \overline{H} \subset V. \tag{13}$$

By virtue of (12) and (13), the set $U = H \cup \{Y^* \cap [(X^* \setminus X_\alpha) \times G]\}$ satisfies the condition $A \subset U \subset \overline{U} \subset V$. Since $\operatorname{Fr} U \subset (X^* \setminus X_\alpha) \times \operatorname{Fr} G$ and $\operatorname{Fr} G$ is a finite set, we infer from Theorem 8 that $\operatorname{Ind} \operatorname{Fr} U \leqslant 0$, i.e. $\operatorname{Ind} Y^* \leqslant 1$.

Let us observe, finally, that the equality $\operatorname{Ind} Y^* = 1$ and Theorems 1 and 2 yield $\operatorname{ind} Y^* = 1$.

It can be shown, similarly, that $\dim Y^* \leqslant 1$; this follows also from Theorem 2.6 below. We have finally

$$\operatorname{ind} Y = 0 \neq 1 = \operatorname{ind} Y^*, \quad \operatorname{Ind} Y = 1 = \operatorname{Ind} Y^*, \quad \text{and} \quad \dim Y = 1 = \dim Y^*. \ ∎$$

EXERCISES

A (P. Erdös [1940]). Verify that the Menger-Urysohn dimension of the space X described in Example 6.2.2 is equal to 1.

Hint: It is sufficient to show that for every natural number n the point $x_0 = (0, 0, \ldots, 0, \ldots)$ has a neighbourhood $V_n \subset X$ such that $\delta(V_n) < 1/n$ and $\operatorname{ind} \operatorname{Fr} V_n = 0$. Make use of the fact that the set $\{x \in X: \varrho(x, x_0) = r\}$ is homeomorphic to a subset of the Hilbert cube consisting of points whose coordinates are all rational.

B. Show that for every normal space Y obtained from a non-empty normal space X by adding a point, the inequality $\operatorname{Ind} X \leqslant n$ yields $\operatorname{Ind} Y \leqslant n$.

C. Show that for every Tychonoff space Y obtained from a non-empty space X by adding a point, the inequality $\dim X \leqslant n$ yields $\dim Y \leqslant n$.

Hint: Notice that if $\dim X \leqslant n$, then every finite functionally open covering of the space X has a functionally open shrinking of order $\leqslant n$.

D. Show that if X and Y are compact spaces and $\dim Y = 0$, then $\dim(X \times Y) = \dim X$.

§ 2. Further properties of the dimension dim. We begin with two theorems which will frequently be used in this paragraph and in the following one. They are called the *sum-theorems*. Before formulating those theorems and giving their proof we shall make a remark on coverings. Let $\mathfrak{A} = \{A_s\}_{s \in S}$ and $\mathfrak{B} = \{B_t\}_{t \in T}$ be two coverings of the set X. Then for every $x \in X$ one can find an $s_x \in S$ and a $t_x \in T$ such that $x \in A_{s_x} \cap B_{t_x}$. In other words, the family $\{A_s \cap B_t\}_{s \in S, t \in T}$ is a covering of the set X. We shall denote it by the symbol $\mathfrak{A} \wedge \mathfrak{B}$. It can easily be verified that it is a refinement of the coverings $\mathfrak{A}$ and $\mathfrak{B}$. For every finite sequence $\mathfrak{A}_1, \mathfrak{A}_2, \ldots, \mathfrak{A}_k$ of coverings of the set X the covering $\mathfrak{A}_1 \wedge \mathfrak{A}_2 \wedge \ldots \wedge \mathfrak{A}_k$ of this set is defined inductively by means of the formula: $\mathfrak{A}_1 \wedge \mathfrak{A}_2 \wedge \ldots \wedge \mathfrak{A}_k = \mathfrak{A}_1 \wedge (\mathfrak{A}_2 \wedge \mathfrak{A}_3 \wedge \ldots \wedge \mathfrak{A}_k)$.

THEOREM 1. *If a normal space X has a countable closed covering $\{F_j\}_{j=1}^{\infty}$ such that $\dim F_j \leqslant n$ for $j = 1, 2, \ldots$, then $\dim X \leqslant n$.*

Proof. Let $\mathfrak{U} = \{U_i\}_{i=1}^{k}$ be an arbitrary finite open covering of the space X. For every $j = 0, 1, \ldots$ we define, by means of induction, a family of open subsets $\mathfrak{B}_j = \{V_i^j\}_{i=1}^{k}$ which satisfies the following conditions:

(1) $\overline{V_i^j} \subset U_i$ for $i = 1, 2, \ldots, k$.

(2) $V_i^{j-1} \subset V_i^j$ for $j > 0$ and $i = 1, 2, \ldots, k$.

(3) $F_1 \cup F_2 \cup \ldots \cup F_j \subset \bigcup_{i=1}^{k} V_i^j$.

(4) $\operatorname{ord}(\{\overline{V_i^j}\}_{i=1}^{k}) \leqslant n$.

Conditions (1)-(4) are satisfied for $j = 0$ if we define $V_i^0 = 0$ for $i = 1, 2, \ldots, k$. Let us assume that the family $\mathfrak{B}_j$ has already been defined for $j \leqslant m-1$ and that it satisfies conditions (1)-(4). By virtue of Theorem 1.4, there exists open sets $W_1, W_2, \ldots, W_k$ such that $\operatorname{ord}(\{W_i\}_{i=1}^k) \leqslant n$ and

(5) $$\overline{V_i^{m-1}} \subset W_i \subset \overline{W}_i \subset U_i \quad \text{for} \quad i = 1, 2, \ldots, k.$$

Let $\mathfrak{A} = \mathfrak{U} \wedge \mathfrak{A}_1 \wedge \mathfrak{A}_2 \wedge \ldots \wedge \mathfrak{A}_k$, where $\mathfrak{A}_i = \{W_i, X \setminus \overline{V_i^{m-1}}\}$ for $i = 1, 2, \ldots, k$.

Intersections of the elements of the covering $\mathfrak{A}$ with the subspace F_m form a covering of this subspace. Since $\dim F_m \leqslant n$, we infer from Theorems 1.6 and 1.5 that there exists a refinement $\mathfrak{F}$ which is a covering of F_m consisting of sets closed in F_m, i.e. also in X, and such that $\operatorname{ord} \mathfrak{F} \leqslant n$. By virtue of Theorem 1.4, there exists a swelling $\{H_j\}_{j=1}^l$ of the family $\mathfrak{F}$ consisting of open subsets of X such that the family $\{\overline{H}_j\}_{j=1}^l$ is of order $\leqslant n$, and for every $j \leqslant l$ the set $\overline{H}_j$ is contained in some element of $\mathfrak{A}$. It follows, in particular, that

(6) if $\overline{H}_j \cap \overline{V_i^{m-1}} \neq 0$, then $\overline{H}_j \subset W_i$ for $j = 1, 2, \ldots, l$ and $i = 1, 2, \ldots, k$.

For every $j \leqslant l$ let us choose an index $i = i(j) \leqslant k$ such that $\overline{H}_j \subset U_{i(j)}$. By virtue of (6) and (5) we can evidently assume that the numbers $i(j)$ have been chosen in such a manner that

(7) if $\overline{H}_j \cap \overline{V_{i_0}^{m-1}} \neq 0$ for some $i_0 \leqslant k$, then $\overline{H}_j \cap \overline{V_{i(j)}^{m-1}} \neq 0$.

Let us now define:

$$V_i^m = V_i^{m-1} \cup \bigcup_{i(j)=i} H_j \quad \text{for} \quad i = 1, 2, \ldots, k.$$

The family $\mathfrak{V}_m = \{V_i^m\}_{i=1}^k$ satisfies conditions (1)-(3) for $j = m$. We shall show that condition (4) is also satisfied. For this purpose it is sufficient to show that no point $x \in \bigcup_{i=1}^k \overline{V_i^m} = \bigcup_{i=1}^k \overline{V_i^{m-1}} \cup \bigcup_{j=1}^l \overline{H}_j$ belongs to the closure of more than $n+1$ elements of $\mathfrak{V}_m$. This is satisfied when $x \notin \bigcup_{i=1}^k \overline{V_i^{m-1}}$, since $\operatorname{ord}(\{\overline{H}_j\}_{j=1}^l) \leqslant n$. We can, therefore, assume that $x \in \overline{V_{i_0}^{m-1}}$ for some $i_0 \leqslant k$. For every $i \leqslant k$ when $x \in \overline{V_i^m}$, either $x \in \overline{V_i^{m-1}}$ or $x \in \overline{H}_j$, for some j, such that $i(j) = i$. It follows from formulas (5), (7), and (6) that in both cases $x \in W_i$. Since $\operatorname{ord}(\{W_i\}_{i=1}^k) \leqslant n$, x does not belong to the closure of more than $n+1$ sets of the family $\mathfrak{V}_m$.

The family $\mathfrak{V} = \{V_i\}_{i=1}^k$, where $V_i = \bigcup_{j=0}^{\infty} V_i^j$, is, according to (3), a finite open covering of the space X. By virtue of (1), this covering is a refinement of the covering $\mathfrak{U}$. Since (2) and (4) yield $\operatorname{ord} \mathfrak{V} \leqslant n$, we infer from Theorem 1.6 that $\dim X \leqslant n$. ■

Since every countable regular space is a Lindelöf space, it is normal, and Theorems 1 and 1.10 yield the following

COROLLARY. *For every non-empty countable regular space X the equalities* $\operatorname{ind} X = \operatorname{Ind} X = \dim X = 0$ *hold.* ∎

The second of the theorems mentioned before will be deduced from Lemma 2. This lemma will be more generally stated in order to enable us to deduce one more theorem, fundamental in the dimension theory of metric spaces.

LEMMA 1. *Let $\mathfrak{U} = \{U_s\}_{s\in S}$ be an open covering of a normal space X. Each closed subspace F of the space X, which satisfies the inequality* $\dim F \leqslant n$ *and intersects only a finite number of elements of the covering $\mathfrak{U}$, has an open covering $\mathfrak{V} = \{V_s\}_{s\in S}$ such that*

$$V_s \subset F \cap U_s \quad \textit{for every } s \in S \quad \textit{and} \quad \operatorname{ord} \mathfrak{V} \leqslant n.$$

Proof. Let $F \cap U_s = 0$ for $s \neq s_i$, where $i = 1, 2, \ldots, k$. The sets $\{F \cap U_{s_i}\}_{i=1}^{k}$ form an open covering of the space F. By virtue of Theorem 1.6, this covering has an open finite refinement $\{W_j\}_{j=1}^{m}$ of order $\leqslant n$. Let us choose an $i = i(j) \leqslant k$ for every $j \leqslant m$ such that $W_j \subset F \cap U_{s_{i(j)}}$. It is easy to verify that the family $\mathfrak{V} = \{V_s\}_{s\in S}$, where

$$V_s = \begin{cases} \bigcup\limits_{i(j)=i} W_j, & \text{if } s = s_i \text{ for some } i \leqslant k, \\ 0, & \text{otherwise}, \end{cases}$$

satisfies the conclusion of the lemma. ∎

LEMMA 2. *Let $\mathfrak{U}$ be an open covering of a normal space X. If the space X has a locally finite closed covering $\mathfrak{F}$ whose every element has the Čech-Lebesgue dimension not exceeding n and intersects only a finite number of elements of the covering $\mathfrak{U}$, then the covering $\mathfrak{U}$ has an open shrinking whose order is not greater than n.*

Proof. Let us arrange the elements of the family $\mathfrak{F}$ in a transfinite sequence $F_0, F_1, \ldots, F_\alpha, \ldots, \alpha \leqslant \xi$ of type $\xi+1$ and let $\mathfrak{U} = \{U_s\}_{s\in S}$ be an open covering of the space X which satisfies the assumptions of the lemma. For every $\alpha \leqslant \xi$ we define, by means of transfinite induction, a family $\mathfrak{F}_\alpha = \{F_{\alpha,s}\}_{s\in S}$ consisting of closed subsets of X and satisfying the conditions:

(8) $$F_{\alpha,s} \subset F_\alpha \text{ for every } s \in S.$$

(9) $$\operatorname{ord}\big(\{F_\beta \cap (U_s \setminus \bigcup_{\gamma \leqslant \alpha} F_{\gamma,s})\}_{s\in S}\big) \leqslant n \text{ for every } \beta \leqslant \alpha.$$

(10) The family $\{U_s \setminus \bigcup\limits_{\gamma \leqslant \alpha} F_{\gamma,s}\}_{s\in S}$ is an open covering of the space X.

Let us suppose either that the families $\mathfrak{F}_\alpha$ satisfying conditions (8)-(10) have already been defined for $\alpha < \alpha_0$ or that $\alpha_0 = 0$. To begin with, we shall show that

(11) $$\bigcup_{s\in S}\big(U_s \setminus \bigcup_{\alpha<\alpha_0} F_{\alpha,s}\big) = X.$$

Formula (11) is evidently valid if $\alpha_0 = 0$. Let us suppose, therefore, that $\alpha_0 > 0$ and let us assume that there exists a point

(12) $$x \in X \setminus \bigcup_{s\in S}\big(U_s \setminus \bigcup_{\alpha<\alpha_0} F_{\alpha,s}\big).$$

Since the point x is an element of a set belonging to the family $\mathfrak{F}$, it belongs only to a finite number $U_{s_1}, U_{s_2}, \ldots, U_{s_k}$ of elements of the covering $\mathfrak{U}$. By virtue of (12), there exists an $\alpha(i) < \alpha_0$ for every $i \leqslant k$ such that $x \in F_{\alpha(i),s_i}$. It follows, however, that for $\alpha = \max\big(\alpha(1), \alpha(2), \ldots$ $\ldots, \alpha(k)\big)$ we have $x \notin \bigcup_{s\in S}\big(U_s \setminus \bigcup_{\gamma\leqslant\alpha} F_{\gamma,s}\big)$, contrary to (10). Thus formula (11) has been proved.

Since the family $\mathfrak{F}$ is locally finite, we infer from formula (8) valid for all $\alpha < \alpha_0$, and from the corollary to Theorem 4.4.1, that the covering $\{U_s \setminus \bigcup_{\alpha<\alpha_0} F_{\alpha,s}\}_{s\in S}$ of the space X is open for $\alpha_0 > 0$. Moreover, if $\alpha_0 = 0$, this is also obvious. It follows from Lemma 1 that there exists an open covering $\mathfrak{V} = \{V_s\}_{s\in S}$ of the space F_{α_0} such that $\operatorname{ord}\mathfrak{V} \leqslant n$ and

(13) $$V_s \subset F_{\alpha_0} \cap \big(U_s \setminus \bigcup_{\alpha<\alpha_0} F_{\alpha,s}\big) \quad \text{for every } s \in S.$$

Let $\mathfrak{F}_{\alpha_0} = \{F_{\alpha_0,s}\}_{s\in S}$, where

(14) $$F_{\alpha_0,s} = \big[F_{\alpha_0} \cap \overline{\big(U_s \setminus \bigcup_{\alpha<\alpha_0} F_{\alpha,s}\big)}\big] \setminus V_s.$$

The family $\mathfrak{F}_{\alpha_0}$ satisfies condition (8) for $\alpha = \alpha_0$. Since it follows from (13) and (14) that

(15) $$F_{\alpha_0} \cap \big(U_s \setminus \bigcup_{\alpha\leqslant\alpha_0} F_{\alpha,s}\big) = F_{\alpha_0} \cap \big(U_s \setminus \bigcup_{\alpha<\alpha_0} F_{\alpha,s}\big) \setminus F_{\alpha_0,s} = V_s$$

and $F_\beta \cap \big(U_s \setminus \bigcup_{\alpha\leqslant\alpha_0} F_{\alpha,s}\big) \subset F_\beta \cap \big(U_s \setminus \bigcup_{\alpha\leqslant\beta} F_{\alpha,s}\big)$ holds for $\beta < \alpha_0$, we infer that (9) is also valid for $\alpha = \alpha_0$. Formula (15) yields that

$$F_{\alpha_0} \cap \bigcup_{s\in S}\big(U_s \setminus \bigcup_{\alpha\leqslant\alpha_0} F_{\alpha,s}\big) = \bigcup_{s\in S} F_{\alpha_0} \cap \big(U_s \setminus \bigcup_{\alpha\leqslant\alpha_0} F_{\alpha,s}\big) = \bigcup_{s\in S} V_s = F_{\alpha_0},$$

so that $F_{\alpha_0} \subset \bigcup_{s\in S}\big(U_s \setminus \bigcup_{\alpha\leqslant\alpha_0} F_{\alpha,s}\big)$, which, together with (11) and (8) for $\alpha = \alpha_0$, proves that (10) is valid for $\alpha = \alpha_0$, because the set $\bigcup_{\alpha\leqslant\alpha_0} F_{\alpha,s}$ is closed by virtue of (8) and by the local finiteness of the family $\mathfrak{F}$.

We may assume, therefore, that the family $\mathfrak{F}_\alpha = \{F_{\alpha,s}\}_{s\in S}$ has already been defined for $\alpha \leqslant \xi$. Conditions (9) and (10) imply, in view of the equality $\bigcup_{\beta\leqslant\xi} F_\beta = X$, that the family $\{U_s \setminus \bigcup_{\alpha\leqslant\xi} F_{\alpha,s}\}_{s\in S}$ is an open shrinking of the covering $\mathfrak{U}$ and its order is not greater than n. ■

Lemma 2 and Theorem 1.6 imply

THEOREM 2. *If a normal space X has a locally finite closed covering $\{F_s\}_{s\in S}$ such that $\dim F_s \leqslant n$ for every $s \in S$, then $\dim X \leqslant n$.* ■

THEOREM 3. *A paracompact space X satisfies the inequality $\dim X \leqslant n$ if and only if for every locally finite open covering of the space X there exists a locally finite open refinement of order which is at most n.*

Proof. Let X be a normal space satisfying the above condition and let $\{U_i\}_{i=1}^k$ denote a finite open covering of X. Let us denote by $\{V_s\}_{s\in S}$ an open refinement of order at most n. For every $s\in S$ let us choose an $i = i(s) \leqslant k$ such that $V_s \subset U_{i(s)}$ and let $V_i = \bigcup_{i(s)=i} V_s$. The open covering $\{V_i\}_{i=1}^k$ is a refinement of the covering $\{U_i\}_{i=1}^k$ and is at most of order n, whence $\dim X \leqslant n$.

Let us now consider a paracompact space X such that $\dim X \leqslant n$ and let $\mathfrak{U}$ be an open locally finite covering of X. For every point $x\in X$ there exists a neighbourhood V_x which meets only a finite number of elements of the covering $\mathfrak{U}$. Let $\mathfrak{F} = \{F_s\}_{s\in S}$ be a locally finite closed refinement of the covering $\{V_x\}_{x\in X}$, which exists by virtue of Theorem 5.1.4. Every element of $\mathfrak{F}$ meets at most a finite number of elements of the covering $\mathfrak{U}$. Moreover, by virtue of Theorem 1.7, $\dim F_s \leqslant n$ for every $s\in S$. It follows from Lemma 2 to Theorem 2 that the covering $\mathfrak{U}$ has an open shrinking of, at most, order n. Since this shrinking is evidently locally finite, the proof of Theorem 3 is completed. ■

We shall now establish some connections between the dimension dim and the dimensions ind and Ind. We shall prove two theorems analogous to Theorem 1.2, which will compare various dimensions of the same space. First, however, we shall prove a lemma which is a generalization of Theorem 6.2.5.

LEMMA. *Let X be a Lindelöf space and let $\mathfrak{B}$ denote a base of the space X. For each pair of closed disjoint subsets A, B of the space X there exist an open set $W \subset X$ and a countable family $\{W_i\}_{i=1}^\infty$ of elements of $\mathfrak{B}$ such that*

$$A \subset W \subset \overline{W} \subset X\setminus B \quad \textit{and} \quad \operatorname{Fr} W \subset \bigcup_{i=1}^\infty \operatorname{Fr} W_i.$$

Proof. For every $x\in X$ there exists a neighbourhood $W_x \in \mathfrak{B}$ such that either $A \cap \overline{W}_x = 0$ or $B \cap \overline{W}_x = 0$. Let us choose a countable subcovering $\mathfrak{W} = \{W_i\}_{i=1}^\infty$ from the covering $\{W_x\}_{x\in X}$. Let $\{U_i\}_{i=1}^\infty$ be the family of all elements of $\mathfrak{W}$ whose closure meets the set A

and let $\{V_i\}_{i=1}^{\infty}$ denote the family of the remaining elements of $\mathfrak{W}$. We thus have

(16) $A \subset \bigcup_{i=1}^{\infty} U_i$, $B \subset \bigcup_{i=1}^{\infty} V_i$, and $\overline{U}_i \cap B = 0 = \overline{V}_i \cap A$ for $i = 1, 2, \ldots$

Let

(17) $$G_i = U_i \setminus \bigcup_{j<i} \overline{V}_j \quad \text{and} \quad H_i = V_i \setminus \bigcup_{j \leqslant i} \overline{U}_j.$$

From formulas (16) and (17) it follows that the open sets $W = \bigcup_{i=1}^{\infty} G_i$ and $V = \bigcup_{i=1}^{\infty} H_i$ satisfy the conditions

$$A \subset W, \quad B \subset V, \quad \text{and} \quad W \cap V = 0.$$

Hence $\overline{W} \cap V = 0$ and $\overline{W} \subset X \setminus V \subset X \setminus B$. Since $\operatorname{Fr} W \subset X \setminus (W \cup V)$, to complete the proof it is sufficient to verify that

$$X \setminus (W \cup V) \subset \bigcup_{i=1}^{\infty} \operatorname{Fr} U_i \cup \bigcup_{i=1}^{\infty} \operatorname{Fr} V_i = \bigcup_{i=1}^{\infty} \operatorname{Fr} W_i.$$

Let x be an arbitrary point of $X \setminus (W \cup V)$ and let F be the first element of the sequence $\overline{U}_1, \overline{V}_1, \overline{U}_2, \overline{V}_2, \ldots$ which contains this point. If $F = \overline{U}_i$, then $x \in \operatorname{Fr} U_i = \overline{U}_i \setminus U_i$, because $x \notin G_i$ and $x \notin \overline{V}_j$ for $j < i$. But if $F = \overline{V}_i$, then $x \in \operatorname{Fr} V_i = \overline{V}_i \setminus V_i$, because $x \notin H_i$ and $x \notin \overline{U}_j$ for $j \leqslant i$. In both cases $x \in \bigcup_{i=1}^{\infty} \operatorname{Fr} U_i \cup \bigcup_{i=1}^{\infty} \operatorname{Fr} V_i$. ∎

THEOREM 4. *For every Lindelöf space X we have* $\dim X \leqslant \operatorname{ind} X$.

Proof. It is sufficient to show that if for an integer $m \geqslant 0$ and a Lindelöf space Y we have $\operatorname{ind} Y \leqslant m$, then also $\dim Y \leqslant m$. By virtue of Theorem 1.10, the implication is valid if $m = 0$. Let us suppose that every Lindelöf space Y satisfying $\operatorname{ind} Y \leqslant n-1$ also satisfies $\dim Y \leqslant n-1$ and let X be a Lindelöf space such that $\operatorname{ind} X \leqslant n$.

Let $\{U_i\}_{i=1}^{k}$ be an arbitrary finite open covering of the space X and let $\{F_i\}_{i=1}^{k}$ denote a closed shrinking, which exists according to Theorem 1.5. From the lemma it follows that for every $i = 1, 2, \ldots, k$ there exist an open set W_i and a family $\{W_j^i\}_{j=1}^{\infty}$ such that

$$F_i \subset W_i \subset \overline{W}_i \subset U_i \quad \text{for} \quad i = 1, 2, \ldots, k,$$

$\operatorname{Fr} W_i \subset \bigcup_{j=1}^{\infty} \operatorname{Fr} W_j^i$ and $\operatorname{ind} \operatorname{Fr} W_j^i \leqslant m-1$ for $i = 1, 2, \ldots, k, j = 1, 2, \ldots$

By virtue of Theorem 3.7.4 and by the inductive assumption, we infer that $\dim \operatorname{Fr} W_j^i \leqslant n-1$. In view of Theorems 1.7, 1, and the formula

$$\operatorname{Fr} W_i = \bigcup_{j=1}^{\infty} [(\operatorname{Fr} W_i) \cap (\operatorname{Fr} W_j^i)],$$

this inequality yields

(18) $$\dim \operatorname{Fr} W_i \leqslant n-1 \quad \text{for} \quad i = 1, 2, \ldots, k.$$

Let $A = \bigcup_{i=1}^{k} \operatorname{Fr} W_i$; by virtue of (18) and Theorem 1, $\dim A \leqslant n-1$. It follows from Theorem 1.5 and 1.4 that there exists a family $\{G_i\}_{i=1}^m$ of open subsets of X such that for $i = 1, 2, \ldots, m$ the set $\overline{G}_i$ is contained in an element of the covering $\{U_i\}_{i=1}^k$ and

(19) $$A \subset G = \bigcup_{i=1}^{m} G_i \quad \text{and} \quad \operatorname{ord}(\{\overline{G}_i\}_{i=1}^m) \leqslant n-1.$$

The sets $\overline{G}_1, \overline{G}_2, \ldots, \overline{G}_m, Z_1, Z_2, \ldots, Z_k$, where

$$Z_i = \overline{W}_i \setminus (G \cup \bigcup_{j<i} W_j),$$

form a closed covering of the space X which is a refinement of the covering $\{U_i\}_{i=1}^k$. Hence, by virtue of Theorem 1.6 and 1.4, it is sufficient to show that the order of this covering is at most n. But this follows immediately from the second formula of (19) and from the fact that for $j < i \leqslant k$ the equality

$$Z_j \cap Z_i \subset \overline{W}_j \cap [\overline{W}_i \setminus (G \cup W_j)] \subset (X \setminus G) \cap \operatorname{Fr} W_j = 0$$

holds. ■

The lemma to Theorem 4 and Theorems 1.10, 1, and 1.2 imply

THEOREM 5. *The conditions* $\operatorname{ind} X = 1$ *and* $\operatorname{Ind} X = 1$ *are equivalent for every Lindelöf space* X. ■

On the other hand, Theorems 1.11, 1.12, 1.2, and 4 yield

THEOREM 6. *For every normal space* X *we have* $\dim X \leqslant \operatorname{Ind} X$. ■

EXAMPLE 1. It follows from Example 1.1 and Theorems 5, 6, and 1.10 that $\operatorname{Ind} R = \operatorname{Ind} S^1 = \operatorname{Ind} I = 1$ and that $\dim R = \dim S^1 = \dim I = 1$. From the same example and from Theorem 4 we infer that $\dim R^n \leqslant n$, $\dim S^n \leqslant n$, and $\dim I^n \leqslant n$ for every natural number n. ■

EXAMPLE 2. For every two integers n, m such that $0 \leqslant m \leqslant n$, let R^n_m denote the subspace of the space R^n consisting of those points which have exactly m rational coordinates.

For an arbitrary choice of m natural numbers $i_1, i_2, \ldots, i_m$ which are not greater than n, and of m rational numbers $r_1, r_2, \ldots, r_m$, the space $\mathbf{P}_{i \leqslant n} R_i$, where $R_{i_k} = \{r_{i_k}\}$ for $k = 1, 2, \ldots, m$ and $R_i = R$ for $i \neq i_k$ and $k = 1, 2, \ldots, m$, is a closed subspace of R^n. The space $R^n_m \cap \mathbf{P}_{i \leqslant n} R_i$ is, therefore, a closed subspace of the space R^n_m. Since $R^n_m \cap \mathbf{P}_{i \leqslant n} R_i$ is homeomorphic to the subspace of R^{n-m} consisting of those points whose coordinates are all irrational, we infer from Example 6.2.1 and Theorem 1.10 that $\dim (R^n_m \cap \mathbf{P}_{i \leqslant n} R_i) = 0$. From Theorem 1 it follows, therefore, that

$\dim R^n_m = 0$, because the number of the spaces $R^n_m \cap \mathbf{P}_{i\leqslant n} R_i$ is countable and they cover the space R^n_m. ∎

To end this paragraph we give a characterization of Tychonoff spaces whose Čech-Lebesgue dimension is not greater than n. Before giving the proof of this theorem, we shall prove three lemmas.

Let A, B be a pair of disjoint subsets of a topological space X. A closed subset $L \subset X$ is called a *partition* between the sets A and B provided that there exist two open sets U and V in X such that

$$(20)\quad A \subset U, \quad B \subset V, \quad U \cap V = 0, \quad \text{and} \quad X \setminus L = U \cup V.$$

LEMMA 1. *If L is a functionally closed partition between disjoint subsets A, B of a topological space X, then the sets U, V satisfying* (20) *are functionally open.*

Proof. By our assumption, there exists a continuous function $f\colon X \to R$ such that $L = f^{-1}(0)$. According to Theorem 2.1.6, the formula

$$g(x) = \begin{cases} f(x) & \text{for} \quad x \in U \cup L, \\ 0 & \text{for} \quad x \in V \cup L \end{cases}$$

defines a continuous function $g\colon X \to R$. Since $U = g^{-1}(R \setminus \{0\})$, we infer that U is functionally open. By the symmetry of our assumptions the set V is also functionally open. ∎

LEMMA 2. *If a Tychonoff* (*normal*) *space X satisfies the condition $\dim X \leqslant n$, then for every family $\{B_i\}_{i=1}^{n+2}$ of functionally closed* (*closed*) *subsets such that $\bigcap_{i=1}^{n+2} B_i = 0$ there exists a functionally closed* (*closed*) *covering $\{F_i\}_{i=1}^{n+2}$ of the space X such that*

$$\bigcap_{i=1}^{n+2} F_i = 0 \quad \textit{and} \quad B_i \subset F_i \quad \textit{for} \quad i = 1, 2, \ldots, n+2.$$

Proof. Let us denote by $\{V_i\}_{i=1}^{n+2}$ a functionally open (open) swelling of the family $\{B_i\}_{i=1}^{n+2}$ and let us define $V_{n+3} = X \setminus \bigcup_{i=1}^{n+2} B_i$. Let $\{A_j\}_{j=1}^{m}$ be a functionally closed (closed) refinement of $\{V_i\}_{i=1}^{n+3}$ whose order is at most n. For every $j \leqslant m$ let us choose $i(j) \leqslant n+3$ such that $A_j \subset V_{i(j)}$ and let us define $E_i = \bigcup_{i(j)=i} A_j$. It is easy to verify that $\{E_i\}_{i=1}^{n+3}$ is a functionally closed (closed) shrinking of the covering $\{V_i\}_{i=1}^{n+3}$ and that $\operatorname{ord}(\{E_i\}_{i=1}^{n+3}) \leqslant n$. In particular, we infer that

$$(21)\quad E_1 \cap E_2 \cap \ldots \cap E_{n+1} \cap E_{n+3} = 0 \quad \text{and} \quad B_i \cap E_{n+3} = 0 \quad \text{for} \quad i = 1, 2, \ldots, n+2,$$

because $E_{n+3} \subset V_{n+3} = X \setminus \bigcup_{i=1}^{n+2} B_i \subset X \setminus B_i$.

The family $\{B_i \cup E_i\}_{i=1}^{n+2}$ is a functionally closed (closed) swelling of the family $\{B_i\}_{i=1}^{n+2}$, and this, together with (21), proves that the sets $\{F_i\}_{i=1}^{n+2}$, where

$$F_i = B_i \cup E_i \quad \text{for} \quad i = 1, 2, \ldots, n+1$$

and

$$F_{n+2} = B_{n+2} \cup E_{n+2} \cup E_{n+3},$$

satisfy the conclusion of the lemma. ∎

LEMMA 3. *If every functionally open (open) covering $\{U_i\}_{i=1}^{n+2}$ of a Tychonoff (normal) space X has a functionally open (open) shrinking $\{W_i\}_{i=1}^{n+2}$ such that $\bigcap_{i=1}^{n+2} W_i = 0$, then $\dim X \leqslant n$.*

Proof. We shall prove that every Tychonoff (normal) space X such that $\dim X > n$ has a functionally open (open) covering $\{U_i\}_{i=1}^{n+2}$ such that its every functionally open (open) shrinking $\{W_i\}_{i=1}^{n+2}$ satisfies the condition $\bigcap_{i=1}^{n+2} W_i \neq 0$. By assumption there exists a functionally open (open) finite covering $\mathfrak{V}$ of the space X which has no functionally open (open) shrinking of order $\leqslant n$. Moreover, we can assume, choosing a suitable shrinking if necessary, that the covering $\mathfrak{V}$ is a swelling of its every functionally open (open) shrinking. Since $\operatorname{ord}\mathfrak{V} > n$, we can assume that $\mathfrak{V} = \{V_i\}_{i=1}^{m}$, where $\bigcap_{i=1}^{n+2} V_i \neq 0$.

Let us now consider the functionally open (open) covering $\{U_i\}_{i=1}^{n+2}$ of the space X, where

$$U_i = V_i \quad \text{for} \quad i = 1, 2, \ldots, n+1 \quad \text{and} \quad U_{n+2} = \bigcup_{i=n+2}^{m} V_i,$$

and an arbitrary functionally open (open) shrinking $\{W_i\}_{i=1}^{n+2}$. The covering $\{W_1, W_2, \ldots, W_{n+1}, W_{n+2} \cap V_{n+2}, \ldots, W_{n+2} \cap V_m\}$ is a functionally open (open) shrinking of the covering $\mathfrak{V}$, whence $\mathfrak{V}$ is its swelling and $\bigcap_{i=1}^{n+2} W_i \supset \bigcap_{i=1}^{n+1} W_i \cap (W_{n+2} \cap V_{n+2}) \neq 0$. ∎

Since the condition considered in Lemma 2 yields, by means of the de Morgan formulas, the condition of Lemma 3 and conversely, we get the following

COROLLARY. *A Tychonoff (normal) space X satisfies the condition $\dim X \leqslant n$ if and only if for every family $\{B_i\}_{i=1}^{n+2}$ of functionally closed (closed) subsets such that $\bigcap_{i=1}^{n+2} B_i = 0$ there exists a functionally closed (closed) covering $\{F_i\}_{i=1}^{n+2}$ of the space X which satisfies the conditions*

$$\bigcap_{i=1}^{n+2} F_i = 0 \quad \textit{and} \quad B_i \subset F_i \quad \textit{for} \quad i = 1, 2, \ldots, n+2,$$

or, equivalently, if and only if every functionally open (open) covering $\{U_i\}_{i=1}^{n+2}$ *of* X *has a functionally open (open) shrinking* $\{W_i\}_{i=1}^{n+2}$ *such that* $\bigcap_{i=1}^{n+2} W_i = 0$. ■

THEOREM 7. *A Tychonoff (normal) space* X *satisfies the inequality* $\dim X \leqslant n$ *if and only if for every sequence*

$$(A_1, B_1), (A_2, B_2), \ldots, (A_{n+1}, B_{n+1})$$

of pairs of subsets of the space X, *which are disjoint and functionally closed (closed), there exist functionally closed (closed) sets* $L_1, L_2, \ldots, L_{n+1}$ *such that* L_i *is a partition between the sets* A_i *and* B_i *for* $i = 1, 2, \ldots, n+1$ *and* $L_1 \cap L_2 \cap \ldots \cap L_{n+1} = 0$.

Proof. We shall first prove that the condition is necessary. Let X be a Tychonoff (normal) space such that $\dim X \leqslant n$ and let (A_1, B_1), $(A_2, B_2), \ldots, (A_{n+1}, B_{n+1})$ denote an arbitrary sequence of $n+1$ pairs of its functionally closed (closed) and disjoint subsets. The family $\{B_i\}_{i=1}^{n+2}$, where $B_{n+2} = \bigcup_{i=1}^{n+1} A_i$, is a family of functionally closed (closed) sets with the empty intersection. Thus, by virtue of Lemma 2 and Theorem 1.4, there exists a functionally open (open) covering $\{U_i\}_{i=1}^{n+2}$ of the space X such that $\bigcap_{i=1}^{n+2} U_i = 0$ and $B_i \subset U_i$ for $i = 1, 2, \ldots, n+2$.

The family $\{V_i\}_{i=1}^{n+2}$, where $V_i = U_i \setminus A_i$ for $i = 1, 2, \ldots, n+1$ and $V_{n+2} = U_{n+2}$, is a functionally open (open) covering of the space X. Let us consider its functionally closed (closed) shrinking $\{F_i\}_{i=1}^{n+2}$ and let us define

$$(22) \qquad E_i = F_{n+2} \setminus U_i \quad \text{and} \quad C_i = A_i \cup E_i, \quad D_i = B_i \cup F_i \quad \text{for} \quad i = 1, 2, \ldots, n+1.$$

Since

$$C_i \cap D_i = (A_i \cup E_i) \cap (B_i \cup F_i) = (A_i \cap B_i) \cup (A_i \cap F_i) \cup (E_i \cap B_i) \cup (E_i \cap F_i) = 0,$$

we infer from Theorem 6.2.2 that for every $i = 1, 2, \ldots, n+1$ there exists a continuous function $f_i \colon X \to I$ such that $f_i(C_i) \subset \{0\}$ and $f_i(D_i) \subset \{1\}$. The set

$$(23) \qquad L_i = f_i^{-1}(1/2) \subset X \setminus (C_i \cup D_i)$$

s a functionally closed (closed) partition between the sets A_i and B_i for $i = 1, 2, \ldots, n+1$. By virtue of (22) and of the equality $\bigcap_{i=1}^{n+2} U_i = 0$

we have

$$\bigcup_{i=1}^{n+1} E_i = F_{n+2} \setminus \bigcap_{i=1}^{n+1} U_i = F_{n+2}.$$

Hence, according to (22) and (23),

$$\bigcap_{i=1}^{n+1} L_i \subset X \setminus \bigcup_{i=1}^{n+1} (C_i \cup D_i) \subset X \setminus (\bigcup_{i=1}^{n+1} E_i \cup \bigcup_{i=1}^{n+1} F_i) = X \setminus \bigcup_{i=1}^{n+2} F_i = 0,$$

which proves that the condition of the theorem is necessary.

Let us now assume that a Tychonoff (normal) space X satisfies this condition. Let $\{U_i\}_{i=1}^{n+2}$ be an arbitrary functionally open (open) covering of the space X and which consists of $n+2$ elements.

Let us consider a functionally closed (closed) shrinking $\{B_i\}_{i=1}^{n+2}$ of the covering $\{U_i\}_{i=1}^{n+2}$ and let us define

$$A_i = X \setminus U_i \quad \text{for} \quad i = 1, 2, \ldots, n+1.$$

The sequence $(A_1, B_1), (A_2, B_2), \ldots, (A_{n+1}, B_{n+1})$ consists of pairs of disjoint and functionally closed (closed) sets. Hence there exist sets V_i, W_i, where $i = 1, 2, \ldots, n+1$, which are functionally open (open) and satisfy

(24) $A_i \subset V_i, \quad B_i \subset W_i, \quad V_i \cap W_i = 0 \quad \text{for} \quad i = 1, 2, \ldots, n+1$

and $\bigcap_{i=1}^{n+1} [X \setminus (V_i \cup W_i)] = X \setminus \bigcup_{i=1}^{n+1} (V_i \cup W_i) = 0$, i.e.

(25) $$\bigcup_{i=1}^{n+1} V_i \cup \bigcup_{i=1}^{n+1} W_i = X.$$

Since (25), (24) and the inclusion $B_{n+2} \subset U_{n+2}$ yield

$$[U_{n+2} \cap \bigcup_{i=1}^{n+1} V_i] \cup \bigcup_{i=1}^{n+1} W_i = [U_{n+2} \cup \bigcup_{i=1}^{n+1} W_i] \cap [\bigcup_{i=1}^{n+1} V_i \cup \bigcup_{i=1}^{n+1} W_i]$$
$$\supset \bigcup_{i=1}^{n+2} B_i = X,$$

the family $\{W_i\}_{i=1}^{n+2}$, where

$$W_{n+2} = U_{n+2} \cap \bigcup_{i=1}^{n+1} V_i,$$

is a functionally open (open) shrinking of the covering $\{U_i\}_{i=1}^{n+2}$. Moreover, in view of (24),

$$\bigcap_{i=1}^{n+2} W_i = \bigcap_{i=1}^{n+1} W_i \cap \left(U_{n+2} \cap \bigcup_{i=1}^{n+1} V_i\right) \subset \bigcap_{i=1}^{n+1} W_i \cap \bigcup_{i=1}^{n+1} V_i = 0,$$

from which, by virtue of Lemma 3, the inequality $\dim X \leqslant n$ follows. ∎

EXERCISES

A. Show that if X is a Tychonoff space and $M \subset X$ is a subspace such that $\dim M \leqslant n$ and such that every function $f: M \to I$ can be extended over X, then for every functionally open finite covering $\mathfrak{A}$ of the space X there exists a functionally open family $\{H_j\}_{j=1}^{l}$ such that $M \subset \bigcup_{j=1}^{l} H_j$, $\operatorname{ord}(\{\overline{H}_j\}_{j=1}^{l}) \leqslant n$ and the set $\overline{H}_j$ is contained in some element of $\mathfrak{A}$, for every $j \leqslant l$.

B (M. Katětov [1950a]). Show that if a Tychonoff space X has a countable covering $\{M_j\}_{j=1}^{\infty}$ such that $\dim M_j \leqslant n$ and such that every function $f: M_j \to I$ can be extended over the space X for $j = 1, 2, \ldots$, then $\dim X \leqslant n$.

Hint: Making use of Exercise A modify the proof of Theorem 1. Another proof can be found by using Problem 2.C and Theorem 1.12.

C (C. H. Dowker [1947]). Prove that for a normal space X the inequality $\dim X \leqslant n$ holds if and only if every star-finite open covering of the space X has a star-finite open refinement of order at most n.

D (K. Morita [1950a]). Generalize Theorem 4, by proving that the inequality $\dim X \leqslant \operatorname{ind} X$ holds for every strongly paracompact space X.

Hint: Adapt the proof of lemma to Theorem 4. Make use of Lemmas 1 and 2 to Theorem 5.3.3 and of Theorem 1.8.

§ 3. Dimension of metrizable spaces. One of the most important theorems of dimension theory is the theorem on the equality of the dimensions Ind and dim for metrizable spaces. We begin the present paragraph with the proof of this theorem. In order to simplify the proof we shall consider one more dimension, which will later be found to be equal to the dimensions Ind and dim.

Let (X, ϱ) be an arbitrary metric space and let n be an integer greater than -2. We shall say that

(DH1) $\operatorname{ds} X \leqslant n$ *if there exists a countable family* $\{\mathfrak{A}_i\}_{i=1}^{\infty}$ *of locally finite open coverings of the space* X *such that*

(a) $\operatorname{ord} \mathfrak{A}_i \leqslant n$ *for* $i = 1, 2, \ldots$;

(b) $\delta(U) \leqslant 1/i$ *for every* $U \in \mathfrak{A}_i$ *and* $i = 1, 2, \ldots$;

(c) *the covering* $\{\overline{U}\}_{U \in \mathfrak{A}_{i+1}}$ *is a refinement of* $\mathfrak{A}_i$ *for* $i = 1, 2, \ldots$

(DH2) $\operatorname{ds} X = n$ *if* $\operatorname{ds} X \leqslant n$ *is true and* $\operatorname{ds} X \leqslant n-1$ *is false.*

(DH3) $\operatorname{ds} X = \infty$ *if* $\operatorname{ds} X \leqslant n$ *is false for every* n.

Conditions (DH1)-(DH3) assign to every metric space X an integer $\operatorname{ds} X$ greater than -2 or the "infinite number" ∞ which is called the *Dowker-Hurewicz dimension* or the *sequential dimension* of the space X. It is easy to see that $\operatorname{ds} X = -1$ if and only if X is the empty space.

LEMMA 1. *For every metric space* X *we have* $\operatorname{ds} X \leqslant \dim X$.

Proof. Assuming that $\dim X \leqslant n$ it is sufficient to construct a countable family $\{\mathfrak{A}_i\}_{i=1}^{\infty}$ of locally finite open coverings of the space X which satisfies conditions (a)-(c). We shall define the coverings $\mathfrak{A}_i$ inductively.

Let us assume that either $k = 1$ or that $k > 1$, that the coverings $\mathfrak{A}_1, \mathfrak{A}_2, \ldots, \mathfrak{A}_{k-1}$ have already been defined and that they satisfy conditions (a)-(c). Let $\mathfrak{B} = \mathfrak{A}_{k-1} \wedge \{B(x, 1/2k)\}_{x \in X}$, where $\mathfrak{A}_0 = \{X\}$. Since according to Corollary 1 to Theorem 5.1.4, X is paracompact, the covering $\mathfrak{B}$ has a locally finite open refinement $\{U_s\}_{s \in S}$. By virtue of Lemma 1 to Theorem 5.1.3, there exists an open covering $\{V_s\}_{s \in S}$ of the space X such that $\overline{V}_s \subset U_s$ for every $s \in S$. This covering is evidently locally finite. It can easily be verified that we can define $\mathfrak{A}_k$ as a locally finite open refinement of $\{V_s\}_{s \in S}$ of order $\leqslant n$, which exists by virtue of Theorem 2.3. ∎

LEMMA 2. *For every metric space X we have* $\operatorname{Ind} X \leqslant \operatorname{ds} X$.

Proof. It is sufficient to show that if for an integer $m \geqslant -1$ and a metric space Y the inequality $\operatorname{ds} Y \leqslant m$ holds, then also $\operatorname{Ind} Y \leqslant m$. This is evidently true for $m = -1$. Let us assume that we have already proved the implication for $m \leqslant n-1$ and let us consider a metric space X such that $\operatorname{ds} X \leqslant n$ and a pair A, B of disjoint closed subsets. In order to complete the proof it is sufficient to construct open sets $M, N \subset X$ such that, by defining $K = X \setminus (M \cup N)$, we have

$$(1) \qquad A \subset M, \quad B \subset N, \quad M \cap N = 0, \quad \text{and} \quad \operatorname{Ind} K \leqslant n-1,$$

for this would yield $A \subset M \subset \overline{M} \subset X \setminus B$, $\operatorname{Fr} M \subset K$, and consequently, according to Theorem 1.3, $\operatorname{Ind} \operatorname{Fr} M \leqslant n-1$.

Let us denote by $\{\mathfrak{A}_i\}_{i=1}^{\infty}$ a family of locally finite open coverings of the space X which satisfy conditions (a)-(c). Let us define $M_0 = N_0 = 0$ and let us define for $i = 1, 2, \ldots$

$$(2) \qquad \mathfrak{A}_{i,1} = \{U \in \mathfrak{A}_i : \overline{U} \cap (B \cup N_{i-1}) = 0\},$$

$$(3) \qquad \mathfrak{A}_{i,2} = \{U \in \mathfrak{A}_i : \overline{U} \cap (A \cup M_{i-1}) = 0 \text{ and } \overline{U} \cap (B \cup N_{i-1}) \neq 0\},$$

$$(4) \qquad \mathfrak{A}_{i,3} = \{U \in \mathfrak{A}_i : \overline{U} \cap (A \cup M_{i-1}) \neq 0 \neq \overline{U} \cap (B \cup N_{i-1})\},$$

$$(5) \qquad G_i = \bigcup_{U \in \mathfrak{A}_{i,1}} U, \quad H_i = \bigcup_{U \in \mathfrak{A}_{i,2}} U, \quad J_i = \bigcup_{U \in \mathfrak{A}_{i,3}} U,$$

$$(6) \qquad M_i = X \setminus (H_i \cup J_i), \quad N_i = X \setminus (G_i \cup J_i).$$

Formulas (2)-(6) define families $\mathfrak{A}_{i,1}, \mathfrak{A}_{i,2}, \mathfrak{A}_{i,3} \subset \mathfrak{A}_i$ and subsets $M_i, N_i \subset X$ for $i = 1, 2, \ldots$ From (2)-(4) it follows that

$$\mathfrak{A}_{i,1} \cup \mathfrak{A}_{i,2} \cup \mathfrak{A}_{i,3} = \mathfrak{A}_i \quad \text{for} \quad i = 1, 2, \ldots,$$

whence we infer that $G_i \cup H_i \cup J_i = X$ and, by virtue of (5) and (6), that

$$(7) \qquad \overline{M}_i = M_i, \quad \overline{N}_i = N_i, \quad M_i \cap N_i = 0 \quad \text{for} \quad i = 1, 2, \ldots$$

Formulas (2), (3), (5), and (6) immediately yield the following relations:

$$\text{(8)} \qquad \text{if } U \in \mathfrak{A}_{i,1}, \text{ then } U \cap N_i = 0 = \overline{U} \cap B;$$

$$\text{(9)} \qquad \text{if } U \in \mathfrak{A}_{i,2}, \text{ then } U \cap M_i = 0 = \overline{U} \cap A;$$

$$\text{(10)} \qquad \text{if } U \in \mathfrak{A}_{i,3}, \text{ then } U \cap M_i = 0 = U \cap N_i.$$

Let us now consider an integer i and a set $V \in \mathfrak{A}_{i+1,3}$. By virtue of (4),

$$\text{(11)} \qquad \overline{V} \cap (A \cup M_i) \neq 0 \neq \overline{V} \cap (B \cup N_i).$$

According to (c) there exists a $U \in \mathfrak{A}_i$ such that $\overline{V} \subset U$. It follows from (8), (9), and (11) that $U \in \mathfrak{A}_{i,3}$ which yields

$$\text{(12)} \qquad J_{i+1} \subset J_i \quad \text{for} \quad i = 1, 2, \ldots$$

and in view of (10) and (11),

$$\text{(13)} \quad \text{if } V \in \mathfrak{A}_{i+1,3}, \text{ then } \overline{V} \cap M_i = 0 = \overline{V} \cap N_i \text{ and } \overline{V} \cap A \neq 0 \neq \overline{V} \cap B.$$

Since the family $\mathfrak{A}_{i+1}$ is locally finite, we infer from (2), (3), (13), (5), and from Theorem 4.4.1 that

$$\text{(14)} \quad M_i \cap \overline{J}_{i+1} = 0 = M_i \cap \overline{H}_{i+1} \quad \text{and} \quad N_i \cap \overline{J}_{i+1} = 0 = N_i \cap \overline{G}_{i+1}.$$

From (14) and (6) we get for $i = 1, 2, \ldots$

$$\text{(15)} \quad M_i \subset X \setminus (\overline{H}_{i+1} \cup \overline{J}_{i+1}) = \operatorname{Int} M_{i+1} \quad \text{and}$$
$$N_i \subset X \setminus (\overline{G}_{i+1} \cup \overline{J}_{i+1}) = \operatorname{Int} N_{i+1}.$$

Hence, in view of the last formula of (7), it follows that the sets

$$M = \bigcup_{i=1}^{\infty} M_i \quad \text{and} \quad N = \bigcup_{i=1}^{\infty} N_i$$

are open and disjoint.

Let us consider an arbitrary point $x \in A$. Since $A \cap B = 0$ and $B = \overline{B}$, we infer from Corollary 1 to Theorem 4.1.5 that $d(x, B) > 0$. It follows from (b) that $B \cap \overline{\operatorname{St}(x, \mathfrak{A}_i)} = 0$ for a certain natural number i. Therefore, for every set $U \in \mathfrak{A}_i$ which contains the point x we have $\overline{U} \cap A \neq 0$ and $\overline{U} \cap B = 0$; hence, from (3) and (13), it follows that $U \notin (\mathfrak{A}_{i,2} \cup \mathfrak{A}_{i,3})$. We deduce from (6) that $x \in M_i$ and, since the point $x \in A$ is arbitrary, that $A \subset M$. It can be proved analogously that $B \subset N$.

To complete the proof of (1) it is now sufficient to show that the large inductive dimension of the set $K = X \setminus (M \cup N)$ is at most $n-1$.

Now for every point $x \in X$, either $d(x, A) > 0$ or $d(x, B) > 0$. Hence, for sufficiently large i and for an arbitrary set $U \in \mathfrak{A}_i$ which contains the point x, either $\overline{U} \cap A = 0$ or $\overline{U} \cap B = 0$, We infer from (13) that $U \notin \mathfrak{A}_{i,3}$, i.e. $x \notin J_i$, so that

$$\bigcap_{i=1}^{\infty} J_i = 0. \tag{16}$$

Let $C_i = K \setminus J_i$ for $i = 1, 2, \ldots$ Since the set K is closed and the set J_i is open, we have, from (12) and (16),

$$K = \bigcup_{i=1}^{\infty} C_i, \quad C_i \subset C_{i+1}, \quad \text{and} \quad \overline{C}_i = C_i \quad \text{for} \quad i = 1, 2, \ldots \tag{17}$$

We shall now show that

$$\operatorname{ds} C_i \leqslant n-1 \quad \text{for} \quad i = 1, 2, \ldots \tag{18}$$

To begin with, let us note that

$$C_i \subset K = X \setminus (M \cup N) \subset X \setminus (M_{i+j} \cup N_{i+j}) = (H_{i+j} \cap G_{i+j}) \cup J_{i+j}$$

for $i, j = 1, 2, \ldots$ By virtue of (17), $C_i \subset C_{i+j} \subset X \setminus J_{i+j}$, whence $C_i \subset H_{i+j} \cap G_{i+j}$ for $i, j = 1, 2, \ldots$

From the last formula it follows that every point $x \in C_i$ belongs to a certain element of the family $\mathfrak{A}_{i+j,1}$ and to a certain element of the family $\mathfrak{A}_{i+j,2}$. Since $\operatorname{ord} \mathfrak{A}_{i+j} \leqslant n$, the family $\mathfrak{A}_j^i = \{U \cap C_i \colon U \in \mathfrak{A}_{i+j,2}\}$ is a covering of the space C_i whose order is at most $n-1$. This covering is obviously open and locally finite, and the diameter of its elements is not greater than $1/j$.

Let us now consider an arbitrary non-empty element $U \cap C_i$ of the covering $\mathfrak{A}_{j+1}^i$. Since $U \in \mathfrak{A}_{i+j+1,2} \subset \mathfrak{A}_{i+j+1}$, we infer from (c) that there exists a $V \in \mathfrak{A}_{i+j}$ such that $\overline{U} \subset V$. It follows from the definition of the set C_i and from (12) that

$$0 \neq U \cap C_i \subset V \cap C_i \subset V \cap (X \setminus J_i) \subset V \cap (X \setminus J_{i+j}).$$

Hence $V \notin \mathfrak{A}_{i+j,3}$. If we assume that $V \in \mathfrak{A}_{i+j,1}$, then by virtue of (8),

$$\overline{U} \cap (B \cup N_{i+j}) \subset V \cap (B \cup N_{i+j}) = 0,$$

which by (3) contradicts $U \in \mathfrak{A}_{i+j+1,2}$. We thus have $V \in \mathfrak{A}_{i+j,2}$ whence $V \cap C_i \in \mathfrak{A}_j^i$ and $\overline{U \cap C_i} \subset \overline{U} \cap C_i \subset V \cap C_i$, which proves that the closures of elements of the family $\mathfrak{A}_{j+1}^i$ form a refinement of the family $\mathfrak{A}_j^i$. Thus the proof of inequality (18) is completed.

By the inductive assumption we have that $\operatorname{Ind} C_i \leqslant n-1$ for $i=1, 2, \ldots$ On the other hand, it follows from Theorems 2.6, 2.1, and from (17) that $\dim K \leqslant n-1$. Making use of Lemma 1 we infer that $\operatorname{ds} K \leqslant n-1$. Hence by virtue of the inductive assumption, we get the inequality $\operatorname{Ind} K \leqslant n-1$ which completes the proof of (1) and of the lemma. ∎

Lemma 1, Lemma 2, and Theorem 2.6 imply

THEOREM 1. *For every metrizable space X we have* $\dim X = \operatorname{Ind} X$. ■

Theorems 1.2, 2.4, 4.1.6, and 1 immediately yield

THEOREM 2. *For every metrizable separable space X we have* $\operatorname{ind} X = \operatorname{Ind} X = \dim X$. ■

In connection with Theorems 1 and 2 the question can be raised whether the small inductive dimension of a metrizable space may be different from the dimensions Ind and dim. This problem had been unsolved for a long time but in 1962 an example of a space X which is metrizable in a complete manner and such that $\operatorname{ind} X = 0$ but $\operatorname{Ind} X = \dim X = 1$ was found. However, the definition of this space and the calculation of its dimensions ind and Ind are rather difficult and will not be presented in this book.

From Lemmas 1 and 2 to Theorem 1 and from Theorem 2.6 it follows also that the sequential dimension of a metric space does not depend on the choice of a metric in that space, because for every metric it is equal to the large inductive dimension and to the covering dimension of that space. Since for every metric space X and a subspace $M \subset X$ with the same metric ϱ the inequality $\operatorname{ds} M \leqslant \operatorname{ds} X$ holds, we get

THEOREM 3. *If M is a subspace of a metrizable space X, then* $\operatorname{Ind} M \leqslant \operatorname{Ind} X$ *and* $\dim M \leqslant \dim X$. ■

Before presenting the next theorem, we prove four lemmas. The proof of the first one can be obtained by a simple modification of the proof of Lemma 1 to Theorem 4.4.5 (cf. the proof of the lemma to Theorem 2.4).

LEMMA 1. *The large inductive dimension of a non-empty normal space, which has a σ-locally finite base consisting of open-and-closed sets, is equal to 0.* ■

LEMMA 2. *Let X be a metrizable space and let $Z \subset X$ denote a subspace. If $\operatorname{Ind} Z \leqslant 0$, then for every closed set $A \subset X$ and for every open set $V \subset X$ containing A, there exists an open set $U \subset X$ such that $A \subset U \subset \overline{U} \subset V$ and $Z \cap \operatorname{Fr} U = 0$.*

Proof. Let $W_1, W_2 \subset X$ denote open sets which satisfy the inclusions:

$$A \subset W_1 \subset \overline{W}_1 \subset W_2 \subset \overline{W}_2 \subset V. \tag{19}$$

Since $\operatorname{Ind} Z = 0$, there exists a set U_0 which is open-and-closed in Z and is such that $Z \cap \overline{W}_1 \subset U_0 \subset Z \cap \overline{U}_0 \subset W_2$. We thus have

$$Z \setminus U_0 \subset Z \setminus (Z \cap W_1) = Z \setminus W_1 \subset X \setminus W_1 \quad \text{and} \quad U_0 \subset \overline{W}_2. \tag{20}$$

By virtue of Theorem 4.1.5 the functions

$$f(x) = d(x, A \cup U_0) \quad \text{and} \quad g(x) = d\big(x, [(X \setminus V) \cup (Z \setminus U_0)]\big)$$

are continuous, whence the set $U = \{x \in X: f(x) < g(x)\}$ is open and $\overline{U} \subset \{x \in X: f(x) \leqslant g(x)\}$. It follows from Corollary 1 to Theorem 4.1.5 and from (19) and (20) that if $x \in A$, then $f(x) = 0$ and $g(x) > 0$. But if $x \in X \setminus V$, then $f(x) > 0$ and $g(x) = 0$. Hence $A \subset U$ and $X \setminus V \subset X \setminus \overline{U}$, i.e. $\overline{U} \subset V$. By the same arguments it follows from the closedness of U_0 and $Z \setminus U_0$ in Z that if $x \in U_0$, then $f(x) = 0$ and $g(x) > 0$. But if $x \in Z \setminus U_0$, then $f(x) > 0$ and $g(x) = 0$. Hence $Z \cap \operatorname{Fr} U = Z \cap (\overline{U} \setminus U) \subset Z \cap \{x \in X: f(x) = g(x)\} = 0$. ■

LEMMA 3. *Every metrizable space X which satisfies the inequality $\operatorname{Ind} X \leqslant n$ for a non-negative integer n has a base $\mathfrak{B} = \bigcup_{i=1}^{\infty} \mathfrak{B}_i$, where $\mathfrak{B}_i = \{U_s\}_{s \in S_i}$ is a locally finite open covering of the space X such that $\delta(U_s) \leqslant 1/i$ and $\operatorname{Ind} \operatorname{Fr} U_s \leqslant n-1$ for every $s \in S_i$, $i = 1, 2, \ldots$*

Proof. Let us consider a metrizable space X satisfying the inequality $\operatorname{Ind} X \leqslant n$. By Corollary 1 to Theorem 5.1.4, there exists for every $i = 1, 2, \ldots$ a locally finite open covering $\{V_s\}_{s \in S_i}$ of the space X such that $\delta(V_s) \leqslant 1/i$ for every $s \in S_i$. From Lemma 1 to Theorem 5.1.3 it follows that for every $i = 1, 2, \ldots$ there exists a closed covering $\{F_s\}_{s \in S_i}$ of the space X such that $F_s \subset V_s$ for every $s \in S_i$. Since $\operatorname{Ind} X \leqslant n$, for every i and every $s \in S_i$ there exists an open set U_s which satisfies the following conditions:

$$(21) \qquad F_s \subset U_s \subset \overline{U}_s \subset V_s \quad \text{and} \quad \operatorname{Ind} \operatorname{Fr} U_s \leqslant n-1.$$

The family $\mathfrak{B}_i = \{U_s\}_{s \in S_i}$ is a locally finite open covering of the space X for $i = 1, 2, \ldots$ Evidently $\delta(U_s) \leqslant 1/i$ for every $s \in S_i$, so that one can easily deduce that $\mathfrak{B} = \bigcup_{i=1}^{\infty} \mathfrak{B}_i$ is a base for the space X. ■

LEMMA 4. *Every metrizable space X which has a σ-locally finite base $\mathfrak{B} = \{U_s\}_{s \in S}$ such that $\operatorname{Ind} \operatorname{Fr} U_s \leqslant n-1$ for every $s \in S$, contains subspaces Y and Z which satisfy the conditions:*

$$X = Y \cup Z, \quad \operatorname{Ind} Y \leqslant n-1, \quad \textit{and} \quad \operatorname{Ind} Z = 0.$$

Proof. Let us represent the set S as the union of sets $S_1, S_2, \ldots$ such that the family $\{U_s\}_{s \in S_i}$ is locally finite for $i = 1, 2, \ldots$ and let us consider the sets

$$Y = \bigcup_{i=1}^{\infty} \bigcup_{s \in S_i} \operatorname{Fr} U_s \quad \text{and} \quad Z = X \setminus Y.$$

It follows from Theorems 1, 2.1, 2.2, and from the corollary to Theorem 4.4.1 that $\operatorname{Ind} Y \leqslant n-1$. Since the family $\{Z \cap U_s\}_{s \in S}$ is a σ-locally finite base of the space Z and the boundary of the set $Z \cap U_s$ in the space Z is contained in $Z \cap \operatorname{Fr} U_s$, i.e. is empty, the equality $\operatorname{Ind} Z = 0$ follows from Lemma 1. ■

THEOREM 4. *A metrizable space X satisfies the inequality* $\operatorname{Ind} X \leqslant n$, *where* $n \geqslant 0$, *if and only if it contains two subspaces Y and Z such that*

$$X = Y \cup Z, \quad \operatorname{Ind} Y \leqslant n-1, \quad \textit{and} \quad \operatorname{Ind} Z = 0.$$

Proof. If X is a metrizable space which satisfies the condition $\operatorname{Ind} X \leqslant n$ for some $n \geqslant 0$, then the required spaces $Y, Z \subset X$ exist by virtue of Lemma 3 and 4.

On the other hand, if a metrizable space X can be represented in the form of the union of two subspaces Y and Z such that $\operatorname{Ind} Y \leqslant n-1$ and $\operatorname{Ind} Z = 0$, then $\operatorname{Ind} X \leqslant n$ by Theorem 1.3 and Lemma 2. ■

Theorem 4 and Lemmas 3 and 4 to that theorem imply

THEOREM 5. *A metrizable space X satisfies the inequality* $\operatorname{Ind} X \leqslant n$, *where* $n \geqslant 0$, *if and only if it has a σ-locally finite base $\mathfrak{B}$ such that* $\operatorname{Ind} \operatorname{Fr} U \leqslant n-1$ *for every* $U \in \mathfrak{B}$. ■

Theorem 4 implies also

THEOREM 6. *A metrizable space X satisfies the condition* $\operatorname{Ind} X \leqslant n$ *if and only if it can be represented as the union of* $n+1$ *subspaces whose large inductive dimension is at most* 0. ■

Theorem 6 implies

THEOREM 7. *For every two subspaces X, Y of a metrizable space the following formula is valid:*

$$\operatorname{Ind}(X \cup Y) \leqslant \operatorname{Ind} X + \operatorname{Ind} Y + 1. \ ■$$

The following theorem, which is a generalization of Lemma 2 to Theorem 4, is also valid.

THEOREM 8. *Let X be a metrizable space and let M denote its subspace. If* $\operatorname{Ind} M \leqslant n$, *where* $n \geqslant 0$, *then for every closed set $A \subset X$ and every open set $V \subset X$ containing A there exists an open set $U \subset X$ such that* $A \subset U \subset \overline{U} \subset V$ *and* $\operatorname{Ind}(M \cap \operatorname{Fr} U) \leqslant n-1$.

Proof. By virtue of Theorem 4, there exist subspaces $Y, Z \subset M$ such that $M = Y \cup Z$, $\operatorname{Ind} Y \leqslant n-1$, and $\operatorname{Ind} Z = 0$. The open set U which satisfies the conclusion of Lemma 2 to Theorem 4 also satisfies the conclusion of our theorem; for we have $M \cap \operatorname{Fr} U \subset M \setminus Z \subset Y$ and $\operatorname{Ind}(M \cap \operatorname{Fr} U) \leqslant n-1$ by virtue of Theorem 1.3. ■

Theorem 8 implies by induction the following corollary, which is a particular case of Theorem 2.7.

COROLLARY. *For every sequence of* $n+1$ *pairs*

$$(A_1, B_1), (A_2, B_2), \ldots, (A_{n+1}, B_{n+1})$$

consisting of disjoint and closed subspaces of a metrizable space X which satisfies the condition $\operatorname{Ind} X \leqslant n$, *there exist open sets* $U_1, U_2, \ldots, U_{n+1}$

such that

$$A_i \subset U_i \subset \overline{U}_i \subset X \setminus B \quad \text{for} \quad i = 1, 2, \ldots, n+1$$

and $\operatorname{Fr} U_1 \cap \operatorname{Fr} U_2 \cap \ldots \cap \operatorname{Fr} U_{n+1} = 0$. ■

EXAMPLE 1. We infer from Theorem 2 and Example 1.1 or 2.1 that $\operatorname{Ind} R^n \leqslant n$, $\operatorname{Ind} S^n \leqslant n$, and $\operatorname{Ind} I^n \leqslant n$ for every natural number n.

The decomposition of the space R^n into the union of $(n+1)$ 0-dimensional sets, which exists by Theorem 6, can, by Example 2.2, be given by the formula:

$$R^n = R_0^n \cup R_1^n \cup \ldots \cup R_n^n.$$

This formula proves, independently of Examples 1.1 and 2.1, that $\operatorname{Ind} R^n \leqslant n$. ■

EXAMPLE 2. Let X_i be a discrete space of power $\mathfrak{m} \geqslant \aleph_0$ for $i = 1, 2, \ldots$ and let the metric ϱ_i in the space X_i be defined by means of the conditions

$$\varrho_i(x, y) = 1 \text{ if } x \neq y \quad \text{and} \quad \varrho_i(x, x) = 0.$$

By virtue of Theorem 4.2.2, the space $B(\mathfrak{m}) = \mathop{\boldsymbol{P}}\limits_{i=1}^{\infty} X_i$ is metrizable and the metric can be defined by means of the formula

$$\sigma(\{x_i\}, \{y_i\}) = \sum_{i=1}^{\infty} \frac{1}{2^i} \varrho_i(x_i, y_i).$$

It can easily be verified that the formula

$$\varrho(\{x_i\}, \{y_i\}) = \begin{cases} 1/k, & \text{if } x_k \neq y_k \text{ and } x_i = y_i \text{ for } i < k, \\ 0, & \text{if } x_i = y_i \text{ for every } i, \end{cases} \tag{22}$$

also defines a metric in the set $\mathop{\boldsymbol{P}}\limits_{i=1}^{\infty} X_i$. A sequence $x_j = \{x_i^j\}$ of points of the space $B(\mathfrak{m})$ is convergent to a point $x = \{x_i\}$ if and only if for every i there exists an $n(i)$ such that $x_j^i = x_i$ for $j \geqslant n(i)$. The same condition is necessary and sufficient in order that the sequence $x_j = \{x_i^j\}$ be convergent to the point $x = \{x_i\}$ in the space $(\mathop{\boldsymbol{P}}\limits_{i=1}^{\infty} X_i, \varrho)$, where ϱ is defined by (22). From Theorem 4.1.2 it follows, therefore, that formula (22) defines a metric in the space $B(\mathfrak{m})$.

The space $B(\mathfrak{m})$ is called the *Baire space* of weight $\mathfrak{m}$. One can easily verify that the weight of the space $B(\mathfrak{m})$ is in fact equal to $\mathfrak{m}$. Speaking of a metric in the space $B(\mathfrak{m})$ we shall always mean the metric defined by (22).

Let us now consider two arbitrary points $x = \{x_i\}$ and $y = \{y_i\}$ in the space $B(\mathfrak{m})$ and a number r such that $0 < r \leqslant 1$. We assume that the intersection $B(x, r) \cap B(y, r)$ is non-empty. It follows that there exists a point $z = \{z_i\}$ such that $x_1 = z_1 = y_1, x_2 = z_2 = y_2, \ldots, x_k = z_k = y_k$, where k is the natural number such that $1/k+1 < r \leqslant 1/k$ and, consequently, that $B(x, r) = B(y, r)$. Thus, in the space $B(\mathfrak{m})$ every pair of balls of the same radius are either disjoint or identical. In particular, for every i the family of all balls of radius $1/i$ is a covering of the space $B(\mathfrak{m})$ consisting of disjoint open-and-closed sets. It follows from Theorem 5 that $\operatorname{Ind} B(\mathfrak{m}) = 0$. ■

THEOREM 9. *For every $\mathfrak{m} \geqslant \aleph_0$ the Baire space $B(\mathfrak{m})$ is a universal space for all metrizable spaces whose large inductive dimension is equal to zero and whose weight is at most $\mathfrak{m}$.*

Proof. By virtue of Example 2 it is sufficient to show that every metrizable space X satisfying the conditions $\operatorname{Ind} X = 0$ and $w(X) \leqslant \mathfrak{m}$ is embeddable in the space $B(\mathfrak{m})$.

According to Lemma 3 to Theorem 4, in the space X there exists a countable family $\{\mathfrak{V}_i\}_{i=1}^{\infty}$ of open-and-closed locally finite coverings, where $\mathfrak{V}_i = \{U_s\}_{s \in S_i}$ and $\delta(U_s) \leqslant 1/i$ for every $s \in S_i$. In view of Theorem 1.1.6 we may assume that $\overline{\overline{S_i}} \leqslant \mathfrak{m}$ for $i = 1, 2, \ldots$ In particular, we can assume that the set S_i is a subset of the discrete space X_i which was used for the definition of the space $B(\mathfrak{m})$. Let us now suppose that each of the sets S_i is well ordered by the relation $<$ and let

$$V_s = U_s \setminus \bigcup_{s' < s} U_{s'} \quad \text{for} \quad s \in S_i.$$

The family $\{V_s\}_{s \in S_i}$ is a covering of the space X consisting of disjoint open-and-closed subsets. Since $S_i \subset X_i$, we infer from Theorem 2.1.5 that by assigning to every point $x \in X$ the element $s \in S_i$ such that $x \in V_s$ we define a mapping $f_i \colon X \to X_i$.

Let x be an arbitrary point of X and let $F \subset X$ be a closed subset which does not contain x. There exists a natural number i such that $d(x, F) > 1/i$. For some $s \in S_i$ we have $x \in V_s$. Since $\delta(V_s) \leqslant \delta(U_s) \leqslant 1/i$, we infer that $V_s \cap F = 0$, i.e. $f_i(x) = s \notin f_i(F) = \overline{f_i(F)}$. Thus the family $\{f_i\}_{i=1}^{\infty}$ separates points from closed sets and $F = \mathop{\triangle}\limits_{i=1}^{\infty} f_i \colon X \to \mathop{\boldsymbol{P}}\limits_{i=1}^{\infty} X_i = B(\mathfrak{m})$ is, according to the Diagonal Lemma, a homeomorphic embedding. ■

Since the Cartesian product of countably many copies of the space $B(\mathfrak{m})$ is homeomorphic to $B(\mathfrak{m})$, Theorems 3 and 9 yield

THEOREM 10. *For every countable family $\{X_i\}_{i=1}^{\infty}$ of metrizable spaces the conditions $\operatorname{Ind}(\mathop{\boldsymbol{P}}\limits_{i=1}^{\infty} X_i) = 0$ and $\operatorname{Ind} X_i = 0$ for $i = 1, 2, \ldots$ are equivalent.* ■

We shall prove one more theorem on the dimension of the Cartesian product of metrizable spaces.

THEOREM 11. *For every two metrizable spaces X and Y we have*

$$\operatorname{Ind}(X\times Y) \leqslant \operatorname{Ind} X + \operatorname{Ind} Y.$$

Proof. The theorem is obviously true if $\operatorname{Ind} X = \infty$ or $\operatorname{Ind} Y = \infty$. Let us, therefore, suppose that $\operatorname{Ind} X$ and $\operatorname{Ind} Y$ are finite. We shall use induction with respect to the number $\operatorname{Ind} X + \operatorname{Ind} Y$. If $\operatorname{Ind} X + \operatorname{Ind} Y = -1$, then either $X = 0$ or $Y = 0$, and the conclusion is valid. Let us suppose that the theorem has already been proved for every pair of metrizable spaces the sum of which dimensions is at most equal to $k-1$, and let X and Y be metrizable spaces such that $\operatorname{Ind} X = m$, $\operatorname{Ind} Y = n$ and $m+n = k$. By virtue of Theorem 5, the space X has a base $\mathfrak{C} = \bigcup_{i=1}^{\infty} \mathfrak{C}_i$, where $\mathfrak{C}_i$ is a locally finite family and $\operatorname{Ind}\operatorname{Fr} U \leqslant m-1$ for every $U \in \mathfrak{C}_i$, where $i = 1, 2, \ldots$ Similarly, the space Y has a base $\mathfrak{D} = \bigcup_{j=1}^{\infty} \mathfrak{D}_j$, where $\mathfrak{D}_j$ is a locally finite family and $\operatorname{Ind}\operatorname{Fr} V \leqslant n-1$ for every $V \in \mathfrak{D}_j$, where $j = 1, 2, \ldots$

The family

$$\mathfrak{B}_{i,j} = \{U\times V\colon U \in \mathfrak{C}_i,\ V \in \mathfrak{D}_j\},$$

consisting of open subsets of the space $X\times Y$, is locally finite. Since

$$\operatorname{Fr}(U\times V) \subset (\operatorname{Fr} U\times Y) \cup (X\times \operatorname{Fr} V),$$

we have by the inductive assumption and Theorems 1 and 2.1, $\operatorname{Ind}\operatorname{Fr}(U\times V) \leqslant k-1$. The family $\{\mathfrak{B}_{i,j}\}_{i,j=1}^{\infty}$ is evidently a base of the space $X\times Y$. Hence, by Theorem 5, $\operatorname{Ind}(X\times Y) \leqslant k = m+n$. ∎

The inequality in Theorem 11 cannot be replaced by an equality, for there exist metrizable (even compact) spaces X and Y such that

$$\operatorname{Ind}(X\times Y) < \operatorname{Ind} X + \operatorname{Ind} Y$$

(cf. Exercise F).

Let us notice that according to Theorem 1, Theorems 4-11 remain valid if we replace "Ind" by "dim".

To end this paragraph we shall prove that the dimensions ind, Ind, and dim of the n-dimensional Euclidean space R^n (and also of the sphere S_n and the cube I^n) are equal to n. This will justify our definitions of the dimensions. At the same time we shall give examples of spaces which have dimension greater than 1. So far we have not shown that such spaces exist.

The proof of the theorem requires deep insight into the structure of the space R^n. From the nature of things the proof contains some combinatorial elements. To preserve the uniformity of the methods developed in this book, we shall deduce this theorem from the fixed-point theorem. The proof of the fixed-point theorem also requires some methods of combinatorial or algebraic topology but the theorem is sure to be known to the readers. To make the book complete we will give the proof of the fixed-point theorem in the Appendix to this chapter.

THEOREM 12 (the fixed-point theorem). *For every natural number* n *and for every mapping* $f: I^n \to I^n$ *there exists a point* $x \in I^n$ *such that* $f(x) = x$. ∎

THEOREM 13. *For every natural number* n *we have* $\operatorname{ind} R^n = \operatorname{Ind} R^n = \dim R^n = n$.

Proof. By virtue of Theorems 2, 1.1 and of Examples 1.1, 2.1, and 1, it is sufficient to prove that $\operatorname{Ind} I^n > n-1$. Let us assume that $\operatorname{Ind} I^n \leqslant n-1$ and define for $i = 1, 2, \ldots, n$

$$A_i = \{\{x_j\} \in I^n : x_i = 0\} \quad \text{and} \quad B_i = \{\{x_j\} \in I^n : x_i = 1\}.$$

From the corollary to Theorem 8 it follows that there exist open sets $U_1, U_2, \ldots, U_n$ such that

$$A_i \subset U_i \subset \overline{U}_i \subset I^n \setminus B_i \quad \text{for} \quad i = 1, 2, \ldots, n$$

and

$$\operatorname{Fr} U_1 \cap \operatorname{Fr} U_2 \cap \ldots \cap \operatorname{Fr} U_n = 0. \tag{23}$$

By virtue of Theorem 2.1.6, the formula

$$f_i(x) = \begin{cases} d(x, \operatorname{Fr} U_i) & \text{for} \quad x \in \overline{U}_i, \\ -d(x, \operatorname{Fr} U_i) & \text{for} \quad x \in I^n \setminus U_i \end{cases}$$

defines a continuous function $f_i: I^n \to R$. For every point $x = \{x_j\} \in U^i$ let us consider the segment J with end-points x and

$$y = \big(x_1, x_2, \ldots, x_{i-1}, \min\big(1, x_i + f_i(x)\big), x_{i+1}, \ldots, x_n\big).$$

Since $J \cap U_i \neq 0$ and $J \cap \operatorname{Fr} U_i \subset \{y\}$, it follows from the corollary to Theorem 6.1.2 that $J \subset \overline{U}_i$, i.e. $0 < x_i + f_i(x) < 1$. It can similarly be verified that $0 < x_i + f_i(x) < 1$ for every point $x \in I^n \setminus \overline{U}_i$. But if $x \in I^n \setminus [U_i \cup (I^n \setminus \overline{U}_i)] = \operatorname{Fr} U_i$, then $x_i + f_i(x) = x_i$. Thus also in this case $0 < x_i + f_i(x) < 1$. Assigning the point $g(x) = \{z_j\} \in I^n$ to $x = \{x_j\} \in I^n$, where $z_j = x_j + f_j(x)$, we define, therefore, a mapping $g: I^n \to I^n$. By the fixed-point theorem, there exists a point $x \in I^n$ such that $g(x) = x$ i.e. $f_j(x) = 0$ for $j = 1, 2, \ldots, n$. We infer that $x \in \operatorname{Fr} U_1 \cap \operatorname{Fr} U_2 \cap \ldots \cap \operatorname{Fr} U_n$, contrary to (23). This contradiction completes the proof of the theorem. ∎

COROLLARY 1. *For every natural number* n *we have* $\operatorname{ind} S^n = \operatorname{Ind} S^n = \dim S^n = n$ *and* $\operatorname{ind} I^n = \operatorname{Ind} I^n = \dim I^n = n$. ∎

COROLLARY 2. *The dimensions* ind, Ind, *and* dim *of the Hilbert cube* $I^{\aleph_0}$ *are equal to* ∞. ∎

EXERCISES

A. Show that a topological space X is metrizable and satisfies the condition $\operatorname{Ind} X \leqslant n$ if and only if it is regular and has a countable family $\{\mathfrak{A}_i\}_{i=1}^{\infty}$ of locally finite open coverings such that

(a) $\operatorname{ord} \mathfrak{A}_i \leqslant n$ for $i = 1, 2, \ldots$;

(b) for every $x \in X$ the family $\{\operatorname{St}(x, \mathfrak{A}_i)\}_{i=1}^{\infty}$ is a base of the space X at the point x;

(c) the covering $\{\overline{U}\}_{U \in \mathfrak{A}_{i+1}}$ is a refinement of the covering $\mathfrak{A}_i$ for $i = 1, 2, \ldots$

Hint: Analyze the proof of Theorem 1.

B (K. Morita [1954]). Show that for every metrizable space X which has a closed countable covering consisting of strongly paracompact spaces the equality $\operatorname{ind} X = \operatorname{Ind} X = \dim X$ holds.

Hint: Make use of Exercise 2.D and of Theorems 2.1 and 2.

C. Give proofs of Theorems 4-11 and of the equality $\operatorname{Ind} R^n = n$ which are independent of Theorem 1.

Hint: Prove counterparts of Theorems 2.1 and 2.2 for metrizable spaces and the dimension Ind, and of Theorem 4, successively for $n = 0, 1, 2, \ldots$

D. Prove that in Theorem 5 σ-local finiteness can be replaced by σ-discreteness.

E (F. Hausdorff [1934], J. de Groot [1956]). A metric ϱ in the set X is called *non-Archimedean* if

$$\varrho(x, z) \leqslant \max[\varrho(x, y), \varrho(y, z)]$$

for every three points $x, y, z \in X$. Show that in a non-empty metrizable space X a non-Archimedean metric exists if and only if $\operatorname{Ind} X = 0$.

Hint: Verify that (22) defines a non-Archimedean metric in $B(\mathfrak{m})$.

F. Show that in Theorem 11 the sign $\leqslant$ cannot be replaced by $=$.

Hint: Make use of Exercise 1.A.

Appendix. Proof of the fixed-point theorem. Let $x = \{x_i\}$ and $y = \{y_i\}$ be points of the n-dimensional Euclidean space R^n. The sum $x+y$ of the points x and y, and the product λx of the point x by a real number λ are defined by the formulas:

$$x+y = \{z_i\}, \quad \text{where} \quad z_i = x_i + y_i, \quad \text{and} \quad \lambda x = \{t_i\}, \quad \text{where} \quad t_i = \lambda x_i.$$

The point of the space R^n whose coordinates are all equal to 0 will be denoted by 0. The distance $\varrho(x, 0)$ will be denoted by $|x|$. It can easily be verified that

$$|x-y| = \varrho(x, y), \qquad |\lambda x| = |\lambda|\,|x|, \qquad \text{and} \qquad |x+y| \leqslant |x|+|y|.$$

The last inequality is equivalent to the triangle inequality in the space R^n.

The points $x_0, x_1, \ldots, x_k \in R^n$ are said to be *linearly independent* provided that for every system $\lambda_0, \lambda_1, \ldots, \lambda_k$ of real numbers the conditions

$$\lambda_0 x_0 + \lambda_1 x_1 + \ldots + \lambda_k x_k = 0 \qquad \text{and} \qquad \lambda_0 + \lambda_1 + \ldots + \lambda_k = 0$$

imply $\lambda_j = 0$ for $j = 0, 1, \ldots, k$.

Let us suppose that a system $a_0, a_1, \ldots, a_m$ of $m+1$ linearly independent points of the space R^n is given. The subset of R^n consisting of all points of the form

(1) $$x = \lambda_0 a_0 + \lambda_1 a_1 + \ldots + \lambda_m a_m,$$

where

(2) $$\lambda_0 + \lambda_1 + \ldots + \lambda_m = 1 \quad \text{and} \quad \lambda_j \geqslant 0 \quad \text{for} \quad j = 0, 1, \ldots, m$$

is called the *m-dimensional simplex* spanned by $a_0, a_1, \ldots, a_m$ and is denoted by $a_0 a_1 \ldots a_m$. Evidently, it does not depend on the order of points $a_0, a_1, \ldots, a_m$.

Let $a_0 a_1 \ldots a_m \subset R^n$ be a simplex. For every system of $k+1$ distinct non-negative integers $j_0, j_1, \ldots, j_k$ which are not greater than m, the points $a_{j_0}, a_{j_1}, \ldots, a_{j_k}$ are linearly independent; consequently they determine a k-dimensional simplex $a_{j_0} a_{j_1} \ldots a_{j_k}$. Every simplex of this form is called a *k-dimensional face* of the simplex $a_0 a_1 \ldots a_m$. 0-dimensional faces $a_0, a_1, \ldots, a_m$ are called *vertices*. The simplex $a_0 a_1 \ldots a_m$ itself is also considerd to be its m-dimensional face. It can easily be verified that the face $a_{j_0} a_{j_1} \ldots a_{j_k}$ is the same as the set of points which are of the form (1) and satisfy condition (2) and the following condition

$$\lambda_j = 0 \quad \text{for} \quad j \neq j^i, \quad \text{where} \quad i = 0, 1, \ldots, k.$$

Since vertices of a simplex are linearly independent, expression (1) for every point of the simplex $a_0 a_1 \ldots a_m \subset R^n$ is unique. The coefficients $\lambda_0, \lambda_1, \ldots, \lambda_m$ in expression (1) are called the *barycentric coordinates* of the point x. They will also be denoted by $\lambda_0(x), \lambda_1(x), \ldots, \lambda_m(x)$.

THEOREM 1. *Let $a_0, a_1, \ldots, a_m$ denote $m+1$ linearly independent points of the space R^n and let S be the simplex with vertices $a_0, a_1, \ldots, a_m$. The simplex S is a compact subspace of R^n and the barycentric coordinates are continuous functions defined on it, $\lambda_j \colon S \to I$ for $j = 0, 1, \ldots, m$.*

Proof. Let $\delta_i^j = 0$ for $i \neq j$ and $\delta_i^i = 1$. The points $d_0, d_1, \ldots, d_m$ of the space R^{m+1}, where $d_j = \{\delta_i^{j+1}\}$ are linearly independent. Let us denote by T the simplex with vertices $d_0, d_1, \ldots, d_m$. The barycentric coordinates of the points of the simplex T are the same as their coordinates in the space R^{m+1} and are, therefore, continuous functions. It follows by (2) that T is a closed and bounded subset of R^{m+1}. Hence, by virtue of Theorem 3.2.7, T is compact.

We infer from Theorem 2.3.3 that the formula

$$f(x) = x_1 a_0 + x_2 a_1 + \ldots + x_{m+1} a_m, \quad \text{where} \quad x = \{x_i\} \in T \subset R^{m+1},$$

defines a mapping $f \colon T \to R^n$. Since the points $a_0, a_1, \ldots, a_m$ are independent, it follows that f is a one-to-one mapping. On the other hand, $f(d_j) = a_j$ for $j = 0, 1, \ldots, m$, whence $f(T) = S$. We infer from Theorem 3.1.10 that f is a homeomorphism of T onto S. This also implies that S is compact and that the functions $\lambda_j: S \to I$ are continuous for $j = 0, 1, \ldots, m$, because $\lambda_j(x) = p_{j+1}f^{-1}(x)$, where $p_j: R^{m+1} \to R$ denotes the projection onto the j-th axis. ■

The fact that f is a homeomorphism can also be deduced from simple theorems of linear algebra. Moreover, the mapping inverse to f can be defined by a formula analogous to that which defines f, the coefficients $a_0, a_1, \ldots, a_m$ being replaced by coefficients $a'_0, a'_1, \ldots, a'_{n-1} \in R^{m+1}$.

The continuity of barycentric coordinates immediately implies the following

COROLLARY. *Every two m-dimensional simplexes are homeomorphic.* ■

By a *simplicial subdivision* of a simplex $S \subset R^n$ we mean a family $\mathfrak{P} = \{S_i\}_{i=1}^k$ of simplexes in R^n which satisfies the conditions:

(3) $$S = \bigcup_{i=1}^{k} S_i.$$

(4) The set $S_i \cap S_j$ is either empty or is the simplex which is a common face of S_i and S_j for every $i, j \leqslant k$.

(5) The family $\mathfrak{P}$, together with every simplex, contains all its faces.

The *mesh* of a simplicial subdivision $\{S_i\}_{i=1}^k$ of a simplex S is the largest of the numbers $\delta(S_1), \delta(S_2), \ldots, \delta(S_k)$.

For every simplex $S = a_0 a_1 \ldots a_m \subset R^n$ the point

$$b(S) = \frac{1}{m+1} a_0 + \frac{1}{m+1} a_1 + \ldots + \frac{1}{m+1} a_m$$

is called the *barycentre* of the simplex S. Evidently $b(S) \in S$ and the point $b(S)$ does not belong to any $(m-1)$-dimensional face of the simplex S.

THEOREM 2. *Let $S = a_0 a_1 \ldots a_m$ be an arbitrary simplex. For every decreasing sequence $S_0 \supset S_1 \supset \ldots \supset S_k$ of distinct faces of the simplex S the points $b(S_0), b(S_1), \ldots, b(S_k)$ are linearly independent. The family of all simplexes of the form $b(S_0)b(S_1) \ldots b(S_k)$ is a simplicial subdivison of the simplex S. Every $(m-1)$-dimensional simplex of this subdivision is a face of one or two of its m-dimensional simplexes — one, if it lies in an $(m-1)$-dimensional face of the simplex S, — two, if it does not lie in such a face.*

Proof. Every decreasing sequence of different faces of the simplex S can be completed to a sequence of $m+1$ elements $S_0 \supset S_1 \supset \ldots \supset S_m$ such that

(6) $$S_0 = a_{i_0} a_{i_1} \ldots a_{i_m}, \quad S_1 = a_{i_1} a_{i_2} \ldots a_{i_m}, \quad \ldots, \quad S_m = a_{i_m},$$

where $i_0, i_1, \ldots, i_m$ is a sequence composed of the numbers $0, 1, \ldots, m$. To prove the first part of the theorem it is sufficient to show that the points $b(S_0), b(S_1), \ldots, b(S_m)$ are linearly independent.

Let us consider the expression:

$$\mu_0 b(S_0) + \mu_1 b(S_1) + \ldots + \mu_m b(S_m). \tag{7}$$

Making use of the definition of the barycentre, we can represent (7) as the linear combination of the points $a_{i_0}, a_{i_1}, \ldots, a_{i_m}$. Namely it is equal to

$$\lambda_{i_0} a_{i_0} + \lambda_{i_1} a_{i_1} + \ldots + \lambda_{i_m} a_{i_m}, \tag{8}$$

where

$$\lambda_{i_j} = \sum_{k=0}^{j} \frac{\mu_k}{(m+1)-k} \quad \text{for} \quad j = 0, 1, \ldots, m. \tag{9}$$

Moreover,

$$\sum_{j=0}^{m} \lambda_{i_j} = \sum_{j=0}^{m} \sum_{k=0}^{j} \frac{\mu_k}{(m+1)-k} = \sum_{i=0}^{m} \sum_{j=i}^{m} \frac{\mu_i}{(m+1)-i} = \sum_{i=0}^{m} \mu_i. \tag{10}$$

In particular, if combination (7) is equal to zero and $\mu_0 + \mu_1 + \ldots + \mu_m = 0$, then, since the points $a_{i_0}, a_{i_1}, \ldots, a_{i_m}$ are linearly independent, it follows from (10) that $\lambda_{i_j} = 0$ for $j = 0, 1, \ldots, m$, which by virtue of (9), yields $\mu_0 = 0, \mu_1 = 0, \ldots, \mu_m = 0$. The points $b(S_0), b(S_1), \ldots$ $\ldots, b(S_m)$ are, therefore, linearly independent and we can consider the simplex $b(S_0) b(S_1) \ldots b(S_m)$. Every simplex of the family under consideration is a face of an m-dimensional simplex of the form $b(S_0) b(S_1) \ldots$ $\ldots b(S_m)$.

It follows also from formulas (7)-(10) that the simplex $b(S_0) b(S_1) \ldots$ $\ldots b(S_m)$ is contained in S. We shall show that it is equal to the set

$$\{x \in S : \lambda_{i_0}(x) \leqslant \lambda_{i_1}(x) \leqslant \ldots \leqslant \lambda_{i_m}(x)\}. \tag{11}$$

By virtue of (9) it suffices to show that each point belonging to the set (11) can be represented in the form of (7), where $\mu_0 + \mu_1 + \ldots + \mu_m = 1$ and $\mu_j \geqslant 0$ for $j = 0, 1, \ldots, m$. The reader can verify without any difficulty that the respresentation can be obtained by defining the coefficients μ_j by means of the formula:

$$\mu_0 = (m+1)\lambda_{i_0}(x) \quad \text{and} \quad \mu_j = [(m+1)-j]\big(\lambda_{i_j}(x) - \lambda_{i_{j-1}}(x)\big) \quad \text{for} \quad j = 1, 2, \ldots, m. \tag{12}$$

It follows from (12) that the faces of the simplex $b(S_0) b(S_1) \ldots b(S_m)$ can be obtained by adding to the conditions which define the set (11) some conditions of the form $\lambda_{i_j}(x) = \lambda_{i_{j-1}}(x)$ and possibly also the condition $\lambda_{i_0}(x) = 0$. Since the intersection of such a set with an anologous set in another simplex $b(S_0')b(S_1')\dots b(S_m')$ (that is corresponding to another sequence $i_0', i_1', \dots, i_m'$ consisting of the numbers $0, 1, \dots, m$) is also a set of this form or is empty, the family of simplexes which is being considered satisfies condition (4). Condition (3) is also satisfied, for, every point of the simplex S belongs to a set of the form (11). Condition (5) is in this case evidently satisfied. The family of such simplexes is, therefore, a simplicial subdivision of the simplex S.

Let us now consider an arbitrary $(m-1)$-dimensional simplex $b(S_0)b(S_1)\dots b(S_{m-1})$ of this subdivision. If it lies in a $(m-1)$-dimensional face of the simplex S, i.e. if $S \neq S_0$, then it is a face of exactly one m-dimensional simplex of our subdivision, namely of the simplex $b(S)b(S_0)\dots b(S_{m-1})$. If, however, this simplex does not lie in a $(m-1)$-dimensional face of the simplex S, i.e. if $S = S_0$, then either there exists a j such that the simplex S_j is obtained from the simplex S_{j-1} by omitting two vertices or S_{m-1} is 1-dimensional. It can easily be verified that in both cases the simplex $b(S_0)b(S_1)\dots b(S_{m-1})$ is a face of exactly two m-dimensional simplexes of the subdivision. ■

The simplicial subdivision described in Theorem 2 is called the *barycentric subdivision*. We define inductively the notion of the *k-th barycentric subdivision*. The subdivision defined above is the first barycentric subdivision. Let $\{S_i\}_{i=1}^k$ be the l-th barycentric subdivision of a simplex S. Making use of the fact that the barycentric subdivision of the simplex S_i induces the barycentric subdivision of every face, we infer that the union of barycentric subdivisions of all simplexes $S_1, S_2, \dots, S_k$ is a simplicial subdivision of the simplex S. We define the $(l+1)$-th barycentric subdivision as being equal to that subdivision.

Let us consider a simplex $a_0a_1\dots a_m \subset R^n$, a point

$$x = \lambda_0 a_0 + \lambda_1 a_1 + \dots + \lambda_m a_m,$$

where $\lambda_0 + \lambda_1 + \dots + \lambda_m = 1$ and $\lambda_j \geqslant 0$ for $j = 0, 1, \dots, m$, and a point $y \in R^n$. In this case we have the inequality

$$\varrho(x, y) \leqslant \max_j \varrho(a_j, y), \tag{13}$$

because

$$|x-y| = \Big|\sum_{j=0}^m \lambda_j a_j - \sum_{j=0}^m \lambda_j y\Big| = \Big|\sum_{j=0}^m \lambda_j (a_j - y)\Big| \leqslant \sum_{j=0}^m \lambda_j |a_j - y|$$
$$\leqslant \max_j |a_j - y| \sum_{j=0}^m \lambda_j.$$

LEMMA 1. *The diameter of the simplex $a_0a_1\dots a_m \subset R^n$ is equal to the diameter of the set of its vertices.*

Proof. Let $x, y \in a_0 a_1 \ldots a_m$. By virtue of (13), $\varrho(x, y) \leqslant \max_j \varrho(a_j, y)$. Making use of (13) again, we get $\varrho(a_j, y) \leqslant \max_i \varrho(a_j, a_i)$, so that $\varrho(x, y) \leqslant \max_{i,j} \varrho(a_i, a_j)$, i.e. $\delta(a_0 a_1 \ldots a_m) = \delta(\{a_0, a_1, \ldots, a_m\})$. ■

LEMMA 2. *The mesh of the barycentric subdivision of a simplex* $S = a_0 a_1 \ldots a_m$ *does not exceed* $\frac{m}{m+1}\delta(S)$.

Proof. By virtue of Lemma 1, it is sufficient to show that the distances between any two points of the form

$$b(S_j) = \frac{1}{j+1}(a_{i_0} + a_{i_1} + \ldots + a_{i_j}) \quad \text{and} \quad b(S_k) = \frac{1}{k+1}(a_{i_0} + a_{i_1} + \ldots + a_{i_k}),$$

where $k < j \leqslant m$ and $i_0, i_1, \ldots, i_m$ denotes a sequence consisting of the numbers $0, 1, \ldots, m$, is not greater than $\frac{m}{m+1}\delta(S)$. Making use of (13), we infer that $\varrho\big(b(S_k), b(S_j)\big) \leqslant \varrho\big(a_{i_l}, b(S_j)\big)$ for some $l \leqslant k < j$. Hence we have

$$\begin{aligned}
&\varrho\big(b(S_k), b(S_j)\big) \leqslant \varrho\big(a_{i_l}, b(S_j)\big) \\
&= |b(S_j) - a_{i_l}| = \left| \frac{1}{j+1}(a_{i_0} + a_{i_l} + \ldots + a_{i_j}) - a_{i_l} \right| \\
&= \frac{1}{j+1}\left| \sum_{h=0}^{j} (a_{i_h} - a_{i_l}) \right| \leqslant \frac{1}{j+1} \sum_{h=0}^{j} |a_{i_h} - a_{i_l}| \leqslant \frac{j}{j+1}\delta(S) \leqslant \frac{m}{m+1}\delta(S). \quad ■
\end{aligned}$$

Lemma 2 immediately implies

THEOREM 3. *For every m-dimensional simplex S and an arbitrary number* $\varepsilon > 0$ *there exists an l such that the mesh of the l-th barycentric subdivision of S is less than* ε. ■

THEOREM 4 (Sperner Lemma). *Let* $\mathfrak{P}_l$ *denote the l-th barycentric subdivision of the simplex* $a_0 a_1 \ldots a_m$ *and let us denote by W the set of vertices of all simplexes belonging to* $\mathfrak{P}_l$. *If we assign to every* $w \in W$ *an integer* $n(w)$ *in such a manner that:*

if $w \in a_{i_0} a_{i_1} \ldots a_{i_k}$, *then* $n(w)$ *is one of the numbers* $i_0, i_1, \ldots, i_k$,

then the number of simplexes of the subdivision $\mathfrak{P}_l$ *on whose vertices the function n assumes all values from 0 to m, is odd.*

Proof. We shall carry out the proof by induction with respect to the dimension m of the simplex.

For $m = 0$ the theorem is obvious, for then $\mathfrak{P}_l = \{a_0\}$ and $n(a_0) = 0$.

Let us assume that the theorem is valid for simplexes of dimension $m-1$ and let us consider a simplex $a_0 a_1 \ldots a_m$. Let us denote by $\mathfrak{P}$ the family of all $(m-1)$-dimensional simplexes of the subdivision $\mathfrak{P}_l$ on whose vertices the function n assumes all the values from 0 to $m-1$. By virtue of the condition satisfied by the function n, the only $(m-1)$-dimensional face of the simplex $a_0 a_1 \dots a_m$ on which simplexes of the family $\mathfrak{P}$ can lie is the face $a_0 a_1 \dots a_{m-1}$. Let us denote by u the number of simplexes of the family $\mathfrak{P}$ which lie on this face. By our assumption, u is an odd number.

Let us write down the sequence $S_1, S_2, \dots, S_h$ of all m-dimensional simplexes of the subdivision $\mathfrak{P}_l$. For every $j \leqslant h$ let v_j denote the number of faces of the simplex S_j belonging to the family $\mathfrak{P}$ and let N_j denote the set of values which the function n assumes on the vertices of the simplex S_j.

The reader can easily verify that:

(14) if $N_j = \{0, 1, \dots, m\}$, then $v_j = 1$;

(15) if $N_j \neq \{0, 1, \dots, m\}$ and $\{0, 1, \dots, m-1\} \subset N_j$, then $v_j = 2$;

(16) if $\{0, 1, \dots, m-1\} \not\subset N_j$, then $v_j = 0$.

Let r be the number of those simplexes of the subdivision $\mathfrak{P}_l$ on whose vertices the function n assumes all the values from 0 to m. It follows from (14), (15), and (16) that there exists an integer s such that

$$r-(v_1+v_2+\dots+v_h) = 2s. \tag{17}$$

If we assign to every simplex S_j, where $j \leqslant h$, its v_j faces belonging to $\mathfrak{P}$, then it easily follows from the last part of Theorem 2, that every simplex belonging to $\mathfrak{P}$ will be assigned to one or two simplexes, depending on whether or not it lies on the face $a_0 a_1 \dots a_{m-1}$. It follows that there exists an integer t such that

$$u-(v_1+v_2+\dots+v_h) = 2t. \tag{18}$$

It follows from (17) and (18) that $r-u = 2(s-t)$, whence r is an odd number. ■

THEOREM 5. *Suppose we are given a simplex $S = a_0 a_1 \dots a_m$ and a family of its closed subsets $\{F_0, F_1, \dots, F_m\}$. If*

$$a_{i_0} a_{i_1} \dots a_{i_k} \subset F_{i_0} \cup F_{i_1} \cup \dots \cup F_{i_k}$$

holds for every face $a_{i_0} a_{i_1} \dots a_{i_k}$ of S, then $F_0 \cap F_1 \cap \dots \cap F_m \neq 0$.

Proof. Let us suppose that the equality $F_0 \cap F_1 \cap \dots \cap F_m = 0$ holds. The family $\{U_i\}_{i=0}^m$, where $U_i = S \setminus F_i$ is a covering of the simplex S. By virtue of Theorems 1 and 4.3.15, there exists an $\varepsilon > 0$ such that every set of diameter less than ε is contained in a set U_i, i.e. it is disjoint with at least one of the sets $F_0, F_1, \dots, F_m$.

According to Theorem 3, there exists an l such that the l-th barycentric subdivision $\mathfrak{P}_l$ of the simplex S is of mesh less than ε. Let us denote the set of vertices of all simplexes belonging to $\mathfrak{P}_l$ by W. For every $w \in W$ let us consider the intersection of all faces of the simplex S which contain w. It is also a face of the simplex S, i.e. a set of the form $a_{i_0} a_{i_1} \ldots a_{i_m}$. Since $w \in a_{i_0} a_{i_1} \ldots a_{i_m}$, we can choose, by assumption, an index i_j such that $w \in F_{i_j}$.

Defining $n(w) = i_j$ we get a function satisfying the assumptions of the Sperner Lemma. There exists, therefore, a simplex $T = w_0 w_1 \ldots w_m \in \mathfrak{P}_l$ such that $n(w_i) = i$ for $i = 0, 1, \ldots, m$. Hence it follows that $w_i \in F_i$, i.e. $T \cap F_i \neq 0$ for $i = 0, 1, \ldots, m$, contrary to the assumption that $\delta(T) < \varepsilon$. This contradiction completes the proof of our theorem. ■

The proof of Theorem 3.12 (the fixed-point theorem). For every n the cube I^n is contained in the n-dimensional simplex $T^n = a_0 a_1 \ldots a_n \subset R^n$, where $a_0 = 0$, $a_j = \{n \cdot \delta_i^j\}$ for $j = 1, 2, \ldots, n$, $\delta_i^j = 0$ if $i \neq j$, and $\delta_i^i = 1$. If there existed a mapping $f\colon I^n \to I^n$, such that $f(x) \neq x$ for every $x \in I^n$, then we would also have $\bar{f}(x) \neq x$ for every $x \in T^n$, where $\bar{f}\colon T^n \to I^n$ denotes an extension of f existing by virtue of Theorems 2.1.3 and 2.3.3. It is, therefore, sufficient to prove that for every mapping $\bar{f}\colon T^n \to T^n$ there exists an $x \in T^n$ such that $\bar{f}(x) = x$.

For every point $x \in T^n$ we have

$$x = \lambda_0(x) a_0 + \lambda_1(x) a_1 + \ldots + \lambda_m(x) a_m, \tag{19}$$

where

$$\lambda_0(x) + \lambda_1(x) + \ldots + \lambda_m(x) = 1 \quad \text{and} \quad \lambda_j(x) \geqslant 0 \text{ for } j = 0, 1, \ldots, m. \tag{20}$$

The point

$$\bar{f}(x) = \lambda_0(\bar{f}(x)) a_0 + \lambda_1(\bar{f}(x)) a_1 + \ldots + \lambda_m(\bar{f}(x)) a_m, \tag{21}$$

where

$$\lambda_0(\bar{f}(x)) + \lambda_1(\bar{f}(x)) + \ldots + \lambda_m(\bar{f}(x)) = 1 \quad \text{and} \quad \lambda_j(\bar{f}(x)) \geqslant 0 \text{ for } j = 0, 1, \ldots, m, \tag{22}$$

is the image of the point $x \in T^n$ under the mapping $\bar{f}$.

The sets

$$F_i = \{x \in T^m\colon \lambda_i(\bar{f}(x)) \leqslant \lambda_i(x)\} \tag{23}$$

are, by virtue of Theorem 1 and by the continuity of $\bar{f}$, closed for every $i = 0, 1, \ldots, m$. We shall show that they satisfy the assumptions of Theorem 5. Let us consider an arbitrary face $a_{i_0} a_{i_1} \ldots a_{i_k}$ of the simplex T^n and a point $x \in a_{i_0} a_{i_1} \ldots a_{i_k}$. We thus have

$$\lambda_{i_0}(x) + \lambda_{i_1}(x) + \ldots + \lambda_{i_k}(x) = 1.$$

Hence, according to (22), it follows that

$$\lambda_{i_0}(\bar{f}(x))+\lambda_{i_1}(\bar{f}(x))+\ldots+\lambda_{i_k}(\bar{f}(x)) \leqslant \lambda_{i_0}(x)+\lambda_{i_1}(x)+\ldots+\lambda_{i_k}(x),$$

i.e. $\lambda_{i_j}(\bar{f}(x)) \leqslant \lambda_{i_j}(x)$ for at least one $0 \leqslant j \leqslant k$. By (23), however, this yields $x \in F_{i_j}$, so that

$$a_{i_0}a_{i_1}\ldots a_{i_k} \subset F_{i_0} \cup F_{i_1} \cup \ldots \cup F_{i_k}.$$

By virtue of Theorem 5, there exists a point $x \in F_0 \cap F_1 \cap \ldots \cap F_m$. In view of (23) we have

$$\lambda_0(\bar{f}(x)) \leqslant \lambda_0(x), \quad \lambda_1(\bar{f}(x)) \leqslant \lambda_1(x), \quad \ldots, \quad \lambda_m(f(x)) \leqslant \lambda_m(x).$$

It follows from (20) and (22) that for any j the inequality $\lambda_j(\bar{f}(x)) < \lambda_j(x)$ does not hold, whence

$$\lambda_0(\bar{f}(x)) = \lambda_0(x), \quad \lambda_1(\bar{f}(x)) = \lambda_1(x), \quad \ldots, \quad \lambda_m(f(x)) = \lambda_m(x),$$

and, by virtue of (19) and (21), we infer that $\bar{f}(x) = x$. ∎

HISTORICAL REMARKS AND BIBLIOGRAPHIC NOTES

An inductive definition of dimension was outlined by Poincaré in [1912]. L. E. J. Brouwer gave another definition in [1913]. For metrizable locally connected continua it is equivalent to the definition of the dimension Ind. In Brouwer's paper, however, the notion of dimension is used only to prove that the spaces R^m and R^n are not homeomorphic for distinct m and n. Dimension theory was established by K. Menger and P. Urysohn. The definition of the dimension ind was given by P. Urysohn in [1922] and by K. Menger in [1923]. The definition of the dimension Ind was given by E. Čech in [1932]. The dimension dim was defined (by means of the condition given in Theorem 1.6) by E. Čech in [1933]. The paper of H. Lebesgue [1911] contains the theorem stating that $\dim I^n = n$. From this theorem Lebesgue deduced that the spaces R^m and R^n are not homeomorphic for $m \neq n$. Lebesgue's proof is not complete and the gap is filled in his paper [1922]. The definition of dimension dim given by Čech was found satisfactory only for normal spaces. A correction of the definition consisting in the consideration of functionally open coverings was introduced by M. Katětov in [1950a]. Another class of coverings giving the same definition of the dimension was considered by Yu. M. Smirnov in [1956b]. In both papers a proof of Theorem 1.7 was given. (E. Čech proved the theorem for normal spaces in [1933]). A first systematic presentation of the dimension theory of Tychonoff spaces based on that definition is given in a book by L. Gillman and M. Jerison [1960].

The definition of the operator Ex and the proof of its properties can be found in Yu. M. Smirnov [1951]. Theorem 1.11 was proved by N. Vedenissoff in [1941], Theorem 1.12 by H. Wallman in [1938] (for normal spaces) and by M. Katětov in [1950a] and Yu. M. Smirnov in [1956b] (for Tychonoff spaces).

Theorem 2.1 was proved by E. Čech in [1933]. An analogous theorem for the dimension ind and compact metric spaces was proved by K. Menger in [1924] and P. Urysohn in [1926] (announcement without proof by P. Urysohn [1922]) and for separable metric spaces by W. Hurewicz in [1927] and L. A. Tumarkin in [1928]. The Lemma 2 to Theorem 2.2 comes from the paper of M. Katětov [1952]. The theorem was proved by K. Morita in [1950a] and M. Katětov in [1952]. C. H. Dowker proved Theorem 2.3 in [1947] (for normal spaces). Theorem 2.4 was proved for compact metric spaces by K. Menger [1924] and P. Urysohn [1926] (announced by Urysohn in [1922]), and for metric separable spaces by W. Hurewicz in [1927a]. The same theorem was proved for compact spaces by P. Alexandroff in [1941] and for Lindelöf spaces by K. Morita in [1950] and Yu. M. Smirnov in [1951b]. Theorem 2.5 was proved by N. Vedenissoff in [1939] and Theorem 2.6 in [1941]. In [1938] S. Eilenberg and E. Otto proved Theorem 2.7 for separable metric spaces; for normal spaces this theorem was proved by E. Hemmingsen in [1946]. The proof presented in this book is taken from a paper by W. Holsztyński [1966].

Theorem 3.1 was proved by M. Katětov in [1952] and K. Morita in [1954]. The proof quoted here is taken from C. H. Dowker and W. Hurewicz [1956]. The equality $\operatorname{ind} X = \operatorname{Ind} X$ for compact metric spaces was proved by L. E. J. Brouwer in [1924] and P. Urysohn in [1926]. For separable metric spaces it was proved by W. Hurewicz [1927] and L. A. Tumarkin in [1928]. P. Urysohn proved in [1926] (announced in [1922]) that $\operatorname{ind} X = \dim X$ for compact metric spaces. For separable metric spaces the theorem was proved by W. Hurewicz in [1927a]. An example of a metric space X such that $\operatorname{ind} X \neq \dim X$ was given by P. Roy in [1962]. Theorems 3.4, 3.6, and 3.7 were proved for compact metric spaces and separable metric spaces (for the dimension ind) by P. Urysohn in [1926] (announced in [1922]) and by W. Hurewicz in [1927], respectively. For arbitrary metric spaces the theorems were proved, together with Theorems 3.8, 3.9, 3.10, and 3.11, by M. Katětov in [1952] and K. Morita in [1954]. Theorem 3.5 can be found in a paper by K. Morita [1954]. Theorem 3.9 was proved for separable metric spaces by W. Sierpiński in [1921] for the case $\mathfrak{m} = \aleph_0$. Theorem 3.11 for metric separable spaces was proved by K. Menger in [1928]. L. S. Pontriagin found in [1930] an example of 2-dimensional compact spaces X and Y such that the Cartesian product $X \times Y$ is of dimension 3. The fixed-point theorem was proved by L. E. J. Brouwer in [1912]. Brouwer's paper [1913] contains the proof of the theorem stating that $\operatorname{Ind} R^n = \dim R^n = n$. The equality $\operatorname{ind} R^n = n$ was proved, independently of Brouwer's results, by K. Menger in [1924] and P. Urysohn in [1925b] (announced in [1922]). An excellent presentation of the dimension theory of metric separable spaces is contained in W. Hurewicz and H. Wallman [1948].

The proof of the fixed-point theorem given in the Appendix was found (together with the preparatory Theorem 5) by B. Knaster, K. Kuratowski, and S. Mazurkiewicz in [1929]. The proof is based on the lemma proved by E. Sperner in [1928].

PROBLEMS

A (P. Urysohn [1925b]). Let X be a hereditarily normal space and let M be a subspace. Show that $\operatorname{ind} M \leqslant n$, where $n \geqslant 0$, if and only if for every point $x \in M$ and every neighbourhood V of x there exists an open set $U \subset X$ such that $x \in U \subset \overline{U} \subset V$ and $\operatorname{ind}(M \cap \operatorname{Fr} U) \leqslant n-1$.

Deduce for every two subspaces X and Y of a hereditarily normal space the inequality

$$\operatorname{ind}(X \cup Y) \leqslant \operatorname{ind} X + \operatorname{ind} Y + 1.$$

Hint: In the proof of the first part make use of Problem 2.B. Prove the second part by induction on the number $\operatorname{ind} X + \operatorname{ind} Y$.

B (Yu. M. Smirnov [1951b]). Let X be a hereditarily normal space and let M be a subspace. Show that $\operatorname{Ind} M \leqslant n$, where $n \geqslant 0$, if and only if for every closed set A and every open set $V \subset X$ which contains A there exists an open set $U \subset X$ such that $A \subset U \subset \overline{U} \subset V$ and $\operatorname{Ind}(M \cap \operatorname{Fr} U) \leqslant n-1$.

Deduce for every two subspaces X and Y of a hereditarily normal space the inequality

$$\operatorname{Ind}(X \cup Y) \leqslant \operatorname{Ind} X + \operatorname{Ind} Y + 1.$$

C (E. Čech [1932a]). Let X be a hereditarily normal space and let M be a subspace. Show that every finite open covering of the space M has a swelling consisting of sets open in X.

Hint: Show, by means of induction, that for every family $\{V_i\}_{i=1}^k$ of open subsets of the space M which satisfies the condition $\bigcap_{i=1}^k V_i = 0$ there exists a family $\{U_i\}_{i=1}^k$ of open subsets of the space X such that $V_i \subset U_i$ for $i = 1, 2, \ldots, k$ and $\bigcap_{i=1}^k U_i = 0$.

D (Yu. M. Smirnov [1951b]). Let X be a hereditarily normal space and let M be a subspace. Show that $\dim M \leqslant n$ if and only if for every finite family $\{U_i\}_{i=1}^k$ of open subsets of X, where $M \subset \bigcup_{i=1}^k U_i$, there exists a family $\{V_i\}_{i=1}^k$ of open subsets of X such that $V_i \subset U_i$ for $i = 1, 2, \ldots, k$, $M \subset \bigcup_{i=1}^k V_i$, and $\operatorname{ord}(\{V_i\}_{i=1}^k) \leqslant n$.

Deduce for every two subspaces X and Y of a hereditaraily normal space the inequality

$$\dim(X \cup Y) \leqslant \dim X + \dim Y + 1.$$

Hint: In the proof of the first part make use of Problem C.

E (O. V. Lokucievskiĭ [1949]; the first example of a compact space X such that $\operatorname{ind} X \neq \dim X$ was given by A. L. Lunc in [1949]). Let L be the space considered in Problem 3.N and let $f: D^{\aleph_0} \to I$ be the function defined in Exercise 3.2.B. Consider the equivalence relation R in the Cartesian product $L \times D^{\aleph_0}$, where $(x_1, y_1)\, R(x_2, y_2)$ if and only if either $(x_1, y_1) = (x_2, y_2)$ or $x_1 = x_2 = \omega_1$ and $f(y_1) = f(y_2)$. Consider the quotient space $X_1 = (L \times D^{\aleph_0})/R$ and prove that $\operatorname{ind} X_1 = \operatorname{Ind} X_1 = \dim X_1 = 1$.

Let $A_1 \subset X_1$ be the subspace consisting of those points which are images of more than one point under the natural mapping φ of the space $L \times D^{\aleph_0}$ onto X_1. Let X_2 be another copy of the space X_1 and let $A_2 \subset X_2$ be the set corresponding to A_1. Making use of Problem 4.E (for $n = 1$), define a matching of the spaces X_1 and X_2 along the segment $\varphi(\{\omega_1\} \times D^{\aleph_0})$ such that no point of the set A_1 is matched with a point of the set A_2. Verify that for the space X so obtained we have $\operatorname{Ind} X = \operatorname{ind} X = 2$ and $\dim X = 1$. Notice that the counterpart of Theorem 2.1 for the dimensions ind and Ind is not valid, even for compact spaces and a finite number of sets.

F (Yu. M. Smirnov [1956b]). Making use of the properties of the space Y described in Example 6.2.2, define a Tychonoff space Z such that $\dim Z = 0$ but $\dim M > 0$ for a certain closed subset $M \subset Z$.

Hint: Let cY be an arbitrary 0-dimensional compactification of the space Y whose weight is equal to $\overline{\omega_1}$. Let T be the space of all ordinal numbers not greater than ω_2. Consider the space

$$Z = T \times cY \setminus \big[\{\omega_2\} \times \big(cY \setminus c(Y)\big)\big]$$

and show that $\beta Z = T \times cY$.

G (Yu. M. Smirnov [1958]). By a modification of the space Y considered in Example 6.2.2, define a normal space Z such that $\operatorname{ind} Z = 0$ and $\dim Z = \infty$.

Hint: Replace the segment with the Hilbert cube and the sets S_a with $S_a^{\aleph_0}$. Make use of the corollary to Theorem 1.12.

H. A *polyhedron* is the union of a family of faces of a simplex. All the vertices of the simplex which belong to the polyhedron are called its *vertices*. The *dimension* of a polyhedron is the greatest dimension of all simplexes in the polyhedron. A polyhedron is a compact space.

Let W be a polyhedron and let $a_0, a_1, \ldots, a_m$ be all its vertices. Show that every point $x \in W$ can be represented in a unique manner as

$$x = \lambda_0(x)a_0 + \lambda_1(x)a_1 + \ldots + \lambda_m(x)a_m,$$

where $\sum_{i=0}^{m} \lambda_i(x) = 1$ and $\lambda_j(x) \geqslant 0$ for $j = 0, 1, \ldots, m$. Verify that the coefficients $\lambda_0(x), \lambda_1(x), \ldots, \lambda_m(x)$ are continuous functions of the point x. The subset of a polyhedron W defined by the condition

$$G_j = \{x \in W: \lambda_j(x) > 0\}$$

is called the *star* of the vertex a_j. Show that for every sequence $a_{j_0}, a_{j_1}, \ldots$ $\ldots, a_{j_k}$ of vertices of a polyhedron W the intersection $G_{i_0} \cap G_{j_1} \cap \ldots \cap G_{j_k}$ is non-empty if and only if $a_{j_0}a_{j_1} \ldots a_{j_k} \subset W$.

Making use of Theorems 2.1, 3.2, and 3.13 show that for every polyhedron W the numbers $\operatorname{ind} W$, $\operatorname{Ind} W$, and $\dim W$ are equal to the dimension of the polyhedron W.

I (P. S. Alexandroff [1928] and W. Hurewicz [1930] for compact metric spaces and separable metric spaces, respectively. The proofs for more general spaces by means of the method given in K. Kuratowski [1933]). Let us suppose that X and Y are two topological spaces and let $\mathfrak{A}$ be a covering of the space X. A mapping $f: X \to Y$ is called an $\mathfrak{A}$-mapping if the covering $\{f^{-1}(y)\}_{y \in Y}$ of the space X is a refinement of $\mathfrak{A}$.

Prove that for a Tychonoff (normal) space X the inequality $\dim X \leqslant n$ holds if and only if for every finite functionally open (open) covering $\mathfrak{A}$ of the space X there exists an $\mathfrak{A}$-mapping of the space X into a polyhedron of dimension $\leqslant n$.

Hint: Consider a functionally open refinement $\{V_i\}_{i=0}^m$ of the covering $\mathfrak{A}$ whose order is at most n, and consider its functionally closed shrinking $\{F_i\}_{i=0}^m$, and an m-dimensional simplex $S = a_0a_1 \ldots a_m$. Define functions $f_0, f_1, \ldots f_m$ on X such that $f_i(X \setminus V_i) \subset \{0\}$ and $f_i(F_i) \subset \{1\}$ and define

$$\lambda_i(x) = \frac{f_i(x)}{f_0(x) + f_1(x) + \ldots + f_m(x)}.$$

Consider the function $f: X \to S$, where $f(x) = \lambda_0(x)a_0 + \lambda_1(x)a_1 + \ldots + \lambda_m(x)a_m$.

Show that in the necessary and sufficient condition the expression "into a polyhedron" can be replaced by "onto a polyhedron".

J (E. Hemmingsen [1946]). Show that for every two compact spaces X and Y the following inequality holds:

$$\dim(X\times Y) \leqslant \dim X + \dim Y.$$

Hint: By means of a modification of the method used in the proof of Theorem 5.1.10, show that every finite open covering of the Cartesian product of compact spaces X and Y has a refinement of the form $\{U\times V\colon U\in\mathfrak{A},\ V\in\mathfrak{B}\}$, where $\mathfrak{A}$ and $\mathfrak{B}$ are finite open coverings of the space X and Y respectively. Make use of the condition of Problem I.

K (C. H. Dowker [1955]). Let X be a normal space and let M denote a closed subspace such that $\dim M \leqslant n$. Show that $\dim X \leqslant n$ if and only if for every closed subspace $N \subset X$, which is disjoint with M, we have $\dim N \leqslant n$.

L (E. Čech [1933], Yu. M. Smirnov [1951]). Let X be a normal space such that $\dim X \leqslant n$. Show that for every space $M \subset X$ which is an F_σ-set or, more generally, a set normally placed in X, we have $\dim M \leqslant n$.

Deduce for every subspace M of a perfectly normal space X the inequality $\dim M \leqslant \dim X$.

Show that the result of Problem J remains valid for every pair of Tychonoff spaces whose Cartesian product is a Lindelöf space.

M (P. S. Alexandroff [1932], W. Hurewicz [1935] for compact metric spaces; E. Hemmingsen [1946], P. S. Alexandroff [1947] for normal spaces; Yu. M. Smirnov [1956b] for Tychonoff spaces). Show that a normal space X satisfies the condition $\dim X \leqslant n$ if and only if every mapping $f\colon A \to S^n$ defined on a closed subset A of the space X can be extended over the space X.

Change the above condition to obtain a characterization of the dimension dim of Tychonoff spaces.

Hint: Make use of the condition given in Theorem 2.7. Instead of the sphere S^n consider the boundary S_1^n of the cube $I^{n+1} \subset R^{n+1}$. Carry out the proof of existence of the extension for a compact space X. Make use of Problem 5.V and of the fact that for every $x_0 \in I^{n+1}\setminus S_1^n$ there exists a mapping $g\colon I^{n+1}\setminus\{x_0\} \to S_1^n$ such that $g(x) = x$ for $x \in S_1^n$. Generalize to normal spaces by Theorem 1.12.

N (E. Čech [1932]). Show that if a perfectly normal space X has a countable closed covering $\{F_j\}_{j=1}^\infty$ such that $\operatorname{Ind} F_j \leqslant n$ for $j = 1, 2, \ldots$, then $\operatorname{Ind} X \leqslant n$.

Deduce for every subspace M of a perfectly normal space X the inequality $\operatorname{Ind} M \leqslant \operatorname{Ind} X$.

Hint: Carry out the proof by induction. Assuming that the theorem is valid for $n \leqslant m-1$ deduce first that it is valid for $n = m$ and a finite covering $\{F_j\}_{j=1}^k$.

Consider the case of the covering consisting of two elements $\{M, N\}$. Let A, V, and U be as in Problem B. Let $\operatorname{Fr} U = \bigcap_{i=1}^{\infty} G_i$, where $\overline{G}_{i+1} \subset G_i$ and $G_i = \operatorname{Int} G_i$ for $i = 1, 2, \ldots$, and $(\operatorname{Fr} U)\setminus M = \bigcup_{i=1}^{\infty} K_i$, where $K_i = \overline{K}_i$ for $i = 1, 2, \ldots$ Find a set W, open and such that $\operatorname{Fr} U \subset W \subset \overline{W} \subset V$, and sets $W_1, W_2, \ldots$, such that $K_i \subset W_i \subset \overline{W}_i \subset (G_i \cap W)\setminus M$ and $\operatorname{Ind} \operatorname{Fr} W_i \leqslant m-1$ for $i = 1, 2, \ldots$ Show that $\operatorname{Fr}\big(U \cup \bigcup_{i=1}^{\infty} W_i\big) \subset \bigcup_{i=1}^{\infty} \operatorname{Fr} W_i \cup M \cap \operatorname{Fr} U$.

When proving the theorem for $n = m$ assume that $F_j \subset F_{j+1}$ for $j = 1, 2, \ldots$ and consider a closed set $A \subset X$, an open set $V \subset X$ containing it and open sets $V_1, V_2, \ldots$ such that $A \subset V_j \subset \overline{V}_j \subset V_{j+1} \subset V$ for $j = 1, 2, \ldots$ Let $F_0 = T_0 = T_{-1} = 0$ and $W_0 = X$; define an open set U_1 and then, inductively, open sets W_j, T_j, U_{j+1} for $j = 1, 2, \ldots$ in such a manner that the following conditions are satisfied:

$$A \cap F_j \subset U_j \subset V_j, \qquad U_{j-1} \subset U_j, \qquad \operatorname{Ind}(F_j \cap \operatorname{Fr} U_j) \leqslant m-1,$$
$$U_j \setminus U_{j-1} \subset W_{j-1}, \qquad (\operatorname{Fr} U_j)\setminus F_{j-1} \subset W_{j-1}, \qquad (\operatorname{Fr} U_{j-1})\setminus F_{j-1} \subset W_{j-1},$$
$$A \subset W_{j-1}, \qquad F_{j-1}\setminus \overline{U}_{j-1} \subset T_{j-1}, \qquad T_{j-2} \subset T_{j-1}, \qquad T_{j-1} \cap W_{j-1} = 0.$$

Show that $\operatorname{Fr}\big(\bigcup_{j=1}^{\infty} U_j\big) \subset \bigcup_{j=1}^{\infty} (F_j \cap \operatorname{Fr} U_j)$.

O (N. Vedenissoff [1939]). Show that for every perfectly normal Lindelöf space X the formula $\operatorname{ind} X = \operatorname{Ind} X$ is valid.

Hint: Make use of Problem N and of the lemma to Theorem 2.4.

P (Yu. M. Smirnov [1951b]). Show that for every perfectly normal space X the equality $\operatorname{ind} \beta X = \operatorname{Ind} X = \operatorname{Ind} \beta X$ is valid.

Hint: Prove inductively the equality $\operatorname{ind} \beta X = \operatorname{Ind} \beta X$. Make use of Theorem 1.11, Lemma 2 to that theorem, and Problem N.

Q (M. Katětov [1952], K. Morita [1954]; for separable spaces L. A. Tumarkin [1928]). Show that for every subspace M of a metrizable space X there exists a G_δ-set $N \subset X$ such that $M \subset N$ and $\operatorname{Ind} M = \operatorname{Ind} N$.

Deduce that every metrizable space is homeomorphic to a dense subspace of a space metrizable in a complete manner whose weight and dimension Ind are equal to the weight and the dimension of the given space.

Hint: Making use of Lemma 2 to Theorem 3.4 and modifying Lemma 3 to that theorem, prove the theorem for the case $\operatorname{Ind} M = 0$. Generalize to an arbitrary dimension by means of Theorem 3.6.

In the proof of the second part, make use of Theorems 4.3.9 and 4.4.7.

R (K. Menger [1924], P. Urysohn [1925b] (announced in [1922])). Show that a subspace M of the n-dimensional Euclidean space R^n is of dimension n if and only if $\operatorname{Int} M \neq 0$.

Deduce that the boundary of every non-empty open subset $U \subset R^n$ such that $\overline{U} \neq R^n$ is of dimension $n-1$.

S. From the fixed-point theorem deduce the Sperner Lemma and the following two corollaries:

There is no mapping $f\colon Q^{n+1} \to S^n$ such that $f(x) = x$ for every $x \in S^n$.

The mapping $\mathrm{id}_{S^n}\colon S^n \to S^n$ is not homotopic to the mapping of S^n into a single point.

Show that each of these corollaries, and also the theorem stating that $\dim I^n = n$, imply the fixed-point theorem.

CHAPTER 8

UNIFORM SPACES. PROXIMITY SPACES

Uniform spaces and proximity spaces can be considered as either axiomatic systems which describe notions related to the notion of a topological space or as tools for examining topological spaces. The theory of uniformities was intended by its author André Weil to be a tool which, in contrast with metrics, can be applied to spaces not necessarily satisfying the axioms of countability. The theory of uniform spaces is analogous to the theory of metric spaces but can be applied to a greater number of spaces. In particular, for every topological group three uniformities are naturally defined which are important in the theory of topological groups. The theory of proximity spaces can also be applied to topological spaces, in the first place to the theory of compactifications. N. Bourbaki, having systematically worked out the theory of uniform spaces, presented it in his book as an axiomatic theory parallel to the theory of topological spaces. The connection between these two theories is established by assigning topological spaces and mappings to uniform spaces and uniformly continuous functions (Theorem 1.1). The transit from uniform spaces to topological spaces can, by Theorems 4.2 and 4.1, be split into two steps by considering proximity spaces.

In Paragraph 1 we define the notion of a uniformity and of a uniform space and show how a uniformity in a set induces a topology in that set. Next, we consider two important concepts which can be used in the definition and examination of uniformities. They are: uniform coverings and pseudo-metrics. From an important property of pseudo-metrics described in Theorem 1.4 we deduce that every space with the topology induced by a uniformity is always a Tychonoff space. Then we examine uniformities induced by metrics and group operations. From Theorem 1.4 we deduce a necessary and sufficient condition that a uniformity be induced by a metric. At the end of the paragraph we prove that the topology of every Tychonoff space can be induced by a uniformity. We also define uniformly continuous functions.

In Paragraph 2 three operations on uniform spaces are examined, namely the subspace, the Cartesian product and the mapping space. In contradistinction to metric spaces, the Cartesian product of a family of uniform spaces is defined without any assumptions concerning the power of the family. By considering a uniformity in the mapping space we are able to define a family of equicontinuous functions and prove counterparts of the classical Ascoli Theorem (Theorems 2.4 and 2.5).

Paragraph 3 is devoted to totally bounded and complete uniformities. It shows clearly the analogy between metric and uniform spaces. Many theorems of that paragraph are generalizations, almost identical in formulation, of theorems of Paragraph 4.3. The proofs of the theorems in Paragraph 3 are often modifications of the proofs of the corresponding theorems of Paragraph 4.3 and are, therefore, sometimes omitted. The end of the paragraph is devoted to the construction of the completion of a uniform space. The conditions for the compactness of a uniform space are also examined.

In Paragraph 4 we deal with proximity spaces. We prove that every proximity induces a topology and examine relations between proximities and uniformities. The theorem of Smirnov which establishes a one-to-one correspondence between proximities in a topological space and compactifications of that space is basic for that paragraph.

§ 1. Uniformities. Uniform spaces. We begin with notations and definitions. Let us consider a set X and subsets A, B of the product $X\times X$, i.e. relations in the set X. The relation *inverse* to A will be denoted by $-A$ and the *composition* of the relations A and B by $A+B$. We thus have

$$-A = \{(x, y): (y, x)\in A\}. \tag{1}$$

$$A+B = \{(x, z): \text{there exists a } y\in X \text{ such that } (x, y)\in A \text{ and } (y, z)\in B\}. \tag{2}$$

It is easy to see that the composition of relations is associative, i.e. that $(A+B)+C = A+(B+C)$. Simple examples show that we may have $A+B \neq B+A$, i.e. the composition of relations is not commutative.

For every $A \subset X\times X$ and a natural number n the set nA is defined inductively by means of the formulas:

$$1A = A, \quad nA = (n-1)A+A. \tag{3}$$

It follows from the associativity of the composition that

$$mA+nA = nA+mA = (m+n)A.$$

The *diagonal* of the product $X\times X$ is the set

$$\Delta = \{(x, x): x\in X\}. \tag{4}$$

Every set V containing Δ and satisfying the condition $V = -V$ is called an *entourage of the diagonal* Δ. The family of all entourages of the diagonal $\Delta \subset X \times X$ will be denoted by $\mathfrak{D}_X$.

If $(x, y) \in V$ for $x, y \in X$ and some $V \in \mathfrak{D}_X$, then we say that x and y are at a *distance less than* V and write $|x-y| < V$. If the condition $|x-y| < V$ is not satisfied, then we write $|x-y| \geqslant V$.

If for every two points of a set $A \subset X$ and an entourage of the diagonal $V \in \mathfrak{D}_X$ the condition $|x-y| < V$ holds, then we say that the *diameter* of A *is less than* V and write $\delta(A) < V$.

It is easy to see that for every $x, y, z \in X$ and $V, V_1, V_2 \in \mathfrak{D}_X$ we have,

(5) $$|x-x| < V,$$

(6) $$|x-y| < V \text{ if and only if } |y-x| < V,$$

(7) $$\text{if } |x-y| < V_1 \text{ and } |y-z| < V_2, \text{ then } |x-z| < V_1+V_2.$$

Suppose we are given an entourage of the diagonal $V \in \mathfrak{D}_X$ and a point $x \in X$. The set $B(x, V) = \{y \in X : |x-y| < V\}$ is called the *ball* with *centre* x and *radius* V. It follows immediately from (7) that the diameter of every ball of radius V is less than $V+V = 2V$. For every set $A \subset X$ and $V \in \mathfrak{D}_X$ the set $\bigcup_{x \in A} B(x, V)$ will be denoted by $B(A, V)$.

A *uniformity* in a set X is a non-empty subfamily of the family $\mathfrak{D}_X$ of entourages of the diagonal Δ of the product $X \times X$, which satisfies the following conditions:

(U1) *If* $V \in \mathfrak{U}$ *and* $V \subset W \in \mathfrak{D}_X$, *then* $W \in \mathfrak{U}$.

(U2) *If* $V_1, V_2 \in \mathfrak{U}$, *then* $V_1 \cap V_2 \in \mathfrak{U}$.

(U3) *For every* $V \in \mathfrak{U}$ *there exists a* $W \in \mathfrak{U}$ *such that* $2W \subset V$.

(U4) $\bigcap_{V \in \mathfrak{U}} V = \Delta$.

A *base* for the uniformity $\mathfrak{U}$ in the set X is any family $\mathfrak{B} \subset \mathfrak{U}$ such that for every $V \in \mathfrak{U}$ there exists a $W \in \mathfrak{B}$ satisfying $W \subset V$. The uniformity $\mathfrak{U}$ may have many bases. A base $\mathfrak{B}_0$ for the uniformity $\mathfrak{U}$ is said to be *minimal* if for every base $\mathfrak{B}$ for the uniformity $\mathfrak{U}$ the inequality $\overline{\overline{\mathfrak{B}_0}} \leqslant \overline{\overline{\mathfrak{B}}}$ holds. All minimal bases for the uniformity $\mathfrak{U}$ are of the same power which is called the *weight* of the uniformity $\mathfrak{U}$ and denoted by $w(\mathfrak{U})$.

A base $\mathfrak{B}$ for a uniformity $\mathfrak{U}$ in the set X has the following properties:

(BU1) *If* $V_1, V_2 \in \mathfrak{B}$, *then there exists a* $V \in \mathfrak{B}$ *such that* $V \subset V_1 \cap V_2$.

(BU2) *For every* $V \in \mathfrak{B}$ *there exists a* $W \in \mathfrak{B}$ *such that* $2W \subset V$.

(BU3) $\bigcap_{V \in \mathfrak{B}} V = \Delta$.

Every entourage of the diagonal $V \in \mathfrak{D}_X$ defines the covering $\mathfrak{C}(V) = \{B(x, V)\}_{x \in X}$ of the set X. Let $\mathfrak{U}$ be a uniformity in the set X. Every covering of the set X, for which there exists a $V \in \mathfrak{U}$ such that $\mathfrak{C}(V)$ is a refinement of it, is called a *uniform covering relative to* $\mathfrak{U}$. The family $\mathbf{C}$ of all coverings of the set X uniform relative to a uniformity $\mathfrak{U}$ has the following properties:

(UC1) *If* $\mathfrak{A} \in \mathbf{C}$ *and* $\mathfrak{A}$ *is a refinement of a covering* $\mathfrak{B}$, *then* $\mathfrak{B} \in \mathbf{C}$.

(UC2) *If* $\mathfrak{A}_1, \mathfrak{A}_2 \in \mathbf{C}$, *then there exists a covering* $\mathfrak{A} \in \mathbf{C}$ *which is a refinement of* $\mathfrak{A}_1$ *and* $\mathfrak{A}_2$.

(UC3) *For every* $\mathfrak{A} \in \mathbf{C}$ *there exists a* $\mathfrak{B} \in \mathbf{C}$ *which is a star-refinement of* $\mathfrak{A}$.

(UC4) *For every two distinct points* $x, y \in X$ *there exists a covering* $\mathfrak{A} \in \mathbf{C}$ *such that no set belonging to* $\mathfrak{A}$ *contains simultaneously* x *and* y.

Property (UC1) is obvious. Property (UC2) follows from (U2) and from the equality $B(x, V_1 \cap V_2) = B(x, V_1) \cap B(x, V_2)$. Property (UC4) follows from (U4) and (U3). Let us now consider $\mathfrak{A} = \mathfrak{C}(V) \in \mathbf{C}$. By virtue of (U3), there exists a $W \in \mathfrak{U}$ such that $4W \subset V$. To prove that the family $\mathbf{C}$ satisfies condition (UC3) it is sufficient to verify that the covering $\mathfrak{B} = \mathfrak{C}(W)$ is a star-refinement of the covering $\mathfrak{A}$. For this purpose let us consider an arbitrary element $B(x, W)$ of the covering $\mathfrak{C}(W)$ and let $y \in X$ satisfy the condition $B(x, W) \cap B(y, W) \neq 0$. It follows that $|x-y| < 2W$. Hence for every $z \in B(y, W)$ we have $|x-z| < 3W \subset 4W \subset V$ and $z \in B(x, V)$. Since the point y is arbitrary, $\mathrm{St}(B(x, W), \mathfrak{B}) \subset B(x, V)$.

A pair $(X, \mathfrak{U})$ consisting of a set X and a uniformity $\mathfrak{U}$ in it is called a *uniform space*. The *weight* of a uniform space is the weight of the uniformity $\mathfrak{U}$.

Every uniformity in X induces a topology in X. Thus every uniform space $(X, \mathfrak{U})$ induces a topological space $(X, \mathfrak{O})$.

THEOREM 1. *If* $\mathfrak{U}$ *is a uniformity in the set* X, *then the family*

$$\mathfrak{O} = \{G \subset X\colon \textit{for every } x \in G \textit{ there exists } V \in \mathfrak{U} \textit{ such that } B(x, V) \subset G\}$$

of subsets of the set X *satisfies conditions* (O1)-(O3); *thus it is a topology in the set* X. *The space* $(X, \mathfrak{O})$ *is a* T_1*-space.*

The topology $\mathfrak{O}$ is called *the topology of the uniformity* $\mathfrak{U}$ or *the topology induced by the uniformity* $\mathfrak{U}$.

Proof. It follows from the definition of the family $\mathfrak{O}$ that this family satisfies conditions (O1) and (O2). Let G_1 and G_2 be elements of $\mathfrak{O}$ and let $x \in G_1 \cap G_2$. By the definition of the family $\mathfrak{O}$, there exist entourages of the diagonal $V_1, V_2 \in \mathfrak{U}$ such that $B(x, V_i) \subset G_i$ for $i = 1, 2$. It follows from (U2) that $V = V_1 \cap V_2 \in \mathfrak{U}$. Since $B(x, V) = B(x, V_1 \cap V_2) = B(x, V_1) \cap B(x, V_2) \subset G_1 \cap G_2$, we infer that $G_1 \cap G_2 \in \mathfrak{O}$.

We shall now prove that $(X, \mathfrak{O})$ is a T_1-space. For this purpose it is sufficient to show that for every $x \in X$ the set $G = X \setminus \{x\}$ is open. Let us consider a point $y \in G$. We thus have $x \neq y$ and, by virtue of (U4), there exists a $V \in \mathfrak{U}$ such that $|x-y| \geqslant V$. Since $B(y, V) \subset G$, G is open. ■

THEOREM 2. *The interior of a set $A \subset X$ in the topology of the uniformity $\mathfrak{U}$ is the set*

$$B = \{x \in X \colon B(x, V) \subset A \text{ for some } V \in \mathfrak{U}\}.$$

Proof. Since every open set $G \subset A$ is contained in the above set, it is sufficient to prove that B is open. Let us consider $x \in B$; we have $B(x, V) \subset A$ for some $V \in \mathfrak{U}$. Let W be an element of $\mathfrak{U}$ such that $2W \subset V$. It follows from (7) that $B(y, W) \subset B(x, V) \subset A$ for every $y \in B(x, W)$. We thus have $B(x, W) \subset B$, and since the point x is arbitrary, this proves that B is open. ■

COROLLARY 1. *For every point $x \in X$ and $V \in \mathfrak{U}$ the set* $\operatorname{Int} B(x, V)$ *is a neighbourhood of the point x in the topology of the uniformity $\mathfrak{U}$.*

Indeed, since $B(x, V) \subset B(x, V)$, x belongs to the interior of the set $B(x, V)$. ■

COROLLARY 2. *For every point x and every subset A of the space X with the topology of the uniformity $\mathfrak{U}$ the relation $x \in \bar{A}$ holds if and only if $B(x, V) \cap A \neq 0$ for every $V \in \mathfrak{U}$.* ■

COROLLARY 3. *Let X be a topological space with the topology of a uniformity $\mathfrak{U}$. Then for every $A \subset X$ and $V \in \mathfrak{U}$*

$$\text{if } \delta(A) < V, \text{ then } \delta(\bar{A}) < 3V.$$

Proof. By virtue of Corollary 2, for every $x, y \in \bar{A}$ there exist $x', y' \in A$ such that $x' \in B(x, V)$ and $y' \in B(y, V)$. We thus have

$$|x-y| < V+V+V = 3V. \blacksquare$$

EXAMPLE 1. Let X be a set. We define $\mathfrak{U} = \mathfrak{D}_X$. Evidently $\mathfrak{U}$ is a uniformity in the set X. This uniformity is called *discrete*. The base for the uniformity $\mathfrak{U}$ is the family $\mathfrak{B} = \{\Delta\}$ consisting of one element, namely the diagonal Δ. Every covering of the set X is a uniform covering. Since $B(x, \Delta) = \{x\}$, every subset $A \subset X$ is open in the topology of the uniformity $\mathfrak{U}$, whence the topology of this uniformity is the discrete topology. ■

It follows from Example 1 that the weight of the topological space X induced by a uniformity $\mathfrak{U}$ in the set X can be greater than the weight of that uniformity. It is, however, easy to see that the weight of the topological space X is, at any point, not greater than the weight of the uniformity $\mathfrak{U}$.

EXAMPLE 2. Let X be a set. For every finite sequence $x_1, x_2, \ldots, x_k \in X$ let us define

$$V(x_1, x_2, \ldots, x_k) = X\times X \setminus \Big\{\bigcup_{i=1}^{k} [(X\times\{x_i\}) \cup (\{x_i\}\times X)]\setminus \Delta\Big\}.$$

The sets $V(x_1, x_2, \ldots, x_k)$ are entourages of the diagonal. Let us consider the family $\mathfrak{U} \subset \mathfrak{D}_X$ consisting of all entourages of the diagonal which contain a set $V(x_1, x_2, \ldots, x_k)$. Elements of the family $\mathfrak{U}$ are, therefore, entourages of the diagonal which can be obtained by removing from the set $X\times X$ one of its subsets which is contained in the union of a finite number of sets of the form $X\times\{x\} \cup \{x\}\times X$, where $x \in X$. We shall show that $\mathfrak{U}$ is a uniformity.

It follows from the definition that $\mathfrak{U}$ satisfies conditions (U1) and (U2). Condition (U3) follows from the formula $2V(x_1, x_2, \ldots x_k) = V(x_1, x_2, \ldots, x_k)$ which can easily be verified. Since $(x, y) \notin V(x)$ for $x \neq y$, condition (U4) is also verified.

Since $B(x, V(x)) = \{x\}$, the uniformity $\mathfrak{U}$ induces the discrete topology in X. If X is infinite, then evidently $\mathfrak{U} \neq \mathfrak{D}_X$. From Example 1 it follows, therefore, that distinct uniformities may induce the same topology in X. ∎

EXAMPLE 3. Let us consider the segment $I = [0, 1]$ and let $\mathfrak{U}$ consist of those entourages of the diagonal Δ of the square which contain a set open in $I\times I$ and containing Δ. The reader can easily verify that $\mathfrak{U}$ is a uniformity and that it induces the natural topology in I. ∎

Let $\mathfrak{U}$ be a uniformity in a set X and let $\mathfrak{O}$ be the topology of the uniformity $\mathfrak{U}$ in X. The topology of the Cartesian product of the space $(X, \mathfrak{O})$ in the set $X\times X$ is said to be *induced* by the uniformity $\mathfrak{U}$. The space $X\times X$ with this topology is very important for examining uniformities in the set X.

Let $(X, \mathfrak{U})$ be a uniform space and let ϱ denote a pseudo-metric in the set X. If for every $\varepsilon > 0$ there exists a $V \in \mathfrak{U}$ such that the condition $|x-y| < V$ implies the inequality $\varrho(x, y) < \varepsilon$, then we say that the pseudo-metric ϱ is *uniform* relative to the uniformity $\mathfrak{U}$.

THEOREM 3. *If a pseudo-metric ϱ in the set X is uniform relative to $\mathfrak{U}$, then it is a continuous function of the set $X\times X$ with the topology induced by $\mathfrak{U}$ into the real-line R.*

Proof. Let us consider a point $(x_0, y_0) \in X\times X$, and a number $\varepsilon > 0$, and let us choose $V \in \mathfrak{U}$ such that

$$\text{if } |x-y| < V, \text{ then } \varrho(x, y) < \varepsilon/2.$$

Since, by virtue of Corollary 1 to Theorem 2, the set $\operatorname{Int} B(x_0, V)\times \operatorname{Int} B(y_0, V)$ is a neighbourhood of the point (x_0, y_0), it is sufficient to prove that

$$|\varrho(x_0, y_0) - \varrho(x, y)| < \varepsilon \text{ for every } (x, y) \in B(x_0, V)\times B(y_0, V).$$

If, however, $(x, y) \in B(x_0, V) \times B(y_0, V)$, then $|x_0 - x| < V$ and $|y_0 - y| < V$, so that, by making use of the triangle inequality, we obtain

$$|\varrho(x_0, y_0) - \varrho(x, y)| \leqslant \varrho(x_0, x) + \varrho(y_0, y) < \varepsilon/2 + \varepsilon/2 = \varepsilon. \blacksquare$$

We shall now prove Theorem 4. It is one of the most important theorems of the theory of uniform spaces. We shall use it often in the sequel. In particular it follows from this theorem that every space with the topology induced by a uniformity is a Tychonoff space.

THEOREM 4. *Let $(X, \mathfrak{U})$ be a uniform space. For every sequence $V_0, V_1, \ldots$ of elements of $\mathfrak{U}$ which satisfy the condition*

$$(8) \qquad V_0 = X \times X \quad \textit{and} \quad 3V_{n+1} \subset V_n \quad \textit{for} \quad n = 1, 2, \ldots$$

there exists a pseudo-metric ϱ in X such that

$$V_n \subset \{(x, y): \varrho(x, y) \leqslant 2^{-n}\} \subset V_{n-1} \quad \textit{for} \quad n = 1, 2, \ldots$$

Proof. Let us define a function f of the product $X \times X$ into the segment I by means of the formula:

$$f(x, y) = \begin{cases} 0, & \text{if } (x, y) \in \bigcap_{n=0}^{\infty} V_n, \\ 2^{-n}, & \text{where } (x, y) \in V_n \setminus V_{n+1}, \text{ otherwise.} \end{cases}$$

It follows from the definition of f that for every $(x, y) \in X$

$$(9) \qquad f(x, x) = 0 \quad \text{and} \quad f(x, y) = f(y, x).$$

For every pair of points $x, y \in X$ let $\varrho(x, y)$ be the greatest lower bound of the set consisting of the numbers of the form $\sum_{i=1}^{m} f(x_{i-1}, x_i)$, where $x_0, x_1, \ldots, x_m$ is a finite sequence of points of the set X such that $x_0 = x$ and $x_m = y$. It follows from (9) that $\varrho(x, x) = 0$ and $\varrho(x, y) = \varrho(y, x)$ for every $x, y \in X$. It follows also from the definiton that ϱ satisfies the triangle inequality, whence it is a pseudo-metric.

The proof of the remaining part of the theorem will be deduced from the inequality

$$(10) \qquad \tfrac{1}{2} f(x, y) \leqslant \varrho(x, y) \leqslant f(x, y).$$

In order to prove (10) it suffices to show that for every $x, y \in X$ and every sequence $x_0, x_1, \ldots, x_m$ such that $x_0 = x$ and $x_m = y$, we have

$$(11) \qquad \tfrac{1}{2} f(x, y) \leqslant \sum_{i=1}^{m} f(x_{i-1}, x_i).$$

We shall prove formula (11) by induction. For $m = 1$ formula (11) is evidently valid. Suppose that $m > 1$ and that (11) is valid for all $n < m$.

Let us consider a sequence $x_0, x_1, \ldots, x_m$ such that $x_0 = x$ and $x_m = y$. Let $a = \sum_{i=1}^{m} f(x_{i-1}, x_i)$. If $a \geqslant \frac{1}{2}$, then inequality (11) is valid, because $f(x, y) \leqslant 1$. We can, therefore, assume that $a < \frac{1}{2}$.

Let us suppose that $a > 0$. Clearly, either $f(x_0, x_1) \leqslant a/2$ or $f(x_{m-1}, x_m) \leqslant a/2$ is valid. By the symmetry of our assumptions we can suppose that $f(x_0, x_1) \leqslant a/2$. Let k denote the greatest integer for which the inequality $\sum_{i=1}^{k} f(x_{i-1}, x_i) \leqslant a/2$ is valid. We thus have $\sum_{i=1}^{k+1} f(x_{i-1}, x_i) > a/2$. Hence $\sum_{i=k+2}^{m} f(x_{i-1}, x_i) \leqslant a/2$ and, by virtue of the inductive assumption, $f(x_0, x_k) \leqslant a$ and $f(x_{k+1}, x_m) \leqslant a$. From the definition of the number a we infer also that $f(x_k, x_{k+1}) \leqslant a$.

Let l denote the smallest non-negative integer such that $2^{-l} \leqslant a$. Since $a < \frac{1}{2}$, we infer that $l \geqslant 2$. Thus, $(x_0, x_k) \in V_l$, $(x_k, x_{k+1}) \in V_l$, and $(x_{k+1}, x_m) \in V_l$, and by virtue of (8), $(x_0, x_m) = (x, y) \in V_{l-1}$. It follows that $f(x, y) \leqslant 2^{-l+1} \leqslant 2a$, i.e. that $\frac{1}{2} f(x, y) \leqslant a$.

Let us now suppose that $a = 0$. We thus have $f(x_{i-1}, x_i) = 0$ for $i = 1, 2, \ldots, m$. By virtue of the definition of the function f, we infer that $(x_i, x_{i-1}) \in V_n$ for $i = 1, 2, \ldots, m$ and $n = 0, 1, 2, \ldots$ It follows that $(x, y) \in mV_n$ for $n = 0, 1, 2, \ldots$ and, by virtue of (8), that $(x, y) \in \bigcap_{n=0}^{\infty} V_n$, i.e. that $f(x, y) = 0$. Thus in the case $a = 0$ the inequality $\frac{1}{2} f(x, y) \leqslant a$ also holds, which, according to the definition of the number a, completes the proof of formulas (11) and (10).

We infer from (10) and from the definition of the function f that

$$V_n \subset \{(x, y) \colon \varrho(x, y) \leqslant 2^{-n}\} \subset V_{n-1} \quad \text{for} \quad n = 1, 2, \ldots \blacksquare$$

COROLLARY 1. *If $\mathfrak{U}$ is a uniformity in the set X, then for every $V \in \mathfrak{U}$ there exists a pseudo-metric ϱ in X which is uniform relative to $\mathfrak{U}$ and is such that*

$$\{(x, y) \colon \varrho(x, y) < 1\} \subset V.$$

Proof. It follows from (U3) that there exists a sequence $V_0, V_1, \ldots$ of elements of $\mathfrak{U}$ which satisfies (8) and is such that $V_1 = V$. The pseudo-metric $\varrho = 4\varrho_0$, where ϱ_0 is a pseudo-metric satisfying the assumption of Theorem 3, has the required properties. $\blacksquare$

The sets

$$W = \{(x, y) \colon \varrho(x, y) < 1\} \quad \text{and} \quad U = \{(x, y) \colon \varrho(x, y) \leqslant \tfrac{1}{2}\},$$

where ϱ is the pseudo-metric defined in the proof of Corollary 1, belong, by virtue of (U1), to $\mathfrak{U}$. Since, by virtue of Theorem 3, the first one is open in $X \times X$ and the second is closed, and since both are contained in V, we have

COROLLARY 2. *Let $\mathfrak{U}$ be a uniformity in a set X. The family of entourages of the diagonal belonging to $\mathfrak{U}$ and open in the topology of $X \times X$ induced by $\mathfrak{U}$ is a base for the uniformity $\mathfrak{U}$. Elements of the uniformity $\mathfrak{U}$ which are closed in $X \times X$ with the topology induced by $\mathfrak{U}$ also form a base for $\mathfrak{U}$.* ■

COROLLARY 3. *The set X with the topology induced by a uniformity $\mathfrak{U}$ in X is a Tychonoff space.*

Proof. For every point $x_0 \in X$ and any closed set F not containing x_0 there exists a $V \in \mathfrak{U}$ such that $B(x_0, V)$ is disjoint from F. The function $f: X \to I$ defined by the formula: $f(x) = \min(1, \varrho(x, x_0))$, where ϱ is the pseudo-metric of Corollary 1, is continuous by Theorem 3 and assumes the value 0 at the point x_0 and the value 1 at points of the set F. ■

Let us now consider a uniform space $(X, \mathfrak{U})$. Let P be the family of all pseudo-metrics in the set X which are uniform relative to $\mathfrak{U}$. We shall show that the family P has the following properties:

(P1) *If $\varrho_1, \varrho_2 \in P$, then* $\max(\varrho_1, \varrho_2) \in P$.

(P2) *For every pair of distinct points $x, y \in X$ there exists a $\varrho \in P$ such that $\varrho(x, y) > 0$.*

Let us consider $\varrho_1, \varrho_2 \in P$ and $\varrho = \max(\varrho_1, \varrho_2)$. Let ε be a positive number. It follows from the definition of a uniform pseudo-metric that there exist $V_1, V_2 \in \mathfrak{U}$ such that the condition $(x, y) \in V_i$ implies the inequality $\varrho_i(x, y) < \varepsilon$ for $i = 1, 2$. Since $V_1 \cap V_2 \in \mathfrak{U}$ and since for $(x, y) \in V_1 \cap V_2$ the inequality $\varrho(x, y) < \varepsilon$ holds, we infer that $\varrho \in P$.

Property (P2) follows from (U4) and Corollary 1 to Theorem 4.

When defining a uniformity in a set X it is sometimes inconvenient to describe all entourages of the diagonal belonging to the uniformity. We shall now give three methods of generating uniformities in a set X. They consist in distinguishing a base, a family of uniform coverings, and a family of pseudo-metrics.

THEOREM 5. *Let X be a set and let $\mathfrak{B} \subset \mathfrak{D}_X$ denote a family of entourages of the diagonal which satisfies conditions* (BU1)-(BU3). *The family $\mathfrak{U}$ consisting of all elements of $\mathfrak{D}_X$ which contain an element of $\mathfrak{B}$ is a uniformity. The family $\mathfrak{B}$ is a base for the uniformity $\mathfrak{U}$.*

The uniformity $\mathfrak{U}$ is said to be *generated by the base* $\mathfrak{B}$. ■

EXAMPLE 4. The reader can note that this method of generating a uniformity was used in Examples 2 and 3. ■

THEOREM 6. *Let X be a set and let $\mathbf{C}$ denote a family of its coverings which satisfies conditions* (UC1)-(UC4). *The family $\mathfrak{B}$ of entourages of the diagonal consisting of sets of the form $\bigcup_{H \in \mathfrak{A}} H \times H$, where $\mathfrak{A} \in \mathbf{C}$, is a base* *for a uniformity* $\mathfrak{U}$ *in the set* X. *The family* $\mathbf{C}$ *is identical with the family of all coverings uniform relative to* $\mathfrak{U}$.

The uniformity $\mathfrak{U}$ is said to be *generated by the family* $\mathbf{C}$ *of uniform coverings.*

Proof. Let

$$V(\mathfrak{A}) = \bigcup_{H \in \mathfrak{A}} H \times H$$

for every covering $\mathfrak{A}$ of the set X. Since evidently $V(\mathfrak{A}) \subset \mathfrak{D}_X$, it is sufficient to verify that $\mathfrak{B} = \{V(\mathfrak{A})\}_{\mathfrak{A} \in \mathbf{C}}$ satisfies conditions (BU1)-(BU3). But these properties follow immediately from the corresponding properties (UC2)-(UC4) by the simple remark that if $\mathfrak{A}$ is a refinement of $\mathfrak{B}$, then $V(\mathfrak{A}) \subset V(\mathfrak{B})$ and if $\mathfrak{A}$ is a star-refinement of $\mathfrak{B}$, then $2V(\mathfrak{A}) \subset V(\mathfrak{B})$. The last part of the theorem follows from (UC1) and the obvious formula $B(x, V(\mathfrak{A})) = \mathrm{St}(x, \mathfrak{A})$. ■

EXAMPLE 5. A *group* is a set G such that for every pair of elements $x, y \in G$ an element $xy \in G$, called the *product* of x and y, is defined and the following three conditions are satisfied:

(G1) $(xy)z = x(yz)$ *for every* $x, y, z \in G$.

(G2) *There exists an element* $e \in G$ *such that* $xe = ex = x$ *for every* $x \in G$.

(G3) *For every* $x \in G$ *there exists an element* $x^{-1} \in G$ *such that* $xx^{-1} = e$.

The element e is called the *unity* of the group and the element x^{-1} is called *inverse* of x. It can be shown that for every $x \in G$ there exists exactly one element $x^{-1} \in G$ which satisfies (G3).

If, moreover, the following condition is satisfied

(G4) $xy = yx$ *for every* $x, y \in G$,

then we say that the group G is *abelian* or *commutative.*

If in a group G a topology is defined with respect to which G is a T_1-space and

(TG1) *The formula* $f(x, y) = xy$ *defines a mapping* $f: G \times G \to G$,

(TG2) *The formula* $f(x) = x^{-1}$ *defines a mapping* $f: G \to G$,

then we call G a *topological group.*

Let us suppose that a group G is given. For every $A, B \subset G$ let us define

$$A^{-1} = \{x^{-1}: x \in A\}, \qquad AB = \{xy: x \in A \text{ and } y \in B\}.$$

For every $A \subset G$ and $x \in G$ we shall write xA and Ax instead of $\{x\}A$ and $A\{x\}$. It can be verified without any difficulty that if A is an open subset of a topological group G, then the set A^{-1} is also open.

Similarly, the set AB is open provided that one of the sets A, B is open in G. In particular, for each open subset $H \subset G$ the sets xH and Hx are open for every $x \in X$.

Let us now consider a topological group G. Let $\mathfrak{B} = \mathfrak{B}(e)$ be a base at the point e. Each element $H \in \mathfrak{B}$ determines three coverings of the space G:

$$\mathfrak{C}_l(H) = \{xH\}_{x \in G}, \quad \mathfrak{C}_r(H) = \{Hx\}_{x \in G}, \quad \mathfrak{C}(H) = \{xHy\}_{x,y \in G}.$$

Let us denote by $\mathbf{C}_l, \mathbf{C}_r$, and $\mathbf{C}$ the family of those coverings of G which have refinements of the form $\mathfrak{C}_l(H), \mathfrak{C}_r(H)$, and $\mathfrak{C}(H)$, respectively. Each of the families of coverings defined above satisfies conditions (UC1)-(UC4), and thus it generates a uniformity in G. We find that the topology of each of these uniformities is the same as the initial topology in the group G. Since the proofs are similar, we shall prove the above only for the family $\mathfrak{C}_l$. Let us notice, however, that if G is abelian, then the three families of coverings under consideration coincide and, therefore, generate the same uniformity in G.

Suppose we are given a topological group G and the family $\mathbf{C}_l$ of its coverings described above. From the definition of $\mathbf{C}_l$ it follows that this family satisfies condition (UC1).

Since for every $H_1, H_2 \in \mathfrak{B} = \mathfrak{B}(e)$ there exists an $H \in \mathfrak{B}$ such that $H \subset H_1 \cap H_2$, we infer that the family $\mathbf{C}_l$ also satisfies condition (UC2).

To prove property (UC3) it is sufficient to show that

(12) for every $H \in \mathfrak{B}$ there exists an $H_1 \in \mathfrak{B}$ such that
$$\operatorname{St}(xH_1, \mathfrak{C}_l(H_1)) \subset xH \text{ for every } x \in G.$$

Let us consider an arbitrary $H \in \mathfrak{B}$. By virtue of (TG1) and (TG2), the formula $f(x_1, x_2, x_3) = x_1 x_2^{-1} x_3$ defines a mapping of the Cartesian product $G \times G \times G$ into G. Since $f(e, e, e) = e$, there exists an $H_1 \in \mathfrak{B}$ such that $f(H_1 \times H_1 \times H_1) = H_1 H_1^{-1} H_1 \subset H$. We shall show that it satisfies condition (12). Indeed, if for a fixed $x \in G$ we have $xH_1 \cap x_1 H_1 \neq 0$, then $xh_0 = x_1 h_1$ and $x_1 = xh_0 h_1^{-1}$ for some $h_0, h_1 \in H_1$. Thus, for every element $x_1 h$ of the set $x_1 H_1$ we have

$$x_1 h = xh_0 h_1^{-1} h \in xH_1 H_1^{-1} H_1 \subset xH$$

and condition (12) is satisfied.

For every pair of distinct elements x, y of the group G we have the inequality $x^{-1}y \neq e$. Since G is a T_1-space, there exists an $H \in \mathfrak{B}$ such that $x^{-1}y \notin H$. For some $H_1 \in \mathfrak{B}$ we have $H_1^{-1}H_1 \subset H$. We shall prove that no element of the covering $\mathfrak{C}_l(H_1)$ contains simultaneously the points x and y. In fact, from the equalities $x = x_0 h_1$ and $y = x_0 h_2$, where $x_0 \in G$ and $h_1, h_2 \in H_1$, it follows that $x^{-1}y = h_1^{-1}h_2 \in H_1^{-1}H_1 \subset H$, contrary to the choice of the neighbourhood H. Thus property (UC4) is also satisfied.

Since for $H \in \mathfrak{B}$ and $V(H) = V(\mathfrak{C}_l(H)) = \bigcup_{x \in G} xH \times xH$ we have

$$B(x, V(H)) = \mathrm{St}(x, \mathfrak{C}_l(H)), \tag{13}$$

we infer that every set open in the topology of the uniformity under consideration is also open in the initial topology of the group G. If U is an open subset of the group G and $x \in U$, then there exists an $H \in \mathfrak{B}$ such that $xH \subset U$. For every H_1 satisfying (12) we have, by (13),

$$x \in B(x, V(H_1)) = \mathrm{St}(x, \mathfrak{C}_l(H_1)) \subset \mathrm{St}(xH_1, \mathfrak{C}_l(H_1)) \subset xH \subset U.$$

Thus the set U is also open in the topology induced by the uniformity. The topology induced in G by this uniformity is, therefore, the same as the initial topology of the group G. It follows, in particular, that every topological group is a Tychonoff space. ∎

THEOREM 7. *Let X be a set and let us suppose that P denotes a family of pseudo-metrics in the set X which satisfies conditions* (P1) *and* (P2). *The family $\mathfrak{B}$ of entourages of the diagonal consisting of the sets of the form $\{(x, y): \varrho(x, y) < 2^{-i}\}$, where $\varrho \in P$ and $i = 1, 2, \ldots$, is a base for a uniformity $\mathfrak{U}$ in the set X. Each pseudo-metric $\varrho \in P$ is uniform relative to the uniformity $\mathfrak{U}$.*

The uniformity $\mathfrak{U}$ is said to be *generated by the family of pseudo-metrics P*. ∎

In connection with the methods here presented of generating a uniformity it is worth noting that if $\mathfrak{U}_0$ is a uniformity in a set X, then for each base $\mathfrak{B}$ for the uniformity $\mathfrak{U}_0$, the family $\mathbf{C}$ of all coverings uniform relative to $\mathfrak{U}_0$, or the family P of all pseudo-metrics uniform relative to $\mathfrak{U}_0$, the uniformity $\mathfrak{U}$ generated in X by $\mathfrak{B}$, $\mathbf{C}$, or P according to Theorem 5, 6, or 7, is identical with the uniformity $\mathfrak{U}_0$.

EXAMPLE 6. Let X be a Tychonoff space. Let us denote the family of all real-valued continuous functions defined on X by $C(X)$ and let $C^*(X)$ denote its subfamily consisting of bounded functions. For every finite number of functions $f_1, f_2, \ldots, f_k \in C(X)$ the formula

$$\varrho_{f_1, f_2, \ldots, f_k}(x, y) = \max\{|f_1(x)-f_1(y)|, |f_2(x)-f_2(y)|, \ldots, |f_k(x)-f_k(y)|\} \tag{14}$$

defines a pseudo-metric in the set X. Let us denote by P the family of pseudo-metrics of the form $\varrho_{f_1, f_2, \ldots, f_k}$, where $f_1, f_2, \ldots, f_k \in C(X)$, and let P^* denote its subfamily consisting of the pseudo-metrics of the form $\varrho_{f_1, f_2, \ldots, f_k}$, where $f_1, f_2, \ldots, f_k \in C^*(X)$.

The families P and P^* satisfy condition (P1) and (P2). Thus according to Theorem 7, they generate uniformities $\mathfrak{C}$ and $\mathfrak{C}^*$ in the set X. We shall show that the topology induced in X by $\mathfrak{C}$ or $\mathfrak{C}^*$ is identical with the initial topology in the space X.

By virtue of (14), the function $\varrho: X\times X \to R$ is continuous for every $\varrho \in P$. The sets $\{(x, y): \varrho(x, y) < 2^{-i}\}$, where $\varrho \in P$ and $i = 1, 2, \ldots$, are, therefore, open in $X\times X$ and every set open in the topology induced by $\mathfrak{C}$ or $\mathfrak{C}^*$ is open in the space X. Let us now suppose that U is an open set in the space X and let $x_0 \in X$ denote a point belonging to it. Since X is a Tychonoff space, there exists a function $f \in C^*(X) \subset C(X)$ such that $f(x_0) = 0$ and $f(x) = 1$ for $x \in X\setminus U$. Since for $V = \{(x, y): \varrho(x, y) < 1/2\}$ we have $B(x_0, V) \subset U$, we infer that the set U is open in the topology induced by $\mathfrak{C}$ or $\mathfrak{C}^*$. ■

Example 6 and Corollary 3 to Theorem 4 imply

THEOREM 8. *The topology of a topological space X can be induced by a uniformity in X if and only if X is a Tychonoff space.* ■

Let us consider a set X and a metric ϱ in it. Since the family $\{\varrho\}$ consisting of only one pseudo-metric ϱ has properties (P1) and (P2), it generates, by Theorem 7, a uniformity $\mathfrak{U}$ in X. The topology induced in X by the metric ϱ is identical with the topology induced by the uniformity $\mathfrak{U}$. Indeed, a set $A \subset X$ is open relative to both topologies if and only if, together with every point x_0, it contains a ball $B(x_0, 2^{-i}) = B(x_0, V_i)$ for a certain i, where $V_i = \{(x, y): \varrho(x, y) < 2^{-i}\} \in \mathfrak{U}$. The uniformity $\mathfrak{U}$ is said to be *induced by the metric* ϱ. The uniform space $(X, \mathfrak{U})$ is called *metrizable* provided that the uniformity $\mathfrak{U}$ can be induced by a metric in the set X.

As we have already noted, every uniformity $\mathfrak{U}$ can be generated by a family of pseudo-metrics, for instance by the family of all pseudo-metrics uniform relative to $\mathfrak{U}$. In connection with this the following question can be raised: which uniformities can be induced by a metric? The following theorem answers the question.

THEOREM 9. *A uniformity $\mathfrak{U}$ in a set X can be induced by a metric in X if and only if $w(\mathfrak{U}) \leqslant \aleph_0$.*

Proof. Every uniformity induced by a metric is of weight $\leqslant \aleph_0$.

If a uniformity $\mathfrak{U}$ in a set X has a countable base $\{U_i\}_{i=1}^{\infty}$, then there exists a sequence $V_0, V_1, \ldots$ of entourages of the diagonal which belong to $\mathfrak{U}$ and such that

$$V_0 = X\times X, \quad 3V_{i+1} \subset V_i \quad \text{and} \quad V_i \subset U_i \quad \text{for} \quad i = 1, 2, \ldots$$

From the last inclusion it follows that $\bigcap_{i=1}^{\infty} V_i = \Delta$. Hence the pseudo-metric corresponding, by Theorem 4, to the sequence $V_0, V_1, \ldots$ is a metric.

It follows from the inclusions of Theorem 4 that $\mathfrak{U}$ is a uniformity induced by ϱ. ■

We note, in connection with the last theorem, that it follows from Example 2 that a metrizable topology can be induced in X by a uniformity which itself cannot be induced by any metric.

To end the paragraph we shall consider uniformly continuous functions. Let us assume that $(X, \mathfrak{U})$ and $(Y, \mathfrak{V})$ are uniform spaces. A function f of the set X into the set Y is called *uniformly continuous* relative to $\mathfrak{U}$ and $\mathfrak{V}$ if for every $V \in \mathfrak{V}$ there exists a $U \in \mathfrak{U}$ such that for every $x, y \in X$ if $|x-y| < U$, then $|f(x)-f(y)| < V$. It follows from the definition that a uniformly continuous function of the space X with the topology induced by $\mathfrak{U}$ into the space Y with the topology induced by $\mathfrak{V}$ is a mapping. We shall use the symbol $f\colon (X, \mathfrak{U}) \to (Y, \mathfrak{V})$ for a uniformly continuous function relative to $\mathfrak{U}$ and $\mathfrak{V}$. Let us consider uniformities $\mathfrak{U}$, $\mathfrak{V}$, and $\mathfrak{W}$ in sets X, Y, and Z, respectively, and functions f of the set X into Y and g of the set Y into Z. The reader can verify that if $f\colon (X, \mathfrak{U}) \to (Y, \mathfrak{V})$ and $g\colon (Y, \mathfrak{V}) \to (Z, \mathfrak{W})$, then $gf\colon (X, \mathfrak{U}) \to Z, \mathfrak{W})$, i.e. that the composition of uniformly continuous functions is a uniformly continuous function.

As in the case of topological spaces one can give some necessary and sufficient conditions for a function to be uniformly continuous in terms of various methods of generating a uniformity.

THEOREM 10. *Let $(X, \mathfrak{U})$ and $(Y, \mathfrak{V})$ be uniform spaces and let f be a function of the set X into the set Y. The following conditions are equivalent:*

(i) *f is uniformly continuous.*

(ii) *If $\mathfrak{B}$ and $\mathfrak{C}$ are bases of the uniformities $\mathfrak{U}$ and $\mathfrak{V}$ respectively, then for every $V \in \mathfrak{C}$ there exists a $U \in \mathfrak{B}$ such that $U \subset f^{-1}(V)$.*

(iii) *For every covering $\mathfrak{A}$ of the set Y, which is uniform with respect to $\mathfrak{V}$, the covering $\{f^{-1}(A)\}_{A \in \mathfrak{A}}$ of the set X is uniform with respect to $\mathfrak{U}$.*

(iv) *For every pseudo-metric ϱ in the set Y, which is uniform with respect to $\mathfrak{V}$, the pseudo-metric σ in X, where $\sigma(x, y) = \varrho\big(f(x), f(y)\big)$, is uniform with respect to $\mathfrak{U}$.* ■

If f is a one-to-one function of X onto Y and both f and f^{-1} are uniformly continuous relative to $\mathfrak{U}$ and $\mathfrak{V}$, and to $\mathfrak{V}$ and $\mathfrak{U}$ respectively, then f is called a *uniform isomorphism* relative to $\mathfrak{U}$ and $\mathfrak{V}$. Uniform isomorphisms are homeomorphisms of topological spaces X and Y with topologies induced by $\mathfrak{U}$ and $\mathfrak{V}$, respectively.

Uniform spaces $(X, \mathfrak{U})$ and $(Y, \mathfrak{V})$ are called *isomorphic* if there exists a uniform isomorphism $f\colon (X, \mathfrak{U}) \to (Y, \mathfrak{V})$. The study of *uniform properties*, i.e. invariants of uniform isomorphisms, is the subject of theory of uniform spaces. Of course, every topological invariant is also a uniform invariant.

EXERCISES

A. Let us suppose that in a set X uniformities $\mathfrak{U}_1$ and $\mathfrak{U}_2$ are given. If $\mathfrak{U}_1 \supset \mathfrak{U}_2$, then we say that $\mathfrak{U}_1$ is *stronger* than $\mathfrak{U}_2$ or that $\mathfrak{U}_2$ is *weaker* than $\mathfrak{U}_1$.

Verify that if a uniformity $\mathfrak{U}_1$ is stronger than a uniformity $\mathfrak{U}_2$, then it induces a stronger topology than the topology induced by $\mathfrak{U}_2$.

Show that every family $\{\mathfrak{U}_s\}_{s \in S}$ of uniformities in a set X has a least upper bound, i.e. that in the set X there exists a uniformity $\mathfrak{U}$ which is the weakest in the set of all uniformities stronger than $\mathfrak{U}_s$ for every $s \in S$. Does there exist a greatest lower bound for every family of uniformities in X?

B. Let us consider a set X, a family of uniform spaces $\{(Y_s, \mathfrak{U}_s)\}_{s \in S}$, and a family of functions $\{f_s\}_{s \in S}$, where f_s is a function of the set X into Y_s. Show that there exists a weakest uniformity $\mathfrak{U}$ in the set X such that $f_s: (X, \mathfrak{U}) \to (Y_s, \mathfrak{U}_s)$ for every $s \in S$. Describe a base for the uniformity $\mathfrak{U}$ and prove that if the space Y_s is considered with the topology induced by $\mathfrak{U}_s$, the topology induced by $\mathfrak{U}$ is identical with the topology generated by the family of mappings $\{f_s\}_{s \in S}$. The uniformity $\mathfrak{U}$ is said to be *generated by the family of functions* $\{f_s\}_{s \in S}$.

C. Let X be a Tychonoff space and let P be the family of all pseudo-metrics in X which are continuous functions of the Cartesian product $X \times X$ into the real-line R. Show that P satisfies conditions (P1) and (P2) and that the topology induced by the uniformity generated by P in X is the same as the initial topology in the space X.

D. Let (X, ϱ) and (Y, σ) be metric spaces. Give a necessary and sufficient condition that a function f of the set X into Y be uniformly continuous relative to the uniformities induced in X and Y by the metrics ϱ and σ, respectively.

§ 2. Operations on uniform spaces. Let us suppose that $(X, \mathfrak{U})$ is a uniform space and let $M \subset X$. The family $\mathfrak{U}_M = \{V \cap (M \times M)\}_{V \in \mathfrak{U}}$ of entourages of the diagonal $\Delta \subset M \times M$ satisfies conditions (U1)-(U4), i.e. $(M, \mathfrak{U}_M)$ is a uniform space. We call it a *subspace* of the space $(X, \mathfrak{U})$. It can easily be verified that the topology induced in M by the uniformity $\mathfrak{U}_M$ is the same as the topology of the set M considered as a subspace of the space X with the topology induced by $\mathfrak{U}$.

If a uniformity $\mathfrak{U}$ in a set X is induced by a metric ϱ, then the uniformity $\mathfrak{U}_M$ is the same as the uniformity induced by the metric of the subspace M of the metric space (X, ϱ).

For every uniform space $(X, \mathfrak{U})$ and for $M \subset X$, the formula $i_M(x) = x$ for $x \in M$ defines a uniformly continuous function $i_M: (M, \mathfrak{U}_M) \to (X, \mathfrak{U})$ called the *embedding* of $(M, \mathfrak{U}_M)$ into $(X, \mathfrak{U})$.

Another important operation on uniform spaces is the Cartesian product. Let us suppose that a family $\{(X_s, \mathfrak{U}_s)\}_{s \in S}$ of uniform spaces is given. The family of entourages of the diagonal $\Delta \subset \mathbf{P}_{s \in S} X_s \times \mathbf{P}_{s \in S} X_s$ consisting of all sets of the form

$$\{(\{x_s\}, \{y_s\}): |x_{s_i} - y_{s_i}| < V_{s_i} \text{ for } i = 1, 2, \ldots, k\},$$

where k is a natural number and $V_{s_i} \in \mathfrak{U}_{s_i}$ for $i = 1, 2, \ldots, k$, has properties (B1)-(B3). According to Theorem 1.5, this family generates a uniformity in the set $\mathbf{P}_{s \in S} X_s$. We call it the *Cartesian product* of the family of uniformities $\{\mathfrak{U}_s\}_{s\in S}$ and denote it by the symbol $\mathop{\boldsymbol{P}}_{s\in S}\mathfrak{U}_s$. The uniform space $(\mathop{\boldsymbol{P}}_{s\in S} X_s, \mathop{\boldsymbol{P}}_{s\in S}\mathfrak{U}_s)$ is called the *Cartesian product* of that family of uniform spaces. The reader can easily verify that the topology induced in $\mathop{\boldsymbol{P}}_{s\in S} X_s$ by the product of uniformities $\mathop{\boldsymbol{P}}_{s\in S}\mathfrak{U}_s$ is identical with the Tychonoff topology of the product $\mathop{\boldsymbol{P}}_{s\in S} X_s$, if we consider X_s with the topology induced by the uniformity $\mathfrak{U}_s$ for every $s\in S$.

If a uniformity $\mathfrak{U}_i$ in a set X_i is induced by a metric ϱ_i bounded by number 1 for $i = 1, 2, \ldots$, then the uniformity $\mathop{\boldsymbol{P}}_{i=1}^{\infty}\mathfrak{U}_i$ in the set $\mathop{\boldsymbol{P}}_{i=1}^{\infty} X_i$ is identical with the uniformity induced by the metric ϱ defined by means of formula (2), Paragraph 4.2.

For every $s\in S$ the formula $p_s(\{x_s\}) = x_s$ defines a function of the product $\mathop{\boldsymbol{P}}_{s\in S} X_s$ onto the set X_s, namely the projection onto the s-th axis. It is easy to notice that this function is uniformly continuous,

$$p_s\colon (\mathop{\boldsymbol{P}}_{s\in S} X_s, \mathop{\boldsymbol{P}}_{s\in S}\mathfrak{U}_s) \to (X_s, \mathfrak{U}_s).$$

The following theorem is parallel to Theorem 2.3.3.

THEOREM 1. *Let us suppose that a uniform space $(Y, \mathfrak{B})$ and a family of uniform spaces $\{(X_s, \mathfrak{U}_s)\}_{s\in S}$ are given. A function f of the set Y into the set $\mathop{\boldsymbol{P}}_{s\in S} X_s$ is uniformly continuous if and only if $p_s f$ is uniformly continuous for every $s\in S$.* ■

EXAMPLE 1. Let us consider the segment I with the uniformity $\mathfrak{U}$ induced by its natural metric. Let us next consider in the Tychonoff cube $I^{\mathfrak{m}}$ of weight $\mathfrak{m} \geqslant \aleph_0$ the uniformity $\mathfrak{U}^{\mathfrak{m}}$, which is the Cartesian product of $\mathfrak{m}$ copies of $\mathfrak{U}$.

It follows from the definition of the Cartesian product of uniformities that $\mathfrak{U}^{\mathfrak{m}}$ has a base of power $\mathfrak{m}$. It can easily be verified that the weight of this uniformity is equal to $\mathfrak{m}$.

Each Tychonoff space X of weight $\mathfrak{m}$ can be considered as a subspace of the cube $I^{\mathfrak{m}}$. Since the uniformity $\mathfrak{U}^{\mathfrak{m}}$ induces the usual topology of the Tychonoff cube $I^{\mathfrak{m}}$, the uniformity $\mathfrak{U}^{\mathfrak{m}}_X$ induces the initial topology in X. Thus, the topology of every Tychonoff space of weight $\mathfrak{m}$ can be induced by a uniformity of weight $\mathfrak{m}$. ■

THEOREM 2. *Every uniform space is uniformly isomorphic to a subspace of the Cartesian product of metrizable uniform spaces.*

Proof. Let $(X, \mathfrak{U})$ be a uniform space. By property (U3), for every $V\in\mathfrak{U}$ there exists a sequence $V_0, V_1, \ldots$ of elements of the uniformity

$\mathfrak{U}$ such that

(1) $V_0 = X\times X, \quad V_1 = V, \quad \text{and} \quad 3V_{n+1} \subset V_n \quad \text{for} \quad n = 1, 2, ..$

For every $V\in\mathfrak{U}$, let ϱ_V denote the pseudo-metric in the set X which exists by Theorem 1.4 and satisfies the condition

(2) $$V_n \subset \{(x, y): \varrho_V(x, y) \leqslant 2^{-n}\} \subset V_{n-1} \text{ for } n = 1, 2, \ldots$$

Let the relation $x \equiv_V y$ hold if and only if $\varrho_V(x, y) = 0$ for every $x, y\in X$. The relation $\equiv_V$ is an equivalence relation in X. Let X_V be the set of its equivalence classes. By the triangle inequality,

$$\varrho_V(x, y) = \varrho_V(x', y')$$

for every $x, x', y, y'\in X$ such that $x \equiv_V x'$ and $y \equiv_V y'$. Defining $\varrho_V([x], [y]) = \varrho_V(x, y)$ for every $[x], [y]\in X_V$, we give X_V the character of a metric space. Let $\mathfrak{U}_V$ be the uniformity induced by the metric ϱ_V in X_V. It follows from (2) that the formula $\varphi_V(x) = [x]$ defines a uniformly continuous function of the space $(X, \mathfrak{U})$ into the space $(X_V, \mathfrak{U}_V)$.

By virtue of Theorem 1, the diagonal $f = \mathop{\triangle}\limits_{V\in\mathfrak{U}} \varphi_V$ is a uniformly continuous function of the space $(X, \mathfrak{U})$ onto a subspace of the Cartesian product $(\mathop{\boldsymbol{P}}\limits_{V\in\mathfrak{U}} X_V, \mathop{\boldsymbol{P}}\limits_{V\in\mathfrak{U}} \mathfrak{U}_V)$ of metrizable uniform spaces. We shall prove that f is a uniform isomorphism.

It follows from property (U4) and from formulas (1) and (2) that for every pair of distinct points $x, y\in X$ there exists a $V\in\mathfrak{U}$ such that $\varrho_V(x, y) > 0$; thus $f(x) \neq f(y)$ and f is a one-to-one mapping.

In order to prove that the function f^{-1} is uniformly continuous we have to show that for every $V_0\in\mathfrak{U}$ there exists a $W\in \mathop{\boldsymbol{P}}\limits_{V\in\mathfrak{U}} \mathfrak{U}_V$ such that if $|f(x)-f(y)| < W$, then $|x-y| < V_0$. It follows from (1) and (2) that this property is possessed by

$$W = \big\{(\{x_V\}, \{y_V\}) \colon \varrho_{V_0}(x_{V_0}, y_{V_0}) < 1/4\big\}. \blacksquare$$

It can easily be verified that by replacing the uniformity $\mathfrak{U}$ by its minimal base in the proof of Theorem 2 we also get a function f which is a uniform isomorphism. Every uniform space of weight $\mathfrak{m}$ is, therefore, uniformly isomorphic to a subspace of the Cartesian product of $\mathfrak{m}$ metrizable uniform spaces.

Let us notice that there is no universal space for uniform spaces of weight $\leqslant \mathfrak{m}$, i.e. there is no space $(X, \mathfrak{U})$ of weight $\leqslant \mathfrak{m}$ which contains a subspace uniformly isomorphic to $(Y, \mathfrak{V})$ for every uniform space $(Y, \mathfrak{V})$ of weight $\leqslant \mathfrak{m}$. Indeed, it follows from Example 1.1 that the weight of a discrete uniform space $(X, \mathfrak{U})$ is always equal to 1, and since the power of the set X can be arbitrarily large, we infer that there is no uniform space which would contain subspaces uniformly isomorphic to, or even of the same power as, all discrete spaces.

In the remaining part of the paragraph we shall consider some problems concerning mapping spaces.

Let us suppose that X is a topological space and $(Y, \mathfrak{U})$ a uniform space. Let us denote by Y^X the family of all mappings of the space X into the space Y with the topology induced by $\mathfrak{U}$. For every $V \in \mathfrak{U}$ let $\hat{V}$ be the entourage of the diagonal of the set $Y^X \times Y^X$ defined by means of the formula:

$$\hat{V} = \{(f, g)\colon |f(x) - g(x)| < V \text{ for every } x \in X\}.$$

From the easily verifiable formulas:

$$\widehat{U \cap V} = \hat{U} \cap \hat{V} \quad \text{and} \quad \hat{U} + \hat{V} \subset \widehat{U + V}$$

it follows that the family $\{\hat{V}\}_{V \in \mathfrak{U}}$ satisfies conditions (BU1)-(BU3). The uniformity generated by this family is called the *uniformity of uniform convergence* induced by $\mathfrak{U}$ and will be denoted by the symbol $\hat{\mathfrak{U}}$. If the uniformity $\mathfrak{U}$ in Y is induced by a bounded metric ϱ, then the uniformity $\check{\mathfrak{U}}$ in Y^X has a countable base and thus, by Theorem 1.9, is induced by a metric. It can easily be verified that the metric $\hat{\varrho}$ defined by formula (6) of Paragraph 4.2, is one of the metrics inducing $\hat{\mathfrak{U}}$. Thus it follows from Example 4.2.2 that if two uniformities $\mathfrak{U}_1, \mathfrak{U}_2$ in the set Y induce the same topology, then the topologies induced in Y^X by $\hat{\mathfrak{U}}_1$ and $\hat{\mathfrak{U}}_2$ may be nevertheless different. Under the assumption of the compactness of the space X the topology in the space Y^X depends, as in the case of metric spaces, only on the topology in Y, for it is identical with the compact-open topology. This will be a corollary to Theorem 3 proved below. We shall define one more uniformity in the set Y^X before we state this theorem.

For every topological space X and every uniform space $(Y, \mathfrak{U})$ we shall denote by $\hat{\mathfrak{U}}|\mathfrak{Z}$ the uniformity in the set Y^X generated by the base consisting of all finite intersections of the sets of the form

$$\hat{V}|Z = \{(f, g)\colon |f(x) - g(x)| < V \text{ for every } x \in Z\},$$

where $V \in \mathfrak{U}, Z \in \mathfrak{Z}$, and $\mathfrak{Z}$ denotes the family of compact subsets of the space X. The uniformity $\hat{\mathfrak{U}}|\mathfrak{Z}$ will be called the *uniformity of uniform convergence on compacta.*

LEMMA. *Let us consider a set X with the topology induced by a uniformity $\mathfrak{U}$. For every compact subspace $Z \subset X$ and any open set $G \subset X$ containing Z there exists a $V \in \mathfrak{U}$ such that $B(x, V) \subset G$ for every $x \in Z$.*

Proof. For every $x \in Z$ there exists a $V_x \in \mathfrak{U}$ such that $B(x, 2V_x) \subset G$. The family $\{Z \cap \operatorname{Int} B(x, V_x)\}_{x \in Z}$ is, by virtue of Corollary 1 to Theorem 1.2, an open covering of the set Z. There exists, therefore, a finite number of points $x_1, x_2, \ldots, x_k \in Z$ such that

(3) $$Z \subset \operatorname{Int} B(x_1, V_{x_1}) \cup \operatorname{Int} B(x_2, V_{x_2}) \cup \ldots \cup \operatorname{Int} B(x_k, V_{x_k}).$$

Let $V = V_{x_1} \cap V_{x_2} \cap \ldots \cap V_{x_k}$ and let x be a point of the set Z. By virtue of (3), there exists an $i \leqslant k$ such that $|x - x_i| < V_{x_i}$. For every $x' \in B(x, V) \subset B(x, V_{x_i})$ we have $x' \in B(x_i, 2V_{x_i}) \subset G$, whence $B(x, V) \subset G$. ■

THEOREM 3. *For every topological space X and every uniform space $(Y, \mathfrak{U})$ the topology induced in the set Y^X by the uniformity $\hat{\mathfrak{U}}|\mathfrak{Z}$ of uniform convergence on compacta is identical with the compact-open topology of the space Y^X, provided that Y is considered with the topology induced by $\mathfrak{U}$.*

Proof. Let us denote by $\mathfrak{O}_1$ the topology induced by the uniformity $\hat{\mathfrak{U}}|\mathfrak{Z}$ in Y^X and let $\mathfrak{O}_2$ denote the compact-open topology. First, we shall prove that $\mathfrak{O}_2 \subset \mathfrak{O}_1$. It is clearly sufficient to show that the sets of the form $M(Z, G)$, where $Z \in \mathfrak{Z}$ and G is an open subset of Y, belong to $\mathfrak{O}_1$. Let us consider $Z \in \mathfrak{Z}$, an open set $G \subset Y$, and a function $f \in M(Z, G)$. Since Y is a Tychonoff space, $f(Z)$ is a compact subspace of G. By the lemma there exists an element V of $\mathfrak{U}$ satisfying the condition $B(f(x), V) \subset G$ for every $x \in Z$. We obviously have $B(f, \hat{V}|Z) \subset M(Z, G)$, which proves that $M(Z, G) \in \mathfrak{O}_1$.

We shall now prove that $\mathfrak{O}_1 \subset \mathfrak{O}_2$. For this purpose it is sufficient to show that for every $Z \in \mathfrak{Z}$, $V \in \mathfrak{U}$, and $f \in Y^X$ there exist compact sets $Z_1, Z_2, \ldots, Z_k \subset X$ and open sets $G_1, G_2, \ldots, G_k \subset Y$ such that

$$f \in \bigcap_{i=1}^{k} M(Z_i, G_i) \subset B(f, \hat{V}|Z).$$

By virtue of Corollary 2 to Theorem 1.4, there exists an entourage $W \in \mathfrak{U}$ of the diagonal which is closed in $Y \times Y$ and satisfies the condition $3W \subset V$. We immediately infer from the compactness of the set $f(Z)$ that for a finite sequence of points $x_1, x_2, \ldots, x_k \in Z$ the inclusion $f(Z) \subset \bigcup_{i=1}^{k} B(f(x_i), W)$ holds. We shall show that the sets

$$Z_i = Z \cap f^{-1}\big(B(f(x_i), W)\big) \quad \text{and} \quad G_i = \operatorname{Int} B\big(f(x_i), 2W\big)$$

have the required properties.

First of all, let us note that the closedness of the set W in $Y \times Y$ yields the closedness of the balls $B(f(x_i), W)$ in the space Y and the compactness of the sets Z_i. Moreover, $f \in \bigcap_{i=1}^{k} M(Z_i, G_i)$. Let us consider an arbitrary $g \in \bigcap_{i=1}^{k} M(Z_i, G_i)$. For every $x \in Z$ we have $x \in Z_i$ for some $i \leqslant k$, whence $g(x) \in B(f(x_i), 2W)$ and $f(x) \in B(f(x_i), W)$. It follows that $|f(x) - g(x)| < 3W \subset V$ for $x \in Z$, i.e. $g \in B(f, \hat{V}|Z)$. ■

COROLLARY. *For a compact space X and a uniform space $(Y, \mathfrak{U})$ the topology induced by the uniformity of uniform convergence in Y^X is identical with the compact-open topology; thus it depends only on the topology induced by $\mathfrak{U}$ in Y.* ■

It is worth noting that Theorem 3.3.2 follows from Theorem 3. In fact, let X be a topological space and Y a Tychonoff space. By virtue of Theorem 1.8, the topology in the space Y can be induced by a uniformity $\mathfrak{U}$. The compact-open topology in the space Y^X is, therefore, identical with the topology induced by the uniformity $\hat{\mathfrak{U}}|\mathfrak{Z}$. Thus, the space Y^X is a Tychonoff space.

For mappings of a topological space X into a topological space Y, whose topology is induced by a uniformity $\mathfrak{U}$, the important notion of an equicontinuous family of functions can be introduced. Namely, we say that the family $F \subset Y^X$ is *equicontinuous* if for every point $x \in X$ and every $V \in \mathfrak{U}$ there exists a neighbourhood G of the point x in X such that $|f(x) - f(x')| < V$ for every $f \in F$ and $x' \in G$. The notion of an equicontinuous family allows us to prove for uniform spaces a theorem analogous to the Ascoli Theorem. Before proving this theorem, however, we give three lemmas.

LEMMA 1. *Let X be locally compact space and let $(Y, \mathfrak{U})$ denote a uniform space. If a family of mappings $F \subset Y^X$, considered as a subspace of the space Y^X with the compact-open topology, is compact, then F is equicontinuous.*

Proof. Let us consider a point $x \in X$ and an entourage of the diagonal $V \in \mathfrak{U}$. Let $W \in \mathfrak{U}$ satisfy the condition $2W \subset V$.

Let us define

$$U_f = \operatorname{Int} B(f(x), W) \quad \text{for every } f \in F. \tag{4}$$

From the local compactness of X it follows that for every $f \in F$ there exists a neighbourhood H_f of the point $x \in X$ such that $\overline{H}_f$ is compact and $f(\overline{H}_f) \subset U_f$. The family of sets $\{F \cap M(\overline{H}_f, U_f)\}_{f \in F}$ is an open covering of the compact space F. There exists, therefore, a finite number of mappings $f_1, f_2, \ldots, f_k \in F$ such that

$$F \subset \bigcup_{i=1}^{k} M(\overline{H}_{f_i}, U_{f_i}).$$

For every mapping $f \in F$ we have $f \in M(\overline{H}_{f_i}, U_{f_i})$ for some $i \leqslant k$. Since by virtue of (4) we have $\delta(U_{f_i}) < 2W$, we infer that for every point x'

belonging to the neighbourhood $G = \bigcap_{j=1}^{k} H_{f_j} \subset \overline{H}_{f_i}$ of the point x, we have $|f(x)-f(x')| < 2W \subset V$. ∎

LEMMA 2. *Let X be a topological space and let $(Y, \mathfrak{U})$ denote a uniform space. For every equicontinuous family $F \subset Y^X$ the pointwise topology and the compact-open topology are identical.*

Proof. Since the compact-open topology is stronger than the pointwise topology, it is sufficient to prove that for every compact $Z \subset X$, open $G \subset Y$, and arbitrary $f_0 \in M(Z, G) \cap F$ there exist points $x_1, x_2, \ldots, x_k \in X$ and open sets $G_1, G_2, \ldots, G_k \subset Y$ such that

$$f_0 \in F \cap \bigcap_{i=1}^{k} M(\{x_i\}, G_i) \subset M(Z, G). \tag{5}$$

By virtue of the lemma to Theorem 3, there exists a $V \in \mathfrak{U}$ such that $B(f_0(x), 2V) \subset G$ for every $x \in Z$. Since the family F is equicontinuous, there exists for every $x \in Z$ a neighbourhood H_x such that

$$|f(x)-f(x')| < V \quad \text{for} \quad f \in F \text{ and } x' \in H_x. \tag{6}$$

By the compactness of the set Z there exists a finite number of points $x_1, x_2, \ldots, x_k$ such that

$$Z \subset H_{x_1} \cup H_{x_2} \cup \ldots \cup H_{x_k}. \tag{7}$$

We shall prove that (5) is satisfied if we assume that $G_i = \operatorname{Int} B(f_0(x_i), V)$ for $i = 1, 2, \ldots, k$.

Let us consider an arbitrary $f \in F \cap \bigcap_{i=1}^{k} M(\{x_i\}, G_i)$ and $x \in Z$. We infer from (7) that $x \in H_{x_i}$ for some $i \leqslant k$. By virtue of (6) this yields

$$|f(x_i)-f(x)| < V.$$

Since $f(x_i) \in G_i \subset B(f_0(x_i), V)$, we have

$$|f(x_i)-f_0(x_i)| < V,$$

and we infer that $f(x) \in B(f_0(x_i), 2V) \subset G$. But the point $x \in Z$ is arbitrary, and thus $f \in M(Z, G)$. Since $f_0 \in F \cap \bigcap_{i=1}^{k} M(\{x_i\}, G_i)$, condition (5) has been proved. ∎

LEMMA 3. *Let X be a topological space and let $(Y, \mathfrak{U})$ denote a uniform space. If $F \subset Y^X$ is an equicontinuous family, then the closure $\overline{F}$ in the space $\mathop{\boldsymbol{P}}_{x \in X} Y_x$, where $Y_x = Y$ for every $x \in X$, is contained in $Y^X \subset \mathop{\boldsymbol{P}}_{x \in X} Y_x$ and is equicontinuous.*

Proof. For each $V \in \mathfrak{U}$ every point $x \in X$ has a neighbourhood $G = G(x, V)$ such that $|f(x) - f(x')| < V$ for every $x' \in G$ and every $f \in F$. If V is an entourage of the diagonal closed in $Y \times Y$ with the topology induced by $\mathfrak{U}$, then the set

$$F(x, V) = \{f \in \mathop{\boldsymbol{P}}_{x \in X} Y_x : |f(x) - f(x')| < V \text{ for every } x' \in G(x, V)\}$$
$$= \bigcap_{x' \in G(x,V)} \{f \in \mathop{\boldsymbol{P}}_{x \in X} Y_x : |f(x) - f(x')| < V\}$$

is closed in the Cartesian product $\mathop{\boldsymbol{P}}_{x \in X} Y_x$. The intersection of all sets $F(x, V)$ for $x \in X$ and closed entourages of the diagonal $V \in \mathfrak{U}$ is closed. Since it contains F, it also contains $\bar{F}$. The family of closed entourages of the diagonal is, by Corollary 2 to Theorem 1.4, a base for the uniformity $\mathfrak{U}$. Thus the intersection and the family $\bar{F}$ are contained in Y^X and are equicontinuous. ■

For every pair of topological spaces X and Y and for every point $x \in X$ the formula: $w_x(f) = f(x)$ defines a mapping of the space Y^X into the space Y, either with the pointwise or with the compact-open topology. In the case of the pointwise topology this follows from Theorem 2.6.3, for, w is the projection onto the axis $Y_x = Y$. In the case of the compact-open topology this follows from the fact that this topology is stronger than the pointwise topology.

THEOREM 4 (Ascoli Theorem). *Let X be a locally compact space and let $(Y, \mathfrak{U})$ denote a uniform space. A closed subspace F of the space Y^X with the compact-open topology is compact if and only if the following conditions are satisfied*:

(a) *F is equicontinuous.*

(b) *For every $x \in X$ the set $w_x(F)$ is a compact subspace of Y.*

Proof. The necessity of conditions (a) and (b) follows from Lemma 1 and Theorem 3.1.8 respectively.

Let us now consider a subset $F \subset Y^X$ which satisfies (a) and (b) and is closed in Y^X with the compact-open topology. Let us denote by $\bar{F}$ the closure of the set $F \subset Y^X$ in the space $\mathop{\boldsymbol{P}}_{x \in X} Y_x$, where $Y_x = Y$ for every $x \in X$. By virtue of Lemmas 3 and 2, the pointwise and the compact-open topologies in $\bar{F}$ are identical. Since F is closed in Y^X with the compact-open topology, $F = \bar{F}$. Since F is a closed subspace of the Cartesian product $\mathop{\boldsymbol{P}}_{x \in X} w_x(F) \subset \mathop{\boldsymbol{P}}_{x \in X} Y_x$ (which is compact by the Tychonoff Theorem), it is compact. ■

Let us now consider spaces X, Y, the space Y^X, and a set $Z \subset X$. For every $F \subset Y^X$ let $F|Z = \{f|Z\}_{f \in F}$, where $f|Z$ denotes the restriction of the mapping $f \in Y^X$ to the set Z. It can easily be deduced from Theorems 3.3.5, 3.2.10, and 4 that the following theorem is also valid.

THEOREM 5 (Ascoli Theorem). *Let X be a k-space, let $\mathfrak{Z}$ be the family of all compact subsets of X and let $(Y, \mathfrak{U})$ denote a uniform space. A closed subspace F of the space Y^X with the compact-open topology is compact if and only if the following conditions are satisfied:*

(a) *$F|Z$ is equicontinuous for every $Z \in \mathfrak{Z}$.*

(b) *For every $x \in X$ the set $w_x(F)$ is a compact subspace of Y.* ■

EXERCISES

A. Let a family $\{(X_s, \mathfrak{U}_s)\}_{s \in S}$ of uniform spaces be given. Prove that the uniformity $\underset{s \in S}{\boldsymbol{P}} \mathfrak{U}_s$ in the set $\underset{s \in S}{\boldsymbol{P}} X_s$ is generated, according to Exercise 1.B, by the family of functions $\{p_s\}_{s \in S}$, where p_s is the projection of the product $\underset{s \in S}{\boldsymbol{P}} X_s$ onto the s-th axis.

B. Let $\{(X_s, \mathfrak{U}_s)\}_{s \in S}$ be a family of uniform spaces such that $X_s \cap X_{s'} = 0$ for $s, s' \in S$ and $s \neq s'$. Define a uniformity $\underset{s \in S}{\oplus} \mathfrak{U}_s$ in the set $\bigcup_{s \in S} X_s$ in such a manner that the topology induced in $\bigcup_{s \in S} X_s$ by the uniformity $\underset{s \in S}{\oplus} \mathfrak{U}_s$ is identical with the topology of the sum $\underset{s \in S}{\oplus} X_s$, where X_s is considered with the topology induced by $\mathfrak{U}_s$.

Define similarly the quotient space of a uniform space and the inverse limit of an inverse system of uniform spaces.

C. Let $(X, \mathfrak{U})$ be a uniform space. Verify that the topology induced by $\mathfrak{U}$ in $X \times X$ and the topology induced by $\mathfrak{U} \times \mathfrak{U}$ in $X \times X$ are identical. Show that a pseudo-metric ϱ in a set X is uniform relative to $\mathfrak{U}$ if and only if it is a uniformly continuous function of the space $(X \times X, \mathfrak{U} \times \mathfrak{U})$ into the real-line R with the uniformity induced by the usual metric.

D. Making use of Theorem 3.3.6, show that the topology induced by the uniformity of uniform convergence in the set Y^X, where X is a topological space and $(Y, \mathfrak{U})$ is a uniform space, is stronger than the compact-open topology.

§ 3. Complete and totally bounded uniform spaces. Compactness in uniform spaces. Let $(X, \mathfrak{U})$ be a uniform space and let $V \in \mathfrak{U}$; we say that a set $D \subset X$ is a *V-net* in X provided that for every point $x \in X$ there exists an $x' \in D$ such that $|x - x'| < V$. If for every $V \in \mathfrak{U}$ there exists in X a finite V-net $\{x_1, x_2, \ldots, x_k\}$, then we say that the uniformity $\mathfrak{U}$ is *totally bounded* or that the uniform space $(X, \mathfrak{U})$ is *totally bounded*.

If a uniformity $\mathfrak{U}$ in a set X is induced by a metric ϱ, then the space $(X, \mathfrak{U})$ is totally bounded if and only if the metric space (X, ϱ) is totally bounded.

The above definition distinguishes a class of uniform spaces. The question arises whether the class of all topological spaces whose topology is induced by a totally bounded uniformity can be topologically characterized. The characterization exists but it not specially interesting. Namely, we shall show below that the topology of every Tychonoff space can be induced by a totally bounded uniformity (cf. Example 1).

We shall now give two theorems on the operations on totally bounded uniform spaces. The proof of the first one can be obtained automatically from the proof of Theorem 4.3.1 by replacing ε with arbitrary $V \in \mathfrak{U}$ and $\varepsilon/2$ with a $W \in \mathfrak{U}$ such that $2W \subset V$. To prove the second theorem it is sufficient to use the base of the uniformity $\underset{s \in S}{\boldsymbol{P}} \mathfrak{U}_s$, described in the preceding paragraph, to argue in the same manner as in the proof of Theorem 4.3.2, and to notice that each of the spaces $(X_s, \mathfrak{U}_s)$ is uniformly isomorphic to a subspace of the space $(\underset{s \in S}{\boldsymbol{P}} X_s, \underset{s \in S}{\boldsymbol{P}} \mathfrak{U}_s)$.

THEOREM 1. *If $(X, \mathfrak{U})$ is a totally bounded uniform space and $M \subset X$, then the uniform space $(M, \mathfrak{U}_M)$ is also totally bounded.* ∎

THEOREM 2. *Let $\{(X_s, \mathfrak{U}_s)\}_{s \in S}$ be a family of non-empty uniform spaces. The uniform space $(\underset{s \in S}{\boldsymbol{P}} X_s, \underset{s \in S}{\boldsymbol{P}} \mathfrak{U}_s)$ is totally bounded if and only if the space $(X_s, \mathfrak{U}_s)$ is totally bounded for every $s \in S$.* ∎

EXAMPLE 1. Let X be a Tychonoff space and let $\mathfrak{C}^*$ denote the uniformity in X defined in Example 1.6. We shall show that the uniform space (X, C^*) is totally bounded.

It is sufficient to prove that for every system of functions $f_1, f_2, \ldots$ $\ldots, f_k \in C^*(X)$ and for every $\varepsilon > 0$ there exists a finite number of points $x_1, x_2, \ldots, x_n \in X$ such that for every $x \in X$ there exists an $i \leqslant n$ with the property

$$\varrho_{f_1, f_2, \ldots, f_k}(x, x_i) = \max\big(|f_1(x) - f_1(x_i)|, |f_2(x) - f_2(x_i)|, \ldots, |f_k(x) - f_k(x_i)|\big) < \varepsilon.$$

The bounded sets $f_1(X), f_2(X), \ldots, f_k(X)$ are contained in a bounded and closed interval $J \subset R$. Let $\{A_j\}_{j=1}^m$ be a covering of the interval J with sets of diameter less than ε. The family of sets of the form

$$f_1^{-1}(A_{j_1}) \cap f_2^{-1}(A_{j_2}) \cap \ldots \cap f_k^{-1}(A_{j_k}), \tag{1}$$

where $1 \leqslant j_i \leqslant m$ for every $i \leqslant k$, is a covering of the space X. The diameter of each of these sets (with respect to the pseudo-metric $\varrho_{f_1, f_2, \ldots, f_k}$) is less than ε. Choosing a point x_i from each of the non-empty sets of the form (1) we get the finite sequence of points $x_1, x_2, \ldots, x_n$ which has the required property.

It can immediately be verified that the real-line R with the uniformity $\mathfrak{C}$ described in Example 1.6 is not totally bounded. ∎

Let a uniform space $(X, \mathfrak{U})$ and a family $\mathfrak{F}$ of subsets of the set X be given. We say that $\mathfrak{F}$ *contains arbitrarily small sets* if

(2) for every $V \in \mathfrak{U}$ there exists an $F \in \mathfrak{F}$ such that $\delta(F) < V$.

We shall say that a uniformity $\mathfrak{U}$ in a set X is *complete* or that a uniform space $(X, \mathfrak{U})$ is *complete* if for each family of closed subsets $\{F_s\}_{s \in S}$ of the space X with the topology induced by $\mathfrak{U}$ which has the finite intersection property and contains arbitrarily small sets the intersection $\bigcap_{s\in S} F_s$ is non-empty. It follows from property (U4) that the intersection contains exactly one point.

The following two theorems are immediate consequences of the definition of completeness.

THEOREM 3. *If a uniformity $\mathfrak{U}$ induces the topology of a compact space in a set X, then the uniform space $(X, \mathfrak{U})$ is complete.* ■

THEOREM 4. *If a uniform space $(X, \mathfrak{U})$ is complete, then the space $(M, \mathfrak{U}_M)$ is complete for each closed set $M \subset X$.* ■

THEOREM 5. *If $(X, \mathfrak{U})$ is a uniform space and $(M, \mathfrak{U}_M)$ a complete subspace, then the set M is closed in X with respect to the topology induced by $\mathfrak{U}$.*

Proof. Let us consider a point $x \in \overline{M}$. Let $\mathfrak{F}$ be the family of all sets of the form $M \cap B(x, V)$, where V runs over the elements of the uniformity $\mathfrak{U}$ which are closed in $X \times X$ with the topology induced by $\mathfrak{U}$. By virtue of Corollary 2 to Theorem 1.2, and of Corollary 2 to Theorem 1.3, the family $\mathfrak{F}$ has the finite intersection property. It is easy to see that the family $\mathfrak{F}$ consists of closed subsets of the space M with the topology induced by $\mathfrak{U}_M$ and contains arbitrarily small sets. From the completeness of $(M, \mathfrak{U}_M)$ it follows that the point x, the only point which may belong to all sets of this family, itself belongs to M. ■

Let us notice that Theorem 4.3.5 implies

THEOREM 6. *If a uniformity $\mathfrak{U}$ in a set X is induced by a metric ϱ, then the space $(X, \mathfrak{U})$ is complete if and only if the metric space (X, ϱ) is complete.* ■

THEOREM 7. *Let $\{(X_s, \mathfrak{U}_s)\}_{s\in S}$ be a family of non-empty, uniform spaces. The uniform space $(\boldsymbol{P}_{s\in S} X_s, \boldsymbol{P}_{s\in S} \mathfrak{U}_s)$ is complete if and only if the space $(X_s, \mathfrak{U}_s)$ is complete for every $s \in S$.*

Proof. If $(\boldsymbol{P}_{s\in S} X_s, \boldsymbol{P}_{s\in S} \mathfrak{U}_s)$ is complete, then each of the spaces $(X_s, \mathfrak{U}_s)$ is complete according to Theorem 4, for it is uniformly isomorphic to a closed subspace of the product $(\boldsymbol{P}_{s\in S} X_s, \boldsymbol{P}_{s\in S} \mathfrak{U}_s)$.

The proof of the completeness of the Cartesian product of complete uniform spaces is analogous to the proof of the Tychonoff Theorem. It is sufficient to notice that if the family $\mathfrak{F}$ under consideration contains arbitrarily small sets, then each of the families $\mathfrak{F}_s$ defined in the proof of the Tychonoff Theorem contains arbitrarily small sets. ■

It follows from Theorems 6, 7, 4, and 3.10.4 that the topology of every real-compact space can be induced by a complete uniformity. It can be proved that if a topology of a space X can be induced by a complete uniformity and the cardinal number $\bar{\bar{X}}$ is non-measurable, then X is real-compact. It can also be proved that the class of topological spaces whose topology can be induced by complete uniformities coincides with the class of closed subspaces of the Cartesian products of metrizable spaces. Proofs of the two theorems lie outside the scope of this book. Let us note that the second theorem implies that the topology of any metrizable space can be generated by a complete uniformity. It can be proved (see Problem O) that every paracompact space has that property. Hence every paracompact space (in particular, every metrizable space) whose power is non-measurable is real-compact.

THEOREM 8. *Let $(X, \mathfrak{U})$ be a uniform space and let $(Y, \mathfrak{V})$ denote a complete uniform space. Every uniformly continuous function f defined on $(A, \mathfrak{U}_A)$, where A is a dense subset of X, with values in $(Y, \mathfrak{V})$ can be extended to a uniformly continuous function F: $(X, \mathfrak{U}) \to (Y, \mathfrak{V})$.*

Proof. The family $\{\overline{f(B(x, U) \cap A)}\}_{U \in \mathfrak{U}}$ has the finite intersection property and contains arbitrarily small sets for every $x \in X$. By the completeness of the space $(Y, \mathfrak{V})$ the formula

$$F(x) = \bigcap_{U \in \mathfrak{U}} \overline{f(B(x, U) \cap A)} \tag{3}$$

defines a function of the set X into the set Y. It can easily be verified that $F(x) = f(x)$ for $x \in A$.

We shall show that F is uniformly continuous. For every $W \in \mathfrak{V}$ let us consider a $V \in \mathfrak{V}$ such that $6V \subset W$ and an open $U \in \mathfrak{U}$ such that for every $a_1, a_2 \in A$ the condition $|a_1 - a_2| < 2U$ implies $|f(a_1) - f(a_2)| < V$. By virtue of Corollary 3 to Theorem 1.2,

(4) for every $M \subset X$ such that $\delta(M) < 2U$ we have $\overline{f(M \cap A)} < 3V$.

Let x, y be points of the space X satisfying the condition $|x - y| < U$ and let $K_1 = B(x, U)$ and $K_2 = B(y, U)$. The set $K_1 \cap K_2$ is a non-empty and open subset of the space X; therefore, from the denseness of A it follows that there exists a point a belonging to $A \cap K_1 \cap K_2$. Hence we have $f(a) \in \overline{f(K_1 \cap A)} \cap \overline{f(K_2 \cap A)}$ and we see from (4) that

$$\delta\left(\overline{f(K_1 \cap A)} \cup \overline{f(K_2 \cap A)}\right) < 6V.$$

Making use of (3), we get $|F(x) - F(y)| < 6V \subset W$. ∎

The theorem, in accordance with Theorem 1.5.2, yields the following

COROLLARY. *Let $(X, \mathfrak{U})$ and $(Y, \mathfrak{V})$ be complete uniform spaces and let A and B be dense subsets of X and Y, respectively. Each uniform isomorphism between the spaces $(A, \mathfrak{U}_A)$ and $(B, \mathfrak{V}_B)$ can be extended to a uniform isomorphism between $(X, \mathfrak{U})$ and $(Y, \mathfrak{V})$.* ∎

LEMMA. *For every metrizable uniform space* $(X, \mathfrak{U})$ *there exists a complete uniform space* $(\tilde{X}, \tilde{\mathfrak{U}})$ *such that* $(X, \mathfrak{U})$ *is uniformly isomorphic to a space* $(A, \tilde{\mathfrak{U}}_A)$, *where* A *is a dense subset of* $\tilde{X}$.

Proof. Let the uniformity $\mathfrak{U}$ be induced by a metric ϱ in the set X. The metric $\varrho_1(x, y) = \min(1, \varrho(x, y))$ induces the same uniformity $\mathfrak{U}$ in the set X. In the proof of Theorem 4.3.10 we constructed a homeomorphic embedding F of the space X into the complete metric space I^X of all continuous functions defined on X into the segment I. From formula (6), Paragraph 4.3 it follows immediately that the mapping is a uniform isomorphism, $F: (X, \mathfrak{U}) \to (F(X), \mathfrak{V}_{F(X)})$, where $\mathfrak{V}$ denotes the uniformity induced by the metric in I^X. It follows from Theorem 6 that we can define $(\tilde{X}, \tilde{\mathfrak{U}})$ as being equal to the subspace $(\overline{F(X)}, \mathfrak{V}_{\overline{F(X)}})$ of the space $(I^X, \mathfrak{V})$. ∎

THEOREM 9. *For every uniform space* $(X, \mathfrak{U})$ *there exists a complete uniform space* $(\tilde{X}, \tilde{\mathfrak{U}})$, *unique up to an uniform isomorphism and called the completion of the space* $(X, \mathfrak{U})$, *such that* $(X, \mathfrak{U})$ *is uniformly isomorphic to a subspace* $(A, \tilde{\mathfrak{U}}_A)$, *where* A *is a dense subset of* X.

If the space $(X, \mathfrak{U})$ *is totally bounded, then the space* $(\tilde{X}, \tilde{\mathfrak{U}})$ *is also totally bounded.*

Proof. The existence of the space $(\tilde{X}, \tilde{\mathfrak{U}})$ follows from Theorem 2.2, from the lemma, and from Theorems 7 and 4. Its uniqueness follows from the corollary to Theorem 8.

Let us suppose that $(X, \mathfrak{U})$, and thus also $(A, \tilde{\mathfrak{U}}_A)$, is totally bounded. For every $V \in \mathfrak{U}$ let us consider $W \in \mathfrak{U}$ such that $2W \subset V$ and let $U = (A \times A) \cap W \in \tilde{\mathfrak{U}}_A$. Let us also assume that the set $\{x_1, x_2, \ldots, x_k\}$ is an U-net in A. By virtue of the denseness of A, for every $\tilde{x} \in \tilde{X}$ there exists an $x \in A \cap B(\tilde{x}, W)$. Thus for some $i \leqslant k$ we have

$$|x - x_i| < U \subset W \quad \text{and} \quad |x - \tilde{x}| < W.$$

It follows that $|\tilde{x} - x_i| < 2W \subset V$, i.e. the set $\{x_1, x_2, \ldots, x_k\}$ is a V-net in X. ∎

The remaining part of the paragraph is devoted to uniformities in compact spaces.

THEOREM 10. *Let* X *be a compact space. There exists exactly one uniformity* $\mathfrak{U}$ *in the set* X *which induces the topology of the space* X. *The base for the uniformity* $\mathfrak{U}$ *consists of all neighbourhoods of the diagonal which are open in the space* $X \times X$.

Proof. The existence of the uniformity $\mathfrak{U}$ inducing the topology of the space X follows from Theorem 1.8. We shall prove that the family of all entourages of the diagonal which are open in $X \times X$ is a base for $\mathfrak{U}$, which will show that there exists exactly one uniformity inducing the topology of the space X.

It follows from Corollary 2 to Theorem 1.4 that every element $V \in \mathfrak{U}$ contains an entourage of the diagonal open in $X \times X$. Let us now consider an entourage W of the diagonal which is open in $X \times X$. By virtue of condition (U4) and Corollary 2 to Theorem 1.4, $\Delta = \bigcap_{V \in \mathfrak{U}} \overline{V} \subset W$, whence, according to Corollary 2 to Theorem 3.1.3 and by the compactness of $X \times X$, there exists a finite number $V_1, V_2, \ldots, V_k$ of elements of the uniformity $\mathfrak{U}$ such that $\Delta \subset V_1 \cap V_2 \cap \ldots \cap V_k \subset \overline{V}_1 \cap \overline{V}_2 \cap \ldots \cap \overline{V}_k \subset W$. By virtue of (U1) and (U2), this yields $W \in \mathfrak{U}$. ∎

THEOREM 11. *If a uniformity $\mathfrak{U}$ induces the topology of a countably compact space in the set X, then the uniform space $(X, \mathfrak{U})$ is totally bounded.*

The proof is analogous to the proof of Theorem 4.3.12 and is omitted. ∎

A uniform space $(X, \mathfrak{U})$ is said to be *compact* if the set X with the topology induced by $\mathfrak{U}$ is a compact space.

THEOREM 12. *A uniform space $(X, \mathfrak{U})$ is compact if and only if it is totally bounded and complete.*

Proof. The necessity of the condition follows from Theorems 11 and 3.

In order to prove its sufficiency let us consider a family $\mathfrak{F} = \{F_s\}_{s \in S}$ of closed subsets of the space X which has the finite intersection property. We shall prove that the intersection $\bigcap_{s \in S} F_s$ is non-empty. Since the finite intersection property is of a finite character, the family $\mathfrak{F}$ is contained in a maximal family of closed subsets of X with the finite intersection property, and it is sufficient to show that the intersection of all elements of this maximal family is non-empty. We can, therefore, assume without any loss of generality that $\mathfrak{F} = \{F_s\}_{s \in S}$ is the maximal family.

From the maximality it follows that the intersection of a finite number of elements of the family $\mathfrak{F}$ belongs to $\mathfrak{F}$ and that

(5) if $\overline{F} = F \subset X$ and $F \cap F_s \neq 0$ for every $s \in S$, then $F \in \mathfrak{F}$.

Moreover,

(6) if $\overline{F}_i = F_i \subset X$ for $i \leqslant k$ and $F = \bigcup_{i=1}^{k} F_i \in \mathfrak{F}$, then

$F_i \in \mathfrak{F}$ for some $i \leqslant k$.

In fact, if $F_i \notin \mathfrak{F}$ for $i = 1, 2, \ldots, k$, then, by virtue of (5), for each $i = 1, 2, \ldots, k$, there would exist $F_i' \in \mathfrak{F}$ such that $F_i \cap F_i' = 0$, so that we would have $0 = \bigcup_{i=1}^{k} F_i \cap \bigcap_{i=1}^{k} F_i' = F \cap \bigcap_{i=1}^{k} F_i' \in \mathfrak{F}$, which is contrary to the assumption.

Let V be an element of the uniformity $\mathfrak{U}$. Let us consider $W \in \mathfrak{U}$ such that $6W \subset V$. From the total boundedness of the space $(X, \mathfrak{U})$ it follows that there exist points $x_1, x_2, \ldots, x_k$ such that

$$\overline{B(x_1, W)} \cup \overline{B(x_2, W)} \cup \ldots \cup \overline{B(x_k, W)} = X.$$

By virtue of (5) and (6), we have $F_i = \overline{B(x_i, W)} \in \mathfrak{F}$ for some $i \leqslant k$. But since $\delta(F_i) < V$, the family $\mathfrak{F}$ contains arbitrarily small sets and has, by the completeness of $(X, \mathfrak{U})$, the non-empty intersection. ∎

EXAMPLE 2. Let X be a Tychonoff space. By virtue of Example 1, the space $(X, \mathfrak{C}^*)$ is totally bounded, so that, by Theorem 9, its completion $(\tilde{X}, \tilde{\mathfrak{C}}^*)$ is also totally bounded. By virtue of Theorem 12, the space $\tilde{X}$ is a compactification of the space X. We shall prove that $\tilde{X}$ is the Čech-Stone compactification of the space X.

It is sufficient to show that every continuous function $f: X \to I$ can be extended over the space $\tilde{X}$. Since the segment I with the unique uniformity $\mathfrak{U}$ inducing its natural topology is, by Theorem 3, a complete space, it is sufficient, by Theorem 8, to prove that f is a uniformly continuous function of the space $(X, \mathfrak{C}^*)$ into the space $(I, \mathfrak{U})$.

The sets $U_i = \{(x, y): \varrho(x, y) < 2^{-i}\}$, where $i = 1, 2, \ldots$ and $\varrho(x, y) = |x-y|$, form a base for the uniformity $\mathfrak{U}$. Since $f \in C^*(X)$, the set

$$W_i = \{(x, y) \in X \times X: \varrho_f(x, y) < 2^{-i}\}$$

belongs to the uniformity $\mathfrak{C}^*$ for every $i = 1, 2, \ldots$ On the other hand, the condition $|x-y| < W_i$ yields the condition $|f(x)-f(y)| < U_i$, whence f is a uniformly continuous function. ∎

EXAMPLE 3. Let X be a Tychonoff space and let $\mathfrak{C}$ denote the uniformity defined in Example 1.6. We shall show that the space $\tilde{X}$, where $(\tilde{X}, \tilde{\mathfrak{C}})$ denotes the completion of the space $(X, \mathfrak{C})$, is the Hewitt real-compactification of the space X.

Let $(R_f, \mathfrak{U}_f)$ be the real-line with the uniformity induced by the natural metric for every $f \in C = C(X)$. By virtue of Theorem 6 and 7, the space $(\underset{f \in C}{\boldsymbol{P}} R_f, \underset{f \in C}{\boldsymbol{P}} \mathfrak{U}_f)$ is complete. It can easily be verified that the diagonal $F = \underset{f \in C}{\triangle} f$ is a uniform isomorphism of the space $(X, \mathfrak{C})$ onto a subspace of the space $(\underset{f \in C}{\boldsymbol{P}} R_f, \underset{f \in C}{\boldsymbol{P}} \mathfrak{U}_f)$. Since the completion is unique, we infer from Theorem 4 that $\tilde{X} = \overline{F(X)} \subset \underset{f \in C}{\boldsymbol{P}} R_f$. From Theorem 3.10.4 it follows, therefore, that $\tilde{X}$ is a real-compact space. Since by the lemma to Theorem 3.10.4, every function $f \in C(X)$ is extendable over $\tilde{X}$, we infer that $\tilde{X}$ is the Hewitt real-compactification of the space X. ∎

Making use of the concepts of a net and a filter, one can state convenient necessary and sufficient conditions that a uniform space $(X, \mathfrak{U})$ be complete. In order to do this, we shall define a class of nets and filters.

We say that a net $\{x_\sigma, \sigma \in \Sigma\}$ in X is a *Cauchy net* in a uniform space $(X, \mathfrak{U})$ if for every $V \in \mathfrak{U}$ there exists a $\sigma_0 \in \Sigma$ such that $|x_\sigma - x_{\sigma'}| < V$ for $\sigma, \sigma' \geqslant \sigma_0$. Similarly, a filter $\mathfrak{F}$ in X is called a *Cauchy filter* in the space $(X, \mathfrak{U})$ if for every $V \in \mathfrak{U}$ there exists an $F \in \mathfrak{F}$ such that $\delta(F) < V$.

The reader can easily verify that Cauchy nets and Cauchy filters correspond to one another under the correspondence established in Paragraph 1.6.

THEOREM 13. *A uniform space $(X, \mathfrak{U})$ is complete if and only if every Cauchy net in this space is convergent.*

The proof of this theorem is analogous to the proof of Theorem 3.1.12. It is sufficient to observe that under the correspondence between nets and families of closed sets satisfying the finite intersection property described there, the Cauchy nets correspond to families containing arbitrarily small sets. ■

The proof of the corresponding theorem for filters is left to the reader.

THEOREM 13F. *A uniform space $(X, \mathfrak{U})$ is complete if and only if every Cauchy filter in this space is convergent.* ■

EXERCISES

A. Let $\{(X_s, \mathfrak{U}_s)\}_{s \in S}$ be a family of uniform spaces and let $(\tilde{X}_s, \tilde{\mathfrak{U}}_s)$ denote the completion of the space $(X_s, \mathfrak{U}_s)$ for every $s \in S$. Prove that the space $(\underset{s \in S}{\boldsymbol{P}} \tilde{X}_s, \underset{s \in S}{\boldsymbol{P}} \tilde{\mathfrak{U}}_s)$ is the completion of the space $(\underset{s \in S}{\boldsymbol{P}} X_s, \underset{s \in S}{\boldsymbol{P}} \mathfrak{U}_s)$.

B. Let $(X, \mathfrak{U})$ be a compact uniform space. Show that every open covering of the space X is a uniform covering with respect to $\mathfrak{U}$.

Deduce that for every uniform space $(Y, \mathfrak{V})$ any mapping of the space X into Y is uniformly continuous relative to $\mathfrak{U}$ and $\mathfrak{V}$.

Hint: Make use of Exercise 5.1.A and of Theorems 1.6 and 10 or prove directly by a modification of the proof of the lemma to Theorem 2.3.

C. Let $\mathfrak{U}$ be a uniformity in a set X and let A denote a dense subset of the space X with the topology induced by $\mathfrak{U}$. Show that if for every family of subsets of the set A, which has the finite intersection property and contains arbitrarily small sets the intersection of closures in X, is non-empty, then the uniform space $(X, \mathfrak{U})$ is complete.

D. Show that the conclusion of Exercise 4.2.C follows from Theorem 1.9 and 10.

E. Let $(X, \mathfrak{U})$ be a compact uniform space. Show that the space X is connected if and only if for every two points $a, b \in X$ and every $V \in \mathfrak{U}$ there exists a finite sequence $x_1, x_2, \ldots, x_k$ of points of the space X such that

$$x_1 = a,\ x_k = b \text{ and } |x_i - x_{i+1}| < V \text{ for } i = 1, 2, \ldots, k-1.$$

§ 4. Proximity spaces. Let X be a set and let δ denote a binary relation defined in the family of its subsets. We shall write $A\delta B$ if the sets A and B are δ-related and $A\bar{\delta}B$ if they are not. The relation δ will be called a *proximity* in the set X provided that the following conditions are satisfied:

(PS1) *$A\,\delta\,B$ if and only if $B\,\delta\,A$.*

(PS2) *$A\,\delta(B\cup C)$ if and only if $A\,\delta\,B$ or $A\,\delta\,C$.*

(PS3) *For every $x,y\in X$ the condition $\{x\}\,\delta\,\{y\}$ is equivalent to the condition $x=y$.*

(PS4) $0\bar{\delta}X$.

(PS5) *If $A\bar{\delta}B$, then there exist sets $C,D\subset X$ such that $C\cup D=X$ and $A\bar{\delta}C$, $B\bar{\delta}D$.*

A pair (X,δ) consisting of a set X and a proximity δ in the set X is called a *proximity space.* Let us suppose that a proximity space (X,δ) is given. Two sets $A,B\subset X$ are said to be *close* in the space (X,δ) if and only if $A\,\delta\,B$. The sets $A,B\subset X$ for which $A\,\bar{\delta}\,B$ holds are called *remote.*

Conditions (PS1)-(PS5) imply the following properties of the relation δ:

(1) If $B\subset C$ and $A\,\delta\,B$, then $A\,\delta\,C$.

(2) If $A\cap B\neq 0$, then $A\,\delta\,B$.

(3) $0\bar{\delta}A$ for every $A\subset X$.

In order to prove (1) it suffices to note that if $B\subset C$, then $B\cup C=C$. Hence if $A\,\delta\,B$, then by (PS2), $A\,\delta\,C$. Condition (2) follows from (PS3), (PS1), and from a double application of (1). For if $x\in A\cap B\neq 0$, then $\{x\}\,\delta\,\{x\}$, $\{x\}\,\delta\,A$, $A\,\delta\,\{x\}$, and $A\,\delta\,B$. To prove (3) it is sufficient to use (PS4) and (1).

A proximity in a set induces a topology in it, i.e. the following theorem is valid.

THEOREM 1. *If δ is a proximity in the set X, then the formula*

$$\bar{A}=\{x\in X\colon \{x\}\,\delta\,A\} \tag{4}$$

defines a closure operator in X which satisfies conditions (CO1)-(CO4) *and thus generates a topology $\mathfrak{O}$ in X.*

The topology $\mathfrak{O}$ is said to be *induced by the proximity δ.*

In the proof of Theorem 1 we shall use the following

LEMMA. *Let (X,δ) be a proximity space. For each $A,B\subset X$*

$$\text{if } B\bar{\delta}A, \text{ then } B\bar{\delta}\bar{A}, \tag{5}$$

where $\bar{A}\subset X$ is defined by means of formula (4).

Proof. Let us assume that $B\bar{\delta}A$. By virtue of (PS5), there exist sets C and D such that

$$C \cup D = X \quad \text{i.e.} \quad X \setminus D \subset C \tag{6}$$

and

$$B\bar{\delta}C \quad \text{and} \quad A\bar{\delta}D. \tag{7}$$

By virtue of (1), it follows from (6) and from the second formula of (7) that $\bar{A} \subset X \setminus D \subset C$, which together with the first part of (7) yields $B\bar{\delta}\bar{A}$. ■

Proof of Theorem 1. Properties (CO1)-(CO3) follow immediately from (3), (2), and (PS2), respectively. In order to prove (CO4) it is sufficient to show that for every $A \subset X$ we have

$$\overline{(\bar{A})} \subset \bar{A}. \tag{8}$$

But this inclusion follows from the lemma if we assume that $B = \{x\}$. ■

The lemma to Theorem 1, formula (1), and property (PS1) yield that for every $A, B \subset X$, a proximity δ in the set X, and for the operator of closure defined by (4), we have:

$$A\,\delta B \text{ if and only if } \bar{A}\,\delta \bar{B}. \tag{9}$$

It follows from (PS3) that X, with the topology induced by a proximity δ, is a T_1-space. We shall prove further that in this manner we can obtain only Tychonoff spaces. When considering a proximity space we shall always understand it to be a topological space with the topology induced by the proximity.

Let us suppose that A, B are two subsets of a proximity space (X, δ) If $A\bar{\delta}(X \setminus B)$, then we say that the set A is *strongly contained* in the set B and write $A \Subset B$. Making use of strong inclusion one can rewrite (PS5) in a simpler form

(PS5′) *If $A\,\bar{\delta} B$, then there exist A_1, B_1 such that $A \Subset A_1$, $B \Subset B_1$ and $A_1 \cap B_1 = 0$.*

We shall show that the strong inclusion $\Subset$ has the following properties:

(SI1) *If $A \Subset B$, then $X \setminus B \Subset X \setminus A$.*

(SI2) *If $A \Subset B$, then $A \subset B$.*

(SI3) *If $A_1 \subset A \Subset B \subset B_1$, then $A_1 \Subset B_1$.*

(SI4) *If $A_i \Subset B_i$ for $i = 1, 2$, then $A_1 \cup A_2 \Subset B_1 \cup B_2$.*

(SI5) *If $A \Subset B$, then there exists an open set $C \subset X$ such that $A \Subset C \subset \bar{C} \Subset B$.*

(SI6) $0 \Subset 0$.

(SI7) *For every point $x \in X$ and its neighbourhood A we have $\{x\} \Subset A$.*

Property (SI1) follows from the definition of the strong inclusion and from the equality $A = X\setminus(X\setminus A)$. Properties (SI2) and (SI3) follow from (2) and (1) respectively.

To prove (SI4) it is sufficient to notice that if $A_i \Subset B_i$ for $i = 1, 2$, then by (1), $A_i\bar{\delta}[(X\setminus B_1) \cap (X\setminus B_2)]$ for $i = 1, 2$. Hence, according to (PS1) and (PS2), $(A_1 \cup A_2)\bar{\delta}[X\setminus(B_1 \cup B_2)]$, i.e. $A_1 \cup A_2 \Subset B_1 \cup B_2$.

The proof of (SI5) is more complicated. If $A \Subset B$, then, by virtue of (PS5′), there exist sets A_1, B_1 such that

$$A \Subset A_1, \qquad X\setminus B \Subset B_1, \qquad \text{and} \qquad A_1 \cap B_1 = 0.$$

We thus have, by (SI1), $A_1 \subset X\setminus B_1 \Subset B$, whence $A_1\bar{\delta}X\setminus B$. Since $A\bar{\delta}X\setminus A_1$, we infer from the lemma to Theorem 1 that $A\bar{\delta}\,\overline{X\setminus A_1}$ i.e. $A\bar{\delta}X\setminus(X\setminus\overline{X\setminus A_1})$. Defining $C = X\setminus\overline{X\setminus A_1} = \operatorname{Int} A_1$ we have $A \Subset C \subset A_1$. Since $A_1\bar{\delta}X\setminus B$, we infer that $C\bar{\delta}X\setminus B$ and $\bar{C}\bar{\delta}X\setminus B$ i.e. $\bar{C} \Subset B$.

Properties (SI6) and (SI7) follow from (PS4) and (4) respectively.

From property (SI1) and the de Morgan formulas it follows immediately that property (SI4) can be expressed in the form

(SI4′) *If* $A_i \Subset B_i$ *for* $i = 1, 2$, *then* $A_1 \cap A_2 \Subset B_1 \cap B_2$.

It can easily be seen that properties (SI4) and (SI4′) remain valid for finite families of sets; i.e. if $A_i \Subset B_i$ for $i = 1, 2, \ldots, k$, then $\bigcup_{i=1}^{k} A_i \Subset \bigcup_{i=1}^{k} B_i$ and $\bigcap_{i=1}^{k} A_i \Subset \bigcap_{i=1}^{k} B_i$.

Let us suppose that (X, δ) and (Y, δ') are two proximity spaces. A function f of the set X into the set Y is called *proximity-preserving* if for every two close sets $A, B \subset X$ the sets $f(A)$ and $f(B)$ are close in Y. The composition of two proximity-preserving functions is evidently a proximity-preserving function. It follows from formula (4) and condition (v) of Theorem 1.4.1 that every proximity-preserving function is a mapping of the topological spaces induced by the proximity spaces.

Suppose that we are given two proximity spaces (X, δ), (Y, δ'), and a one-to-one function f of the set X onto Y. We say that f is an *equimorphism* if both f and f^{-1} are proximity-preserving functions. The proximity spaces (X, δ) and (Y, δ') are said to be *equimorphic* provided there exists an equimorphism of one onto the other. The study of invariants of equimorphisms is the subject of the theory of proximity spaces. Of course, every topological invariant is also an invariant of equimorphisms.

THEOREM 2. *If* $\mathfrak{U}$ *is a uniformity in a set* X, *then assuming that*

$$A\,\delta B \text{ if and only if } V \cap (A \times B) \neq 0 \text{ for every } V \in \mathfrak{U}$$

we define a proximity in the set X.

The proximity δ is said to be *induced by the uniformity* $\mathfrak{U}$.

Proof. To begin with, let us note that $A\,\delta B$ if and only if for every $V \in \mathfrak{U}$ there exists an $x \in A$ and an $y \in B$ such that $|x-y| \geqslant V$.

It is evident that δ satisfies conditions (PS1) and (PS4). Property (PS3) follows from property (U4).

If $A\bar{\delta}B$ and $A\bar{\delta}C$, then there exist $V_1, V_2 \in \mathfrak{U}$ such that $|x-y| \geqslant V_1$ and $|x-z| \geqslant V_2$ for every $x \in A$, $y \in B$, and $z \in C$. Thus, for every $x \in X$ and $t \in B \cup C$ we have $|x-t| \geqslant V_1 \cap V_2$, and by virtue of (U2), $A\bar{\delta}(B \cup C)$ holds. But if $A\,\delta B$ or $A\,\delta C$, then evidently $A\,\delta(B \cup C)$. Thus the relation δ has property (PS2).

In order to complete the proof of Theorem 2 it is sufficient to verify that δ also has property (PS5). For this purpose let us consider sets $A, B \subset X$ satisfying the condition $A\bar{\delta}B$. There exists a $V \in \mathfrak{U}$ such that for every $x \in A$ and $y \in B$ we have $|x-y| \geqslant V$. By virtue of (U3), there exists a $W \in \mathfrak{U}$ such that $2W \subset V$. The reader can easily verify that the sets

$$C = X \setminus B(A, W) \quad \text{and} \quad D = X \setminus B(B, W)$$

satisfy the properties enumerated in (PS5). ■

From Corollary 2 to Theorem 1.2 it follows that the topology induced by a proximity δ in X, which is in turn induced by a uniformity $\mathfrak{U}$ in X, is identical with the topology induced by $\mathfrak{U}$.

Theorem 2 and Theorem 1.8 thus imply the following

COROLLARY. *For every Tychonoff space $(X, \mathfrak{O})$ there exists a proximity δ in the set X which induces the topology $\mathfrak{O}$.* ■

It can easily be verified that if f is a uniformly continuous function of a space $(X, \mathfrak{U})$ into a space $(Y, \mathfrak{V})$, then f, considered as a function of the space X with the proximity induced by $\mathfrak{U}$ into the space Y with the proximity induced by $\mathfrak{V}$, is a proximity-preserving function.

EXAMPLE 1. Let X be a set. For all sets $A, B \subset X$ let us assume that $A\,\delta B$ if and only if $A \cap B \neq 0$. The relation δ is a proximity. Properties (PS1)-(PS4) are evidently satisfied. To prove that (PS5) is also satisfied it is sufficient to note that for every pair of remote, i.e. disjoint, sets A, B the sets $C = X \setminus A$ and $D = X \setminus B$ have the required properties. The topology induced by the proximity δ in X is the discrete topology. ■

EXAMPLE 2. Every metric space (X, ϱ) induces, by Theorem 1.7, a uniform space $(X, \mathfrak{U})$; and this uniform space induces, by the preceding theorem, a proximity space (X, δ). It can easily be verified that non-empty subsets $A, B \subset X$ are closed if and only if $\inf_{x \in A, y \in B} \varrho(x, y) = 0$. Thus, in every metric space (X, ϱ) the formula:

$$A\,\delta B \text{ if and only if } A \neq 0 \neq B \text{ and } \inf_{x \in A, y \in B} \varrho(x, y) = 0,$$

defines a proximity δ, which is said to be *induced by the metric* ϱ. ■

EXAMPLE 3. Let X be a Tychonoff space. For every $A, B \subset X$ let us assume that $A \delta B$ if and only if $A \neq 0 \neq B$ and that there is no continuous function $f: X \to I$ such that $f(x) = 0$ for $x \in A$ and $f(x) = 1$ for $x \in B$, i.e. the sets A and B are not completely separated. We shall show that the relation δ is a proximity.

It follows immediately from the definition that δ has properties (PS1), (PS3), and (PS4).

If $A \bar{\delta} B$ and $A \bar{\delta} C$, then there exist continuous functions $f: X \to I$ and $g: X \to I$ such that $f(x) = g(x) = 0$ for $x \in A$, and such that $f(x) = 1$ for $x \in B$, and $g(x) = 1$ for $x \in C$. The function $h: X \to I$ defined by the formula: $h(x) = \min(f(x)+g(x), 1)$ assumes the value 0 on the set A and the value 1 on the set $B \cup C$. Hence $A \bar{\delta} (B \cup C)$. If $A \delta B$ or $A \delta C$, then evidently $A \delta (B \cup C)$, whence δ also has property (PS2).

To prove condition (PS5) let us notice that if $A \bar{\delta} B$, i.e. if there exists a continuous function $f: X \to I$ such that $f(x) = 0$ for $x \in A$ and $f(x) = 1$ for $x \in B$, then the sets

$$C = f^{-1}([1/2, 1]) \quad \text{and} \quad D = f^{-1}([0, 1/2])$$

have the required properties.

It follows from the definition of a Tychonoff space that the relation δ induces the initial topology in the set X. ∎

THEOREM 3. *If $(X, \mathfrak{O})$ is a compact space, then there exists exactly one proximity in the set X which induces the topology $\mathfrak{O}$, namely the relation δ defined by the condition*

$$(10) \qquad A \delta B \text{ if and only if } \bar{A} \cap \bar{B} \neq 0.$$

Proof. It follows from Example 3 that formula (10) defines a proximity inducing the topology $\mathfrak{O}$ in X.

Let δ' be a proximity inducing the topology $\mathfrak{O}$ in the set X. It follows from (2) and (9) that if $A \delta B$, then $A \delta' B$. To complete the proof it is, therefore, sufficient to show that if A and B are disjoint closed sets, then $A \bar{\delta}' B$. For every point $x \in A$ we have $\{x\} \bar{\delta}' B$, whence, by virtue of (SI5), there exists an open set V_x such that

$$(11) \qquad x \in V_x \quad \text{and} \quad V_x \bar{\delta}' B.$$

The family $\{A \cap V_x\}_{x \in A}$ is an open covering of the compact set A. There exists, therefore, a finite number of points $x_1, x_2, \ldots, x_k \in A$ such that

$$(12) \qquad A \subset V_{x_1} \cup V_{x_2} \cup \ldots \cup V_{x_k}.$$

From property (PS2) and from (1), (11), and (12) it follows immediately that $A \bar{\delta}' B$. ∎

We proceed now to an examination of the connection between proximity spaces and uniform spaces. Let us begin with the definition of the basic concept of a δ-uniform covering.

Let (X, δ) be a proximity space. A finite covering $\mathfrak{A} = \{A_i\}_{i=1}^k$ of the set X is called *uniform relative to the proximity* δ, or simply δ-*uniform*, if there exists a covering $\mathfrak{B} = \{B_i\}_{i=1}^k$ of the set X such that

$$B_i \Subset A_i \text{ for } i = 1, 2, \ldots, k. \tag{13}$$

LEMMA. *If δ is a proximity in the set X, then for every $A, B \subset X$ the relation $A \delta B$ holds if and only if every δ-uniform covering $\mathfrak{A} = \{A_i\}_{i=1}^k$ of the set X contains a set A_j such that $A \cap A_j \neq 0 \neq B \cap A_j$.*

Proof. Let us consider $A, B \subset X$ such that $A \delta B$ and a δ-uniform covering $\mathfrak{A} = \{A_i\}_{i=1}^k$ of the set X. Let a covering $\mathfrak{B} = \{B_i\}_{i=1}^k$ of the set X satisfy condition (13) and let

$$C = \mathrm{St}(A, \mathfrak{B}), \qquad D = \mathrm{St}(A, \mathfrak{A}). \tag{14}$$

It follows from property (SI4) that $C \Subset D$. Since $A \subset C$, we have $A \bar{\delta} (X \setminus D)$. Hence

$$B \cap D \neq 0, \tag{15}$$

for if this were not true, $B \subset X \setminus D$ and $A \bar{\delta} B$, contrary to the assumption. It follows from the second formula of (14) and from inequality (15) that there exists a $j \leqslant k$ such that $A \cap A_j \neq 0 \neq B \cap A_j$.

Let us now consider $A, B \subset X$ such that $A \bar{\delta} B$. By virtue of (PS5′), there exist sets $B_1, B_2 \subset X$ such that $A \Subset X \setminus B_1$, $B \Subset X \setminus B_2$ and $(X \setminus B_1) \cap (X \setminus B_2) = 0$. The sets $A_1 = X \setminus A$ and $A_2 = X \setminus B$ form a covering of the set X. Since, by virtue of (SI1),

$$B_1 \Subset A_1, \qquad B_2 \Subset A_2, \qquad \text{and} \qquad B_1 \cup B_2 = X,$$

$\mathfrak{A} = \{A_1, A_2\}$ is a δ-uniform covering of the set X, of which no element meets A and B simultaneously. ∎

THEOREM 4. *If δ is a proximity in the set X, then the family $\mathbf{C}$ of all coverings which have a δ-uniform refinement satisfies conditions* (UC1)-(UC4). *The uniformity generated, according to Theorem* 1.6, *by the family $\mathbf{C}$ in the set X, is totally bounded. The proximity induced in X by this uniformity is identical with δ.*

The uniformity generated by the family $\mathbf{C}$ is said to be *induced by the proximity* δ.

Proof. Let us denote by $\mathbf{C}_0$ the family of all δ-uniform coverings of the set X. Since the family $\mathbf{C}$ evidently satisfies condition (UC1), to prove the theorem it is sufficient to verify that $\mathbf{C}_0$ has properties (UC2)-(UC4).

Let us begin with condition (UC2). Consider $\mathfrak{A}_1, \mathfrak{A}_2 \in \mathbf{C}_0$ and let $\mathfrak{A}_1 = \{A_1^1, A_2^1, \ldots, A_k^1\}$, $\mathfrak{A}_2 = \{A_1^2, A_2^2, \ldots, A_m^2\}$. Let $\mathfrak{B}_1 = \{B_1^1, B_2^1, \ldots, B_k^1\}$ and $\mathfrak{B}_2 = \{B_1^2, B_2^2, \ldots, B_m^2\}$ be coverings such that

(16) $B_i^1 \Subset A_i^1$ for $i = 1, 2, \ldots, k$ and $B_i^2 \Subset A_i^2$ for $i = 1, 2, \ldots, m$.

It follows immediately from formula (16) and property (SI4′) that the finite covering $\mathfrak{A} = \{A_i^1 \cap A_j^2\}_{i \leqslant k, j \leqslant m}$ of the set X is δ-uniform. Since $\mathfrak{A}$ is a refinement of $\mathfrak{A}_1$ and of $\mathfrak{A}_2$, the family $\mathbf{C}_0$ has property (UC2).

The verification that the family $\mathbf{C}_0$ satisfies condition (UC3) is a little longer. First of all, let us notice that, by virtue of Lemma 2 to Theorem 5.1.5, it suffices to show that every covering $\mathfrak{A} \in \mathbf{C}_0$ has a pointwise star-refinement $\mathfrak{B} \in \mathbf{C}_0$.

Let us consider a covering $\mathfrak{A} = \{A_1, A_2\} \in \mathbf{C}_0$ consisting of two elements. Let the sets $B_1, B_2 \subset X$ satisfy the conditions:

(17) $$B_1 \Subset A_1, \quad B_2 \Subset A_2, \quad \text{and} \quad B_1 \cup B_2 = X.$$

The family $\mathfrak{B} = \{A_1 \setminus B_2, A_2 \setminus B_1, A_1 \cap A_2\}$ is, by (17), a covering of the space X. Since $(A_1 \setminus B_2) \cap (A_2 \setminus B_1) = 0$, the covering $\mathfrak{B}$ is a pointwise star-refinement of the covering $\mathfrak{A}$. By virtue of property (SI5), there exist sets $C_1, C_2 \subset X$ such that

(18) $$B_1 \Subset C_1 \Subset A_1 \quad \text{and} \quad B_2 \Subset C_2 \Subset A_2,$$

From properties (SI1), (SI4′) and from formulas (17) and (18) it follows that

$$C_1 \setminus C_2 \Subset A_1 \setminus B_2, \quad C_2 \setminus C_1 \Subset A_2 \setminus B_1, \quad C_1 \cap C_2 \Subset A_1 \cap A_2,$$

and

$$(C_1 \setminus C_2) \cup (C_2 \setminus C_1) \cup (C_1 \cap C_2) = X,$$

i.e. that $\mathfrak{B} \in \mathbf{C}_0$. We have thus shown that every covering $\mathfrak{A} \in \mathbf{C}_0$, consisting of two elements, has a pointwise star-refinement $\mathfrak{B} \in \mathbf{C}_0$.

Let us now consider a covering $\mathfrak{A} = \{A_i\}_{i=1}^k \in \mathbf{C}_0$. Let us suppose that the sets $B_1, B_2, \ldots, B_k \subset X$ satisfy the conditions

(19) $B_i \Subset A_i$ for $i = 1, 2, \ldots, k$ and $B_1 \cup B_2 \cup \ldots \cup B_k = X$.

By virtue of properties (SI5) and (SI1), $\mathfrak{A}_i = \{A_i, X \setminus B_i\} \in \mathbf{C}_0$ for every $i = 1, 2, \ldots, k$. By virtue of the part of the theorem already proved, there exists for every $i = 1, 2, \ldots, k$ a covering $\mathfrak{B}_i \in \mathbf{C}_0$ which is a pointwise star-refinement of $\mathfrak{A}_i$, and a covering $\mathfrak{B} \in \mathbf{C}_0$ which is a refinement of each of the coverings $\mathfrak{B}_1, \mathfrak{B}_2, \ldots, \mathfrak{B}_k$. For every point $x \in X$ and $i = 1, 2, \ldots, k$ we have $\mathrm{St}(x, \mathfrak{B}) \subset \mathrm{St}(x, \mathfrak{B}_i)$. Hence

$$\text{either} \quad \mathrm{St}(x, \mathfrak{B}) \subset A_i \quad \text{or} \quad \mathrm{St}(x, \mathfrak{B}) \subset X \setminus B_i.$$

By virtue of (19), the second of these conditions cannot be valid for a fixed point $x \in X$ and for every i. Thus, for some $i \leqslant k$ we have $\mathrm{St}(x, \mathfrak{B}) \subset A_i$, i.e. the covering $\mathfrak{B}$ is a pointwise star-refinement of the covering $\mathfrak{A}$ and the family $\mathbf{C}_0$ has property (UC3).

It follows immediately from the lemma that the family $\mathbf{C}_0$ satisfies condition (UC4) and that the proximity induced in X by the uniformity generated by $\mathbf{C}$ is identical with the proximity δ.

By virtue of Theorem 1.6, the base for the uniformity generated by the family $\mathbf{C}$ consists of the sets

$$V(\mathfrak{A}) = \bigcup_{i=1}^{k} A_i \times A_i,$$

where $\mathfrak{A} = \{A_1, A_2, \ldots, A_k\} \in \mathbf{C}_0$. Choosing a point from any non-empty element of $\mathfrak{A}$ we get a $V(\mathfrak{A})$-net in the space X. Thus the uniformity generated by $\mathbf{C}$ is totally bounded. ■

Theorem 4 and the corollary to Theorem 2 imply

THEOREM 5. *In order that a topology of a topological space X be induced by a proximity in the set X it is necessary and sufficient that X be a Tychonoff space.* ■

Let X be a topological space. Every proximity in the set X inducing the topology identical with the initial topology of the space X will be called a *proximity in the space X*. The corollary to Theorem 2 states that in every Tychonoff space X there exists at least one proximity. In general, however, many proximities may exist in the space X. To end the paragraph we shall prove a theorem which will imply that proximities in a Tychonoff space are in a one-to-one correspondence with compactifications of this space.

LEMMA 1. *Let X be a Tychonoff space and let cX denote a compactification of X. The relation $\delta(c)$ defined by the formula*

$$A\,\delta(c)\,B \text{ if and only if } \overline{c(A)} \cap \overline{c(B)} \neq 0,$$

is a proximity in the space X.

If cX and $c'X$ are compactifications of X, then $\delta(c) = \delta(c')$ if and only if cX and $c'X$ are equivalent.

Proof. The verification that $\delta(c)$ is a proximity in the space X is left to the reader. The validity of the second part of the theorem follows immediately from Theorem 3.4.5. ■

LEMMA 2. *For each proximity δ in a Tychonoff space X there exists a compactification cX of this space such that $\delta = \delta(c)$.*

Proof. Let us consider the uniformity $\mathfrak{U}$ induced in X by the proximity δ. Let $(\tilde{X}, \tilde{\mathfrak{U}})$ be the completion of the uniform space $(X, \mathfrak{U})$. Since

$\mathfrak{U}$ is totally bounded, we infer from Theorems 3.9 and 3.12 that the space $\tilde{X}$ is compact. Let us denote by c the uniform isomorphism of the space X onto the dense subset $c(X)$ of the space $\tilde{X}$. Since c is also a homeomorphism of the topological spaces, $\tilde{X} = cX$ is a compactification of the space X.

Let δ' be the proximity in the set $\tilde{X}$ induced by the uniformity $\tilde{\mathfrak{U}}$. Since the uniformity $\mathfrak{U}$ induces, by Theorem 4, the proximity δ in the set X, and since c is a uniform isomorphism, we have for every $A, B \subset X$ that

$$A \delta B \text{ if and only if } c(A)\delta' c(B). \tag{20}$$

Since the space $\tilde{X}$ is compact, it follows from Theorem 3 that

$$c(A)\delta' c(B) \text{ if and only if } \overline{c(A)} \cap \overline{c(B)} \neq 0, \tag{21}$$

which, together with (20), proves that $\delta = \delta(c)$. ∎

Lemmas 1 and 2 imply

THEOREM 6 (Yu. M. Smirnov). *The assigning to every compactification cX of a Tychonoff space X the proximity $\delta(c)$ in this space is a one-to-one function of the family of all compactifications of the space X onto the family of all proximities in the space X.* ∎

EXAMPLE 4. The reader can verify without any difficulty that the proximity defined in Example 3 for the Tychonoff space X corresponds, in the sense of the Smirnov Theorem, to the Čech-Stone compactification of the space X. ∎

EXERCICES

A. Let X be a compact space, let Y denote a topological space and let $f: X \to Y$ be a mapping. Show that for every choice of proximities δ and δ' in the spaces X and Y, respectively, f is a proximity-preserving function.

B. Let δ and δ' be proximities in sets X and Y respectively, and let $\mathfrak{U}$ and $\mathfrak{U}'$ be uniformities induced by δ and δ'. Verify that any proximity-preserving function f of the set X into the set Y is uniformly continuous relative to $\mathfrak{U}$ and $\mathfrak{U}'$.

Hint: Show that a function f of the set X into the set Y is proximity-preserving if and only if for every δ'-uniform covering $\{A_i\}_{i=1}^k$ of the space Y the covering $\{f^{-1}(A_i)\}_{i=1}^k$ of the space X is δ-uniform.

C. Suppose we are given a set X and two proximities δ and δ' in X. We say that the relation δ is *stronger* than δ' or that δ' is *weaker* than δ and write $\delta' \leqslant \delta$ if and only if for every $A, B \subset X$ we have if $A\delta B$, then $A\delta' B$.

Show that the relation $\leqslant$ is a partial order in the family of all proximities in X.

Show also that if cX and $c'X$ are two compactifications of the space X, then $c'X \leqslant cX$ if and only if $\delta(c') \leqslant \delta(c)$.

D. Give a direct description of the proximity corresponding to the Alexandroff compactification of a locally compact space.

HISTORICAL REMARKS AND BIBLIOGRAPHIC NOTES

The concept of a uniform space was introduced by A. Weil in [1937]. The definition adopted in this book differs slightly from that of Weil, for by an entourage of the diagonal he understands every set $V \subset X \times X$ containing Δ (i.e. the condition of symmetry $V = -V$ is not necessarily satisfied) and by a uniformity a family $\mathfrak{U}$ of entourages of the diagonal satisfying conditions (U1)-(U4) and the condition: (U5) *If* $V \in \mathfrak{U}$, *then* $-V \in \mathfrak{U}$. Limiting oneself to symmetric entourages permits a simplification of the theory. Some simplifications can also be obtained by using the symbols $|x-y| < V$ (instead of $(x, y) \in V$) and $B(x, V)$ (instead of $V[x]$), which emphasize the analogy with metric spaces. This notation, together with the term "ball of radius V with centre x", was introduced by R. Sikorski.

In [1937] A. Weil also proved most of the theorems of the first three paragraphs of this chapter. Theorems 1.4 and 1.9 were proved earlier for topological groups by G. Birkhoff [1936] and S. Kakutani [1936]. Theorem 1.9 can be considered as a reformulation of the metrization theorem of Alexandroff and Urysohn [1923] in terms of uniformities.

Another but equivalent concept of a uniform space described by a uniform covering system (see Theorem 1.6) was considered by J. W. Tukey in [1940]. The description of uniformities by families of pseudo-metrics (see Problem E) is used by L. Gillman and M. Jerison in [1960]. The presentation of Examples 1.6, 3.1, 3.2, and 3.3 is taken from that work.

The theorems of Paragraph 2, dealing with mapping spaces, were proved in such a general manner for the first time by N. Bourbaki in [1949]. A weaker form of the Ascoli Theorem was given by R. Arens in [1946].

In [1952] T. Shirota proved that under the assumption of the non-measurability of the power of these spaces, the class of real-compact spaces is identical with the class of spaces whose topology can be induced by a complete uniformity. J. Dieudonné proved in [1939] that the existence of a complete uniformity in a space X is equivalent to the embeddability of X as a closed subspace in a Cartesian product of metrizable spaces.

In [1908] F. Riesz defined axiomatically a concept of closeness for pairs of sets, similar to the proximity relation. However, neither he nor any other mathematician of his time took interest in a precise study of that idea. The notion of a proximity space was introduced by V. A. Efremovič in the papers [1951] and [1952], in which he also proved Theorems 4.1 and 4.3. A full analysis of those spaces was carried out by Yu. M. Smirnov in [1952]. Theorems 2, 4, 5, and 6 of Paragraph 4 come from that paper.

PROBLEMS

A (J. L. Kelley [1955]). Show that if an open covering $\mathfrak{U} = \{U_s\}_{s \in S}$ of a topological space X has a closed locally finite refinement $\mathfrak{F} = \{F_t\}_{t \in T}$, then there exists an entourage V of the diagonal Δ open in $X \times X$ and such that the covering $\{B(x, V)\}_{x \in X}$ is a refinement of $\mathfrak{U}$.

Hint: For every $t \in T$ let $F_t \subset U_{s(t)}$ and $V_t = (U_{s(t)} \times U_{s(t)}) \cup \cup [(X \setminus F_t) \times (X \setminus F_t)]$. Verify that $V = \bigcap_{t \in T} V_t$ has the required properties.

B (J. L. Kelley [1955]). Prove that a regular space X is paracompact if and only if every open covering $\{U_s\}_{s \in S}$ has a refinement of the form $\{B(x, V)\}_{x \in X}$, where V is an open entourage of the diagonal $\Delta \subset X \times X$.

Hint: Proving that X is paracompact make use of condition (ii), Theorem 5.1.5. Find a refinement $\{B(x, V)\}_{x \in X}$ of the open covering and for every $x \in X$ choose a $W(x)$ such that $W(x) \times W(x) \subset V$; then consider the covering $\{W(x)\}_{x \in X}$.

C. Let Z be the set of integers and let p denote a prime number. Show that the family $\{W_n\}_{n=1}^{\infty}$ of entourages of the diagonal $\Delta \subset Z \times Z$, where $W_n = \{(x, y) \in Z \times Z: x \equiv y \,(\mathrm{mod}\, p^n)\}$ and the relation $k \equiv l \,(\mathrm{mod}\, m)$ denotes that $k - l$ is divisible by m, is a base for a uniformity in Z. This uniformity is called the *p-adic uniformity*.

Prove that for distinct prime numbers p_1 and p_2 the uniformities described above and the topologies induced by them in the set Z are not comparable.

Find a metric in Z which induces the p-adic uniformity. Show that the metric can be extended to a metric in the set of all rational numbers.

D. Let $\{G_s\}_{s \in S}$ be a family of topological groups. Verify that the Cartesian product $\boldsymbol{P}_{s \in S} G_s$ is a topological group if we define the product of elements $\{x_s\}, \{y_s\} \in \boldsymbol{P}_{s \in S} G_s$ to be equal to $\{z_s\} \in \boldsymbol{P}_{s \in S} G_s$, where $z_s = x_s y_s$ for every $s \in S$.

Show that the uniformity induced in $\boldsymbol{P}_{s \in S} G_s$ by any of the families of uniform coverings defined in Example 1.5 is the Cartesian product of analogous uniformities in the groups G_s.

Formulate and prove an analogous theorem for subgroups.

E. Let P be a family of pseudo-metrics in the set X which satisfy conditions (P1), (P2) and the condition

(P3) *If for a pseudo-metric σ in the set X and every $\varepsilon > 0$ there exists a $\varrho \in P$ and $\delta > 0$ such that for every $x, y \in X$ the condition $\varrho(x, y) < \delta$ implies the inequality $\sigma(x, y) < \varepsilon$, then $\sigma \in R$.*

Verify that P is the family of all pseudo-metrics which are uniform relative to the uniformity $\mathfrak{U}$ generated by the family P.

There exists, therefore, a one-to-one correspondence between uniformities and families of pseudo-metrics satisfying (P1)-(P3).

F. Give a necessary and sufficient condition for metrics ϱ_1 and ϱ_2 to induce the same uniformity in a set X.

G. Give an example of a non-normal topological group.

Hint: Make use of Problem 2.T.

H. Let $(X, \mathfrak{U})$ be a uniform space and let 2^X denote the family of all non-empty closed subsets of the space X. Show that the family of sets of the form

$$2^V = \{(A, B) \in 2^X \times 2^X: A \subset B(B, V) \text{ and } B \subset B(A, V)\},$$

where $V \in \mathfrak{U}$, is a base for a uniformity (denoted by $2^{\mathfrak{U}}$) in the set 2^X.

Verify that if a uniformity $\mathfrak{U}$ is induced by a bounded metric ϱ, then the uniformity $2^{\mathfrak{U}}$ can be induced by the Hausdorff distance (see Problem 4.H).

Verify that if X is compact, then the topology in the set 2^X induced by the uniformity $2^{\mathfrak{U}}$ is identical with the Vietoris topology (see Problem 3.J).

I. Let us consider a Tychonoff space X. A uniformity $\mathfrak{U}$ in the set X is called a *uniformity in the space* X if $\mathfrak{U}$ induces the initial topology in X. Show that in the family of all uniformities in a Tychonoff space X there exists a strongest uniformity, called the *universal uniformity* in the space X.

Hint: The universal uniformity is defined in Exercise 1.C.

Show that every mapping of the space X into a Tychonoff space Y is a uniformly continuous function relative to the universal uniformity in X and an arbitrary uniformity $\mathfrak{V}$ in Y.

J. Let $(X, \mathfrak{U})$ be a uniform space. Show that there exists in X a totally bounded uniformity $\mathfrak{U}_0$ which is weaker than $\mathfrak{U}$ and induces the same topology in the set X.

Hint: Repeat the construction of Example 1.6, considering uniformly continuous functions of the uniform space $(X, \mathfrak{U})$ into the segment I with the uniformity induced by the natural metric (cf. Problems V and Y).

K. Show that in the set of all uniformities in a Tychonoff space X a weakest uniformity exists if and only if X is locally compact.

Hint: Make use of Problem J and of Theorems 3.8, 3.12 and 3.6.8.

L (R. Doss [1947]). Show that for a Tychonoff space X the following conditions are equivalent:

(i) X is pseudo-compact.
(ii) Every uniformity in the space X is totally bounded.
(iii) The uniformities $\mathfrak{C}$ and $\mathfrak{C}^*$ in the space X are equal.

Hint: To prove the implication (i) $\Rightarrow$ (ii) show that if (ii) is not satisfied, then there exists a discrete family $\{G_i\}_{i=1}^{\infty}$ of open subsets of X, and make use of Theorem 2.1.5. To prove the inverse implication make use of Problem I. Implication (iii) $\Rightarrow$ (i) follows from Exercise 3.10.D. The inverse implication is obvious.

M (J. Dieudonné [1939a]). Give an example of a Tychonoff space X such that the space $(X, \mathfrak{U})$ is not complete for any uniformity $\mathfrak{U}$ in X.

Hint: Make use of the preceding problem.

N (R. Doss [1949]). Show that for a Tychonoff space X the following conditions are equivalent:

(i) The space X has only one compactification (up to equivalence).
(ii) There exists only one uniformity in the space X.
(iii) There exists only one totally bounded uniformity in the space X.

Hint: To prove the implication (i) $\Rightarrow$ (ii) make use of Problems 3.Q and L.

O (J. Nagata [1950a]). Show that in every paracompact space there exists a uniformity $\mathfrak{U}$ such that the space $(X, \mathfrak{U})$ is complete.

Hint: Verify that the family of all open coverings of the space X satisfies conditions (UC1)-(UC4). Consider a family $\mathfrak{F}$ of closed subsets of X which has the finite intersection property, contains arbitrarily small sets, and has the empty intersection. For every $x \in X$ let $U(x)$ be a neighbourhood of the point x disjoint with a set of the family $\mathfrak{F}$. Consider the covering $\{U(x)\}_{x \in X}$ of the space X.

P. Show that if X is a topological space and $(Y, \mathfrak{U})$ is a complete uniform space, then the space $(Y^X, \hat{\mathfrak{U}})$ is also complete.

Q. Let $(X, \mathfrak{U})$ be a uniform space. Let us denote by $\mathring{X}$ the set of all families of closed subsets of X which have the finite intersection property and contain arbitrarily small sets. Suppose that for every $V \in \mathfrak{U}$
$\mathring{V} = \{(\mathfrak{F}_1, \mathfrak{F}_2) \in \mathring{X} \times \mathring{X}$: there exists an $F \in \mathfrak{F}_1 \cap \mathfrak{F}_2$ such that $\delta(F) < V\}$.

Show that the family $\{\mathring{V}\}_{V \in \mathfrak{U}}$ of entourages of the diagonal of the set $\mathring{X} \times \mathring{X}$ satisfies conditions (BU1) and (BU2). By the identification of every pair F_1, F_2 of points of the set $\mathring{X}$ for which $(\mathfrak{F}_1, \mathfrak{F}_2) \in \bigcap_{V \in \mathfrak{U}} \mathring{V}$ we get a set $\tilde{X}$ in which the sets $\tilde{V}$ obtained by the identification from the sets $\mathring{V}$ form a base for the uniformity $\tilde{\mathfrak{U}}$. Verify that $(\tilde{X}, \tilde{\mathfrak{U}})$ is the completion of the space $(X, \mathfrak{U})$.

Hint: Make use of Exercise 3.C.

R. Let G be an abelian topological group. Let us consider a uniform space $(G, \mathfrak{U})$, where $\mathfrak{U}$ is the uniformity described in Example 1.5 and let $(\tilde{G}, \tilde{\mathfrak{U}})$ denote the completion of this space. Show that we can give the character of a topological group to the set $\tilde{G}$ in such a manner that for elements belonging to G, the product and the inverse element in $\tilde{G}$ and G are identical.

S (P. S. Alexandroff and V. I. Ponomarev [1959]). Let X be a T_1-space, let $\mathfrak{O}$ denote the family of its open subsets, and let $\mathfrak{D}$ be the family of its closed subsets. A binary relation $\Subset$ which holds between the elements of the family $\mathfrak{D}$ and of the family $\mathfrak{O}$ is called a *strong inclusion* in the space X if it satisfies conditions (SI1)-(SI7) of Paragraph 4.

Show that there exists a one-to-one correspondence between the relations of strong inclusion and the proximities in the space X.

T (V. A. Efremovič [1952]). Let (X, ϱ) and (Y, ϱ') be metric spaces and let (X, δ) and (Y, δ') denote the proximity spaces induced by virtue of Example 4.2. Show that the function f of the set X into Y is proximity-preserving if and only if for every $\varepsilon > 0$ there exists a $\delta > 0$ such that for every pair of points $x, x' \in X$ which satisfies the condition $\varrho(x, x') < \delta$, the inequality $\varrho'(f(x), f(x')) < \varepsilon$ holds (cf. Exercise 1.D).

Hint: Show that if $\{y_n\}$ and $\{y'_n\}$ denote two sequences in the space Y such that for some $\varepsilon > 0$ and every $n = 1, 2, \ldots$ we have $\varrho'(y_n, y'_n) > \varepsilon$, then there exists an increasing sequence of natural numbers $n_1, n_2, \ldots$ such that $\{y_{n_i}\}_{i=1}^{\infty} \bar{\delta}' \{y'_{n_i}\}_{i=1}^{\infty}$. Begin with the assumption that one of the sequences $\{y_n\}, \{y'_n\}$ contains a subsequence satisfying Cauchy's condition.

U (V. A. Efremovič [1952]). Let δ be a proximity in a topological space X. Show that for every pair A, B of remote subsets of X there exists a proximity-preserving function f of the space X into the segment I (with the proximity induced by the natural metric) such that $f(A) \subset \{0\}$ and $f(B) \subset \{1\}$.

Hint: Make use of Theorem 4.6 and Exercise 4.A.

V (Yu. M. Smirnov [1952]). Show that in the family of all uniformities which induce a fixed proximity in a set X there exists the weakest uniformity.

Hint: This is the uniformity described in Theorem 4.4.

W (Yu. M. Smirnov [1952]). Let (X, δ) be a proximity space. A covering $\mathfrak{A} = \{U_s\}_{s \in S}$ of the set X is said to be *weakly δ-uniform* if there exists a sequence $\mathfrak{A}_1, \mathfrak{A}_2, \ldots$ of coverings of the set X such that

(a) $\mathfrak{A}_1 = \mathfrak{A}$.
(b) $\mathfrak{A}_{i+1}$ is a star-refinement of $\mathfrak{A}_i$ for $i = 1, 2, \ldots$
(c) For every two close subsets A, B of X and every $i = 1, 2, \ldots$ there exists a $C_i \in \mathfrak{A}_i$ such that $A \cap C_i \neq 0 \neq B \cap C_i$.

Show that every δ-uniform covering is weakly δ-uniform.

Prove that for every weakly δ-uniform covering $\mathfrak{A}$ of a set X there exists a uniformity $\mathfrak{U}$ in X which induces the proximity δ and contains the set $\bigcup_{A\in\mathfrak{A}} A\times A$ as an element.

X (C. H. Dowker [1961], M. Katětov [1959]). Let N be the set of natural numbers with the discrete topology. Verify that the family of all coverings of the set $X = N\times N$ which have refinements of the form $\{\{x\}\times A\}_{x\in N, A\in\mathfrak{A}}$, where $\mathfrak{A}$ is a finite covering of the set N consisting of disjoint sets, satisfies conditions (UC1)-(UC4), and thus generates a uniformity $\mathfrak{U}$ in X. Let δ be the proximity induced by $\mathfrak{U}$ in X; verify that $\Delta\delta(N\times N\setminus\Delta)$. Show that the coverings $\{\{x\}\times N\}_{x\in N}$ and $\{N\times\{y\}\}_{y\in N}$ are weakly δ-uniform and that the only common refinement of these two coverings is the covering consisting of individual points of the set X.

Deduce that a strongest uniformity inducing the proximity δ in X does not exist.

Y (Yu. M. Smirnov [1952]). Show that the weakest uniformity $\mathfrak{U}$ inducing a fixed proximity δ in the set X is the unique totally bounded uniformity inducing this proximity. Deduce that for every Tychonoff space X there exists a one-to-one correspondence between the proximities and the totally bounded uniformities in X.

BIBLIOGRAPHY

Alexander, J. W.

1939. *Ordered sets, complexes and the problem of compactification,* Proc. Nat. Acad. Sci. USA 25 (1939), 296-298.

Alexandroff, P.

1924. *Sur les ensembles de la première classe et les ensembles abstraits,* C. R. Acad. Paris 178 (1924), 185-187.

1924a. *Über die Struktur der bikompakten topologischen Räume,* Math. Ann. 92 (1924), 267-274.

1924b. *Über die Metrisation der in kleinen kompakten topologischen Räume,* Math. Ann. 92 (1924), 294-301.

1927. *Über stetige Abbildungen kompakter Räume,* Math. Ann. 96 (1927), 555-571.

1928. *Über den allgemeinen Dimensionsbegriff und seine Beziehungen zur elementaren geometrischen Anschauung,* Math. Ann. 98 (1928), 617-636.

1929. *Untersuchungen über Gestalt und Lage abgeschlossener Mengen beliebiger Dimension,* Ann. of Math. 30 (1929), 101-187.

1932. *Dimensionstheorie. Ein Beitrag zur Geometrie der abgeschlossenen Mengen,* Math. Ann. 106 (1932), 161-238.

1936. *Zur Theorie der topologischen Räume,* C. R. (Doklady) Acad. Sci. URSS 2 (1936), 55-58.

1939. *Bikompakte Erweiterungen topologischer Räume,* Mat. Sbornik 5 (1939), 403-423 (Russian; German summary).

1941. *Der endliche dimensionstheoretische Summensatz für bikompakte Räume.* Soobšč. Akad. Nauk Gruzin. SSR 2 (1941), 1-6 (Russian; German summary),

1947. *On the dimension of normal spaces,* Proc. Roy. Soc. London 189 (1947), 11-39.

1960. *On the metrization of topological spaces,* Bull. Acad. Pol. Sci. sér. math. 8 (1960), 135-140 (Russian; English summary).

Alexandroff, P. and **Hopf, H.**

1935. *Topologie I,* Berlin 1935.

Alexandroff, P. and **Ponomarev, V. I.**

1959. *On bicompact extensions of topological spaces,* Vestnik Mosk. Univ. ser. mat. No 5 — 1959, 93-108 (Russian).

Alexandroff, P. and **Urysohn, P. S.**

1923. *Une condition nécessaire et suffisante pour qu'une classe (L) soit une classe (D),* C. R. Acad. Sci. Paris 177 (1923), 1274-1276.

1923a. *Sur les espaces topologiques compacts,* Bull. Intern. Acad. Pol. Sci. Sér. A année 1923, 5-8.

1924. *Zur Theorie der topologischen Räume,* Math. Ann. 92 (1924), 258-266.

1929. *Mémoire sur les espaces topologiques compacts,* Verh. Akad. Wetensch. Amsterdam 14 (1929), 1-96.

Arens, R.

1946. *A topology for spaces of transformations*, Ann. of Math. 47 (1946), 480-495.
1950. *Note on convergence in topology*, Math. Mag. 23 (1950), 229-234.
1952. *Extension of functions on fully normal spaces*, Pacific Journ. of Math. 2 (1952), 11-22.

Arens, R. and **Dugundji, J.**

1950. *Remark on the concept of compactness*, Portugaliae Math. 9 (1950), 141-143.

Arhangel'skiĭ, A. V.

1959. *An addition theorem for weight of sets lying in bicompacta*, Dokl. Akad. Nauk SSSR 126 (1959), 239-241 (Russian).
1960. *On exterior bases of sets lying in bicompacta*, Dokl. Akad. Nauk SSSR 132 (1960), 495-496 (Russian).
1960a. *On the metrization of topological spaces*, Bull. Acad. Pol. Sci. sér. math. 8 (1960), 589-595 (Russian; English summary).
1961. *On topological spaces full in Čech's sense*, Vestnik Mosk. Univ. ser. math. No 2 — 1961, 37-40 (Russian; English summary).

Bagley, R. W., Connel, E. H. and **McKnight, J. D.**

1958. *On properties characterizing pseudo-compact spaces*, Proc. Amer. Math. Soc. 9 (1958), 500-506.

Bing, R. H.

1951. *Metrization of topological spaces*, Canad. Journ. of Math. 3 (1951), 175-186.
1953. *A connected countable Hausdorff space*, Proc. Amer. Math. Soc. 4 (1953), 474.

Birkhoff, G.

1936. *A note on topological groups*, Comp. Math. 3 (1936), 427-430.

Bockstein, M.

1948. *Un théorème de séparabilité pour les produits topologiques*, Fund. Math. 35 (1948), 242-246.

Borsuk, K.

1932. *Über Schnitte der n-dimensionalen Euklidischen Räume*, Math. Ann. 106 (1932), 239-248.
1933. *Über Isomorphie der Funktionalräume*, Bull. Intern. Acad. Pol. Sci. Sér. A année 1933, 1-10.
1937. *Sur les prolongements des transformations continues*, Fund. Math. 28 (1937), 99-110.

Bourbaki, N.

1949. *Topologie générale*, Ch. 10, Paris 1949.
1958. *Topologie générale*, Ch. 9, second ed., Paris 1958 (first ed. Paris 1948).
1961. *Topologie générale*, Ch. 1 and 2, third ed., Paris 1961 (first ed. Paris 1940).

Brouwer, L. E. J.

1911. *Beweis der Invarianz der Dimensionenzahl*, Math. Ann. 70 (1911), 161-165.
1912. *Über Abbildung von Mannigfaltigkeiten*, Math. Ann. 71 (1912), 97-115.
1913. *Über den natürlichen Dimensionsbegriff*, Journ. für die reine und angew. Math. 142 (1913), 146-152.
1924. *Bemerkungen zum natürlichen Dimensionsbegriff*, Proc. Acad. Amsterdam 27 (1924), 635-638.

Cartan, H.

1937. *Théorie des filtres,* C. R. Acad. Paris 205 (1937), 595-598.

Čech, E.

1932. *Sur la dimension des espaces parfaitement normaux,* Bull. Intern. Acad. Tchèque Sci. 33 (1932), 38-55.

1932a. *Théorie générale de l'homologie dans un espace quelconque,* Fund. Math. 19 (1932), 149-183.

1933. *Contribution à la théorie de la dimension,* Časopis Pěst. Mat. Fys. 62 (1933), 277-291 (Czech; French summary).

1937. *On bicompact spaces,* Ann. of Math. 38 (1937), 823-844.

1959. *Topological spaces,* Prague 1959 (Czech).

Čech, E. and **Pospíšil, B.**

1938. *Sur les espaces compacts,* Publ. Fac. Sci. Univ. Masaryk Brno, 258 (1938), 3-7.

Chevalley, C. and **Frink, O., jr.**

1941. *Bicompactness of Cartesian products,* Bull. Amer. Math. Soc. 47 (1941), 612-614.

Colmez, J.

1951. *Sur les espaces précompacts,* C. R. Acad. Paris 233 (1951), 1552-1553.

Corson, H. H.

1959. *Normality in subsets of product spaces,* Amer. Journ. of Math. 81 (1959), 785-796.

Corson, H. H. and **Isbell, J. R.**

1960. *Some properties of strong uniformities,* Quart. Journ. of Math. Oxford 11 (1960), 17-33.

Dieudonné, J.

1939. *Sur les espaces uniformes complets,* Ann. École Normale 56 (1939), 277-291,

1939a. *Un exemple d'espace normal non susceptible d'une structure d'espace complet,* C. R. Acad. Paris 209 (1939), 145-147.

1939b. *Sur les espaces topologiques susceptibles d'être munis d'une structure uniforme d'espace complet,* C. R. Acad. Paris 209 (1939), 666-668.

1944. *Une généralisation des espaces compacts,* Journ. Math. Pures et Appl. 23 (1944), 65-76.

Doss, R.

1947. *On continuous functions in uniform spaces,* Ann. of Math. 48 (1947), 843-844.

1949. *On uniform spaces with a unique structure,* Amer. Journ. of Math. 71 (1949), 19-23.

Dowker, C. H.

1947. *Mapping theorems for non-compact spaces,* Amer. Journ. of Math. 69 (1947), 200-242.

1947a. *An imbedding theorem for paracompact metric spaces,* Duke Math. Journ. 14 (1947), 639-645.

1951. *On countably paracompact spaces,* Canad. Journ. of Math. 3 (1951), 219-224.

1952. *On a theorem of Hanner,* Ark. för Mat. 2 (1952), 307-313.

1955. *Local dimension of normal spaees,* Quart. Journ. of Math. Oxford 6 (1955), 101-120.

1961. *Mappings of proximity structures,* Proceedings of the Symposium on General Topology Prague 1961, Prague 1962, 139-141.

Dowker, C. H. and **Hurewicz, W.**

1956. *Dimension of metric spaces,* Fund. Math. 43 (1956), 83-88.

Dugundji, J.

1951. *An extension of Tietze's theorem,* Pacific Journ. of Math. 1 (1951), 353-367.

Efimov, B.

1963. *On dyadic bicompact spaces,* Dokl. Akad. Nauk SSSR 149 (1963), 1011-1014 (Russian).

1963a. *On dyadic spaces,* Dokl. Akad. Nauk SSSR 151 (1963), 1021-1024 (Russian).

Efremovič, V. A.

1951. *Infinitesimal spaces,* Dokl. Akad. Nauk SSSR 76 (1951), 341-343 (Russian).

1952. *Proximity geometry,* I, Mat. Sbornik 31 (1952), 189-200 (Russian).

Eilenberg, S. and **Otto, E.**

1938. *Quelques propriétés caractéristiques de la théorie de la dimension,* Fund. Math. 31 (1938), 149-153.

Eilenberg, S. and **Steenrod, N.**

1952. *Foundations of algebraic topology,* Princeton 1952.

Engelking, R. and **Mrówka, S.**

1958. *On E-compact spaces,* Bull. Acad. Pol. Sci. sér. math. 6 (1958), 429-436.

Engelking, R. and **Pełczyński, A.**

1963. *Remarks on dyadic spaces,* Coll. Math 11 (1963), 55-63.

Erdös, P.

1940. *The dimension of the rational points in Hilbert space,* Ann. of Math. 41 (1940), 734-736.

Esenin-Vol'pin, A. S.

1949. *On the relation between the local and integral weight in dyadic bicompact spaces,* Dokl. Akad. Nauk SSSR 68 (1949), 441-444 (Russian).

Fichtenholz, G. and **Kantorovitch, L.**

1934. *Sur les opérations linéaires dans l'espace des fonctions bornées,* Studia Math. 5 (1934), 69-98.

Fomin, S.

1943. *Extensions of topological spaces,* Ann. of Math. 44 (1943), 471-480.

Fort, M. K., jr.

1951. *A note on pointwise convergence,* Proc. Amer. Math. Soc. 2 (1951), 34-35.

Fox, R. H.

1945. *On topologies for function spaces,* Bull. Amer. Math. Soc. 51 (1945), 429-432.

Fréchet, M.

1906. *Sur quelques points du Calcul Fonctionnel,* Rend. del Circ. Math. di Palermo 22 (1906), 1-74.

1910. *Les dimensions d'un ensemble abstrait,* Math. Ann. 68 (1910), 145-168.

1926. *Les espaces abstraits,* Paris 1926.

Frolík, Z.

1959. *Generalizations of Compact and Lindelöf spaces*, Czech. Math. Journ. 9 (1959), 172-217 (Russian; English summary).

1960. *Generalizations of the G_δ-property of complete metric spaces*, Czech. Math. Journ. 10 (1960), 359-379.

Gelfand, I. M. and **Kolmogoroff, A. N.**

1939. *On rings of continuous functions on topological spaces*, C. R. (Doklady) Acad. Sci. URSS 22 (1939), 11-15.

Gęba, K. and **Semadeni, Z.**

1960. *Spaces of continuous functions (V)*, Studia Math. 19 (1960), 303-320.

Gillman, L. and **Jerison, M.**

1960. *Rings of continuous functions*, New York 1960.

Glicksberg, I.

1959. *Stone-Čech compactifications of products*, Trans. Amer. Math. Soc. 90 (1959), 369-382.

de Groot, J.

1956. *Non-archimedean metrics in topology*, Proc. Amer. Math. Soc. 7 (1956), 948-953.

Hahn, H.

1914. *Mengentheoretische Charakterisierung der stetigen Kurve*, Sitzungsberichte Akad. Wiss. Wien 123 (1914), 2433-2489.

Halmos, P. R.

1963. *Lectures on Boolean Algebras*, Princeton 1963.

Hanner, O.

1951. *Solid spaces and absolute retracts*, Ark. för Mat. 1 (1951), 375-382.

Hausdorff, F.

1914. *Grundzüge der Mengenlehre*, Leipzig 1914.

1927. *Mengenlehre*, Berlin 1927.

1930. *Erweiterung einer Homöomorphie*, Fund. Math. 16 (1930), 353-360.

1934. *Über innere Abbildungen*, Fund. Math. 23 (1934), 279-291.

1936. *Über zwei Sätze von G. Fichtenholz und L. Kantorovitch*, Studia Math. 6 (1936), 18-19.

1938. *Erweiterung einer stetigen Abbildung*, Fund. Math. 30 (1938), 40-47.

Hemmingsen, E.

1946. *Some theorems in dimension theory for normal Hausdorff spaces*, Duke Math. Journ. 13 (1946), 495-504.

Henriksen, M. and **Isbell, J. R.**

1958. *Some properties of compactifications*, Duke Math. Journ. 25 (1958), 83-106.

Hewitt, E.

1943. *A problem of set-theoretic topology*, Duke Math. Journ. 10 (1943), 309-333.

1946. *On two problems of Urysohn*, Ann. of Math. 47 (1946), 503-509.

1946a. *A remark on density characters*, Bull. Amer. Math. Soc. 52 (1946), 641-643.

1947. *Certain generalizations of the Weierstrass approximation theorem*, Duke Math. Journ. 14 (1947), 419-427.
1948. *Rings of real-valued continuous functions*, I, Trans. Amer. Math. Soc. 64 (1948), 45-99.

Holsztyński, W.

1966. *Topological dimension of lattices*, Bull. Acad. Pol. Sci. sér. math. 14 (1966), 63-69.

Hurewicz, W.

1927. *Normalbereiche und Dimensionstheorie*, Math. Ann. 96 (1927), 736-764.
1927a. *Über das Verhältnis separabler Räume zu kompakten Räumen*, Proc. Acad. Amsterdam 30 (1927), 425-430.
1930. *Einbettung separabler Räume in gleich dimensional kompakte Räume*, Monatsh. für Math. und Phys. 37 (1930), 199-208.
1935. *Über Abbildungen topologischer Räume auf die n-dimensionale Sphäre*, Fund. Math. 24 (1935), 144-150.

Hurewicz, W. and **Wallman, H.**

1948. *Dimension theory*, second ed., Princeton 1948 (first ed. Princeton 1941).

Iseki, K. and **Kasahara, S.**

1957. *On pseudo-compact and countably compact spaces*, Proc. Japan Acad. 33 (1957), 100-102.

Janiszewski, Z.

1912. *Sur les continus irréductibles entre deux points*, Journ. École Polyt. 16 (1912), 79-170.

Jones, F. B.

1937. *Concerning normal and completely normal spaces*, Bull. Amer. Math. Soc. 43 (1937), 671-677.

Kakutani, S.

1936. *Über die Metrisation der topologischen Gruppen*, Proc. Imp. Acad. Tokyo 12 (1936), 82-84.

Katětov, M.

1940. *Über H-abgeschlossene und bikompakte Räume*, Časopis Pěst. Mat. Fys. 69 (1940), 36-49.
1948. *Complete normality of Cartesian products*, Fund. Math. 35 (1948), 271-274.
1950. *On nearly discrete spaces*, Časopis Pěst. Mat. Fys. 75 (1950), 69-78.
1950a. *A theorem on the Lebesgue dimension*, Časopis Pěst. Mat. Fys. 75 (1950), 79-87.
1951. *Measures in fully normal spaces*, Fund. Math. 38 (1951), 73-84.
1951a. *On real-valued functions in topological spaces*, Fund. Math. 38 (1951), 85-91.
1952. *On the dimension of non-separable spaces*, I, Czech. Math. Journ. 2 (1952), 333-368 (Russian; English summary).
1958. *On extension of locally finite coverings*, Coll. Math. 6 (1958), 145-151 (Russian).
1959. *Fully normal spaces*, appendice to E. Čech's book "Topological spaces", Prague 1959 (Czech).

Keisler, H. J. and **Tarski, A.**

1964. *From accessible to inaccessible cardinals*, Fund. Math. 53 (1964), 225-308.

Kelley, J. L.

1950. *Convergence in topology*, Duke Math. Journ. 17 (1950), 277-283.
1955. *General topology*, New York 1955.

Kerstan, J.

1957. *Zur Charakterisierung der pseudokompakten Räume*, Math. Nachr. 16 (1957), 289-293.

Knaster, B. and **Kuratowski, K.**

1921. *Sur les ensembles connexes*, Fund. Math. 2 (1921), 206-255.

Knaster, B., Kuratowski, K. and **Mazurkiewicz, S.**

1929. *Ein Beweis des Fixpunktsatzes für n-dimensionale Simplexe*, Fund. Math. 14 (1929), 132-137.

Kowalsky, H. J.

1957. *Einbettung metrischen Räume*, Arch. der Math. 8 (1957), 336-339.

Kuratowski, K.

1921. *Solution d'un problème concernant les images continues d'ensembles de points*, Fund. Math. 2 (1921), 158-160.
1922. *Une méthode d'élimination des nombres transfinis des raisonnements mathématiques*, Fund. Math. 3 (1922), 76-108.
1922a. *Sur l'opération $\bar{A}$ de l'Analysis Situs*, Fund. Math. 3 (1922), 182-199.
1933. *Sur un théorème fondamental concernant le nerf d'un système d'ensembles*, Fund. Math. 20 (1933), 191-196.
1935. *Quelques problèmes concernant les espaces métriques non-separables*, Fund. Math. 25 (1935), 534-545.
1948. *Une méthode de prolongement des ensembles relativement fermés ou ouverts*, Coll. Math. 1 (1948), 273-278.
1958. *Topologie I*, fourth ed., Warszawa 1958 (first ed. Warszawa 1933).
1961. *Topologie II*, third ed., Warszawa 1961 (first ed. Warszawa 1950).
1961a. *Introduction to set theory and topology*, Warszawa-Oxford 1961.

Kuratowski, K. and **Sierpiński, W.**

1921. *Le théorème de Borel-Lebesgue dans la théorie des ensembles abstraits*, Fund. Math. 2 (1921), 172-178.
1921a. *Sur les différences de deux ensembles fermés*, Tôhoku Math. Journ. 20 (1921), 22-25.
1926. *Sur un problème de M. Fréchet concernant les dimensions des ensembles linéaires*, Fund. Math. 8 (1926), 193-200.

Lavrentieff, M.

1924. *Contribution à la théorie des ensembles homéomorphes*, Fund. Math. 6 (1924), 149-160.

Lebesgue, H.

1911. *Sur la non-applicabilité de deux domaines appartenant respectivement à des espaces de n et n+p dimensions*, Math. Ann. 70 (1911), 166-168.
1921. *Sur les correspondences entre les points de deux espaces*, Fund. Math. 2 (1921), 256-285.

Lefschetz, S.

1942. *Algebraic topology*, New York 1942.

Levšenko, B. T.

1957. *On the concept of compactness and point-finite coverings,* Mat. Sbornik 42 (1957), 479-484 (Russian).

Lindenbaum, A.

1926. *Contributions à l'étude de l'espace métrique,* I, Fund. Math. 8 (1926), 209-222.

Lokucievskiĭ, O. V.

1949. *On the dimension of bicompacta,* Dokl. Akad. Nauk SSSR 67 (1949), 217-219 (Russian).

Lunc, A. L.

1949. *A bicompactum whose inductive dimension is greater than its dimension defined by means of coverings,* Dokl. Akad. Nauk SSSR 66 (1949), 801-803 (Russian).

Mackey, G. W.

1944. *Equivalence of a problem in measure theory to a problem in the theory of vector lattices,* Bull. Amer. Math. Soc. 50 (1944), 719-722.

Mansfield, M. J.

1957. *On countably paracompact normal spaces,* Canad. Journ. of Math. 9 (1957), 443-449.

Marczewski, E. (Szpilrajn, E.)

1941. *Remarque sur les produits cartésiens d'espaces topologiques,* C. R. (Doklady) Acad. Sci. URSS 31 (1941), 525-527.

1947. *Séparabilité et multiplication cartésienne des espaces topologiques,* Fund. Math. 34 (1947), 127-143.

Mather, M. R.

1964. *Paracompactness and partitions of unity,* preprint 1964.

Mazur, S.

1952. *On continuous mappings on Cartesian products,* Fund. Math. 39 (1952), 229-238.

Mazurkiewicz, S.

1920. *Sur les lignes de Jordan,* Fund. Math. 1 (1920), 166-209.

McAuley, L. F.

1956. *Paracompactness and an example due to F. B. Jones,* Proc. Amer. Math. Soc. 7 (1956), 1155-1156.

1958. *A note on complete collectionwise normality and paracompactness,* Proc. Amer. Math. Soc. 9 (1958), 796-799.

Menger, K.

1923. *Über die Dimensionalität von Punktmengen.* I, Monatsh. für Math. und Phys. 33 (1923), 148-160.

1924. *Über die Dimensionalität von Punktmengen,* II, Monatsh. für Math. und Phys. 34 (1924), 137-161.

1928. *Dimensionstheorie,* Leipzig 1928.

Mibu, Y.

1944. *On Baire functions on infinite product spaces,* Proc. Imp. Acad. Tokyo 20 (1944), 661-663.

Michael, E.

1951. *Topologies on spaces of subsets*, Trans. Amer. Math. Soc. 71 (1951), 152-182.
1953. *A note on paracompact spaces*, Proc. Amer. Math. Soc. 4 (1953), 831-838.
1955. *Point-finite and locally finite coverings*, Canad. Journ. of Math. 7 (955,1) 275-279.
1957. *Another note on paracompact spaces*, Proc. Amer. Math. Soc. 8 (1957), 822-828.
1961. *On a theorem of Rudin and Klee*, Proc. Amer. Math. Soc. 12 (1961), 921.
1963. *The product of a normal space and a metric space need not be normal*, Bull. Amer. Math. Soc. 69 (1963), 375-376.

Mokobodzki, G.

1964. *Nouvelle méthode pour démontrer la paracompacité des espaces métrisables*, Ann. Inst. Fourier 14 (1964), 539-542.

Moore, E. H.

1939. *General analysis I*, Pt. II, Philadelphia 1939.

Moore, E. H. and **Smith, H. L.**

1922. *A general theory of limits*, Amer. Journ. of Math. 44 (1922), 102-121.

Moore, R. L.

1916. *On the foundations of plane analysis situs*, Trans. Amer. Math. Soc. 17 (1916) 131-164.

Morita, K.

1948. *Star-finite coverings and the star-finite property*, Math. Japonicae 1 (1948), 60-68.
1950. *On the dimension of normal spaces*, I, Jap. Journ. of Math. 20 (1950), 5-36.
1950a. *On the dimension of normal spaces*, II, Journ. of Math. Soc. Japan 2 (1950), 16-33.
1954. *Normal families and dimension theory for metric spaces*, Math. Ann. 128 (1954), 350-362.

Morita, K. and **Hanai, S.**

1956. *Closed mappings and metric spaces*, Proc. Japan Acad. 32 (1956), 10-14.

Mrówka, S.

1956. *On universal spaces*, Bull. Acad. Pol. Sci. Cl. III 4 (1956), 479-481.
1956a. *Remark on the paper by P. Alexandroff "On two Yu. Smirnov's theorems"*, Fund. Math. 43 (1956), 399-400 (Russian).
1957. *Some properties of Q-spaces*, Bull. Acad. Pol. Sci. Cl. III 5 (1957), 947-950.
1959. *On the potency of subsets of βN*, Coll. Math. 7 (1959-60), 23-25.
1959a. *An outline of the theory of Q-spaces*, Warszawa 1959 (Polish).

Nagami, K.

1955. *Paracompactness and strong screenability*, Nagoya Math. Journ. 8 (1955), 83-88.

Nagata, J.

1950. *On a necessary and sufficient condition of metrizability*, Journ. Inst. Polyt. Osaka City Univ. 1 (1950), 93-100.
1950a. *On topological completness*, Journ. of Math. Soc. Japan 2 (1950), 44-47.
1963. *On the metrizability of topological spaces*, lecture on the meeting of the Pol. Math. Soc., Warszawa May 14, 1963.

Nakamura, M. and **Kakutani, S.**

1943. *Banach limits and the Čech compactification of a countable discrete set*, Proc. Imp. Acad. Tokyo 19 (1943), 224-229.

Niemytzki, V. and **Tychonoff, A.**

1928. *Beweis des Satzes dass ein metrisierbarer Raum dann und nur dann kompakt ist, wenn er in jeder Metrik vollständing ist*, Fund. Math. 12 (1928), 118-120.

Novák, J.

1937. *Sur deux espaces réguliers et dénombrables sans points de caractère dénombrable*, Časopis Pěst. Mat. Fys. 67 (1937-38), 97-99 (Czech; French summary).

1948. *Regular space, on which every continuous function is constant*, Časopis Pěst. Mat. Fys. 73 (1948), 58-68 (Czech; English summary).

1953. *On the Cartesian product of two compact spaces*, Fund. Math. 40 (1953), 106-112.

Parovičenko, I. I.

1957. *Certain special classes of topological spaces and δs-operations*, Dokl. Akad. Nauk SSSR 115 (1957), 866-868 (Russian).

Poincaré, H.

1912. *Pourquoi l'espace a trois dimensions*, Revue de Metaph. et de Morale 20 (1912). 483-504.

Pondiczery, E. S.

1944. *Power problems in abstract spaces*, Duke Math. Journ. 11 (1944), 835-837.

Pontriagin, L. S.

1930. *Sur une hypothèse fondamentale de la théorie de la dimension*, C. R. Acad, Sci. Paris 190 (1930), 1105-1107.

1954. *Continuous groups*, Moscow 1954 (Russian).

Pospíšil, B.

1937. *Remark on bicompact spaces*, Ann. of Math. 38 (1937), 845-846.

1937a. *Trois notes sur les espaces abstraits*, Publ. Fac. Sci. Univ. Masaryk Brno 249 (1937), 3-9.

Riesz, F.

1907. *Die Genesis des Raumbegriffs*, Math. u. Naturwiss. Berichte aus Ungarn 24 (1907), 309-353.

1909. *Stetigkeitsbegriff und abstrakte Mengenlehre*, Atti del IV Congresso Intern. dei Matem. Roma 1908, v. II, 18-24, Roma 1909.

Ross, K. A. and **Stone, A. H.**

1964. *Products of separable spaces*, Amer. Math. Month. 71 (1964), 398-403.

Roy, P.

1962. *Failure of equivalence of dimension concepts for metric spaces*, Bull. Amer. Math. Soc. 68 (1962), 609-613.

Rudin, M. E.

1955. *Countable paracompactness and Souslin's problem*, Canad. Journ. of Math. 7 (1955), 543-547.

Rudin, M. E. and Klee, V. L., jr.

1956. *A note on certain function spaces*, Arch. der Math. 7 (1956), 469-470.

Saks, S.

1921. *Sur l'equivalence de deux théorèmes de la théorie des ensembles*, Fund. Math. 2 (1921), 1-3.

Šanin, N. A.

1943. *On the theory of bicompact extensions of topological spaces*, C. R. (Doklady) Acad. Sci. URSS 38 (1943), 110-113.
1944. *On imbedding in a power of a topological space*, Izv. Akad. Nauk SSSR ser. mat. 8 (1944), 233-242 (Russian; English summary).
1948. *On the product of topological spaces*, Trudy Inst. Steklova 24, Moscow 1948 (Russian).

Šediva, V.

1959. *On collectionwise normal and hypocompact spaces*, Czech. Math. Journ. 9 (1959), 50-62 (Russian; English summary).

Shirota, T.

1952. *A class of topological spaces*, Osaka Math. Journ. 4 (1952), 23-40.

Sierpiński, W.

1920. *Sur une condition pour qu'un continu soit une courbe jordanienne*, Fund. Math. 1 (1920), 44-60.
1921. *Sur les ensembles connexes et non connexes*, Fund. Math. 2 (1921), 81-95.
1928. *Sur les projections des ensembles complémentaires aux ensembles (A)*, Fund. Math. 11 (1928), 117-122.
1933. *Sur les espaces métriques localement séparables*, Fund. Math. 21 (1933), 107-113.
1965. *Cardinal and ordinal numbers*, second ed., Warszawa 1965 (first ed. Warszawa 1958).

Smirnov, Yu. M.

1948. *On the theory of completely regular spaces*, Dokl. Akad. Nauk SSSR 62 (1948) 749-752 (Russian).
1951. *On coverings of topological spaces*, Uč. Zapiski Mosk. Gos. Univ. 148 (1951), 204-215 (Russian).
1951a. *On metrization of topological spaces*, Uspehi Mat. Nauk 6 (1951), 100-111 (Russian).
1951b. *Some relations in the theory of dimension*, Mat. Sbornik 29 (1951), 157-172 (Russian).
1951c. *On normally disposed sets of normal spaces*, Mat. Sbornik 29 (1951), 173-176 (Russian).
1952. *On proximity spaces*, Mat. Sbornik 31 (1952), 543-574 (Russian).
1956. *On strongly paracompact spaces*, Izv. Akad. Nauk SSSR ser. mat. 20 (1956), 253-274 (Russian).
1956a. *On the metrizability of bicompacta decomposable into an union of sets with countable bases*, Fund. Math. 43 (1956), 387-393 (Russian).
1956b. *On the dimension of proximity spaces*, Mat. Sbornik 38 (1956), 283-302 (Russian).
1958. *An example of a zero-dimensional normal space having infinite covering dimension*, Dokl. Akad. Nauk SSSR 123 (1958), 40-42 (Russian).

Šneĭder, V. E.

1945. *Continuous images of Suslin and Borel sets. Metrizations theorems*, Dokl. Akad. Nauk SSSR 50 (1945), 77-79 (Russian).

Sorgenfrey, R. H.

1947. *On the topological product of paracompact spaces*, Bull. Amer. Math. Soc. 53 (1947), 631-632.

Sperner, E.

1928. *Neuer Beweis für die Invarianz der Dimensionszahl und des Gebietes*, Abh. Math. Semin. Hamburg. Univ. 6 (1928), 265-272.

Steenrod, N.

1936. *Universal homology groups*, Amer. Journ. of Math. 58 (1936), 661-701.

Stone, A. H.

1948. *Paracompactness and product spaces*, Bull. Amer. Math. Soc. 54 (1948), 977-982.
1956. *Metrizability of decomposition spaces*, Proc. Amer. Math. Soc. 7 (1956), 690-700.
1963. *A note on paracompactness and normality of mapping spaces*, Proc. Amer. Math. Soc. 14 (1963), 81-83.

Stone, M. H.

1937. *Applications of the theory of Boolean rings to general topology*, Trans. Amer. Math. Soc. 41 (1937), 375-481.
1937a. *Algebraic characterization of special Boolean rings*, Fund. Math. 29 (1937), 223-303.
1947. *The generalized Weierstrass approximation theorem*, Math. Mag. 21 (1947-8), 167-184 and 237-254.
1948. *On the compactification of topological spaces*, Ann. Soc. Pol. Math. 21 (1948), 153-160.

Šura-Bura, M. R.

1941. *Zur Theorie der bikompakten Räume*, Mat. Sbornik 9 (1941), 385-388 (Russian; German summary).

Taĭmanov, A. D.

1952. *On extension of continuous mappings of topological spaces*, Mat. Sbornik 31 (1952), 459-463 (Russian).

Terasaka, H.

1952. *On Cartesian product of compact spaces*, Osaka Math. Journ. 4 (1952), 11-15.

Tietze, H.

1915. *Über Funktionen die auf einer abgeschlossenen Menge stetig sind*, Journ. für die reine und angew. Math. 145 (1915), 9-14.
1923. *Beiträge zur allgemeinen Topologie*, I, Math. Ann. 88 (1923), 290-312.

Tong, H.

1948. *Some characterizations of normal and perfectly normal spaces*, Bull. Amer. Math. Soc. 54 (1948), 65.

1949. *On some problems of Čech*, Ann. of Math. 50 (1949), 154-157.

1952. *Some characterizations of normal and perfectly normal spaces*, Duke Math. Journ. 19 (1952), 289-292.

Tukey, J. W.

1940. *Convergence and uniformity in topology*, Princeton 1940.

Tumarkin, L. A.

1928. *Über die Dimension nicht abgechlossener Mengen*, Math. Ann. 98 (1928), 637-656.

Tychonoff, A.

1925. *Über einen Metrisationssatz von P. Urysohn*, Math. Ann. 95 (1925), 139-142.

1930. *Über die topologische Erweiterung von Räumen*, Math. Ann. 102 (1930), 544-561.

1935. *Über einen Funktionenraum*, Math. Ann. 111 (1935), 762-766.

Ulam, S.

1930. *Zur Masstheorie in der allgemeinen Mengenlehre*, Fund. Math. 16 (1930), 140-150.

Urysohn P.,

1922. *Les multiplicités Cantoriennes*, C. R. Acad. Sci. Paris 157 (1922), 440-442.

1924. *Über die Metrisation der kompakten topologischen Räume*, Math. Ann. 92 (1924), 275-293.

1925. *Über die Mächtigkeit der zusammenhängenden Mengen*, Math. Ann. 94 (1925), 262-295.

1925a. *Zum Metrisationsproblem*, Math. Ann. 94 (1925), 309-315.

1925b. *Mémoire sur les multiplicités Cantoriennes*, Fund. Math. 7 (1925), 30-137.

1926. *Mémoire sur les multiplicités Cantoriennes* (suite), Fund. Math. 8 (1926), 225-359.

1927. *Beispiel eines nirgends separablen metrischen Raumes*, Fund. Math. 9 (1927), 119-121.

Vaĭnšteĭn, I. A.

1947. *On closed mappings of metric spaces*, Dokl. Akad. Nauk SSSR 57 (1947), 319-321 (Russian).

Vedenissoff, N.

1936. *Sur les fonctions continues dans les espaces topologiques*, Fund. Math. 27 (1936), 234-238.

1939. *Remarques sur la dimension des espaces topologiques*, Uč. Zapiski Mosk. Gos. Univ. 30 (1939), 131-140 (Russian; French summary).

1940. *Généralisation de quelques théorèmes sur la dimension*, Comp. Math. 7 (1940), 194-200.

1941. *Sur la dimension au sens de E. Čech*, Izv. Akad. Nauk SSSR ser. mat. 5 (1941), 211-216 (Russian; French summary).

Vietoris, L.

1921. *Stetige Mengen,* Monatsh. für Math. und Phys. 31 (1921), 173-204.
1922. *Bereiche zweiter Ordnung,* Monatsh. für Math. und Phys. 32 (1922), 258-280.
1923. *Kontinua zweiter Ordnung,* Monatsh. für Math. und Phys. 33 (1923), 49-62.

Wallman, H.

1938. *Lattices and topological spaces,* Ann. of Math. 39 (1938), 112-126.

Weil, A.

1937. *Sur les espaces à structure uniforme et sur la topologie générale,* Paris 1937.

Zorn, M.

1935. *A remark on method in transfinite algebra,* Bull. Amer. Math. Soc. 41 (1935), 667-670.

LIST OF SPECIAL SYMBOLS

$A \cup B$ 13

$A \cap B$ 13

$A \setminus B$ 13

0 13

$x \in A$ 13

$x \notin A$ 13

$A \subset B, B \supset A$ 13

$\{x \in X: \varphi(x)\}, \{x: \varphi(x)\}$ 13

$\{x_1, x_2, \ldots, x_k\}, \{x_i\}_{i=1}^{k}$ 13

(x, y) 13

$A \times B$ 14

$f(M)$ 14

$f^{-1}(N)$ 14

$\bigcup_{s \in S} A_s, \bigcup_{i=1}^{\infty} A_i$ 14

$\bigcap_{s \in S} A_s, \bigcap_{i=1}^{\infty} A_i$ 14

$\{x_i\}_{i=1}^{\infty}$ 14

$\mathop{\boldsymbol{P}}_{s \in S} A_s, \mathop{\boldsymbol{P}}_{i=1}^{\infty} A_i$ 14

$\{x_s\}, \{x_i\}$ 14

$\overline{\overline{A}}$ 15

$\aleph_0$ 15

$\mathfrak{c}$ 15

$\mathfrak{m}+\mathfrak{n}$ 15

$\mathfrak{m} \cdot \mathfrak{n}$ 15

$\sum_{s \in S} \mathfrak{m}_s$ 15

$2^{\mathfrak{m}}$ 15

$\mathfrak{m} \leqslant \mathfrak{n}, \mathfrak{n} \geqslant \mathfrak{m}$ 16

α 18

$\alpha < \beta$ 18

$\xi + 1$ 18

$\omega_0, \omega_1, \omega_2$ 18

$(a, b), [a, b], (a, b], [a, b)$ 22, 23

$w((X, \mathfrak{O})), w(X)$ 26, 31

$\overline{A}$ 28

$\operatorname{Int} A$ 29

R 31

I 31

$\operatorname{Fr} A$ 37

A^{d} 38

$f: X \to Y$ 40

gf 42

$|f|, f+g, f \cdot g, 1/f$ 42

$\max(f, g), \min(f, g)$ 42

$\lim f_n$ 43

id_X 45

$\{x_\sigma, \sigma \in \Sigma\}$ 53

$\lim \{x_\sigma, \sigma \in \Sigma\}$ 53

$\lim \mathfrak{F}, \lim \mathfrak{H}$ 57

i_M 65

$f|M$ 66

$\bigoplus_{s \in S} X_s, X_1 \oplus X_2 \oplus \ldots \oplus X_k$ 70

$\mathop{\boldsymbol{P}}_{s \in S} X_s, X_1 \times X_2 \times \ldots \times X_k, X^{\mathfrak{m}}$ 73

p_s 73

$\mathop{\boldsymbol{P}}_{s \in S} f_s, f_1 \times f_2 \times \ldots \times f_k$ 75

$\mathop{\triangle}_{s \in S} f_s, f_1 \triangle f_2 \triangle \ldots \triangle f_k$ 75

R^n, I^n, S^n, Q^n 75

$I^{\mathfrak{m}}, I^{\aleph_0}$ 78

$F^{\mathfrak{m}}$ 80

$D^{\mathfrak{m}}, D^{\aleph_0}$ 80

X/R 83

$\underleftarrow{\lim} \{X_\sigma, \pi_\varrho^\sigma, \Sigma\}$ 87

Y^X 91

$M(A, B)$ 92
cX 125
$\mathfrak{C}(X)$ 126
βX 129
ωX 137
$\delta(M) < \mathfrak{A}$ 143
vX 156
$\varrho(x, y)$ 169
$B(x_0, r)$ 169
$\lim x_n$ 171
$\delta(A)$ 171
$J(\mathfrak{m})$ 173
H 173
$d(x, A)$ 175
$\hat{\varrho}(f, g)$ 180
$\mathrm{St}(M, \mathfrak{A})$ 212
$\mathrm{St}(x, \mathfrak{A})$ 212
X_M 215
$\mathrm{ind}\, X$ 264
$\mathrm{Ind}\, X$ 265
$\mathrm{ord}\, \mathfrak{A}$ 265
$\dim X$ 266
$\mathrm{Ex}\, U$ 269
$\mathfrak{A} \wedge \mathfrak{B}, \mathfrak{A}_1 \wedge \mathfrak{A}_2 \wedge \ldots \wedge \mathfrak{A}_k$ 274
$\mathrm{ds}\, X$ 285
$B(\mathfrak{m})$ 292
$b(S)$ 298
$-A$ 313
$A+B$ 313
nA 313
Δ 313
$|x-y| < V, |x-y| \geqslant V$ 314
$\mathfrak{D}_X$ 314
$\delta(A) < V$ 314
$B(x, V)$ 314
$B(A, V)$ 314
$w(\mathfrak{U})$ 314
$C(X), C^*(X)$ 323
$\mathfrak{C}, \mathfrak{C}^*$ 324
$f: (X, \mathfrak{U}) \to (Y, \mathfrak{B})$ 325
$\mathfrak{U}_M$ 326
$\underset{s \in S}{\boldsymbol{P}} \mathfrak{U}_s$ 327
$\hat{V}, \hat{V}|Z$ 329
$\hat{\mathfrak{U}}, \hat{\mathfrak{U}}|Z$ 329
$(\tilde{X}, \tilde{\mathfrak{U}})$ 338
$\delta, \bar{\delta}$ 342
$A \Subset B$ 343
(O1)-(O3) 25, 26
(B1)-(B2) 26
(BP1)-(BP4) 27, 47
(C1)-(C3) 27
(CO1)-(CO4) 29
(I1)-(I4) 30
(M1)-(M3) 169
(U1)-(U4) 314
(BU1)-(BU3) 314
(UC1)-(UC4) 315
(P1)-(P3) 320, 352
(PS1)-(PS5) 342
(SI1)-(SI7) 343

AUTHOR INDEX

Alexander, J. W. 160
Alexandroff, P. 59, 94, 151, 157, 158, 159, 161, 162, 165, 199, 200, 202, 230, 233, 305, 308, 309, 351, 355
Arens, R. 109, 158, 163, 231, 234, 235, 351
Arhangel'skiĭ, A. V. 158, 159, 166, 233, 236

Bagley, R. W. 151
Bing, R. H. 199, 231, 258
Birkhoff, G. 351
Bockstein, M. 98
Borsuk, K. 234, 237, 258
Bourbaki, N. 59, 94, 203, 351
Brouwer, L. E. J. 304, 305, 306

Cantor, G. 58, 199, 258
Cartan, H. 59
Čech, E. 60, 158, 159, 161, 164, 199, 203, 304, 305, 306, 309
Chevalley, C. 158
Colmez, J. 151
Connel, E. H. 151
Corson, H. H. 98, 165

Dieudonné, J. 165, 230, 232, 351, 354
Doss, R. 353, 354
Dowker, C. H. 220, 231, 232, 236, 237, 258, 259, 285, 305, 309, 356
Dugundji, J. 231, 234

Efimov, B. 162, 202, 203
Efremovič, V. A. 351, 355
Eilenberg, S. 119, 158, 258, 305
Engelking, R. 159, 162, 202, 203
Erdös, P. 259, 274
Esenin-Vol'pin, A. S. 162

Fichtenholz, G. 164
Fomin, S. 159
Fort, M. K., jr. 200
Fox, R. H. 158
Fréchet, M. 58, 159, 198, 199, 200
Frink, O. jr. 158
Frolík, Z. 159

Gelfand, I. M. 166
Gęba, K. 235
Gillman, L. 157, 159, 164, 259, 261, 304, 351
Glicksberg, I. 158
de Groot, J. 296

Hahn, H. 260
Halmos, P. R. 202
Hanai, S. 203, 204
Hanner, O. 231
Hausdorff, F. 23, 58, 160, 164, 199, 201, 202, 235, 258, 259, 296
Hemmingsen, E. 305, 309
Henriksen, M. 167, 232
Hewitt, E. 59, 94, 96, 159, 164, 165, 166, 167
Holsztyński, W. 158, 305
Hopf, H. 59
Hurewicz, W. 305, 306, 308, 309

Isbell, J. R. 98, 167, 232
Iseki, K. 237

Janiszewski, Z. 157
Jerison, M. 157, 159, 164, 259, 261' 304, 351
Jones, F. B. 59
Jordan, C. 258

Kakutani, S. 158, 351
Kantorovitch, L. 164
Kasahara, S. 237
Katětov, M. 94, 95, 158, 159, 161, 200, 231, 236, 237, 285, 304, 305, 310, 356
Keisler, H. J. 159
Kelley, J. L. 63, 352
Kerstan, J. 237
Klee, V. L., jr. 142

Knaster, B. 258, 306
Kolmogoroff, A. N. 58, 166
Kowalsky, H. J. 199
Kuratowski, K. 23, 58, 59, 82, 96, 157, 159, 183, 198, 199, 200, 233, 258, 259, 261, 306, 308

Lavrentieff, M. 202
Lebesgue, H. 304
Lefschetz, S. 231
Levšenko, B. T. 237
Lindelöf, E. 159
Lindenbaum, A. 193
Lokucievskiĭ, O. V. 307
Lunc, A. L. 307

Mackey, G. W. 157
Mansfield, M. J. 236
Marczewski, E. 94, 96, 162
Mather, M. R. 231
Mazur, S. 97
Mazurkiewicz, S. 260, 306
McAuley, L. F. 220, 234
McKnight, J. D. 151
Menger, K. 304, 305, 306, 311
Mibu, Y. 120
Michael, E. 142, 163, 201, 204, 231, 232, 233, 238,
Mokobodzki, G. 231
Moore, E. H., 59
Moore, R. L. 260
Morita, K. 203, 204, 231, 285, 296, 305, 310
Mrówka, S. 97, 158, 159, 166

Nagami, K. 231
Nagata, J. 199, 204, 233, 354
Nakamura, M. 158
Niemytzki, V. 59, 236
Novák, J. 59, 94, 158, 159

Otto, E. 305

Parovičenko, I. I. 134
Pełczyński, A. 162, 202, 203
Poincaré, H. 304
Pondiczery, E. S. 94, 96
Ponomarev, V. I. 355
Pontriagin, L. S. 159, 305
Pospíšil, B. 99, 158, 161

Riesz, F. 58, 59, 351
Ross, K. A. 98
Roy, P. 305
Rudin, M. E. 142, 231

Saks, S. 157
Šanin, N. A. 97, 159, 162
Šediva, V. 232, 237
Semadeni, Z. 235
Shirota, T. 157, 159, 351
Sierpiński, W. 23, 96, 157, 159, 200, 202, 233, 259, 260, 305
Sikorski, R. 351
Słodkowski, Z. 158
Smirnov, Yu. M. 60, 96, 158, 199, 203, 231, 233, 304, 305, 306, 307, 309, 310, 351, 355, 356
Smith, H. L. 59
Šneĭder, V. E. 183
Sorgenfrey, R. H. 94, 159
Sperner, E. 306
Steenrod, N. 119, 158, 258
Stone, A. H. 98, 99, 124, 199, 203, 204, 230, 232
Stone, M. H. 61, 120, 134, 158, 166, 259
Šura-Bura, M. R. 258

Taĭmanov, A. D. 158
Tarski, A. 159
Terasaka, H. 159
Tietze, H. 59, 94
Tong, H. 164, 236
Tukey, J. W. 23, 230, 351
Tumarkin, L. A. 305, 310
Tychonoff, A. 59, 94, 158, 164, 199, 236

Ulam, S. 159
Urysohn, P. 59, 61, 94, 95, 151, 157, 158, 159, 161, 165, 199, 258, 304, 305, 306, 311, 351

Vaĭnšteĭn, I. A. 167, 204
Vedenissoff, N. 60, 259, 305, 310
Vietoris, L. 59, 157, 159, 163, 259

Wallman, H. 305, 306
Weierstrass, K. 199
Weil, A. 351

Zorn, M. 23

SUBJECT INDEX

(C = corollary, E followed by three numbers = example, E followed by two numbers and a letter = exercice, L = lemma, P = problem, T = theorem)

abelian group 321
absolutely closed space P 3.DE
accumulation point of a set 38
— point of a set, complete P 3.A
additive property 71
aleph, first strongly inaccessible 154
— zero 15
Alexandroff compactification 138
and proximity E 8.4.D
examples E 3.6.2-3
existence T 3.6.7-8
see also compactification unique
— cube 80
universality T 2.3.9
— theorem 114, 137
antecedent of an ordered pair 13
arcwise connected space P 6.HJN
Ascoli theorem 333, 334
axiom of choice 21
— of countability, first 27, *see* space satisfying the first axiom of countability
— of countability, second 27, *see* space satisfying the second axiom of countability
axioms of separation 46-53, *see also* T_0-space, T_1-space, Hausdorff space, semi-regular space, Urysohn space, Tychonoff space, normal space, hereditarily normal space, collectionwise normal space *and* perfectly normal space

Baire space E 7.3.2
universality T 7.3.9
— theorem 145, E 4.3.D
ball in an Euclidean space 75
— in a metric space 169
— in a uniform space 314

barycentre 298
barycentric coordinates 297
— subdivision 300
base for a uniformity 314
— for a uniformity, minimal 314
— of a topological space 26, *see also* weight of a topological space
— of a topological space at a point 26, *see also* space satisfying the first axiom of countability
— of a topological space, minimal 26, *see also* weight of a topological space
—, point-regular P 5.I
—, regular P 5.H
binary relation 14
Bing theorem 197
bound, greatest lower 20
—, least upper 20
boundary of a set 37, E 4.4.A
— set 38, E 1.3.A
bounded mapping 180
— metric 171, *see* metric bounded by a real number
— set in an Euclidean space 114
— set in a metric space 171
Brouwer-Čech dimension 265, *see* large inductive dimension

Cantor cube 80
and quasi-components P 6.P
compact spaces are images of closed subsets T 3.2.2
universality T 6.2.11
see also dyadic space
— set 80, E 3.2.B, P 4.LO, *see also* Cantor cube
— theorem 187
Cantor-Bernstein theorem 16

cardinal number 15
— number less 16
— number non-measurable 154
— number not greater 16
— number not less 16
Cartesian product of mappings 75
— product of sets 14
— product of topological spaces 73-75
characterization E 2.3.F
dense subsets T 2.3.7, P 2.KL
embedding into 78, P 2.MN
weight P 2.J
see also mapping depending on a countable number of coordinates *and* universal space
— product of uniform spaces 327, E 8.2.A
— product of uniformities 326
Cauchy filter 341
— net 341
Cauchy's condition 186
Čech-Lebesgue dimension 266, *see* covering dimension
Čech-Stone compactification 129
and Hewitt's real-compactification E 3.10.D
and proximity E 8.4.4
and uniformity E 8.3.2
characterizations T 3.5.1 and C 1-3
constructions E 3.5.C, P 3.V, E 8.3.2, E 8.4.4
dimension E 6.2.3, T 7.1.11-12, P 7.P
examples E 3.5.1, E. 3.5.4, P 3.LNP
extremal disconnectedness T 6.2.12
of a subspace C 6-7, T 3.5.1
of Cartesian product E 3.5.E, P 6.R
see also compactification unique *and* remainder of β
— compactification of N (discrete space of power $\aleph_0$) 132
Cartesian product P 6.R
construction E 3.5.4
is extremally disconnected C T 6.2.12
power and weight T 3.5.2
subsets T 3.5.3-4
see also remainder of βN
centre of a ball in a metric space 169
— of a ball in a uniform space 314
chain in a family of sets 228
circle 76
class of a cut, lower 16
— of a cut, upper 16
class of spaces, perfect P 3.Y, P 5.C
close sets 342
closed covering 101
— domain E 1.1.C
— equivalence relation 84
in a compact space T 3.2.9
— mapping 44
projection parallel to a compact axis is T 3.2.8
— set 27
— subspace 65
compact subspace of a T_2-space is T 3.1.6
closure of a set 28-29, E 1.1.AB, T 1.6.2, T 1.6.2F, P 1.A, T 4.1.1, C 1 T 4.1.5, C 2 T 8.1.2, T 8.4.1
closure-preserving family of sets P 5.A
cluster point of a filter 57, E 1.6.A
— point of a filter-base 57
— point of a net 54
cofinal subset 20
collectionwise normal space 214
characterizations E 5.1.C, P 5.E
countably paracompact P 5.U
non-paracompact E 5.1.1
operations E 5.1.C, P 5.L
weakly paracompact is paracompact T 5.3.2
combination of mappings 69
is a mapping T 2.1.5-6, E. 4.4.B
commutative group 321
compact space 101
and Cantor cube T 3.2.2
Cartesian product T 3.2.4, E 3.2.F, E 3.7.D, E 3.9.BE, T 5.1.10, L T 5.2.2, E 5.2.C
characterizations T 3.1.1, T 3.1.12, T 3.1.12F, T 3.9.1, T 3.10.3, P 3.ABDVW
compact subspace T 3.1.3-6, E 3.2.H
examples E 3.1.1-2, E 3.1.E, E 3.9.C, P 3.CN
in an Euclidean space T 3.2.7
inverse systems T 3.2.10-11
is normal T 3.1.7
mappings and functions T 3.1.8-10, C 2 T 3.1.11, C T 3.2.7, T 3.2.12, E 3.2.DFGH, P 3.VWY
metrizable T 4.2.3, E 4.2.C, T 4.3.13-14, P 4.FOR, P 5.O, E 8.3.D

compact space
power and weight T 3.1.11 and C 1-2, E 3.2.G, P 3.FG, P 4.O
quotient space T 3.2.9, E 3.2.E
subspaces T 3.1.2, T 3.2.6
uniformities in T 8.3.3, T 8.3.10-12
unique proximity T 8.4.3
universal space T 3.2.5
see also countably compact space, dyadic space, *and* pseudo-compact space
— uniform space 339
all coverings are uniform E 8.3.B
characterization T 8.3.12
connectedness E 8.3.E
compactification 125, E 3.4.DE
and proximity T 8.4.6
equivalent T 3.4.4-5
existence T 3.4.1-2
of Cartesian product E 3.4.B
one-point T 3.6.7
power and weight T 3.4.2-3
unique E 3.6.3, P 3.Q, P 8.N
0-dimensional C T 6.2.11
see also Alexandroff compactification, Čech-Stone compactification, *and* family of compactifications
—, Alexandroff 138, *see* Alexandroff compactification
—, Čech-Stone 129, *see* Čech-Stone compactification
—, not less 126
compactifications, equivalent 125, T 3.4.4-5
compact-open topology 121-122, E 3.3.AE, E 3.7.E, P 3.K
and the topology of uniform convergence on compacta T 8.2.3, E 8.2.D
compact subspaces T 8.2.4-5
metrizability T 4.2.6, E 4.2.F
see also space of mappings
compatible mappings 69, *see also* combination of mappings
complete accumulation point of a set P 3.A
— metric space 186
characterizations T 4.3.4-5
operations T 4.3.6-9
see also completion of a metric space
— uniform space 335-337
characterization T 8.3.13
see also completion of a uniform space
complete uniformity 335
existence 337, P 8.O
completely separated sets 51, C 1 T 3.5.1, T 6.2.2
completion of a metric space P 4.I
— of a uniform space 338, P 8.Q
and Cartesian product E 8.3.A
component of a family of sets 228
— of a point 245
and quasi-component T 6.1.7-8, E 6.1.4
in Cartesian product T 6.1.6
composition of mappings 42
— of relations 313
condensation point P 1.P
condition, Cauchy's 186
connected family of sets 228
— space 240
Cartesian product T 6.1.4
characterizations T 6.1.1 and C 1, C 3-4, T 6.1.3, E 6.1.C, P 6.A
connected subspace T 6.1.2, T 6.1.3 and C 1-3, E 6.1.B
countable E 6.1.2
equivalence of strong paracompactness and the Lindelöf property E 6.1.D
mappings C 3 T 6.1.1
power C 2 T 6.1.1, E 6.1.2
quotient space P 6.D
continuous image of a space 42
— real-valued function 42
continuum (cardinal number) 15
— (space) 244
intersection C T 6.1.5
limit of an inverse system T 6.1.5
locally connected P 6.M
metrizable and locally connected P 6.JKL
convergent filter 57
— filter-base 57
— net 54
— sequence in a metric space 171
convex set E 3.2.C
coordinate of a point in the Cartesian product 14
coordinates, barycentric 297
countable intersection property 101
— set 15

countably additive two-valued measure 154
— compact space 146
Cartesian product E 3.9.4, E 3.9.B
characterizations T 3.9.2, T 3.9.6, E 3.9.A, P 5.W
is pseudo-compact T 3.9.9
mappings T 3.9.5, T 3.9.7, P 3.Y
metrics C 1 T 4.3.4, T 4.3.12
metrizable C T 4.3.12, T 4.3.13
non-compact E 3.9.1-3
non-regular P 3.O
normal is collectionwise normal C L T 5.1.7
satisfying the first axiom of countability is regular P 3.O
subspaces T 3.9.3
weakly paracompact is compact T 5.3.1
— paracompact space 220
and collectionwise normal P 5.U
characterizations T 5.2.1-2, E 5.2.A, P 5.RT
mappings P 5.C
perfectly normal is P 5.Q
covering 101
—, closed 101
— dimension 266
and operations T 7.1.7, E 7.1.CD, T 7.3.3, E 7.3.F, P 7.DFJKL
and other dimensions T 7.1.9-10, E 7.1.2, T 7.2.4, T 7.2.6, E 7.2.D, T 7.3.1-2, E 7.3.B, P 7.E
characterizations T 7.1.6, T 7.2.3, CL 3 T 7.2.7, T 7.2.7, E 7.2.C, P 7.IMK
examples E 7.1.2, E 7.2.1-2, T 7.3.13 and C 1-2, P 7.FG
of β T 7.1.12
of metrizable space, *see* large inductive dimension
sum theorems T 7.2.1-2, E 7.2.B
zero, *see* strongly 0-dimensional space
—, δ-uniform 347
—, irreducible 225
—, open 101
—, point finite 207, LT 5.3.1
—, star-finite 220
—, uniform 315
—, weakly δ-uniform P 8.W
cube, Alexandroff 80, *see* Alexandroff cube
—, Cantor 80, *see* Cantor cube
—, Hilbert 79, *see* Hilbert cube
— in an Euclidean space 75
—, Tychonoff 78, *see* Tychonoff cube
cut of an ordered set 16

dense in itself, set 38, E 1.3.C, P 1.O
— set 38
countable, *see* separable space
of power $\leqslant \mathfrak{m}$ T 1.3.7, P 1.F, P 2.L, L 1 T 3.4.3, T 4.1.6
— subspace 65
derived set 38, P 1.E
in a T_1-space E 1.5.B
n-th E 1.3.B
diagonal in the Cartesian product E 2.3.E, 313
— lemma 78
— of a family of mappings 75
diameter less than $\mathfrak{A}$ 143
— less than V 314
— of a set 171
dimension, Brouwer-Čech 265, *see* large inductive dimension
—, Čech-Lebesgue 266, *see* covering dimension
—, covering 266, *see* covering dimension
—, Dowker-Hurewicz 285
—, large inductive 265, *see* large inductive dimension
—, Menger-Urysohn 264, *see* small inductive dimension
—, sequential 285
—, small inductive 264, *see* small inductive dimension
directed set 20
discrete family of sets 193
— space 30
Cartesian product need not be normal P 2.T, E 3.1.F
condition for real-compactness E 3.10.E
is metrizable E 4.1.1
— uniformity 316
distance between points 169
— from a point to a set 175
— less than V 314
domain, closed E 1.1.C
—, open E 1.1.C
Dowker-Hurewicz dimension 285

dyadic space P 3.HI, P 4.LMN
δ-uniform covering 347
— , first 16
—, last 16
element, maximal 21
embeddable space 65
into the Cartesian product P 2.MN, *see also* universal space
embedding, homeomorphic 65
— of a subspace in a topological space 65
— of a subspace in a uniform space 326
entourage of the diagonal 314
equicontinuous mappings 331
equimorphic proximity spaces 344
equimorphism 344
equivalence class 15
— relation 15
— relation, closed 84, *see* closed equivalence relation
— relation, open 84
equivalent compactifications 125, T 3.4.4-5
— metrics 171
Euclidean space 75
extendable mapping 66, *see also* extension of functions and mappings
extension of a homeomorphism P 4.K, P 5.O
— of a metric P 5.O,
— of a uniformly continuous mapping T 8.3.8
— of closed and open subsets P 4.D
— of functions and mappings 66, T 2.1.4, P 4.JK, P 5.O
existence T 2.1.3, T 3.2.1, E 3.2.AH
linear P 5.MN
over a compactification T 3.5.1 and C 2
extremally disconnected space 256
characterizations T 6.2.12, T. 6.2.14, P 6.Q
is strongly 0-dimensional T 6.2.13
metrizable is discrete E 6.2.E
operations T 6.2.15, E 6.2.4, E 6.2.D
ε-net 184

F_σ-set 39
the set of irrational numbers is not E 3.8.A
face of a simplex 297
family of compactifications T 3.4.6, T 3.6.6-8, E 3.6.C, T 3.8.1, P 3.R
family of mappings separating points 77
— of mappings separating points from closed sets 77
— of sets, closure-preserving P 5.A
— of sets, connected 228
— of sets, containing arbitrarily small sets 335
— of sets, discrete 193
— of sets, functionally closed 248
— of sets, functionally open 248
— of sets, locally finite 193, E. 4.4.AB
— of sets, star-countable 228
— of sets, star-finite 228
— of sets, σ-discrete 193
— of sets, σ-locally finite 193
— of sets with countable intersection property 101
— of sets with finite intersection property 101
filter 56-57, T 2.3.11F, T 3.1.12F
—, Cauchy 341
—, convergent 57
—, finer 57
filter-base 56
—, convergent 57
finer filter 57
— net 54
finite intersection property 101
first axiom of countability 27, *see* space satisfying the first axiom of countability
— element of an ordered set 16
— strongly inaccessible aleph 154
fixed-point theorem 296
consequences T 7.3.13, P 7.S
proof 303
function 14, *see also* mapping
—, monotone 20
—, one-to-one 14
— onto 14
— preserving an ordering 17
—, real-valued continuous 42
—, semi-continuous P 5.RS
—, uniformly continuous 325, *see* uniformly continuous function
functional determined by a point P 3.W
—, multiplicative linear P 3.W
—, non-trivial P 3.W
functionally closed family of sets 248
— closed set 248, E 6.2.A
— open family of sets 248
— open set 248

G_δ-set 39
closed set in a metric space is C 2 T 4.1.5
gap 17
generation of a topology 33, *see* topology generated
graph of a mapping P 2.I
greatest lower bound 20
grid 104
group 321
—, abelian (commutative) 321
—, topological 321, P 8.DGR

Hausdorff distance P 4.H, P 8.H
— space 47
characterizations T 1.6.4, T 1.6.4F, E 2.3.E
non-regular E 1.5.1
hedgehog E 4.1.3
hereditarily collectionwise normal space P 5.L
— Lindelöf space E 3.7.BE, E 3.9.C
— normal space P 2.BDEFU, E 3.7.E, P 3.C, P 7.ABCD
— paracompact space P 5.D
— separable space E 3.7.E
hereditary property 66
Hewitt's real-compactification 156
and β E 3.10.D
and uniformity E 8.3.3
example P 3.P
Hilbert cube 79
and Hilbert space E 4.2.D
metrizability C 1 T 4.2.2
universality C T 4.2.4
— space E 4.1.5
homeomorphic embedding 65
— spaces 45
characterizations P 3.V, P 4.P
homeomorphism 45
homotopic mappings P 5.V
homotopy P 5.V

ideal P 3.V
—, maximal P 3.V
identifying 85
identity mapping 45
image 14
—, continuous 42
—, inverse 14
inclusion, strong 343, P 8.S
independent sets P 3.L
initial number 18
interior of a set 29-30
invariant of homeomorphisms 46
inverse image 14
— in a group 321
— relation 313
— system of topological spaces 87
irreducible covering 225
isolated point 38
isometry E 4.2.E, E 4.3.F
isomorphic uniform spaces 325
isomorphism, uniform 325

jump 17

k-space 123
locally compact space is T 3.6.10
mappings T 3.3.4-5, T 8.2.4
subspaces E 3.3.C
T_2-space satisfying the first axiom of countability is T 3.3.3
Kuratowski-Zorn lemma 21

$\mathscr{L}^*$ space P 1.STU
metrizable space is E 4.1.A
large inductive dimension 265
and operations T 7.1.3, E 7.1.B, T 7.3.3, T 7.3.11, E 7.3.F, P 7.BN
and other dimensions T 7.1.2, T 7.1.9-10, E 7.1.2, T 7.2.5-6, T 7.3.1-2, E 7.3.B, P 7.O
examples E 7.1.2, E 7.2.1, E 7.3.1-2, T 7.3.13 and C 1-2
of β T 7.1.11
of metrizable spaces T 7.3.1-11, E 7.3.A-F, P7.QR
sum theorem P 7.N
zero, *see* strongly 0-dimensional space
last element of an ordered set 16
least upper bound 20
left topology induced by a partial ordering P 1.BC
less, cardinal number 16
—, ordinal number 18
lexicographic order P 3.C
limit mapping 90
— number 18
— of a filter 57
— of a filter-base 57
— of a net 54
— of a sequence (in a metric space) 171
— of an inverse system 87
base T 2.5.3

Lindelöf property 140, *see* Lindelöf space
— space 140-141
characterizations T 3.7.2, P 3.R
dimension T 7.2.4-5
is paracompact C 2 T 5.1.4
is real-compact T 3.10.2
is strongly paracompact C T 5.3.3
locally compact E 3.7.C
mappings P 3.Y
metrizable C T 4.1.6
operations E 3.7.ABD
linearly independent points 296
— ordered subset 20
locally arcwise connected space P 6.IJKLN
— closed set P 2.H
— compact space 135
Cartesian product T 3.6.5
compactifications T 3.6.7-8, E 3.6.C
is a k-space T 3.6.10
Lindelöf E 3.7.C
mappings T 3.6.11, P 3.Y, T 8.2.4
paracompact E 5.3.CD
subspaces T 3.6.3, E 3.6.B
weakest uniformity P 8.K
weight T 3.6.9
— connected space P 6.EFG
— finite family of sets 193, E 4.4.AB
— finite partition of unity 207
lower class of a cut 16
— semi-continuous function P 5.RS

mapping 40-45
characterizations T 1.4.1, T 1.6.3, T 1.6.3F, C T 2.1.5, E 3.2.D, T 4.1.4, E 4.1.C
—, bounded 180
—, closed 44, *see* closed mapping
— depending on a countable number of coordinates P 2.R, E 3.2.F
—, extendable 66, *see* extension of functions and mappings
—, identity 45
—, limit 90
—, natural 83
— of an inverse system 89
induces a homeomorphism T 2.5.4
—, open 44
—, perfect P 3.X
mappings, compatible 69, *see also* combination of mappings
—, equicontinuous 331
mappings, homotopic P 5.V
maximal element 21
— ideal P 3.V
measure, countably additive two-valued 154
Menger-Urysohn dimension 264, *see* small inductive dimension
mesh of a simplicial subdivision 298
metric 169
— bounded by a real number 171
equivalent T 4.1.3, E 4.1.B
— in a topological space 170
extension from a closed subspace P 5.O
—, non-Archimedean E 7.3.E
— "river" E 4.1.4
— space 169
compact T 4.3.13-15, E 4.3.EF
completion P 4.I
embedding in the space of functions E 4.2.E, T 4.3.10
examples E 4.1.1-5
mappings T 4.2.5-8, T 4.3.8
see also complete metric space *and* totally bounded metric space
metrics, equivalent 171
metrizable topological space 170
Cartesian product T 4.2.2, E 4.2.1, E 4.2.B, P 5.G
characterizations T 4.2.3-4, E 4.2.C, T 4.4.5-6, P 4.F, P 5.HI
compact T 4.2.3, E 4.2.C, T 4.3.13-14, E 4.3.E, P 4.FHLOR, P 5.O
dimension T 7.3.1-11
embedding in a complete metric space E 4.2.E, T 4.3.10, P 4.I
equivalence of compactness and countable compactness T 4.3.13
equivalence of separability, Lindelöf property, and of the second axiom of countability C T 4.1.6
functions and mappings T 4.2.5-8, P 4.JK, P 5.MO
has a σ-discrete base T 4.4.4
is normal C 3 T 4.1.5
is paracompact C 1 T 5.1.4
metrizability of unions of metrizable subspaces P 4.QV, P 5.J
quotient space P 4.STU
universal space T 4.4.7
see also space metrizable in a com-

plete manner *and* space metrizable in a totally bounded manner
metrizable uniform space 324
characterization T 8.1.9
minimal base for a uniformity 314
— base of a topological space 26, *see also* weight of a topological space
monotone function 20
de Morgan formulas 13
multiplicative linear functional P 3.W
— property 76

Nagata-Smirnov theorem 196
natural mapping 83
— topology of *I* 31
— topology of *R* 31
neighbourhood of a point 26
— system 27
net 53-56, T 1.6.5-6, P 1.V, T 2.3.11, T 2.6.4. T 3.2.11
—, Cauchy 341
—, convergent 54
— eventually in a set 53
—, finer 54
— frequently in a set 53
non-Archimedean metric E 7.3.E
non-measurable cardinal number 154
non-trivial functional P 3.W
normal space 49
Cartesian product E 2.3.2, P 2.T, E 3.1.F
characterizations E 1.6.E, P 1.J, T 2.1.3, E 5.1.A
coverings L 1 T 5.1.3, L T 5.2.1
functions and mappings E 1.5.E, T 2.1.3, P 5.S
non-collectionwise normal E 5.1.3
quotient space T 2.4.5
pseudo-compact is countably compact T 3.9.10
separation of subsets E 1.6.D, C T 2.1.6, E 5.1.D
subspaces E 2.3.3, P 2.CG, *see also* hereditarily normal space
normally placed set P 1.K, P 2.G, P 3.R
not greater cardinal number 16
— less cardinal number 16
— less compactification 126
nowhere dense set 38
union T 3.8.6, E 4.4.A
number, cardinal 15
number, initial 18
—, limit 18
—, ordinal 17

one-to-one function 14
open covering 101
— domain E 1.1.C
— equivalence relation 84
— mapping 44
— set 26
— subspace 65
open-and-closed set 27
order, lexicographic P 3.C
— of a family of sets 265
— topology P 1.D, *see* topology induced by an ordering
— type 17
ordered pair 13
— set 16
ordering 16
—, partial 20
ordinal number 17
— number less 18
oscillation of a mapping P 4.J

p-adic uniformity P 8.C
pair, ordered 13
paracompact space 206
Cartesian product E 5.1.4-5, T 5.1.10, P 5.FK
characterizations T 5.1.3-5, P 5.B, P 8.B
covering dimension T 7.2.3
equivalence of compactness and countable compactness T 5.1.7
existence of complete uniformity P 8.O
is collectionwise normal T 5.1.6
is normal T 5.1.2
Lindelöf space is C 2 T 5.1.4
locally compact E 5.3.CD
metrizable space is C 1 T 5.1.4
subspaces T 5.1.8, P 5.D
partial ordering 20
partially ordered set 20
partition between sets 281
— of unity 207
— of unity, locally finite 207
— of unity subordinate to a covering 207
perfect class of spaces P 3.Y, P 5.C
— mapping P 3.X
— set P 1.O

perfectly normal space P 1.GHIK, P 2.EF, P 4.W, P 5.DFQ, P 7.NOP
plank, Tychonoff P 3.O
point finite covering 207, L T 5.3.1
—, isolated 38
— of a metric space 169
— of a topological space 26
point-regular base P 5.I
points, linearly independent 296
pointwise star-refinement 212, L 2 T 5.1.5
— topology 92-94, E 3.3.A, E 3.7.E, P 4.G, *see also* space of mappings
polyhedron P 7.H
power of a set 15
— of a topological space, *see* dense subset *and* weight of a topological space
— of an ordinal number 18
predecessor of an ordinal number 18
product, Cartesian, *see* Cartesian product
— in a group 321
— of cardinal numbers 15
projection onto an axis of the Cartesian product 73
  parallel to a compact axis is closed T 3.2.8
property, additive 71
—, countable intersection 101
—, finite intersection 101
—, hereditary 66
— hereditary with respect to closed subsets 66
—, Lindelöf 140, *see* Lindelöf space
—, $\mathfrak{m}$-additive 71
—, $\mathfrak{m}$-multiplicative 76
—, multiplicative 76
— of finite character 21
—, topological 46
—, uniform 325
proximity 342
  and compactifications T 8.4.6, E 8.4.4, E 8.4.D
  and strong inclusion P 8.S
  and uniformity T 8.4.2, T 8.4.4, P 8.VWXY
  examples E 8.4.1-3
— in a topological space 349
  existence T 8.4.5
  in a compact space T 8.4.3, E 8.4.A
— induced by a metric E 8.4.2, P 8.T
— induced by a uniformity 344
proximity preserving function 344
— space 342
  separation of points from closed sets P 8.U
—, stronger E 8.4.C
—, weaker E 8.4.C
pseudo-compact space 149
  Cartesian product E 3.9.5, E 3.9.E
  characterizations E 3.9.DF, E 3.10.D, P 3.S, P 5.X, P 8.L
  mappings T 3.9.11, P 3.Y
  non-countably compact E 3.9.5
  normal is countably compact T 3.9.10
  real-compact is compact T 3.10.3
  subspaces E 3.9.5
pseudo-metric 169
— bounded by a real number 171
— uniform relatively to a uniformity 317, E 8.2.C
pseudo-weight at a point P 3.F

quasi-compact space 106
quasi-component of a point 246
  and component T 6.1.7-8, E 6.1.4
  as element of a quotient space P 6.P
  in the Cartesian product P 6.O
quotient space 83-85, E 2.4.ABC, P 2.VW, T 3.2.9, E 3.2.2
— topology 83

radius of a ball in a metric space 169
— of a ball in a uniform space 314
ray E 3.2.C
real-compact space 151
  and complete uniformity 336-337
  characterizations T 3.10.1, T 3.10.4, T 3.10.7, P 3.W
  discrete space as E 3.10.E
  non-Lindelöf E 3.10.2
  non-normal P 2.T, E 3.1.F, E 3.10.C
  operations T 3.10.5-6, E 3.10.AB, P 3.U
real-compactification, Hewitt's 156, *see* Hewitt's real-compactification
real-valued continuous function 42
refinement 101
regular base P 5.H
— space 47-48
  conditions for normality T 1.5.6, L 1 T 4.4.5
  non-Tychonoff E 2.4.4
regularly placed set P 3.U

relation, binary 14
—, inverse 313
remainder of a compactification 128
and mappings T 3.4.7, P 3.X
closed T 3.6.6
E_σ-set T 3.8.1
— of β E 3.5.F, P 3.MS
— of βN E 3.5.A
extension of functions from P 5.N
non-extremally disconnected E 6.2.4
open disjoint subsets E 3.5.2
remote sets 342
restriction of a mapping 66
retraction 44
ring of functions 116
on a compact space T 3.2.12, P 3.VW
on a real-compact space P 3.W
scattered set P 1.O
second axiom of countability 27, *see* space satisfying the second axiom of countability
— axiom of countability at a point P 4.B
segment E 3.2.C
semi-continuous function P 5.RS
semi-regular space P 1.MN, P 2.A, P 3.E
separable space 39, P 1.QR
Cartesian product T 2.3.7, T 2.3.10, P 2.KPQRS
normal and non-paracompact E 5.1.F
separated sets 242
sequence, convergent 171
— of functions, uniformly convergent 43
— of mappings, uniformly convergent 182, T 4.2.7
—, transfinite 18
sequences, similar P 4.E
sequential dimension 285
set, bounded (in an Euclidean space) 114
—, bounded (in a metric space) 171
—, Cantor 80, *see* Cantor set
—, closed 27
—, convex E 3.2.C
—, countable 15
—, dense 38, *see* dense set
—, dense in itself 38, E 1.3.C, P 1.O
—, directed 20
—, functionally closed 248, E 6.2.A
—, functionally open 248
— in general position P 4.E
—, locally closed P 2.H
set, normally placed P 1.K, P 2.G, P 3.R
—, nowhere dense 38, *see* nowhere dense set
—, open 26
—, open-and-closed 27
—, ordered 16
— ordered in a continuous manner 17
— ordered in a dense manner 17
—, partially ordered 20
—, perfect P 1.O
—, regularly placed P 3.U
—, scattered P 1.O
—, Souslin 224
—, well-ordered 17
sets, close 342
—, completely separated 51, C 1 T 3.5.1 T 6.2.2
—, independent P 3.L
— of the same power 15
—, remote 342
—, separated 242
—, similarly ordered 17
shrinking of a covering 267
similar sequences P 4.E
similarly ordered sets 17
simplex 297
simplicial subdivision 298
small inductive dimension 264
and operations T 7.1.1, P 7.A
and other dimensions T 7.1.2, T 7.1.10, E 7.1.2, T 7.2.4-5, E 7.2.D, T 7.3.2
examples E 7.1.1-2, E 7.1.A, T 7.3.13 and C 1-2, P 7.G
of β E 6.2.3, P 7.P
zero, *see* 0-dimensional space
Smirnov theorem 350
Souslin set 224
space 26, 169
—, absolutely closed P 3.DE
—, arcwise connected P 6.HJN
—, Baire E 7.3.2, *see* Baire space
—, collectionwise normal 214, *see* collectionwise normal space
—, compact 101, *see* compact space
— complete in the sense of Čech 142
Cartesian product T 3.8.5
characterizations T 3.8.2, T. 4.3.11
mappings P 3.Y
metrizable T 4.3.11
power and weight P 3.GT

space complete in the sense of Čech subspace T 3.8.3
—, complete metric 186, *see* complete metric space
—, connected 240, *see* connected space
—, countably compact 146, *see* countably compact space
—, countably paracompact 220, *see* countably paracompact space
—, discrete 30, *see* discrete space
—, dyadic P 3.HI, P 4.LMN
—, embeddable 65, *see* embeddable space
—, Euclidean 75
—, extremally disconnected 256, *see* extremally disconnected space
—, Hausdorff 47, *see* Hausdorff space
—, hereditarily collectionwise normal P 5.L
—, hereditarily Lindelöf E 3.7.BE, E 3.9.C
—, hereditarily normal P 2.BDEFU, E 3.7.E, P 3.C, P 7.ABCD
—, hereditarily paracompact P 5.D
—, hereditarily separable E 3.7.E
—, Hilbert E 4.1.5
—, -k 123, *see* k-space
—, $\mathscr{L}^*$ P 1.S, *see* $\mathscr{L}^*$ space
—, locally arcwise connected P 6.IJKLN
—, locally compact 135, *see* locally compact space
— locally complete in the sense of Čech P 5.P
—, locally connected P 6.EFG
—, metric 169, *see* metric space
—, metrizable 170, *see* metrizable space
— metrizable in a complete manner 186, T 4.3.9, T 4.3.11, E 4.3.D, P 4.JK
— metrizable in a totally bounded manner 184, T 4.3.3
—, normal 49, *see* normal space
— of continuous functions 91, *see* topology of uniform convergence *and* space of mappings
— of mappings
  axioms of separation C T 2.6.3, E 2.6.1, T 3.3.1-2, E 3.7.E
  mapping $\varphi(f, x) = f(x)$ T 3.3.6, T 3.6.11, P 3.K, T 4.2.5
  see also compact-open topology *and* pointwise topology
space of subsets P 3.J, P 4.H, P 6.C, P 8.H
—, paracompact 206, *see* paracompact space
— perfectly normal P1.G, *see* perfectly normal space
—, pseudo-compact 149, *see* pseudo-compact space
—, quasi-compact 106
—, quotient 83, *see* quotient space
—, real-compact 151, *see* real-compact space
—, regular 47, *see* regular space
— satisfying locally the second axiom of countability P 4.BC
— satisfying the first axiom of countability 27
  countable space not satisfying E 3.1.4, E 3.1.CD, E 3.5.A
  is a k-space T 3.3.3
  sequences instead of nets E 1.6.C
— satisfying the second axiom of countability 27, P 1.QR
  Cartesian product P 2.Q
  is separable C T 1.3.7
  is the union of a perfect and a countable set P 1.P
  metrizable C T 4.1.6, T 4.2.4, C T 4.3.3
  regular is normal T 1.5.6
—, semi-regular P 1.MN, P 2.A, P 3.E
—, separable 39, *see* separable space
—, strongly paracompact 228-230, E 5.3.ABC
—, strongly 0-dimensional 249, *see* strongly 0-dimensional space
—, topological 25
—, totally bounded metric 184-185, E 4.3.A
—, totally disconnected 247, *see* totally disconnected space
—, Tychonoff 48, *see* Tychonoff space
—, uniform 315, *see* uniform space
—, universal 78, *see* universal space
—, Urysohn P 1.LN, P 2.A
—, weakly paracompact 225, *see* weakly paracompact space
—, 0-dimensional 247, *see* 0-dimensional space
spaces, homeomorphic 45, *see* homeomorphic spaces
Sperner lemma 301

sphere in an Euclidean space 75
star of a point 212
— of a set 212
star-countable family of sets 228
star-finite covering 220
— family of sets 228
star-refinement 212
—, pointwise 212, L 2 T 5.1.5
A. H. Stone theorem 194
Stone-Weierstrass theorem 118
strong inclusion 343, P 8.S
stronger proximity E 8.4.C
— topology 31
— uniformity E 8.1.A
strongly paracompact space 228-230, E 5.3.ABC
— 0-dimensional space 249
and other kinds of disconnectedness T 6.2.5-6, E 6.2.3, E 7 3.B, P 7.E
characterizations T 6.2.3-4, T 6.2.8
metrizable T 7.3.9-10, E 7.3.E
operations T 6.2.7, E 6.2.BC
see also covering dimension *and* large inductive dimension
subbase 26
subcovering 101
subdivision, barycentric 300
—, simplicial 298
subset, cofinal 20
—, linearly ordered 20
subspace, closed 65, *see* closed subspace
—, dense 65
— of a topological space 65-66, E 2.1.ABC
— of a uniform space 326
—, open 65
succesor of an ordered pair 13
— of an ordinal number 18
sum of cardinal numbers 15
— of spaces 70-72
— theorems in dimension theory T 7.2.1-2, E 7.2.B, P 7.N
swelling of a family of sets 266
system of topological spaces, inverse 87
σ-discrete family of sets 193
σ-locally finite family of sets 193

T_0-space 46
characterization E 1.5.A
universal space T 2.3.9
T_1-space 46
is the union of a perfect and a scattered set P 1.O
T_2-space 47, *see* Hausdorff space
T_3-space 47, *see* regular space
$T_{3\frac{1}{2}}$-space 48, *see* Tychonoff space
T_4-space 49, *see* normal space
theorem on defining by transfinite induction 18
thread of an inverse system 87
Tietze-Urysohn theorem 67, E 3.5.D
topological group 321, P 8.DGR
— property 46
— space 25
topology 26
—, compact-open 121, *see* compact-open topology
— generated by a base 34, E 1.2.B
— generated by a closure operator 35-36
— generated by convergent nets P 1.V
— generated by a family of closed sets 35
— generated by a family of mappings 44
— generated by a neighbourhood system 35, T 1.5.1
— generated by an operator of interior 36
— induced by a metric 170, *see* metrizable space
— induced by a partial ordering P 1.BC
— induced by a proximity 342, *see* proximity *and* proximity in a topological space
— induced by a uniformity 315 *see* uniform space, uniformity, *and* uniformity in a topological space
— induced by an ordering P 1.D
compactness P 3.C
connectedness P 6.B
— induced by convergent sequences P 1.TU
— induced in a subspace 65
— induced in $X \times X$ by a uniformity 317, E 8.2.C
— natural of I 31
— natural of R 31
— of a uniformity 315, *see* uniform space, uniformity, *and* uniformity in a topological space
— of pointwise convergence 92, *see* pointwise topology
— of uniform convergence 92, T 2.6.5, T 4.2.8
—, stronger 31

topology, Tychonoff 73
—, weaker 31
—, Vietoris P 3.J, P 4.H, P 6.C, P 8.H
torus 76
totally bounded metric space 184-185, E 4.3.A
— bounded uniform space 334-335
— bounded uniformity 334
all uniformities in a space are P 8.L
weaker than a uniformity P 8.J
— disconnected space 247
and other kinds of disconnectedness T 6.2.1, T 6.2.6, E 6.2.2
operations T 6.2.7, T 6.2.8-10
transfinite sequence 18
triangle inequality 169
Tukey's lemma 21
Tychonoff cube 78
universality T 2.3.8, T 3.2.5
— plank P 3.O
— space 48-49
characterization T 3.2.6
existence of a proximity T 8.4.5
existence of a uniformity T 8.1.8
non-normal E 1.5.2, E 2.1.2, P 2.T, E 3.1.F, E 3.5.3, P 3.O, E 5.1.4, P 5.K
— theorem 112, P 3.B
— topology 73

uniform covering 315
— isomorphism 325
— property 325
— pseudo-metric 317, E 8.2.C
— space 315
embedding in the Cartesian product of metrizable uniform spaces T 8.2.2
induced topology T 8.1.1
— space, compact 339, *see* compact uniform space
— space, complete 335, *see* complete uniform space
— space, metrizable 324, *see* metrizable uniform space
— space, totally bounded 334-335
— spaces, isomorphic 325
uniformity 314
and proximity T 8.4.2, T 8.4.4, P 8.VWXY
examples E 8.1.1-6, E 8.2.1, P 8.C
in a topological group E 8.1.5, P 8.DR
unique P 8.N
uniformity, complete 335, *see* complete uniformity
—, discrete 316
— generated by a base 320
— generated by a family of functions E 8.1.B
— generated by a family of pseudc-metrics 323, P 8.E
— generated by a family of uniform converings 321
— in a topological space P 8.I
existence T 8.1.8
weakest P 8.K
— induced by a metric 324, P 8.F
characterization T 8.1.9
uniformly continuous functions E 8.1.D
— induced by a proximity 347, E 8.4.B
—, metrizable 324, *see* metrizable uniform space
— of uniform convergence 329
completeness P 8.P
— of uniform convergence on compacta 329
and compact-open topology T 8.2.8
—, p-adic P 8.C
—, stronger E 8.1.A
—, totally bounded 334, *see* totally bounded uniformity
—, universal P 8.I
—, weaker E 8.1.A
uniformly continuous function 325
characterization T 8.1.10
— convergent sequence of functions 43
— convergent sequence of mappings 182, T 4.2.7
unity of a group 321
universal space 78
for compact spaces T 3.2.5
for compact metrizable spaces C T 4.2.4
for metrizable spaces T 4.4.7
for separable metrizable spaces C T 4.2.4
for strongly 0-dimensional metrizable spaces T 7.3.9
for T_0-spaces T 2.3.9
for Tychonoff spaces T 2.3.8
for 0-dimensional spaces T 6.2.11

universal uniformity P 8.I
upper class of a cut 16
— semi-continuous function P 5.RS
Urysohn lemma 50
— space P 1.LN, P 2.A
$\mathcal{V}$-net 334
vertex of a polyhedron P 7.H
— of a simplex 297
Vietoris topology P 3.J, P 4.H, P 6.C, P 8.H

weaker proximity E 8.4.C
— topology 31
— uniformity E 8.1.A
weakly δ-uniform covering P 8.W
— paracompact space 225-226, E 5.3.AB, P 5.YZ
weight of a topological space 26, T 1.1.6-7
and a dense subset T 1.3.7, L 1 T 3.4.3
and power T 3.1.11 and C 1-2, L 2 T 3.4.3, E 3.4.A, T 3.6.9, P 3.GT, P 4.O
weight of a topological space
and pseudo-weight P 3.F
of the Cartesian product P 2.J
see also space satisfying the second axiom of countability
— of a topological space at a point 27, *see also* space satisfying the first axiom of countability
— of a uniform space 315
— of a uniformity 314
well-ordered set 17
well-ordering 17

Zermelo's theorem 21
0-dimensional space 247
and other kinds of disconnectedness T 6.2.1, T 6.2.5-6, E 6.2.2-3
operations T 6.2.7, T 6.2.9-10
universal space T 6.2.11
0-dimensional compactification C T 6.2.11
see also small inductive dimension

ERRATA

Page, line	For	Read
58^{12}	S	S_ξ
64^{11}	here spaces	spaces
64^{12}	described	described here
81^{11}	Σ_0	Σ
87^{15}	π^τ_σ	π^σ_τ
112^{6}	$f^{-1}(B_i) = A \cap K_i$	$\overline{f^{-1}(B_i)} = \overline{A \cap K_i}$
116^{4}	$y_\varrho = \pi^\varrho_\sigma(y_\varrho)$	$y_\sigma = \pi^\varrho_\sigma(y_\sigma)$
118_{16}	*and is identical*	*is identical*
138^{19}	ωX for	ωX, for
182_{17}	$i = 1,2, \ldots$	$i = 1, 2, \ldots, k$
252^{2}	$\underset{s \in S}{\boldsymbol{P}} X_s$	$\underset{s \in S}{\boldsymbol{P}} X_s,$
314_{17}	subfamily	subfamily $\mathfrak{U}$
337^{15}	$\{f(B(x, U) \cap A)\}_{U \in \mathfrak{U}}$	$\{\overline{f(B(x,U) \cap A)}\}_{U \in \mathfrak{U}}$
337_{13}	$\overline{f(M \cap A)} < 3V$	$\delta(\overline{f(M \cap A)}) < 3V$
338_{16}	$\mathfrak{U}$	$\tilde{\mathfrak{U}}$
338_{10}	X	$\tilde{X}$
345^{2}	$\lvert x-y \rvert \geqslant V$	$\lvert x-y \rvert < V$
345_{4}	closed	close
346_{14}	$\bar{A}\ \delta\ \bar{B} \neq 0$	$\bar{A} \cap \bar{B} \neq 0$

R. Engelking, *Outline of General Topology*